Don. Haske
Pine Bluff Ct.
Bath, Mich.

W9-CHE-960

820

162-185
200-365

McGraw-Hill Series in Civil Engineering

HARMER E. DAVIS, *Consulting Editor*

WATER SUPPLY ENGINEERING

McGraw-Hill Series in Civil Engineering

HARMER E. DAVIS, *Consulting Editor*

BABBITT · Engineering in Public Health

DAVIS, TROXELL, AND WISKOCIL · The Testing and Inspection of Engineering Materials

DUNHAM · Foundations of Structures

DUNHAM · The Theory and Practice of Reinforced Concrete

GOLZÉ · Reclamation in the United States

LINSLEY AND FRANZINI · Elements of Hydraulic Engineering

LINSLEY, KOHLER, AND PAULHUS · Applied Hydrology

TSCHEBOTARIOFF · Soil Mechanics, Foundations, and Earth Structures

Water Supply Engineering

HAROLD E. BABBITT, M.S.

Professor of Sanitary Engineering, University of Illinois

JAMES J. DOLAND, M.S., C.E., D.Sc.

Professor of Civil Engineering, University of Illinois

FIFTH EDITION

McGRAW-HILL BOOK COMPANY, INC.

New York   Toronto   London

1955

WATER SUPPLY ENGINEERING

Copyright © 1955 by the McGraw-Hill Book Company, Inc.

Copyright, 1929, 1931, 1939, 1949, by the McGraw-Hill Book Company, Inc. Printed in the United States of America. All rights reserved. This book, or parts thereof, may not be reproduced in any form without permission of the publishers.

Library of Congress Catalog Card Number 54-11257

II

THE MAPLE PRESS COMPANY, YORK, PA.

PREFACE

This fifth edition differs from the fourth probably more than any earlier edition differs from its immediate predecessor. The attempt has been made, in the preparation of this edition, to present information on the latest accepted practices in the field of water works, and the scope of the book has been slightly increased to include information on industrial water supplies. Since water-works practices are changing rapidly, many changes in the book have been necessary in order to meet the objective. The inclusion of new material without increasing the length of the book has forced the deletion of some older material. The substitution of the new for the old may not always represent improvement but it does keep the reader informed on the more recent practices.

Design is emphasized by the material in the book. Information is given on financing, operation, and management primarily as they may affect design. The applicability of the book to advanced study has been improved by numerous references, in the form of footnotes, to source material, thus facilitating further study in the various branches of the subject. These leads should be especially useful to graduate students and to practicing engineers.

H. E. Babbitt

CONTENTS

WATER SUPPLY ENGINEERING

CHAPTER 1

INTRODUCTION

1-1. The Importance of Water Works. As a community develops, the need for a public water supply becomes apparent.[1,2] Dependence can no longer be placed on private sources of water supply such as wells and cisterns. The increasing concentration of population makes satisfactory wells more difficult to locate, and unpolluted sources of both surface and ground water are less readily available to the individual. It is less the unavailability of private sources of water supply than the need for community protection against fire, however, that emphasizes the need for a public water supply.

1-2. Fire Protection. A large percentage of the cost of water works in small communities is chargeable to fire protection, as is shown in Table 1-1. In the rating system of the National Board of Fire Underwriters, there are

TABLE 1-1. Proportion of Cost of Water Works Chargeable to Fire Protection*

Population, thousands	Percentage of total cost of water works chargeable to fire protection	Percentage of cost of distribution system chargeable to fire protection
10	60	56
50	32	29
100	23	17.5
300	13	4

* Estimated by the National Board of Fire Underwriters.

31 main items which are of value in checking a design or in studying an existing water works. These items are:
   1. Appointment of employees
   2. Efficiency of executive

[1] See also W. J. Diamond, *Military Eng.*, 1947, pp. 105, 168, 330, 430, 527; 1948, p. 6.
[2] See also: M. N. Baker, "The Quest for Water," American Water Works Association, 1948; J. O. Draffin, "The Story of Man's Quest for Water," Garrard Press, Champaign, Ill., 1939; and the 4th edition of this book.

3. Records and plans
4. Emergency provisions
5. Receipt of alarms by fire department
6. Normal adequacy of entire system
7. Reliability of source of supply
8. Sufficiency of reserve pump capacity
9. Sufficiency of reserve boiler capacity
10. Condition, arrangement, and reliability of plant equipment
11. Fuel and accessories for transmission of power
12. Construction of pumping station
13. Fire protection of pumping station
14. Hazards of pumping station
15. Exposures of pumping station
16. Reliability of supply mains as affecting adequacy
17. Reliability of installation of supply mains
18. Completeness of arterial system
19. Reliability of installation of mains
20. Effect of small mains in high-value district considered
21. 4-in. mains in system
22. Dead ends, 4- and 6-in. mains
23. Completeness of gridiron of 6-in. mains
24. Quality and condition of pipe
25. Conditions affecting fire protection in other than section graded
26. Spacing of gate valves
27. Condition of gate valves
28. Distribution of hydrants in high-value district considered
29. Distribution of hydrants in residential and other districts
30. Condition of hydrants
31. Size and installation of hydrants

1-3. Reliability of Water Works. Reliability of water works is provided through the development of an inexhaustible source or by supplementing a precarious source of supply with adequate storage; by the construction of permanent and substantial structures and equipment; by foresight in minimizing the dangers of fire, flood,[1] earthquake, sabotage, and other emergencies; and by the duplication of such structures and machinery, the breakdown of a single unit of which might be disastrous to the continuous supply of water.

Some sources of supply and methods of distribution offer greater safety and reliability than others. It is to be noted that a supply requiring purification is not so reliable as one that is sufficiently pure at its source. Aside from the question of purity, the relative order of reliability is:

---

[1] See also Symposium, Meeting Flood Problems, *J.A.W.W.A.*, September, 1952, p. 811.

1. A surface- or ground-water supply taken from a never-failing source from which the water is led to, and is distributed throughout, the city by gravity

2. A surface supply requiring impounding reservoirs from which the water is led to, and is distributed throughout, the city by gravity

3. A never-failing surface supply which requires pumping for distribution

4. A surface supply requiring impounding reservoirs from which the water must be pumped

5. A ground-water supply which must be pumped

The reliability of any one of these types of water works depends on the design, construction, or maintenance of the works for securing or distributing the water. For example, in the third type the construction of a large storage reservoir with several days capacity, at an elevation sufficient to distribute the water by gravity, will materially improve the reliability of the water works.

In rating a public water supply for the purpose of fixing insurance rates, the reliability of the works is taken into account by the National Board of Fire Underwriters. A gravity supply is preferred by them over one requiring pumping unless there is adequate storage under pressure. Under the circumstances "there is no deficiency charged if, with the two largest (pumping) units out of commission, the remaining pumps, in connection with storage, will furnish the maximum consumption plus fire flow for a 10-hr. period."

1-4. Rating of Public Water Supplies. Numerical ratings, or "scorecard" systems, are used for expressing various features of a public water supply,[1] the condition of the works, the sanitary safety of the water, and other features. For example, the system may be rated in accordance with the numerical method of the National Board of Fire Underwriters, or the sanitary quality according to the method of the Minnesota State Board of Health.[2]

Rating systems can be irrational and may fail to make proper allowance for extreme conditions. On the other hand, their advantages include: (1) avoidance of "approved" ratings which may be interpreted as equivalent to perfect; (2) the degree of seriousness of defective items and of total works is indicated numerically; (3) comparison of consecutive ratings shows effect of improvement or of neglect; and (4) intelligibility to the layman.

1-5. Governmental Regulation. Within the area served by a public water supply it is customary for a single enterprise, either publicly or privately owned, to enjoy a monopoly of supplying the general public,

---

[1] See also O. E. Brownell, *J.A.W.W.A.*, September, 1947, p. 922.
[2] *Ibid.*, p. 924.

under governmental regulation.[1]   However, institutional and industrial
water supplies within the area are, sometimes, competitive with such
apparent monopolies.   Governmental control is exercised by public
utility commissions and commerce commissions, whose jurisdiction
extends to equipment, capacities, rates, and financial policies; by water
commissions whose rulings may affect the availability of the sources of
supply;[2] by health departments who deal with questions of quantity and
quality; and by other governmental and quasi-governmental organizations, such as the National Board of Fire Underwriters, which exerts its
influence through the regulation of fire insurance rates based on the
equipment of the water works.

1-6. Legal Rights and Liabilities.[3]   The supplying of water is a legally
recognized governmental activity[4] and, as such, the water-works organization possesses the right of eminent domain[5] in the condemnation of
private property for public use.[6]   The right to sell water is not, however,
a governmental prerogative.[7]   Balancing the extensive rights and powers
possessed by a water-works enterprise are its legal liabilities.   For example, a water works can be sued successfully for damages if, through
negligence, polluted water is supplied to a consumer who would have no
reasonable means of knowing that the water was polluted.[8]   This liability applies alike to privately and publicly owned public water supplies.[9]

1-7. Legal Rights to Sources of Supply.   The law and usages governing the right to take water from sources of supply are not uniform in the
various states.[10]   One is impressed with the lack of agreement among
authorities respecting many of the points at issue.[11]   The following principles govern in different states, and in some states combinations of these
principles determine the right to water.   The general principles on which
rights are based include:

[1] See also: W. E. Crawford and F. E. Crawford, "Public Utility Regulation," Harper
& Brothers, New York, 1933; J. A. Beck, *J.A.W.W.A.*, October, 1935, p. 1323.

[2] See also Committee Report, *J.A.W.W.A.*, August, 1950, p. 755.

[3] See also J. H. Murdoch, Jr., *J.A.W.W.A.*, December, 1952, p. 1085.

[4] See *J.A.W.W.A.*, May, 1937, p. 699.

[5] L. T. Parker, *Water Works Eng.*, June 10, 1936, p. 765.

[6] Parker, *ibid.*, Nov. 24, 1937, p. 1675.

[7] Parker, *ibid.*, July 27, 1932, p. 901.

[8] See: Jones vs. Mount Holly Water Co., 87 *N.J.L.* 106; Parker, *ibid.*, Jan. 5, 1938,
p. 20; Illinois State Department of Public Health, Responsibilities of Cities, Water
Companies, and Individuals for Illness Caused by Water, *Educational Health Circ.* 15.

[9] J. H. Howard, *J.A.W.W.A.*, March, 1945, p. 260.

[10] H. Conkling, *Trans. Am. Soc. Civil Engrs.*, Vol. 102, p. 753, 1937; see also: *J.A.-
W.W.A.*, January, 1944, p. 102; July, 1945; p. 601; C. D. Harris, *J.A.W.W.A.*, January, 1954, p. 10.

[11] L. T. Parker, *Water Works Eng.*, Sept. 6, 1933; Water Rights of Riparian Owners,
Water Works Eng., July 25, 1934; A. P. Black, *J.A.W.W.A.*, October, 1947, with 15
references.

1. *Priority of Appropriation to Beneficial Use.* This is the principle that "the first in time shall be the first in right," but it is modified in that the use must be beneficial and also by the amount of water available for various preferred purposes.

2. *Ownership Rights.* Ownership rights are acquired through the purchase of land, the rights being specified in the deed thereto. In some cases the rights may include the right to take water from within the boundaries embraced by the deed. This is a common condition in the location of a well, and insofar as surface waters are concerned, it is similar to the common-law doctrine of riparian rights which gives the owner the right to have the stream flow by or through his land undiminished in quantity and unchanged in quality and permitting him the right to use any amount necessary for domestic use.

3. *Reasonable Use.* Only reasonable use may be made of the water beneath or contiguous to the land, with due regard to the rights of others above or adjacent to such water.

4. *Right Is Granted by an Administrative Body.* In some states a just allocation of water rights is attempted through an administrative body acting under legislative authority.

5. *Special Legislation.* The right to use water may be either granted or restricted through special legislative action.[1]

Stevenson and Ryder[2] summarize the guiding principles that have been developed in the appropriation of interstate waters, as follows: (1) the doctrine of equitable apportionment controls the division and use of interstate waters; (2) priority of appropriation creates no superiority of right in interstate waters; (3) the highest use of interstate waters is for drinking and other domestic uses; (4) injunctive relief will be granted only on proof of present and substantial damages; (5) diversion will be allowed from one watershed to another; (6) states may select sources of water supply provided no substantial damage is done to sister riparian states; (7) release of compensating water depends on downstream conditions and needs; (8) judicial allowance of diversion affecting navigation or navigable capacity is conditioned on Federal approval.[3]

Johnson[4] divides underground water into two classes: (1) water flowing in defined and known channels, and (2) water passing through the ground below the surface, either without a definite channel or in courses that are unknown. In the conception of the law, waters of the first class are to be dealt with as though they were surface streams. The fundamental principle on which the law regulating the use of waters of the second class

---

[1] See also *J.A.W.W.A.*, June, 1947, p. 527.

[2] W. L. Stevenson and C. E. Ryder, *Civil Eng.*, August, 1931, p. 991.

[3] See also T. Merriman, *J. New Engl. Water Works Assoc.*, Vol. 45, p. 199, 1931; F. E. Winsor, *ibid.*, p. 267.

[4] See also *U.S. Geol. Survey, Water Supply Paper* 122, 1905.

is based is that such waters are a part of the land and belong absolutely to the proprietor within whose territory they are. The percolating waters within his territory are as truly his absolute property as are the rocks, ores, and minerals.

Conkling[1] states four doctrines of the law on which the use of underground waters in the United States is based, as follows: (1) absolute ownership, or the "doctrine of unreasonable use"; (2) ownership to the extent of reasonable use on the land beneath which the water is found, or the "doctrine of reasonable use"; (3) ownership coequal with that of every other owner of land overlying the underground basin, termed the "California doctrine"; and (4) ownership by the state.

The practice of rain making by inducing precipitation from the clouds has raised legal questions not yet solved.

Under any circumstances it may be desirable for the engineer to consult legal advice concerning the rights to any particular source before its use is recommended as a source for a public water supply.

1-8. The Parts of a Water-works System. Water works may be classified for purposes of study and design as: works for the collection of water, works for the purification of water, works for the pumping of water, and works for the distribution of water. The personnel of a comprehensive water-works organization includes: (1) an engineering organization for the design of structures, machines, and other equipment; (2) an operating force; (3) a maintenance force; and (4) an office force. In some states professional engineers, certain grades of operating engineers, and responsible operators must be legally registered.[2]

Works for the collection of water include wells, galleries, collecting works for springs, lake and river intakes, impounding reservoirs, aqueducts, and long pipe lines. Works for the purification of water are represented by filtration plants, softening equipment, chlorinating equipment, aerators, and similar devices. Pumps and pumping stations and their equipment represent works for the pumping of water. Works for the distribution of water include the system of underground pipes, distributing and equalizing reservoirs, service connections, and, in some cases, meters.

1-9. The Business of Supplying Water. A public water supply, whether publicly or privately owned, is usually conducted as a self-supporting business. The design, operation, and maintenance of a water works should be conducted so that expenditures are justified and are economical.

1-10. Public Relations.[3] The maintenance of public good will is essential to the continued successful and profitable operation of a public water

---

[1] H. Conkling, *Trans. Am. Soc. Civil Engrs.*, Vol. 102, p. 753, 1937.

[2] See *J.A.W.W.A.*, February, 1949, p. 111.

[3] See also *J.A.W.W.A.*, January, 1947, p. 41.

works. Public good will can be created and maintained through education of the public in the problems of the water works; by supplying water adequate in both quantity and quality; by the proper type of publicity; by a uniform billing system; by the beautification and careful maintenance of the building, equipment, and grounds belonging to the water works; and by other means. The American Water Works Association published, in 1947, a "Check List of Public Relations Activities" valuable in planning and maintaining good public relations. Among bad practice in public relations may be listed so-called "nuisance charges" such as "turn-on" charges and "meter-purchase" charges.[1] Methods of maintaining public good will represent a special field in water-works management.

1-11. Appearance of Water-works Properties. Public good will is essential to the ability of a water works to attain its principal objective, the provision of an adequate and satisfactory water supply. No water works whose structures are dilapidated, whose equipment is uncared for, whose buildings are unkempt, and whose grounds are neglected can furnish a *satisfactory* water supply. Pleasing architectural style and well-kept property arouse, on the part of the public and the water consumers, a feeling of confidence and friendship which is measured in financial returns. The value of water-works beautification has been proved by experience.

The creation of parks and playgrounds is an effective means of winning public favor. Water-works parks are maintained in many cities with the provision of playgrounds for sports, picnicking, boating, fishing, and bathing. All can be provided without danger to the quality of the water supplied to the consumers if proper precautions are taken to prevent the passage of contamination through the water-purification plant.

1-12. Water-works Management and the Engineer.[2] Among those problems of water-works management which affect the design, operation, and maintenance of the enterprise may be included customer relations; policies in the preparation for emergencies; financial policies and procedures; governmental regulation; legal rights and liabilities; methods of measuring water for sale, particularly the use of meters; and the provision of safety measures. Although practically all public water works in the United States are locally managed, the promise of improvement in safety and efficiency, especially in the smaller communities, lies in increased regional and state advice and participation. Among those important water-works activities which do not materially affect the engineer may be included methods of accounting and billing, meter reading and its admin-

---

[1] See also E. E. Norman, *J.A.W.W.A.*, September, 1946, p. 1031.

[2] See also H. E. Jordan, "The Management of Water Works," published jointly by the Illinois Section of the American Water Works Association and the Illinois State Department of Public Health, 1951.

istration, and certain legal responsibilities and obligations such as liability for damages for shutting off the water or for injuries committed on a citizen by a water-works employee.

1-13. Starting a Water Works. The starting of a water works in a community is usually a result of the activities of an individual or a group which focuses attention on the need. Water works usually have small beginnings and grow with the community. The design of a complete water works on a large scale is unusual. The principal work of the water-works engineer is the design of improvements and extensions to existing works.

An investigation of the possibilities of obtaining water, purifying it, if necessary, and distributing it, all at a reasonable cost, should be made by a competent engineer whose report may be used as a basis of publicity aimed at winning the support of the citizens, or other responsible body, when the matter is considered and a decision is made. The engineer's report[1] should include a thorough study of all possible sources of supply and of methods of treatment, pumping, and distribution, together with an estimate of the cost of each project. The report should be written in an attractive manner in language easily comprehensible to laymen. An outline of a report is given in Appendix 1.

The work of the engineer in connection with a water-works system can be divided into four periods: development, design, construction, and operation. The duties of the engineer during the period of development are to gather all data necessary for his report, to write and present the report, and possibly to make public addresses and to explain to laymen the salient features of the plan or plans presented for consideration.

1-14. Preparation for Emergencies. It is the duty of a water-works administration to prepare for the continuation of water supply under any emergency. Emergencies may include such natural cataclysms as earthquakes, floods, and droughts and such man-made catastrophes as fires, riots, and war. In many states preparation against disaster is administered by the Civil Defense authority created under state statute. Preparation for emergencies may include the assembly of maps of the distribution system and supply sources; inventories of pumping equipment; the pooling of resources and equipment with neighboring cities; location of emergency sources of supply and its transportation and distribution; equipment and personnel for the disinfection of the water supply; and the organization, training, and equipment of repair crews.[2]

[1] See also J. S. Watkins, *J.A.W.W.A.*, January, 1954, p. 31.
[2] See also: L. A. Greenberg, *Public Works*, April, 1952, p. 144; L. S. Vance, *Water Works Eng.*, May 26, 1937, p. 699; *Water Works Eng.*, Aug. 18, 1937, p. 1170; J. C. Crenshaw, *J.A.W.W.A.*, Vol. 29, pp. 1230, 1737*ff.*, 1937; J. D. Wedeman, *ibid.*, June, 1954, p. 514.

Finances

1-15. Financial Principles. All the items entering into the over-all cost of a water works can be classified as: (1) first cost, (2) operating and maintenance cost, and (3) depreciation or renewal allowance. The sum of these three items may be called the over-all cost. This is an amount of money which, if set aside at simple interest, would provide enough money to purchase, operate, maintain, and renew the water works forever at the then existing costs and rate of interest. The over-all cost is much greater than the capital invested, which is represented by the first cost of the works. The over-all cost can be formulated as

$$OC = C + \frac{O}{r} + C \frac{1}{(1 + r)^n - 1} \qquad (1\text{-}1)$$

[handwritten annotation: Capitalized Depreciation]

[handwritten annotation: Multiply form. By r Gives Annual Cost.]

where OC = over-all cost

   C = first cost or invested capital

   O = periodic, usually annual, operating cost

   r = periodic, usually annual, rate of interest

   n = life of enterprise in interest periods, usually in years

The product of the over-all cost and the rate of interest may be called the annual expense. A comparison of the over-all costs, or the annual expenses, of two or more enterprises capable of doing the same thing will show which enterprise is the most economical.

In financing an enterprise, the rates to be charged for the services rendered must be sufficient to return annually a sum equal to the annual expense. The low rates of interest that may exist during times of financial inflation may mitigate the financial restrictions on water-works extensions[1] resulting from inflation. Fick[2] reports cost indexes for various types of water-works equipment from 1913 to 1952 which are helpful in the determination of prices and in indicating price trends.

1-16. Methods of Raising Money. Money may be raised, or borrowed, to finance a business enterprise such as a water works, by (1) direct taxation, (2) special assessment, (3) the sale of general-obligation tax bonds, (4) the sale of revenue bonds, (5) the sale of mortgage bonds, (6) the sale of stock in the enterprise, and (7) governmental grants and loans. In general, all but the fifth and sixth methods are used for the financing of publicly owned water works. These two are used for financing private enterprises.

---

[1] See also: L. R. Howson, *J.A.W.W.A.*, August, 1944, p. 803; N. T. Veatch, *ibid.*, p. 811; C. B. Burdick, *ibid.*, p. 821; E. J. Taylor, *ibid.*, January, 1947, p. 57; F. A. Marston, *Water Works Eng.*, February, 1952, p. 132.

[2] H. H. Fick, *J.A.W.W.A.*, August, 1953, p. 779.

The financial record of water-works enterprises is sufficiently excellent to make water-works securities so attractive to investors that the securities enjoy relatively low rates of interest charges. In general, water-works obligations secured by water-works revenues are more attractive than obligations secured by the power to tax because experience has shown that it is easier to collect from revenues than from delinquent taxes.

Whenever financial obligations are undertaken that must be retired at some future date, many state laws, together with sound business principles, required the obligations to be retired within a reasonable time, and usually in not more than 20 years. Publicly owned water works are usually limited by state laws and constitutional provisions in matters of raising money for new works and extensions and rehabilitations of existing works. The laws vary among the states.

1-17. Direct Taxation. Direct taxes, commonly based on the value of the real estate of a community, are usually placed in the general municipal fund and are used for such non-self-supporting services as police and fire protection. Such direct taxes are seldom used for special and for self-supporting services such as the water works. However, when water works are financed from direct taxes, only a small portion of them can be so used and all property owners must benefit from the improvement.

1-18. Special Assessments. A special assessment is a tax levy against property to pay for improvements that ordinarily are required to be of direct benefit to the property taxed, and in some cases, the improvements must be contiguous with the property. Special-assessment bonds, subject to statutory limitations, may be issued to provide immediate funds needed for construction purposes. They are secured by the power of the municipality to make and to collect the assessment. Limitations imposed by statute frequently prevent the use of special assessments for the financing of water works.

1-19. Bonds. The sale of bonds is the most common method of financing publicly owned water-works enterprises. Water-works bonds, classified as to security, are, in general, of two types: (1) general-obligation bonds, secured by the power of the governmental agency to tax, and by the public property owned by the taxing authority; and (2) special-lien bonds, payable from the revenues of the enterprise, sometimes called "revenue bonds." The physical properties and the earning power of the enterprise serve as security for the bonds. Revenue bonds are, however, sometimes issued without hypothecation of the physical properties of the utility and are not a financial obligation of the issuing municipality.[1] Such bonds, despite their apparent lack of sound security, have proved to be financially attractive where the income of the utility is adequate to retire the bonds.

[1] See also L. N. Thompson, *J.A.W.W.A.*, October, 1947, p. 1032.

Special-lien bonds may also be secured by direct mortgage of the physical property of the utility, in which case provision is usually made for the operation of the utility by the bondholders in case of default. Under such conditions a receiver may be appointed who is empowered to adjust rates, if necessary and if permitted by the utility commission, in order to protect the investor's interest.

Bonds may be classified also as long-term bonds, which provide for payment of the entire indebtedness at maturity; or serial bonds, which provide for periodic payments of portions of the indebtedness until the whole is discharged. Provision for the retirement of long-term bonds is usually made by the establishment of a sinking fund. The issuance of serial bonds avoids the hazards of long-term sinking funds, because the bonds themselves are retired with payments that would be invested in the sinking fund.

Limitations of the amount of bonded indebtedness, rate of interest, and life of bonds are usually regulated by statute or constitutional provisions; indebtedness limitation is commonly between $2\frac{1}{2}$ and 5 per cent of the value of taxable property; the interest rate is limited to not more than 6 per cent; and the greatest length of time that bonds may run is usually 20 years. There is a growing tendency to exempt public-utility debts from provisions limiting the total bonded indebtedness of a municipality. Refunding of bonds is not generally permitted.

1-20. Governmental Grants and Loans. During periods of economic emergency the Federal government has established financial agencies for the purpose of making grants and loans, especially to self-supporting public enterprises such as water works. Among such agencies have been the Reconstruction Finance Corporation (RFC), the Public Works Administration (PWA), the Civil Works Administration (CWA), and the Works Progress Administration (WPA). None of these is functioning. The establishment of such bureaus has had far-reaching effects on the financing of publicly owned water works. For example, under the PWA, grants were made not exceeding 45 per cent of the cost of labor and materials employed in the construction of the project, and the remainder of the cost was financed by reasonably secured loans.

1-21. Water Districts, Sanitary Districts, and Miscellaneous. Some states permit the organization of quasi-municipal corporations for the purpose of providing needed construction or improvement to water works, sewer systems, and similar public utilities. The formation of such districts is advantageous where two or more communities desire to operate a public service under a single administration. Another important advantage of the plan is the power of the newly created municipal organization, or district, to levy taxes and to incur bonded indebtedness up to the legal limitation without regard to any existing bonded debt of overlapping municipal corporations.

Where a municipality finds itself unable to finance a water-works improvement because of legal restrictions on the bonded indebtedness, the following methods have been used:

1. An overlapping municipal district has been incorporated, as described above.

2. A holding company is formed which is capitalized for an amount sufficient to cover the cost of the needed improvements. The stock of the company is purchased by private individuals, banks, and commercial establishments interested in the civic welfare. The net earnings from the sale of water are used by the municipality to repurchase the stock gradually and to pay a fair return on the remaining outstanding stock. Thus, the municipality eventually becomes the sole owner of the holding company.

3. Certain private corporations will agree to finance a water-works installation or improvement under what is known as a "lease form" of contract. In other words, the corporation agrees to build the necessary works and to lease them to the city. The latter agrees to make periodic payments of an amount such that at the end of a term of years the cost, profit, and interest charges will be repaid to the financing corporation, and the city becomes the owner of the plant.

1-22. Financing Extensions.[1] Established water works may be expected to extend their services, either by supplying water to suburbs owning their own distribution systems, or by extending the pipes of the distribution system into newly developed territory. The fact must not be overlooked that the extension of mains will result in an increased load on the plant which will subsequently involve additional capital charge. The amount to be charged for the supplying of water usually does not involve new capital charges directly.

Since the water works is now a going concern, current income can be used for financing, or money may be raised through charges made to those to be benefited by the extension. Bases for these charges include (1) population served, (2) acreage served, (3) length of frontage benefited, (4) number of services or meters installed, (5) length of pipe installed, and (6) prospective use or sale of water. In some cities, a minimum length of 50 or 100 ft of pipe is installed without charge to the consumer. In others, where the number of potential customers along the extended lines gives assurance of adequate water sales, no initial charge is made to those benefited. In other cities, the initial payment advanced by the beneficiaries is refunded when the sale of water exceeds a predetermined amount sufficient to pay for the extension.

1-23. Free Water. Some municipally owned water works receive no income for water supplied for public purposes such as fire fighting, schools,

---

[1] See also: D. D. Heffelfinger, *J.A.W.W.A.*, March, 1947, p. 257; Committee Report, *ibid.*, August, 1949, p. 729.

or the city building. The custom of supplying "free" water for public use is misleading because the burden is placed on the water consumer, who must carry it in the place of the taxpayer.

1-24. Fire-protection Charges.[1] The cost of public fire protection by publicly owned water works is commonly paid by the water users. The equity of such a policy is debatable. Privately owned public water works are commonly reimbursed by payments from the public treasury taken from the general tax fund. The rate of payment may be based on the number of hydrants or otherwise "fixed by some sort of capricious agreement . . . ," as stated by Witherspoon. An equitable system might involve the determination of the total cost of that portion of the water works chargeable to fire protection. This is expressed in the Metcalf, Kuichling, and Hawley formula[2] as

$$Y = \frac{147}{P^{0.83}} - 12.1 \qquad (1\text{-}2)$$

where Y = percentage of cost of plant chargeable to fire protection, dollars

P = population, thousands

1-25. Water Rates.[3] The rates to be charged for water sold to a user are based on a variety of considerations, such as the cost of the water based on the over-all cost of the works. Other factors that may be considered include (1) the average and peak rates at which water is used, (2) the pressure required, (3) the distance of the customer from the pumping station, (4) the cost of water purification, (5) the percentage of leakage and unaccounted-for water, (6) changing cost levels, usually rising,[4] and (7) reserve capacity required. The competitive nature of public water supplies must sometimes be considered in the fixing of rates to customers who might be able to develop their own private supplies at a lower cost than an exorbitant rate charged for the public supply. The base on which most water bills are fixed is the amount of water consumed, regardless of how inequitable or inaccurate such a measure may be.

Methods for estimating the quantity of water used so that the charge to be paid by the customer may be fixed are based on various conditions such as the number of fixtures, faucets, or users on the service; the number of rooms or the number of windows in the building; the floor area of the building; and the record of a meter. Although sliding scales, in which a

---

[1] See also: F. R. Witherspoon, *J.A.W.W.A.*, July, 1947, p. 623; P. A. Reynolds and P. K. Hood, *ibid.*, April, 1950, p. 333; R. H. Ellis, *ibid.*, November, 1950, p. 1009.

[2] L. Metcalf, E. Kuichling, and W. C. Hawley, *Proc. A.W.W.A.*, 1911, p. 83.

[3] See also: A. P. Leonard, *J.A.W.W.A.*, July, 1947, p. 666; F. R. Theroux, *Water Works Eng.*, October, 1948, p. 946; Committee Report, *J.A.W.W.A.*, March, 1954, p. 187.

[4] See also L. R. Howson, *J.A.W.W.A.*, September, 1947, p. 819.

lower charge is made per gallon for larger quantities of water used, are customary in the water business, it has been pointed out[1] that such a scale is inequitable and illogical since the greater burden is placed on the small domestic-water user.

Some charges for water in various cities are shown in Table 1-2.

TABLE 1-2. Annual Water Bill, Dollars, in Some Large American Cities*

City	Annual use, gal	
	30,000	120,000
San Francisco	18.54	43.51
Buffalo	13.20	16.50
Los Angeles	13.20	22.50
Washington, D.C.	10.94	17.69
Boston	8.00	22.50
Baltimore	8.00	30.00
Philadelphia	8.00	12.95
Pittsburgh	8.00	24.20
Detroit	6.56	16.68
New York	6.00	22.50
St. Louis	6.00	21.30
Cleveland	5.75	14.00
Milwaukee	5.70	13.13
Chicago	2.40	

* From *Water Works Eng.*, August, 1952, p. 753.

[1] See G. B. Schunke, *J.A.W.W.A.*, July, 1946, p. 838.

Residential Single Family $= \dfrac{15,000}{3.5 \times 90} = 48$ gal/day/capita

SINKING Fund

$C \dfrac{r}{(1+r)^n - 1} =$ Sinking Fund = Amount to set aside at end of each year to provide for first cost C

= Depreciation Item of Capt. Cost.

CHAPTER 2

HYDRAULICS·

2-1. Problems Involved. The design, maintenance, and operation of water works involve problems of hydrostatics and hydrodynamics in the collection, pumping, storage, distribution, and treatment of water. Hydrostatics includes problems in intensity of pressure, total pressure, and center of pressure. Hydrodynamics includes problems in the flow of water in pipes, conduits, and distribution systems, and water hammer.

2-2. Intensity of Pressure. The intensity of static pressure on a surface submerged in water can be expressed as

$$p = w\bar{h} \qquad (2\text{-}1)$$

where p = intensity of pressure

w = unit weight of water

$\bar{h}$ = vertical distance from water surface to centroid of area on which pressure is exerted

Since the weight of water is approximately 62.5 lb per cu ft, the intensity of pressure in pounds per square inch at the foot of a column of water 100 ft high can be computed as

$$p = w\bar{h} = \frac{62.5 \times 100}{144} = 43.4 \text{ psi}$$

The height of a column of water above a point where the pressure is 100 psi can be computed as

$$\bar{h} = \frac{p}{w} = \frac{100 \times 144}{62.5} = 231 \text{ ft}$$

2-3. Total Pressure on a Plane Surface. The total pressure normal to a submerged plane surface can be expressed as

$$P = w\bar{h}A \qquad (2\text{-}2)$$

where P = total pressure

A = area of submerged surface

and other nomenclature is as in Eq. (2-1). The direction of action of the resultant of the total pressure is normal to the plane surface and its point of application is at the center of pressure of the surface.

2-4. Components of Total Pressure on a Curved Surface. The direction of action of pressure against a submerged surface is normal to the surface. The magnitude of the resultant of all the components of the total pressure in any direction can be expressed as

$$P = \int wH \cos \alpha \, dA \qquad (2\text{-}3)$$

where new nomenclature is $H =$ depth of submergence of a differential area of submerged surface

$\alpha =$ angle between a line parallel to direction of P and a line normal to dA

Both H and α are variable, and unless the relation between them is known the expression cannot be integrated. Where H or α is constant, the expression becomes

$$\int H \cos \alpha \, dA = \int H \, dA' = \bar{H} A' \qquad \text{and} \qquad P = wA'\bar{H} \qquad (2\text{-}4)$$

where A' is the area of the projection of the curved surface in a direction parallel to the resultant P onto a plane surface normal to this direction, H is approximately constant where the depth of submergence is great and the area is small, and α is constant where the submerged surface is plane. Where A' is a vertical plane

$$\int H \cos \alpha \, dA = \int H \, dA' = \bar{H} A' \qquad \text{and} \qquad P = wA'\bar{H} \qquad (2\text{-}5)$$

where $\bar{H}$ is the depth of submergence of the centroid of the surface.

Hence, the pressure in a horizontal direction against any surface is equal to the horizontal pressure against the horizontal projection of that surface against a vertical plane.

2-5. Center of Pressure. The distance to the center of pressure of a submerged plane surface, in the plane of the submerged surface, from and normal to the axis formed by the intersection of the plane surface, extended, with the water surface, is indicated by z_s in Fig. 2-1. It can be expressed as

$$z_s = \frac{I_s}{S_s} \qquad (2\text{-}6)$$

$$I_s = I_{c.g} + A z_{c.g.}^2$$

$$S = A z_{cg}$$

where $I_s =$ moment of inertia of submerged surface about axis formed by intersection of submerged surface, extended, with surface of water

$S_s =$ gravity moment of the same surface around the same axis

The distance x_1 of the center of pressure of a plane surface from any axis in the plane of the submerged surface and normal to the above-described axis is

$$x_1 = \frac{\int xz \, dA}{\int z \, dA} \qquad (2\text{-}7)$$

where x = horizontal distance from axis to differential area $dA = dx\,dz$

  z = distance from axis in the surface of the liquid to differential area dA

Loweke[1] states that

$$x_1 = \frac{I_{zz}}{\bar{z}A} \tag{2-8}$$

$$I_{xz} = I_{\bar{x}\bar{z}} + \overline{xz}A \tag{2-9}$$

where $I_{\bar{x}\bar{z}}$ = product of inertia about parallel axes through the centroid of the submerged plane at a distance $\overline{xz}$ from the original axes

  $\bar{x}$ = horizontal distance from the sloping axis in the plane of the submerged surface of the centroid of the area

  $\bar{z}$ = distance in the plane of the submerged surface from and normal to the axis formed by the intersection of the plane surface, extended, with the water surface, to the centroid of the submerged area

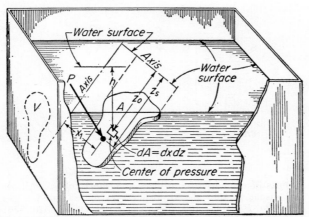

Fig. 2-1. Diagram showing the location of the center of pressure of a submerged surface.

Where the submerged surface is nonplanar, the vertical distance from the water surface to the center of pressure can be expressed as

$$h = \frac{\int h^2\,dA}{\int h\,dA} \tag{2-10}$$

and the distance x is as shown in Eq. (2-7). An integrable relation must exist between h and A to permit the solution of such a problem. Approximate solutions may be reached by assuming the curved surface to be composed of a series of plane surfaces.

[1] G. P. Loweke, *J. Am. Soc. Eng. Education,* June, 1951, p. 633.

2-6. Flow through Orifices and Nozzles. Knowledge of the rate of flow through an orifice may be applied to the determination of the rate of discharge through a valve, the rate of lowering the water in a storage tank, or the measurement of the rate of flow from a pump or in the test of a well. The rate of flow through an orifice or nozzle can be expressed as

$$Q = C_1 A C_2 \sqrt{2gh} \qquad (2\text{-}11)$$
$$Q = K_o A \sqrt{2gh} \qquad (2\text{-}12)$$

where Q = rate of flow
$\quad C_1$ = coefficient of area of reduction
$\quad C_2$ = coefficient of velocity
$\quad K_o$ = coefficient of discharge
$\quad g$ = acceleration due to gravity
$\quad h$ = head on center of orifice, or centroid of orifice opening
$\quad A$ = area of orifice opening

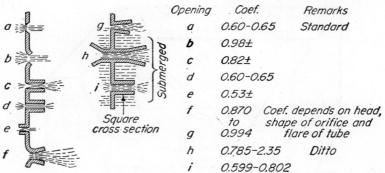

FIG. 2-2. Coefficients of discharge for orifices and short tubes. All are circular in cross section and discharge into the atmosphere except as noted. (*See also: Univ. Illinois Eng. Expt. Sta. Bulls.* 96, 100; *Eng. News, Vol.* 76, pp. 520, 826; *Eng. News-Record, Vol.* 86, p. 24.)

Coefficients for various orifices and nozzles are shown in Fig. 2-2. Values of K_o have been found to vary between 0.58 and 0.71, and values for smooth conical nozzles between 0.95 and 0.99. Rates of flow through fire nozzles are discussed in Secs. 2-24 and 21-14.

Where a large orifice is discharging under a low head, *i.e.*, where the height of the opening is large compared with the depth of water over it, modification of the formula is necessary. For a rectangular orifice the formula becomes

$$Q = mL(H_1^{3/2} - H_2^{3/2}) \qquad (2\text{-}13)$$

where Q = rate of discharge through orifice
$\quad L$ = width of orifice

H_1 = head on bottom of orifice

H_2 = head on top of orifice

m = a coefficient depending on the shape and the condition of installation of the orifice

The order of magnitude of m and some conditions affecting it were illustrated in a test on the crest gates of the Wilson Dam.[1] The spillway has 58 gates with clear openings of 58 ft each. With a gate opened at different heights, and adjacent gates closed, it was found that the value of m varied between 3.23 for small openings and 3.83 for full opening. Different openings for one gate, with adjacent gates fully open, gave values of m from 3.33 for small heads to 4.17 for full opening.

2-7. Discharge under Falling Head. Problems involving the time required to lower the elevation of the water surface in a reservoir or tank by opening a submerged orifice, or the distance the water surface will fall in a given time under similar conditions, are illustrative of the principle of discharge under a falling head.

The relation between the time and the distance of fall can be expressed as

$$t = \frac{A}{ca \sqrt{2g}} \int_{h_2}^{h_1} \frac{dh}{\sqrt{h}} \tag{2-14}$$

where t = time

A = surface area of reservoir or tank

c = coefficient of discharge of orifice or gate

a = area of opening of orifice or gate

h_1 = head on orifice at start of time t

h_2 = head on orifice at end of time t

h = head on orifice at any time

If A is a function of h, as frequently happens in tanks, then

$$t = \frac{1}{ca \sqrt{2g}} \int_{h_2}^{h_1} f(h) \frac{dh}{\sqrt{h}} \tag{2-15}$$

2-8. Discharge over Measuring Weirs.[2] A measuring weir is a device or structure over which water falls in such a manner that the rate of flow can be computed from the depth or head on the crest of the weir. Measuring weirs may be standard, broad-crested, sharp, curved, or flat; suppressed or contracted; rectangular, V-notch, trapezoidal, semicircular, or hyperbolic; free-falling or submerged; or other shapes or conditions.

A standard weir consists of a sharp horizontal edge of a flat plate placed vertically in such a manner that there is air beneath the nappe of the falling water. The rate of flow over such a weir is:

---

[1] L. G. Puls, *Trans. Am. Soc. Civil Engrs.*, Vol. 95, p. 316, 1931.

[2] See also F. T. Mavis, *Eng. News-Record*, Jan. 6, 1949, p. 77.

For a suppressed weir, *i.e.*, without end contractions of the falling stream:

Without velocity of approach $Q = clh^{3/2}$ (2-16)

With velocity of approach $Q = cl\left[\left(h + \dfrac{V^2}{2g}\right)^{3/2} - \left(\dfrac{V^2}{2g}\right)^{3/2}\right]$ (2-17)

For a contracted weir, *i.e.*, with the ends of the falling streams contracted:

Without velocity of approach $Q = c\left(l - \dfrac{nh}{10}\right)h^{3/2}$ (2-18)

With velocity of approach

$$Q = c\left(l - \frac{nh}{10}\right)\left[\left(h + \frac{V^2}{2g}\right)^{3/2} - \left(\frac{V^2}{2g}\right)^{3/2}\right] \qquad (2\text{-}19)$$

where Q = rate of discharge, cfs
     c = coefficient, usually 3.33 for standard sharp-crested weirs
     h = head on weir, ft
     l = length of crest, ft
     n = number of end contractions, either 1 or 2

The discharge Q_s over a submerged weir may be taken as a function of the discharge over a free-discharge weir, Q_f. Using the formula $Q_s = KQ_f$, values of K, determined through model tests by the U.S. Deep Waterways Commission,[1] are given in Table 2-1.

TABLE 2-1. Coefficients for Submerged Weirs

Hd/H*	K	Hd/H	K
0	1.000	0.5	0.937
0.1	0.991	0.6	0.907
0.2	0.983	0.7	0.856
0.3	0.972	0.8	0.778
0.4	0.956	0.9	0.620

* H = upstream head on weir, H_d downstream head on weir.

For a triangular-notch weir $Q = C \tan \alpha \, h^{5/2}$ (2-20)
where α = angle of sides of notch with vertical
     h = depth of water from bottom of notch to water surface in approach channel
    C = a coefficient
Tests[2] indicate that measurements with heads less than 0.3 ft, on triangular-notch weirs, are not dependable.

2-9. Broad-crested Weirs. A broad-crested weir is "an overflow structure on which the nappe is supported for an appreciable length with

[1] *U.S. Geol. Survey, Water Supply and Irrigation Paper* 200, 1907.
[2] See F. W. Blaisdell, *Civil Eng.*, August, 1939, p. 495.

a significant dimension in the direction of the stream."[1] This condition exists on the spillways of many dams. The formula $Q = Clh^{3/2}$ is often used to determine the discharge over a broad-crested weir. The value of the coefficient C varies, with the head and shape, from 2.5 to 3.1.[2]

2-10. Ogee Spillway Crests. Masonry crests are now frequently designed to fit, nearly, the curve of the lower nappe which would be

formed by a jet flowing over a sharp-crested weir at a head corresponding to the design crest of the spillway. Under such conditions it can be shown that[3] $Q = 4.10lH^{3/2}$ where H is the head on a perfectly shaped ogee crest discharging at the designed head, which would give a rise of $0.11h$ to the lower nappe

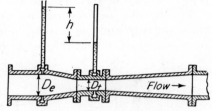

FIG. 2-3. Venturi meter.

discharging over a standard sharp-crested weir. Coefficients for rounded crests usually lie between 3.0 or less for low heads and 4.0 for well-shaped crests at designed heads.

2-11. Velocity Meters. The venturi meter, shown in Fig. 2-3, was invented by Clemens Herschel.[4] The rate of flow through the meter can be expressed as

$$Q = C \left(\frac{\pi}{4}\right) \frac{D_e^2 D_t^2}{\sqrt{D_e^4 - D_t^4}} \sqrt{2gh} \qquad (2\text{-}21)$$

where D_e and D_t = diameters at the entrance and at the throat, respectively

h = difference between pressure at entrance and pressure at throat of meter

C = a coefficient; for most meters it is unity

Equation (2-21) can be derived directly from an algebraic expression of Bernoulli's theorem.

Indicating and recording mechanisms are available to indicate the momentary rate of flow or to totalize the accumulated volume of flow through the meter.[5]

Elbows, orifices, valves, and other constrictions in pipe lines may be used to measure the rate of flow of water in the pipe line. The velocity

[1] American Society of Civil Engineers, Manual of Engineering Practice, No. 11, 1936.

[2] From J. G. Woodburn, *Trans. Am. Soc. Civil Engrs.*, Vol. 96, p. 387; see also *U.S. Geol. Survey, Water Supply Paper* 200, 1907.

[3] See H. E. Babbitt and J. J. Doland, "Water Supply Engineering," 3d ed., p. 36, McGraw-Hill Book Company, Inc., New York, 1939.

[4] C. Herschel, *Trans. Am. Soc. Civil Engrs.*, Vol. 17, p. 288, 1887.

[5] See also R. T. Regester, *Water Works & Sewerage*, June, 1941, p. R-31.

of flow in a pipe can be expressed as $V = Kh^n$, where K and n are constants for which the constriction is calibrated, and h is the difference in pressures at standardized points above and below the constriction. h is commonly measured by a differential-pressure gage. For almost all constrictions[1] and for an elbow gage n is $\frac{1}{2}$. Tests made by Lansford[2] indicate that K for an elbow varies, in English units, from 7.0 for 1-in. pipe to about 5.0 for 24-in. pipe.

Among other devices used for the measurement of velocity of flow are the pitot tube and the current meter. The tube is more commonly used in closed conduits and the meter in open channels.

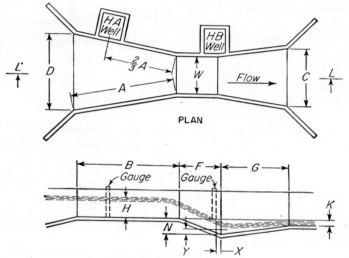

FIG. 2-4. A Parshall flume.

2-12. Measuring Flumes. Open flumes with a constricted throat section, sometimes called "venturi flumes," can be used for measuring the rate of flow of water. A true venturi flume requires the measurement of the depth of flow in the flume and in the throat. A Parshall flume, shown in Fig. 2-4, is a special type of venturi flume requiring the measurement of only the head H at the point shown in the figure. The rate of flow through the flume can be expressed as

$$Q = 4.1WH^{3/2} \qquad (2\text{-}22)$$

where the nomenclature is indicated in the figure. The use of venturi flumes is not common in water-works practice because public water supplies are not commonly conveyed in open channels.

[1] See also Jacobs and Sooy, *J. Elec. Power Gas*, July 22, 1911; Yarnell and Nagler, *Trans. Am. Soc. Civil Engrs.*, Vol. 100, p. 1018, 1935; W. M. Lansford, *Univ. Illinois Eng. Expt. Sta. Bull.* 289, 1936.

[2] *Loc. cit.*

2-13. Salt-velocity Method of Measurement. Allen and Taylor[1] introduced a method for the measurement of the rate of flow of water in which a salt solution is placed in the conduit and the time of passage of the solution between pairs of electrodes in the conduit is observed. Among the conditions affecting the accuracy[2] of the method are the uniformity of the cross section between electrodes, and the presence of large-scale eddies between electrodes.

2-14. Hazen and Williams Formula. Numerous formulas are available for the expression of the rate of flow of water in closed conduits, particularly in circular pipes, but the formula that finds almost exclusive use in water-works practice is that of Hazen and Williams,[3] originally expressed as

$$V = CR^{0.63}S^{0.54}0.001^{-0.04} \qquad (2\text{-}23)$$

$$V = 1.318 \, CR^{0.63}S^{0.54}$$

where V = velocity of flow
  R = hydraulic radius = $D/4$ for circular pipes $R = \dfrac{D}{4}$
  D = diameter of a circular pipe
  S = slope of the hydraulic grade line
  C = coefficient depending on the roughness and age[4] of the pipe, and on units used

The formula can be expressed also as

$$H_1 = \frac{3{,}030}{C^{1.85}D^{1.17}} \qquad (2\text{-}24)$$

$$H_1 = K_1 \frac{V^{1.85}}{D^{1.17}} \qquad (2\text{-}25)$$

where H_1 = head loss, ft per 1,000 ft of pipe, and other units in feet and seconds

Values of C and of K_1 are given in Table 2-2.

Solutions of problems involving the Hazen and Williams formula have been simplified by the use of slide rules and charts. Nomographic charts are shown in Fig. 2-5, based on the value of $C = 100$, and in Fig. 21-3, for special application to 8-in. pipes. Since V and Q vary directly with C, Fig. 2-5 can be read directly with $C = 100$. The true value of V or Q is then the product of the true value of C and the value of V or Q read from Fig. 2-5, divided by 100.

[1] C. M. Allen and E. A. Taylor, *Trans. Am. Soc. Civil Engrs.*, Vol. 45, p. 285, 1923.

[2] M. M. Mason, *J. Boston Soc. Civil Engrs.*, Vol. 27, p. 207, 1940.

[3] G. S. Williams and Allen Hazen, "Hydraulic Tables," 1st ed., John Wiley & Sons, Inc., New York, 1905, with subsequent editions; see also: *J. New Engl. Water Works Assoc.*, September, 1935; Julian Hinds, *J.A.W.W.A.*, November, 1946, p. 1226.

[4] See also P. Lamont, *J. Inst. Water Engrs.*, February, 1954, p. 53.

TABLE 2-2. Values of C and of K_1 in Hazen and Williams Formula
(For circular pipes running full)

Material	C	K_1
New tar-coated pipes:		
Supply and transmission mains larger than or equal to 16 in...	135	0.35
Distribution mains smaller than 16 in......................	125	0.405
New cement-lined pipes:		
Centrifugal method, based on actual diam. where diam. is		
between 4 and 24 in.................................	150	0.28
New cast-iron pipe, pit cast.................................	120–130	
New cast-iron pipe, centrifugally cast........................	125–135	
Cement lining, applied by hand.............................	125–135	
Bitumastic enamel, hand brushed...........................	135–145	
Bitumastic enamel, centrifugally applied.....................	145–155	
Concrete, best workmanship, large diam.....................	145–155	
Ordinary tar-dipped cast-iron, 20 years service in inactive water..	110–125	
Ordinary tar-dipped cast-iron after long service with severe tuber-		
culation...	30–40	
Ordinary tar-dipped cast iron; average effect of tuberculation on		
values of C: new, 135; 5 years old, 120; 10 years old, 110; 15		
years old, 105; 20 years old, 95; 30 years old, 85; 40 years old, 80		
New bituminous enamel-lined pipes		
Supply and transmission pipes 16 in. or larger...............	155	0.27
Smaller than 16 in..	145	0.30
Transite pipe:		
6-in..	140+	0.32
Old tuberculated cast-iron pipe after 20 years of service.........	100	0.61

Example. Find the rate and the velocity of flow in a bituminous-lined pipe 16 in. in diameter, when the head loss is 1 ft per 1,000 ft, and $C = 160$.

Solution. Reading from Fig. 2-5, $Q = 1,000$ and $V = 1.6$. The correct value of Q is $1,000 \times {}^{160}\!/_{100} = 1,600$ gpm, and of V is $1.6 \times {}^{160}\!/_{100} = 2.6$ fpm.

The values of S or of H for values of C other than 100 must be computed by multiplying the value read from Fig. 2-5 by $(100/C)^{1.85}$.

Example. Find the head lost, in feet, and the velocity in feet per second, in 2,000 ft of 16-in. bitumastic-lined pipe when Q is 1,600 gpm, and C is 160.

Solution. Reading from Fig. 2-5, $H = 2.4$ and $V = 2.6$. The head loss in 2,000 ft is $(2.4 \times 2,000/1,000)(100/160)^{1.85} = 2.0$ ft.

When two of the three terms Q, V, and D are known the third can be read directly from the nomograph without regard to the value of C because the three parameters are related independently of C in the form $Q = AV = \pi V D^2/4$. Hence, in the preceding example, $V = 2.6$ fps.

The Hazen and Williams formula is so widely used in water-works practice that engineers refer to it indirectly when describing the characteristics of a pipe as "100" pipe or "140" pipe, depending on the coefficient of roughness.

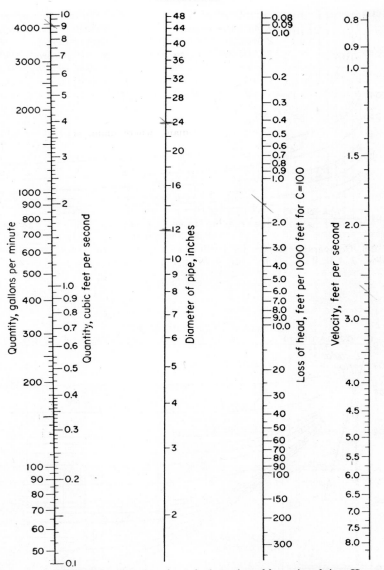

FIG. 2-5. A nomographic chart for the solution of problems involving Hazen and Williams formula. Use of diagram: Place a straightedge on two known points and read at the intersection of the straightedge with the verticals the values of the other two hydraulic elements which satisfy the condition. When only Q and V are given the problem is indeterminate. The values of loss of head are good only for $C = 100$.

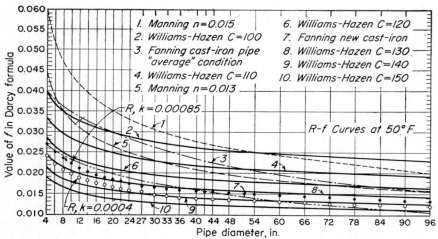

FIG. 2-6. Comparative curves for f values at a mean velocity of 3 fps. (*From Leo Hudson, J.A.W.W.A., June, 1947, p. 570.*)

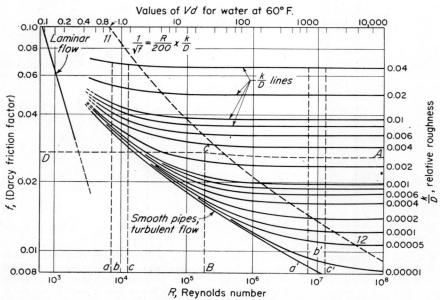

FIG. 2-7. Solution of Colebrook formula for rough pipe. (*From G. H. Hickox, Proc. Am. Soc. Civil Engrs., April, 1947.*)

2-15. The Weisbach or Darcy Formula, and the Chézy Formula. The Weisbach or Darcy formula[1] is expressed as

$$H = f \frac{lV^2}{D2g} \tag{2-26}$$

and the Chézy formula is expressed as

$$V = C_1 \sqrt{RS} \tag{2-27}$$

where f and C_1 are friction coefficients, l is the length of the pipe, and other nomenclature is as in Eq. (2-23). The two formulas are algebraically identical and both are rational formulas since they can be developed mathematically from Bernoulli's formulation of the principle of the conservation of energy. Values of f are shown in Figs. 2-6 and 2-7. It has been shown by various investigators that f is not a constant depending on the roughness of the pipe but that it is also a function of the head loss and of the pipe diameter, or both of them. Harris[2] has shown that

$$f = 0.0061 + \frac{f_1 + 0.0061}{D^{1/3}} \tag{2-28}$$

TABLE 2-3. Values of f_1 in Eq. (2-28)*

Material	f_1	Turbulent velocity, fps at 55°F V_t	Material	f_1	Turbulent velocity, fps at 55°F V_t
Metallized stainless steel..............	0.0146	3.5	Concrete drain tile....	0.024	1.6
Wood stave, old surface..............	0.0150	3.0	Cast-iron pipe, average for city mains...	0.028	
Cement-lined steel...	0.0173	1.6	Cast-iron pipe, old and foul...........	0.042	
Black pipe surface only..............	0.018	1.5	Riveted steel, 25 years old, tuberculated....	0.062	
Cast-iron pipe, bare surface..........	0.023		Wood stave, continuous................	0.023	3.0

* From Harris, *Proc. Am. Soc. Civil Engrs.*, May, 1949, p. 555.

with values of f_1 given in Table 2-3.

Formulas for flow in the turbulent region involving the use of the Reynolds number R_n for the determination of f include:[3]

[1] "Recherches expérimentales relative au mouvement de l'eau dans les tuyaux," Paris, 1857.

[2] Harris, *Proc. Am. Soc. Civil Engrs.*, May, 1949, p. 555.

[3] See also Julian Hinds, *J.A.W.W.A.*, November, 1946, p. 1226.

von Kármán, Nikuradse, for smooth pipe,

$$\frac{1}{\sqrt{f}} = 2.0 \log \frac{R_n \sqrt{f}}{2.51} = 2.0 \log R_n \sqrt{f} - 0.8 \tag{2-29}$$

For rough pipe, complete turbulence,

$$\frac{1}{\sqrt{f}} = 1.14 - 2.0 \log \frac{k}{D} = 2 \log \frac{3.7D}{k} \tag{2-30}$$

Colebrook, for rough pipes,

$$\frac{1}{\sqrt{f}} = -2 \log \left(\frac{k}{3.7D} + \frac{2.51}{R_n \sqrt{f}} \right) \tag{2-31}$$

where R_n = Reynolds number = $VD\rho/\mu$
   k = absolute roughness, or height of surface roughness or some linear dimension representing height, form, and distribution of such projections
   ρ = density
   μ = relative viscosity

2-16. The Kutter Formula[1] and the Manning Formula.[2] The Kutter formula is commonly expressed as

$$V = \left\{ \frac{(1.81/n) + 41.67 + (0.0028/S)}{1 + (n/\sqrt{R})[41.67 + (0.0028/S)]} \right\} \sqrt{RS} \tag{2-32}$$

and the Manning formula as

$$V = \frac{1.486}{n} R^{\frac{2}{3}} S^{\frac{1}{2}} \tag{2-33}$$

where additional nomenclature is n = coefficient of roughness
Values of n are given in Table 2-4.

TABLE 2-4. Values of Absolute Roughness k in von Kármán, Nikuradse, and Colebrook Formulas and of n in the Manning and Kutter Formulas

Material	k	Kutter's and Manning's n
Drawn tubing	0.000005	0.0105
Commercial steel or wrought iron	0.00015	0.011
Asphalted cast iron	0.0004	0.012
Galvanized iron	0.0005	0.013
Wood stave	0.0006–0.003	0.014
Cast iron	0.00085	0.015
Concrete	0.001 –0.01	0.016
Riveted steel	0.003 –0.03	

[1] E. Ganguillet and W. R. Kutter, "A General Formula for Flow of Water in Rivers and Other Channels," translated by J. C. Trautwine, John Wiley & Sons, Inc., New York, 1907.

[2] R. Manning, *Trans. Inst. Civil Engrs. Ireland*, Vol. 20, 1890.

The Kutter and Manning formulas are most commonly used for the solution of problems in open-channel flow. Results obtained by the use of the two formulas are close, and the relative simplicity of the Manning formula leads to its use more often than the Kutter formula.

2-17. Other Formulas. Among many other formulas devised, but not now extensively used in water-works practice, are:

Bazin:[1]
$$V = \frac{87}{0.522 + m/\sqrt{R}} \sqrt{RS} \qquad (2\text{-}34)$$

Capen:[2] $\quad V = F_m D^{0.625} H_1^{0.5}$ (2-35)

Flamant:[3] $\quad V = CR^{\frac{3}{4}}S^{\frac{4}{7}}$ (2-36)

Rhodes:[4] $\quad V = 17.5R_n{}^{0.085}F_n{}^{-0.02}D^{0.5}S^{0.5}$ (2-37)

Scobey:[5] $\quad V = H_1^{0.5}(12D)^{0.625}$ (2-38)

where nomenclature not previously given is

$$C, m, \text{ and } F_m = \text{friction factors depending on roughness}$$
$$F_n = \text{Froude number[6]} = V/\sqrt{Dg}$$

2-18. The Reynolds and the Froude Numbers. The inclusion of the Reynolds number[7] and of the Froude number[6] in problems involving the

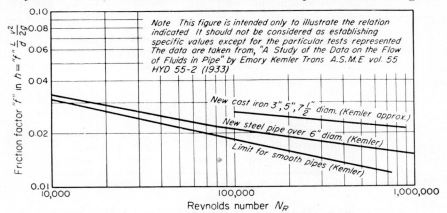

Note This figure is intended only to illustrate the relation indicated It should not be considered as establishing specific values except for the particular tests represented The data are taken from, "A Study of the Data on the Flow of Fluids in Pipe" by Emory Kemler Trans A.S.M.E vol. 55 HYD 55-2 (1933)

New cast iron 3", 5", 7½" diam. (Kemler approx.)

New steel pipe over 6" diam. (Kemler)

Limit for smooth pipes (Kemler)

Friction factor "f" in $h = "f" \frac{L}{d} \frac{v^2}{2g}$

Reynolds number N_R

FIG. 2-8. Relation between friction factor f and Reynold's number.

flow of fluids other than cold water facilitates the solutions. Both numbers are useful, particularly the Reynolds number, in the prediction of the performance of large conduits based on experiments made on small ones. Relations between R_n, k, and f are indicated in Figs. 2-7 and 2-8, and in Table 2-4.

[1] M. Basin, *Ann. ponts et chaussées*, October, 1888.

[2] *J.A.W.W.A.*, Vol. 33, p. 1, 1941.

[3] A. Flamant, *Ann. ponts et chaussées*, September, 1892.

[4] *Eng. News-Record*, Aug. 15, 1940, p. 45.

[5] *U.S. Dept. Ag. Bull.* 376, 1916; *Bull.* 852, 1924; *Bull.* 150, 1930.

[6] W. Froude, *Trans. Inst. Naval Arch.*, Vol. 11, p. 80, 1870.

[7] Osborn Reynolds, *Phil. Trans. Roy. Soc. (London)*, 1882 and 1885; see also C. H. Capen, *Water & Sewage Works*, April, 1948, p. 125.

2-19. Effect of Temperature and of Pressure on Flow. In general, the effect of temperature and of pressure variation on the formulas for rates or velocities of flow, involved in the field of water works, is negligible, so that the formulas used do not allow for these factors. However, where temperatures are involved that are higher than those normally permitted for potable water, some allowance may be made for them. This can be done partly through the information in Tables 2-5 and 2-6 and Fig. 2-8.

TABLE 2-5. Density and Viscosity of Water at Different Temperatures

Temp, °F	Density ρ, lb per cu ft	Viscosity μ, lb per ft sec	$\rho/\mu = 1/\nu$	Temp, °F	Density ρ, lb per cu ft	Viscosity μ, lb per ft sec	$\rho/\mu = 1/\nu$
32	62.42	0.001206	51,754	90	62.12	0.000513	121,091
40	62.42	0.001039	60,082	100	62.00	0.000458	135,371
50	62.41	0.000880	70,918	150	61.20	0.000291	210,309
60	62.37	0.000759	82,173	175	60.69	0.000241	251,825
70	62.30	0.000660	94,393	200	60.14	0.000205	293,365
80	62.22	0.000579	107,611	212	59.84	0.000141	313,314

TABLE 2-6. Effect of Temperature on R_n and f in Pipes*

Smooth pipe			Rough pipe		
Temp, °F	R_n, in thousands	f	Temp, °F	R_n, in thousands	f
40	7,300	0.0336	40	7,300	0.00849
60	10,000	0.0309	60	10,000	0.00810
80	13,200	0.0287	80	13,200	0.00779

* See also Julian Hinds, *J.A.W.W.A.*, November, 1946, p. 1226.

Example. What will be the effect on the friction loss in a 12-in. new steel pipe carrying water at 6 fps if the temperature of the water changes from 40 to 90°F? Suggestion: use Table 2-5 and Fig. 2-8 where necessary.

Solution. $R_n = VD\rho/\mu$. Hence

$$R_n \text{ at } 40°F = \frac{6 \times 1 \times 62.42}{0.001039} = 360,000$$

$$R_n \text{ at } 90°F = \frac{6 \times 1 \times 62.12}{0.000513} = 728,000$$

Hence, from Fig. 2-8 f at 40°F = 0.0173 and at 90°F it equals 0.0159.

Answer. The friction loss would be decreased $(0.0173 - 0.0159)/0.0173$, or by about 8 per cent. The carrying capacity would be 8 per cent greater for the 90°F water than for the 40°F water.

2-20. Losses of Head Due to Pipe Fittings and Valves. Losses of head due to friction in pipe fittings can be expressed in the general form $h = k \dfrac{V^2}{2g}$ where the values of k, for foot and second units, are as shown in Table 2-7.[1]

TABLE 2-7. Values of k for Pipe Fittings and Valves

Sudden contraction				Bend				Fittings			
A_2/A_1*	k	A_2/A_1*	k	D/r†	k	D/r†	k	Fitting	k	Fitting	k
0.1	0.362	0.6	0.164	0.2	0.131	1.2	0.440	Globe valve wide open	10	Medium-radius elbow	0.75
0.2	0.388	0.7	0.105	0.4	0.138	1.4	0.661	Angle valve wide open	5	Long-radius elbow	0.60
0.3	0.308	0.8	0.053	0.6	0.158	1.6	0.977	Close return bend	2.2	40-deg elbow	0.42
0.4	0.267	0.9	0.005	0.8	0.206	1.8	1.40	Tee, through side outlet	1.8	Gate valve wide open	0.19
0.5	0.221	1.0	0.000	1.0	0.294	2.0	1.98	Short-radius elbow	0.9	Submerged discharge	1.0

* A_1 = area of pipe above contraction, and A_2 = area below contraction.
† D = diameter of pipe, and r = radius of bend.

The values of k for bends, shown in the table, are primarily for small pipes up to 2 in. in diameter. Their applicability to larger pipes has not been demonstrated. In a sudden enlargement, if d represents the diameter of the smaller pipe and D that of the larger pipe, then, when $d/D = \frac{1}{4}$, $k = 0.92$; $d/D = \frac{1}{2}$, $k = 0.56$; and when $d/D = \frac{3}{4}$, $k = 0.19$.

2-21. Hydraulic Grade Line and Total-energy Line. A hydraulic grade line is a line joining points whose vertical distances from the centroid of the cross section of the stream flowing in a closed channel are proportional to the pressures in the pipe at the point. In open-channel flow the hydraulic grade line lies in the surface of the stream. The slope of the hydraulic grade line is known as the "hydraulic gradient." The total-energy line is the locus of points lying one velocity head above the hydraulic grade line. The hydraulic grade line and the total-energy lines shown in Fig. 2-9 indicate the effect of friction losses and changes in velocity on the pressures and the energies in the pipe line.

2-22. Equivalent Pipes and Compound Pipes. Two pipes, two systems of pipes, or a single pipe and a system of pipes are said to be equivalent when the losses of head for equal rates of flow in them are equal. Problems involving equivalent pipes are common in water-works practice.

A compound pipe is made up of two or more pipes of different diameters connected end to end (in series), or of two or more pipes of the same or of

[1] Additional values are given by F. E. Giesecke in *Bull. Univ. Texas*, Oct. 20, 1917; and by H. E. Babbitt in "Plumbing," 2d ed., Chap. 2, McGraw-Hill Book Company, Inc., New York, 1950.

different diameters connected in parallel. The two conditions are illustrated in Fig. 2-10. Compound pipes exist in water-distribution systems and in long pipe lines.

Many methods have been devised for the solution of problems involving head losses and rates of flow in compound pipes.[1] The first step in the method presented here involves changing all the pipes of the system to

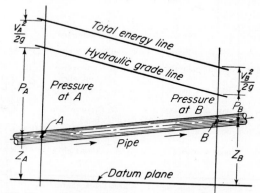

FIG. 2-9. Bernoulli's theorem applied to closed-channel flow.

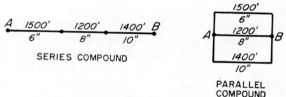

FIG. 2-10. Compound pipe. $C = 120$.

equivalent lengths of 8-in. pipe with $C = 100$. This can be done by substitution in the expression

$$l_8 = \left(\frac{100}{C_n}\right)^{1.85} \left(\frac{8}{d_n}\right)^{4.87} l_n \qquad (2\text{-}39)$$

where l_8 = equivalent length of 8-in. pipe, ft
$\quad C_n$ = hydraulic coefficient for pipe whose diameter is d_n, in.
$\quad l_n$ = length, ft, of pipe whose diameter is d_n, in.
Values of this expression of l_8 are recorded in Table 21-2.

A problem involving a series-compound pipe solved by the use of Eq. (2-39) or Table 21-2 and Fig. 2-5 or Fig. 21-3 is as follows:

[1] See also: Q. B. Graves, *Civil Eng.*, February, 1944; J. R. Arbuthnot, *Water & Sewage Works*, August, 1946, p. 306; G. E. Hinds, *Civil Eng.*, October, 1950, p. 43; B. C. Seal, *ibid.*, January, 1951, p. 54.

Example. Find the flow in the series-compound pipe in Fig. 2-10, when the pressure at A is 100 psi, and at B is 50 psi. Assume C in all pipes is 120.

Solution. From Table 21-2, 1,500 ft of 6-in. pipe with $C = 120$ are equivalent to $1,500 \times 2.9 = 4,350$ ft of 8-in. pipe with $C = 100$; 1,200 ft of 8-in. pipe with $C = 120$ are equivalent to $1,200 \times 0.713 = 855$ ft of 8-in. pipe with $C = 100$; and 1,400 ft of 10-in. pipe with $C = 120$ are equivalent to $1,400 \times 0.242 = 338$ ft of 8-in. pipe with $C = 100$. If these lengths are added the total equivalent length of 8-in. pipe with $C = 100$ is 5,543 ft. The head loss given in the data is 50 psi, equivalent to $50 \times 2.31/1,000 = 115.5$ ft per 1,000 ft. The rate of flow with this head loss, from Fig. 2-5, is 2,000 gpm.

In the solution of a problem involving a parallel-compound pipe each pipe should be converted, as before, to an equivalent length of 8-in. pipe with $C = 100$. If the total rate of flow through the system is known the rate of flow through each pipe will be inversely proportional to its length to the 0.54 power, and the head loss through the system will be equal to the head loss through any one pipe.

Example. If the flow from A to B in the parallel-compound pipe shown in Fig. 2-10 is 2,000 gpm, and $C = 120$ for each pipe, what is the head loss, in feet, from A to B?

Solution. Convert all pipes to equivalent lengths of 8-in. pipe with $C = 100$. These lengths are given in the preceding solution.

Now
$$Q_6 + Q_8 + Q_{10} = 2,000$$

where $Q_6 =$ flow in 6-in. pipe, etc.

and
$$\frac{Q_{10}}{Q_6} = \left(\frac{4,350}{338}\right)^{0.54} = 3.96 \qquad \frac{Q_8}{Q_6} = \left(\frac{4,350}{855}\right)^{0.54} = 2.4$$

hence
$$Q_6 + 2.43Q_6 + 3.96Q_6 = 2,000$$
and
$$Q_6 = 270 \qquad Q_8 = 650 \qquad \text{and} \qquad Q_{10} = 1,080 \text{ gpm}$$

The head loss in each pipe, reading from Fig. 2-5, is: 10-in., $33 \times 0.338 = 11$ ft; 8-in., $13 \times 0.855 = 11$ ft; and 6-in., $2.5 \times 4.35 = 11$ ft.

2-23. Crossovers and Intersections. Crossovers and intersections occur in distribution systems, as indicated in Fig. 2-11. The head losses,

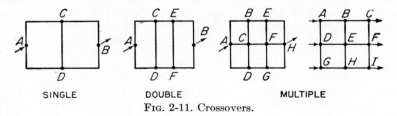

FIG. 2-11. Crossovers.

rates of flow, and other conditions cannot be computed by the equivalent-pipe method. A method for the solution of such problems, devised by Hardy Cross, is explained in Sec. 21-5.

2-24. Fire Streams. The determination of the head loss or the rate of flow in a fire hose and nozzle attached to a hydrant presents no special difficulty when the coefficients of friction in the hose and nozzle and the

TABLE 2-8. Friction Factors in $2\frac{1}{2}$-in. Fire Hose*

Description of hose	Values of f for velocities, fps				
	4	6	10	15	20
Unlined canvas..............	0.038	0.038	0.037	0.035	0.034
Rough rubber-lined cotton....	0.032	0.031	0.031	0.030	0.029
Smooth rubber-lined cotton...	0.024	0.023	0.022	0.019	0.018

* From H. N. Lendall, Hydraulics and Water Works Engineering, *J.A.W.W.A.*, December, 1939, p. 207.

discharge from the nozzle are known.   Ordinarily, standard fire hose is $2\frac{1}{2}$ in. in diameter and it is rubber-lined.   The rate of flow through it can be computed by the Weisbach formula, Eq. (2-26), using values of f given in Table 2-8.   The rate of flow through a fire nozzle can be expressed as

$$Q = C_d a \sqrt{2gh_n} \qquad (2\text{-}40)$$

where Q = rate of flow, cfs
$\qquad a$ = area of contracted jet, sq ft
$\qquad g$ = acceleration of gravity, ft per sec^2
$\qquad h_n$ = pressure at base of nozzle, ft
$\qquad C_d$ = coefficient of discharge of the nozzle
Values of C_d for the nozzle shown in Fig. 2-12 are shown in the same figure.

TABLE 2-9. Heights and Distances, Feet, That Fire Streams Can Be Thrown*

Pressure at base of nozzle, psi	Angle with horizontal, deg	$1\frac{1}{2}$- to 2-in. jets		3-in. jets		Theoretical	
		Max height	Horizontal distance at max height	Max height	Horizontal distance at max height	Max height	Horizontal distance at max height
50	20	15	75	15	75	15	75
	50	60	100	62	100	70	115
100	20	30	140	30	140	30	140
	50	110	165	120	180	140	230
200	20	45	210	50	220 ±	50	220 ±
	50	175	180	180	250 ±	>200	250 ±

* Based on information presented by H. Rouse and J. W. Howe, *Proc. Am. Soc. Civil Engrs.*, October, 1951.

Heights and distances that fire streams can be thrown are given in Table 2-9.

The rate of discharge from fire hydrants has been reported by Wilson[1] as

$$Q = 27d^2p^{0.5} \qquad (2\text{-}41)$$

where Q = discharge, gpm

d = internal diameter of hydrant nozzle, in.

p = pressure at hydrant, psi

Additional information concerning fire hydrants is given in Sec. 18-19.

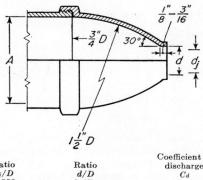

Ratio d_i/D	Ratio d/D	Coefficient of discharge C_d
0.250	0.279	0.805
0.300	0.335	0.806
0.350	0.391	0.807
0.400	0.446	0.811
0.450	0.501	0.817
0.500	0.557	0.825

Fig. 2-12. Characteristics of recommended fire nozzle. (*From Hunter Rouse, Proc. Am. Soc. Civil Engrs., Vol. 77, Separate 92, October, 1951, p. 26.*)

The effective reach of a fire stream can be computed by the Goldsmith[2] formula

$$H = \sqrt{(240P - P^2 - 1,900)} - 15 \qquad (2\text{-}42)$$

where H = height for ¾-in. nozzle, ft

P = pressure at base of nozzle, psi

For larger nozzles increase H by 1 ft for each additional ⅛-in. nozzle size for pressures below 50 psi, and by 2 ft for pressures above 50 psi.

If more than one line of hose is attached to a hydrant and the lengths of all hoses, the sizes and types of all nozzles, and the rate of discharge from one nozzle are all known, the rates of flow and the pressures at the bases of all nozzles can be determined by a method of trial and error.

Example. Let it be required to determine the pressure at the hydrant, the pressure at the base of each nozzle, and the rate of flow from each nozzle shown in Fig. 2-13, where C_d for each nozzle is 0.97, and f for the hose is 0.032. The rate of flow from nozzle A is 356 gpm.

[1] P. S. Wilson, *Water Works & Sewerage*, April, 1935, p. 115.

[2] C. Goldsmith, *J.A.W.W.A.*, December, 1939, p. 2027.

Solution.   1. Determine the pressure at the base of nozzle A:

$$P = \frac{Q^2}{2gC_a^2a^2} = \frac{(356/60 \times 7.5)^2}{64.4 \times 2.31 \times 0.97^2 \times [(\pi \times 1.5^2)/(4 \times 144)]^2}$$
$$= 30 \text{ psi}$$

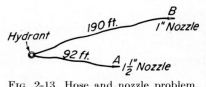

FIG. 2-13. Hose and nozzle problem.

2. Determine the head loss in hose A:

$$P = \frac{h}{2.31} = \frac{flV^2}{2.31D2g} = \left(\frac{92 \times 12}{2.5 \times 64.4 \times 2.31}\right) \times \left(\frac{356 \times 4 \times 144}{450 \times 6.25}\right)^2 = 50 \text{ psi}$$

3. Determine the pressure at the hydrant:

$$30 + 50 = 80 \text{ psi}$$

4. Assume, as a trial, that Q from nozzle B is 200 gpm.

5. Determine the pressure at nozzle B with the above rate of flow, following the procedure in step 1. $P = 47.1$ psi.

6. Determine the loss of head in hose B, following the procedure in step 2. $P = 32.9$ psi.

7. Determine the pressure in the hydrant, as in step 3. $47.1 + 32.9 = 80$ psi.

This checks the pressure in the hydrant computed from the known rate of flow from nozzle A.   Hence, the assumed flow of 200 gpm from nozzle B is correct. If it is not correct, another assumption must be made and the procedure continued until the correct rate of flow is found.

CHAPTER 3

DEMAND FOR WATER

3-1. Estimates of Demand. The making of an estimate of the probable rate of demand for water by a community is among the first steps to be taken in the design of water works therefor. The determination of the demand is important because it fixes the capacity and sizes of the parts of the system. The rate of demand changes with the growth of the city, and it is obviously undesirable to construct a system which might be outgrown in a short time.

The period into the future for which the estimate of demand is to be made depends, to some extent, on the portion of the water works being designed and how it is to be financed. If the structure is long-lived and will benefit future generations, it will be unfair to the present generation to put the full financial burden upon it. On the other hand, it is unwise and uneconomical to build for too short a period. In some states 20 years is the legal limit of time in which municipal bonds must be retired. Such a period is a fair guide to the judgment of the designer when no better information is available.

In making an estimate of future demand, information on present usage is frequently available. This information may be in the form of pumpage records, meter readings, or otherwise. In using it, allowance should be made for the changed conditions that will result from the proposed improvement.

3-2. Population and Rate of Demand. Some rates of the use of water are shown in Table 3-1. No correlation is indicated in this table between population and rate of use per capita. Nevertheless, it is generally assumed that rate of use per capita is greater in large than in small communities, and that as a community grows the per capita rate of use will increase. This may be due, in part, to greater industrial demands and to increased use for municipal purposes.

Studies reported by Capen[1] show that the following expressions may be used to indicate, approximately, the rate of increase of per capita rate of use with population:

[1] C. H. Capen, Jr., *J.A.W.W.A.*, Vol. 29, p. 201, 1937; *Water Works Eng.*, Feb. 17, 1937, p. 212.

For completely metered, low-waste systems

$$G = 53 \, P^{0.11}$$

For well-metered, average systems

$$G = 54 \, P^{0.125}$$

where G = gallons per capita per day
P = population, thousands

TABLE 3-1. Rates of Water Usage

Location	Year	Population, thousands	% metered		Use, gpcpd	
			Domestic	Industrial	Before meters	After meters
Fayetteville, Ark............	1910	5	0	0	100	
	1932	.....	100	100	...	65
Jonesboro, Ark.............	1924	9	50	50	111	
	1932	11	100	100	...	69
San Francisco, Calif.........	1910	417	0	24	85	
	1920	508	100	100	...	71
Lewiston, Idaho.............	1920	6.6	79	79	215	
	1932	15	100	100	...	175
Madisonville, Ky............	1920	8	0	0	225	
	1932	9	100	100	...	105
Quincy, Mass...............	1910	33	36	...	88	
	1920	49	92	...	93	
	1932	74	100	...	...	69
Flint, Mich.................	1910	39	15	50	113	
	1932	150	100	100	...	91
Hastings, Mich..............	1900	5.1	10	0	180	
	1932	5.1	98	100	...	80
Reading, Pa.................	1900	78	0	80	92	
	1932	118	100	100	...	91
Greenville, Tenn............	1920	3.8	15	80	117	
	1932	6.2	100	100	...	60
Avg.....................	....	.....	...	...	133	88

3-3. Prediction of Population.[1] Methods for the prediction of future population can be classified as (1) mathematical or graphical, (2) projections based on migrations and on natural increase, and (3) forecasts based on specific estimates of future employment. Mathematical or graphical methods, modified by rational application of knowledge of the economy and other conditions of the area, are most commonly used in water-works practice.

[1] See also Van Buren Stanbery, Better Population Forecasting for Areas and Communities, *U.S. Dept. Commerce, Domestic Commerce Series* 32, 1952.

The mathematical or graphical methods may be classified as:

1. *Arithmetical progression,* in which a constant increment of growth is added periodically. For example, if the population increased from 100,000 to 110,000 in the past decade, it would increase by an increment of 10,000 to 120,000 in the next decade.

2. *Geometrical progression,* in which a constant percentage of growth is assumed for equal periods of time. For example, if the population increased from 100,000 to 110,000 during the past decade, it would increase 10 per cent to 121,000 during the next decade.

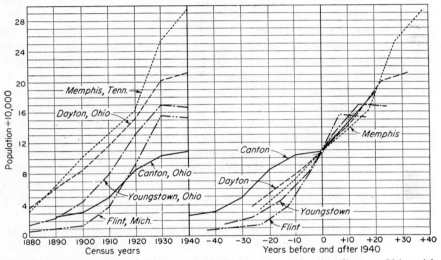

FIG. 3-1. Population prediction by graphical comparison, showing Canton, Ohio, with a population of 176,000 in 1970.

3. *Decreasing rate of increase* is similar to the geometrical progression but with an arbitrary assumption of a decreasing, rather than a constant, rate of increase.

4. *Graphical extension* of the population-time curve into the future by mathematical or statistical methods or by eye guided by judgment based on knowledge of probable conditions.

5. *Graphical extension* based on Verhulst's[1] logistic grid.   The method is based on a modification of Verhulst's theory by Velz and Eich.[2]

6. *Graphical comparison* involving the extension of the population-time curve of the community into the future based on a comparison with population-time curves of similar and larger communities.   In this method, the population-time curves are plotted as indicated in Fig. 3-1 with the

---

[1] See P. F. Verhulst, Recherches mathématiques sur la loi d'acroissement de la population, *Mem. acad. roy. Bruxelles,* Vol. 18, pp. 1–58, 1844.

[2] C. S. Velz and H. F. Eich, *Civil Eng.,* October, 1940, p. 619.

curves for all cities passing through the same point, represented by the present population of the city for which the prediction is to be made. Projections based on studies of migrations, natural increases, future employment and economic conditions, and on other predicted factors may be used to modify the results of the "graphical-comparison" method. This method, based as it is on a logical study of past and future conditions, gives promise of a reliable prediction.

Information on the past and present population of a community can be obtained from such sources as the Federal census, school censuses, the chamber of commerce, the post office, public utilities, health districts, and the city directory.

3-4. Rates of Water Usage. A man, under normal conditions of comfort and physical effort, consumes *as a beverage* less than a quart of water a day. However, his demand for water for other purposes, on a desirable living standard, is relatively large. These other purposes include the kitchen, the laundry, and the bath and, communally, the industrial plant and the municipality. Statistics in Table 3-1 show how different are the rates of water use in various communities. The U.S. Army sets, as an absolute minimum, 2 quarts per day for no longer than 3 days.[1] Some of our larger cities use more than a billion gallons of water in a day, with per capita rates greater than 300. When a rough approximation of water demand is to be made, and other information is not available, it is usually assumed that 100 gal per capita per day is fairly representative of rate of water usage.[2]

Studies of statistics[3] of water usage in the United States reveal an increasing trend in per capita use of water and conflicting conclusions concerning average rates. Langbein[4] gives the information shown in Tables 3-2 and 3-3. He states, "The increased use of water . . . has

TABLE 3-2. Comparison of Population and Water Use Increase*

Item	1890	1945
Number of water works............	1,878	15,400
Population served, millions.........	22.8	94.39
% of total in U.S..................	36	71
Avg use, gpcpd....................	90	127
Total estimated usage, mgd.........	2,050	12,030

* From W. B. Langbein, *J.A.W.W.A.*, November, 1949, p. 997.

[1] Military Water Supply and Purification, *War Dept. Tech. Manual* TM5-295, August, 1945.

[2] See also B. O. Larson and H. E. Hudson, Jr., *J.A.W.W.A.*, August, 1951, p. 603.

[3] A Survey of Operating Data for Water Works in 1945, *J.A.W.W.A.*, February, 1948, p. 167; "Inventory of Water and Sewage Facilities in the U.S.," U.S. Public Health Service, 1948.

[4] W. B. Langbein, *J.A.W.W.A.*, November, 1949, p. 997.

raised this figure to a general average of 127 gal per capita per day and to more than 300 gal per capita per day in many of the western communities." MacKichan[1] states that "municipal water systems served 93.5 million people in 1950, an average of 145 gal per day per person. . . ."

TABLE 3-3. Relation of Size of City to Per Capita Use of Water*

Population, thousands	0.5	1.0	5.0	10	50	100
Avg water use, gpcpd	60	85	135	140	140	140

* From W. B. Langbein, *J.A.W.W.A.*, November, 1949, p. 997.

Rates in European cities are generally lower than in the United States, varying between 15 and 100 gal per capita per day. The lower rate of demand in European as compared with American cities may be attributed to the greater percentage of European dwellings with fewer plumbing fixtures, to the somewhat lower standard of living in major portions of some European cities, and to the less wasteful attitude of the European householder.

3-5. Use of Water for Specific Purposes. The amounts of water that may be used for specific purposes may be expressed, roughly, in percentages of the total use as domestic, 35; industrial and commercial, 39; public, 10; and waste and miscellaneous, 16. Under public uses may be included any use by the city government such as cleaning and flushing streets, public fountains, schools, and other municipal purposes except fire for

TABLE 3-4. Rates of Usage of Water for Various Purposes[a]

Purpose	Amount, gpcpd unless otherwise stated	Purpose	Amount, gpcpd unless otherwise stated
Domestic only	10	Office buildings[b]	27–45
Cities in N.Y., N.J., and New England	26–44.5	Hospitals[b]	125–350[c]
		Hospitals[d]	66–1144[e]
Single-family houses in 1927:		Hotels[b]	306–525[e]
West Haven, Conn.	36.8	Laundries[b]	3–5.7[f]
New Haven, Conn.	59.4	Restaurants[b]	0.5–4[g]

[a] From M. A. Pond, *J.A.W.W.A.*, December, 1939, p. 2003.
[b] From H. E. Jordan, *ibid.*, January, 1946, p. 65.
[c] Gallons per bed per day.
[d] From G. C. St. Laurent, *Hotel Eng.*, 1940.
[e] Gallons per day per occupied room, with average of 400 for hospitals.
[f] Gallons per pound.
[g] Gallons per meal.

[1] K. A. MacKichan, Estimated Use of Water in the United States, *U.S. Geol. Survey*, *Bull.* 115, May, 1951.

which the amount used is normally negligible. In some cities, industrial demand is greater than municipal demand.

Information on the use of water for specific purposes, other than industrial, is given in Tables 3-4 to 3-6.

TABLE 3-5. Water Required by Livestock, Gal per Animal per Day*

Horses	10	Milk cows	15	Sheep	3
Cattle	10	Hogs	4	Turkeys	0.05
Mules	10	Chickens	0.02	Goats	3

* From K. A. MacKichan, *U.S. Geol. Survey, Bull.* 115, May, 1951.

TABLE 3-6. Rates of Water Usage for Various Purposes, Gal per Day*

Single-family homes†	35–50	High schools‡	15– 20
Multifamily homes†	50–90	Hospitals§	125–225
Grade schools‡	5–10		

* From *Am. City*, November, 1951, p. 115.
† Per person.
‡ Per pupil.
§ Per patient.

3-6. Water Required by Industry.[1]   Information on industrial demands for water is given in Table 3-7.

3-7. Fire Demand.[2]   Fire protection is an important function of a water works. The total amount of water used in a year for extinguishing fires is usually a negligible part of the total use, but during a fire the rate of demand is so great as to be the deciding factor, in all but the largest communities, in fixing the capacities of pumps, reservoirs, and distributing pipes.

The fire demand is a function of population, with a minimum limit, because the greater the population the greater the number of buildings and the greater the risk of fire. The minimum limit of fire demand is the amount and rate of supply that are required to extinguish the largest probable fire that could be started in a community. A minimum of four fire streams available at all points is desirable within the area protected. Such streams should each throw at least 175 gpm in a low-risk district, and 250 gpm in high-risk districts. In rating a public water supply, the National Board of Fire Underwriters[3] fixes the required fire flow with

[1] See also: H. E. Jordan, *J.A.W.W.A.*, January, 1946, p. 65; *ibid.*, March, 1953, p. 289; Task Group Report, *ibid.*, December, 1953, p. 1249.

[2] See also: A. C. Huston, *J.A.W.W.A.*, September, 1948, p. 936; R. H. Ellis, *ibid.*, November, 1953, p. 1151.

[3] Standard Schedule for Grading Cities and Towns of the U.S., *J.A.W.W.A.*, October, 1942, p. 1584.

TABLE 3-7. Water Used for Industrial Purposes

Industry[a]	No. of industries	Production		Use, gal, estimated		Industry[b]	Unit	Gal per unit
		Units	10^6	Per unit 10^3	Year 1947 10^9			
Steel, finished..........	419	Tank	61.86	65	4,021	Rayon yarn..........	Ton	250-404
Oil refining.............	437	Bbl	1,888	0.77	1,454	Cotton bleaching.......	Ton	60-80
Gasoline................	.....	Bbl	791	0.36	791	Wool cloth............	M sq yd	40-510
Wood pulp:						Soap.................	Ton	0.5-4.5
Sulphate..............	.....	Ton	5.36	64	343	Ice, manufacturing.....	Ton	0.25-9.0
Sulphite..............	.....	Ton	2.80	60	168	Steam, electric genera-		
Soda.................	.....	Ton	0.49	85	4.17	tion.................	M kwhr	52-170
Paper...................	.....	Ton	10.6	39	415	Cane sugar...........	Ton	4-30
Paperboard.............	665	Ton	9.19	15	138	Whisky..............	M gal	70
Beer...................	440	Bbl	88.0	0.47	41.37	Fluid milk...........	Cwt	$(63-207)10^6$
Coke..................	167	Ton	79.1	3.6	284.5	Canned corn, No. 2....	Case	0.0072
Milk, cream, butter......	.....	Lb	72,440	c	12.3	Canned beans, No. 2...	Case	0.0035
Canning[d,e].............	2,265	Case	391	f	8.5[e]	Meat packing, no hogs..	Ton (live)	6.0
Ice, manufacturing.....	3,423	Ton	36.1	0.24	8.8	Steel, finished..........	Ton	65
Soft drinks.............	5,618	Case	928	0.0025	6.25	Cold-rolled..........	Ton	6.0
Wool scouring..........	74	Lb	210	0.0013	2.65	Hot-rolled..........	Ton	15-110
Tanning...............	561	Lb	239	0.008	1.9	Aviation gasoline.......	Bbl	1.05
Meat packing, hogs......	2,153	Hog	51.7	0.011	0.57	Petroleum products....	Bbl	0.15-15
Rayon, all types........	38	Lb	747	0.00016	0.12	Soap.................	Ton	0.5-4.5

[a] From "U.S. Census of Manufacturers, 1947." See *Sewage and Ind. Wastes*, February, 1951, p. 212.

[b] From "Water and Industry," National Association of Manufacturers, New York, December, 1950.

[c] 0.00011-0.00025.

[d] Excluding fish.

[e] This includes water used in processing only. The total amount used is probably two or three times higher.

[f] 0.0075-0.250.

respect to the population and the general structural condition of the district. The requirements vary between 1,000 gpm for 1,000 persons and 12,000 gpm for 200,000 persons, with a maximum of 20,000 gpm. There must be enough water to provide for a 5-hr fire for towns of less than 2,500 persons and a 10-hr fire for larger cities.[1] The pressure to be provided at the hydrant should, in general, not be less than about 20 psi where mobile fire-pumping engines are used, and 75 to 90 psi otherwise.

Authoritative recommendations concerning allowance to be made for peak fire demands in water-works design are listed in Table 3-8. The maximum rate of demand to be provided for in design is the sum of the fire demand and the general-service demand occurring simultaneously.

3-8. Fluctuations in Rates of Demand.[2,3] The rate of use of water varies greatly with the time over which the rate is computed, as shown in

[1] R. H. Ellis (*J.A.W.W.A.*, November, 1953, p. 1151) presents a method for the computation of storage deficiency convertible into N.B.F.U. units.

[2] See *Water Works Eng.*, June 12, 1946, p. 702.

[3] See M. P. Hatcher, *Water & Sewage Works*, May, 1947, p. 157.

TABLE 3-8. Empirical Formulas for Rates of Fire Demand

Name of originator or authority	Formula: Q = demand, gpm P = population, thousands	Gpm for 100,000 population
Kuichling (on basis of fire streams of 250 gpm).........................	$Q = 700 \sqrt{P}$	7,000
John R. Freeman....................	$Q = 250 \left(\dfrac{P}{5} + 10 \right)$	7,500
National Board of Fire Underwriters..	$Q = 1{,}020 \sqrt{P}\,(1 - 0.01\sqrt{P})$	9,180

Table 3-9.   The shorter the time the greater the deviation from the long-time average.   Deviations of rates from the annual average are indicated in Table 3-9.

TABLE 3-9. Maximum and Minimum Rates of the Use of Water*

Condition	Pumpage observed in five cities					Period of time	Design recommendations, % annual avg			
	Character of city						Less than 100,000 population		More than 100,000 population	
	Resi-dential	Indus-trial	Resi-dential	Resi-dential	Indus-trial		Max	Min	Max	Min
Population, thousands........	37.4	100.4	110.5	307	320	Month	120–150	75–90	110–130	80–90
Avg pumpage, gpcpd...........	99	96	63	57	137	Day	150–250	50–75	125–175	60–80
Max day, % avg day............	138	182	196	175	160	Hr	300–400	25–50	200–300	50–75
Max hr,										
% max day......	158	205	222	172	165					
% avg day.......	218	384	440	305	262					
Storage to equalize hourly peaks:										
Gal per capita....	24	33	31	14	50					
% max day......	18	19	25	14	23					
Reduced pumpage peak by storage:										
Gal per capita....	80	184	154	73	140					
% max day......	37	51	55	42	39					

* From C. B. Burdick, *Water & Sewage Works*, April, 1952, p. R-35.

Rates in the summer and in the winter in temperate climates are usually above the annual average.   In summer, water usage is high because of lawn watering, bathing, and cooling.   In winter, usage may be high because of waste of water to prevent freezing.   Monthly rates in some cities in Massachusetts are shown in Table 3-10.   In vacation cities,

TABLE 3-10. Water Used during Different Months*
(Averages for 10 year period in Massachusetts cities)

Month	Annual average percentage	Month	Annual average percentage
January	90	July	124
February	92	August	118
March	89	September	108
April	87	October	96
May	100	November	90
June	113	December	92

* *J. New Engl. Water Works Assoc.*, Vol. 27, p. 85, 1913.

demands for the maximum month are reported[1] as varying between 125 and 252 per cent of the annual average.

Daily and hourly rates of demand are shown in Figs. 3-2 and 3-3. Such hydrographs show some habits of water users. For example, marked

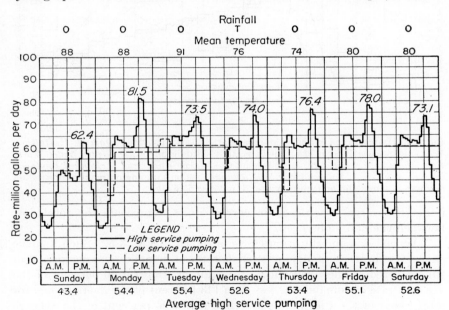

FIG. 3-2. Demand curve for week of July 12 to 18, 1936, at Toledo, Ohio. (*Courtesy of Burns and McDonnell Engineering Co.*)

fluctuations of pressure, indicating variations in rate of water use, have been observed to follow some events of public interest such as air-raid

[1] S. S. Keller, *J.A.W.W.A.*, September, 1951, p. 694.

warnings and certain radio and television programs.[1]   In general, rate of
demand in small cities is greatest during morning hours and on Monday.
In cities of all sizes, the lowest rate of use falls on Sunday, the extreme
minimum falling in the small hours of Monday morning.   A typical
weekly chart showing hourly variations in rate of pumping at Springfield,
Mass., is shown in Fig. 3-4.[2]   A study of this figure will reveal much concerning hourly and daily variations in demand.   For example, the area

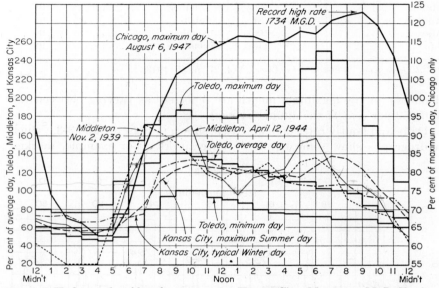

Fig. 3-3. Hydrographs of hourly pumpage at Kansas City, Mo. (*from M. P. Hatcher,
Water & Sewage Works, May,* 1947, *p.* 158), Middleton, Mass. (*from Water Works
Eng., July* 12, 1944, *p.* 822), and Toledo, Ohio (*from Burns and McDonnell Engineering Co.,* 1937.)   At Kansas City, Mo., average rate of pumping on maximum summer
day was 87.4 mg, and on typical winter day it was 55.6 mg.

under the curve, when read in correct units, represents the total flow
between the hours observed.

A typical demand-duration curve is shown in Fig. 3-5.   Such a curve
shows the duration of time of various rates of demand over the period of
time covered.   The curve shows, for example, that for 90 per cent of the
year the rate of demand was less than 143 per cent of the average, and for
50 per cent of the year it was less than about 96 per cent of the average
rate of demand.

3-9. Conditions Affecting Rates of Demand.   Rates of water use are
affected by the size of the community, its location, the standards of living

[1] See also: M. H. Finch, *Water and Water Eng.,* October, 1948, p. 467; G. J. Van Dorp,
Public Works, March, 1953, p. 64.

[2] From C. G. Richardson, *Water Works Eng.,* July 28, 1943, p. 831.

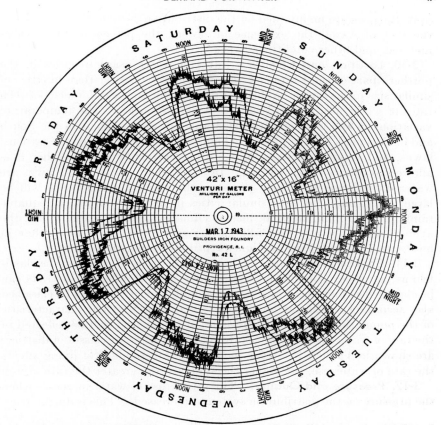

FIG. 3-4. Hourly variations in rate of pumping for week of Mar. 17, 1943 at Spring-field, Mass.   Inside curve represents week of Mar. 24, 1943, and outside curve represents week of Mar. 17, 1943.   (*From C. G. Richardson, Water Works Eng., July 28, 1943, p. 831.*)

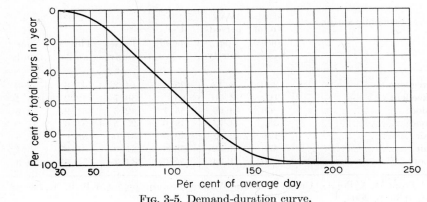

FIG. 3-5. Demand-duration curve.

in it, the pressure maintained on the distribution system, the quality and the cost of water, the existence of sewers, the percentage of services metered, and other conditions.

3-10. Location and Climate. Rates of water usage in cities in the northern part of the United States are generally greater than in cities of similar size in the South. This fact offers a clue to the difference between rates of water use in European and American cities. The temperature variations in the northern United States are greater than in the South and in Europe. During protracted hot periods, water is used for gardens, lawns, and cooling purposes, and during extremely cold weather it is allowed to run to avoid freezing. In cities where gardens and lawns are watered, particularly in arid climates, the rates of water usage will be large when compared with similar cities in districts with more equable rainfall. In humid, tropical, insular climates, as at Havana, Cuba, the average annual rate of use of 80 gal per capita per day is lower than in most cities of similar size in higher latitudes in the United States.

3-11. Character of District. Cities and districts of cities can be classified as industrial, commercial, and residential. Residential districts can be classified as high class, medium class, and poor. They can be classified also according to the predominating racial or antecedent characteristic of the population. The characteristics of the district will be reflected in the rate of water use therein. Rates of use in different classes of districts are shown in Table 3-11. It is found that the standard of living affects the rate of water use, the higher the standard the greater the rate of use.

3-12. Pressure and Quality. The rate of use of water increases when the pressure on the distribution system is increased. This is due, in part,

TABLE 3-11. Rates of Water Demand for Domestic Use at New Haven, Conn., in 1937, Showing the Effect of the Character of the District*

Economic status	Single-family houses			Multiple-family houses		
	No. of houses	Avg persons per family	Use, gpcpd	Gpcpd		
				Two-family	Three-family	Four-family
Excellent.................	290	3.13	125	44.2	41.6	52.0
Excellent.................	162	3.20	85	39.7	42.2	43.1
Good.....................	66	3.07	55.7	42.3	51.2	44.6
Good.....................	335	3.77	38.0	27.5	37.6	27.0
Fair.....................	176	2.92	39.0	37.0	38.6	45.9
Fair.....................	470	3.82	33.9	31.0	31.9	36.7
Poor.....................	20	4.34	54.0	34.2	35.7	29.3

* From M. A. Pond, "Urban Domestic Water Consumption," *J.A.W.W.A.*, December, 1939, p. 2003.

to the greater loss through leaks and the greater amount run to waste through open faucets. Increases in the rate of use of water with pressure have been known to reach 30 per cent for a change from 25 to 45 psi. This fact should lead the designer to provide the lowest pressure that will give satisfactory service. Excess pressure means waste of water.

Improvement of the quality of the water supply will result in increased use of water, in part because of the availability of the water for more uses and a feeling of safety on the part of the public in using it.

3-13. Intermittent Pumping. If water is supplied for less than 24 hr daily, as is the practice in some foreign cities, the rate of water use may be reduced but not in proportion to the time that it is supplied, and undesirable conditions may develop. When water is supplied intermittently, waste increases to such an extent that the amount of water used may be undiminished. Where an intermittent supply is not metered, it may become the custom of the consumers to place receptacles under faucets and hydrants which are left open during periods of nonsupply so that the receptacles will be filled when the supply is turned on. The receptacle remains unattended and, when filled, overflows to waste. Just before the resumption of supply is expected, the water remaining in the receptacle may be thrown away to assure a fresh and clean supply in the receptacle.

3-14. Air Conditioning.[1] Water requirements for air conditioning can be calculated for individual installations, but it is difficult to predict what the over-all future demand will be.[2,3] The demand for water for air conditioning is seasonal and is affected by the summer temperatures that prevail.

3-15. Sewers. The effect of the installation of sewers is to increase the rate of water use because of the increase in plumbing facilities and the freedom from concern over the capacity of the private sewage-disposal facilities. Data on this effect are given in Table 3-12.

3-16. Cost of Water. The use of water increases if the cost is reduced. This is indicated by the information in Table 3-13.

3-17. Effect of Meters on Demand.[4] The effect of meters is generally to diminish the use of water. This fact is shown by the data in Table 3-1. In unmetered communities, where water is paid for at a flat rate, there is no incentive to conserve water and more may be used than is required.

3-18. Policy of Metering. The desirability of the installation of meters is controversial.[5] Some points in the controversy are presented in Table 3-14.

[1] See also: Committee Report, *J.A.W.W.A.*, August, 1953, pp. 867ff.; A. D. Henderson, *Water Works Eng.*, April, 1948, p. 333.

[2] See also Anon., *Public Works*, April, 1948, p. 91.

[3] L. D. Gayton, *J.A.W.W.A.*, Vol. 29, p. 808, 1937; Vol. 30, p. 892, 1938; H. E. Babbitt, *ibid.*, Vol. 30, p. 454, 1938.

[4] See also K. T. Hoomon, *J.A.W.W.A.*, May, 1950, p. 509.

[5] See also *Water Works Eng.*, November, 1952, p. 1058.

TABLE 3-12. Average Use of Water before and after the Introduction of Sewers*

(Gallons per capita per day)

City	Years previous to the introduction of sewers							Years after the introduction of sewers									
	7	6	5	4	3	2	1	1	2	3	4	5	6	7	8	9	10
Marlborough, Mass...............	13	17	20	21	24	24	25	30	30	35	34	37	37	38	38	36	37
Newton, Mass...................	28	31	33	33	31	36	40	50	52	60	65	63	60	57	63	62	63
Waltham, Mass..................	37	36	39	33	31	32	33	47	53	61	59	71	70	76	88	90	88
Madison, Wis...................	Unsewered residences 14 gpcpd							Sewered residences 68 gpcpd									

* Report of Committee on Water Consumption Statistics and Records, *J. New Engl. Water Works Assoc.*, Vol. 27, p. 70, 1913.

TABLE 3-13. Relation between Demand and Cost of Water*

% increase in cost	% decrease in rate of water consumption
20	13
40	22
60	29
80	35
100	40

* Leonard Metcalf, Effect of Water Rates and Growth in Population upon per Capita Consumption, *J.A.W.W.A.*, Vol. 15, p. 1, 1926.

TABLE 3-14. Some Points for and against Metering

For	*Against*
1. It is only just that the consumer should pay in proportion to the amount he uses	1. Limited use of water may result in unhygienic conditions and disease
2. Waste is diminished, resulting in financial saving to all	2. Meters cost money to buy, to install, to maintain, to read, partly defeating their own purpose
3. The poor actually pay more through taxes where meters are not used	3. Pressure losses through meters are appreciable and add to pumping cost
4. Loads on purification plants and pumps, etc., are minimized	4. The poor suffer more than the rich through water charges
5. Waste surveys are easier to conduct; leaks are more easily found	5. Consumer resents stand-by charge made when meter shows no water used
6. Most privately owned water works are 100 per cent metered*	6. The use on gardens is diminished, affecting economy and appearance of community
7. The careful consumer benefits; the careless consumer is penalized	7. Meter money might better be spent on water-works improvement
	8. Waste can be more economically checked by inspection than by meter

* It is illegal in Nevada for a private company to sell water by meter. (See *Water Works Eng.*, Feb. 26, 1941, p. 241.)

The argument that meters require pressure for their operation is valid. Specifications of the American Water Works Association permit a head loss of 20 psi through the meter at rated capacity.[1] The argument that meters are costly is likewise valid. In 1950, the cost of a $\frac{5}{8}$-in. meter, installed, was between $18 and $25. Despite this fact, Sopp[2] has shown that, from the water-works management viewpoint, they "earn their keep."

Water-works engineers generally favor the metering of water supplies where cost of the works is important, the quantity of water available is not unlimited, and purification is required.[3]

[1] See also: *Eng. News-Record*, Dec. 12, 1918, p. 1074; J. R. Garratt, *J.A.W.W.A.*, Vol. 8, pp. 127, 130, 1921.

[2] G. C. Sopp, *J.A.W.W.A.*, September, 1947, p. 905.

[3] See also *Water Works Eng.*, November, 1950, p. 1002.

CHAPTER 4

GROUND WATER

4-1. Occurrence and Use of Ground Water.[1] A portion of the rain that falls on the ground percolates through it and fills the interstices of the substrata until the water reappears at the surface to join a river, a lake, or the sea. Conditions affecting the amount of rainfall that may percolate into the ground include the amount and intensity of the rainfall and its distribution, the topography and permeability of the ground surface, and the water capacity of the ground. Ground water is an important source of water for industrial, private, and public water supplies.[2]

Water is not contained in all underground materials. An *aquifer* is an underground stratum holding water. Aquifers may be regarded as natural storage reservoirs from which water may be withdrawn and which must be replaced as withdrawn, in order that the underground reservoir may not be depleted. The free flow of water as an open stream in a subterranean cavern is an unusual natural phenomenon, and such a stream is seldom available for use as a public water supply. The *free surface* of the ground water is the surface that is subject to atmospheric pressure under the ground. This surface generally rises and falls with the season, the rate of withdrawal, the rate of restoration, and other conditions. It is seldom static. It is known as the *ground-water table*.

The elevation of the ground-water table fluctuates with the rainfall, temperature, barometric pressure, tides, rate of pumping from wells, and other conditions. Water spreading, or artificial recharge,[3] is practiced under favorable conditions to raise or to maintain the elevation of the ground-water table. Practically all ground water is in motion. Hence, its surface is not level, the slope depending on the imperviousness of the aquifer and the velocity of the flow of water through it. The shape of

---

[1] See also: *U.S. Geol. Survey, 19th Ann. Rept.*, Part II, p. 381, 1897–1898; *U.S. Geol. Survey, Water Supply Paper* 67, 1902; *U.S. Geol. Survey, Water Supply Paper* 120, 1903; E. W. Bennison, "Ground Water," E. E. Johnson, Inc., St. Paul, Minn., 1947.

[2] See W. F. Guyton, in abstract and references by C. L. McGuinness, The Water Situation in the U.S., *U.S. Geol. Survey, Circ.* 114, p. 67, 1951.

[3] See also: J. H. Adamson, Jr., *J.A.W.W.A.*, August, 1947, p. 739; O. E. Meinzer, *Econ. Geol.*, May, 1946, with bibliography.

the ground-water table follows, roughly, the topography of the ground surface above it, as indicated in Fig. 4-1.

4-2. Water-bearing Formations. Among the forms in which ground water occurs are buried river valleys or beds of ancient lakes, extensive sedimentary deposits such as occur beneath prairies and the Western plains of the United States where the water may be held in porous rock or held under pressure in pervious strata, and porous strata in which the resistance to flow together with the rate of percolation from the surface are sufficient to maintain a reservoir of ground water well above the elevation of the natural surface outlet. Ground water occurs also as a lens of fresh water supported above the level of adjacent salt water,[1] and as

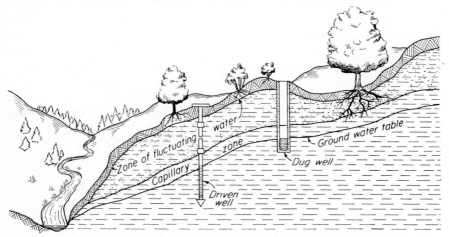

FIG. 4-1. Relation between ground-water table and ground surface.

perched water, i.e., water held in porous material supported by an impervious, basinlike, underground stratum. The occurrence of ground water in permafrost regions[2] offers a special problem in the Arctic.

Ground water that is available for public water supplies is most commonly found in strata of gravel and sand. The porosity of natural sands and gravels may be as high as 30 to 35 per cent.[3] Igneous rocks have a pore space of about 1 per cent; shale, 4 per cent; limestone, about 5 per cent; American oölites, between 3 and 12 per cent, averaging about 7 per cent; sandstones, 13 to 30 per cent; and some clays as high as 50 per cent. It is necessary to distinguish between porosity and perviousness, for it is upon the latter that the availability of water from underground strata depends. *Porosity* is the volume of the pores of a substance. It is

---

[1] See also: J. P. Lawlor, *Eng. News-Record*, June 27, 1946, p. 83; F. Ohrt, *J.A.-W.W.A.*, October, 1947, p. 979; and McGuinness, *loc. cit.*

[2] See also *U.S. Geol. Survey, Circ.* 275, Mar. 3, 1949.

[3] See also B. Smith, *Water and Water Eng.*, April, 1936, p. 223.

usually expressed as the percentage of its total volume.   It represents the volume of water that the dry material will soak up divided by the total volume of the material.   *Perviousness* is the capacity of a substance to allow water to pass through it, which is equivalent to the water available for a supply.   Although some clays may be 50 per cent porous, they may be practically impervious, whereas an igneous rock only $\frac{1}{2}$ to 1 per cent porous may yield all its water.   Nearly all the porosity in coarse materials is perviousness.   Large cracks or channels in an underground stratum, through which water may flow, should not be confused with the pores and interstices of the material which determine its perviousness.

Permeability and *transmissibility*[1] express the relative ease with which water will flow through a porous medium.[2]   Permeability is frequently expressed as the velocity of flow for a hydraulic slope of unity.   The coefficient of permeability may be expressed as the gallons of water which, in one day, will flow through 1 sq ft cross-sectional area of the sample of material, when the hydraulic gradient is unity and the temperature is 60°F.   Wenzel[3] states that the coefficient of transmissibility is equal to the product of the "field coefficient of permeability and the thickness of the saturated portion of the aquifer."   His definition of the *field coefficient of permeability* is "the number of gallons per day that percolates under prevailing conditions through each mile of a water-bearing bed under investigation (measured at right angles to the direction of flow) for each foot of thickness of the bed and for each foot per mile of hydraulic gradient."   The coefficients of permeability and of transmissibility are not usually equal since the former is determined on a sample in the laboratory and the latter on the undisturbed aquifer in the field.   Predictions of underground-flow conditions based on transmissibility may therefore be expected to be more dependable.   The *coefficient of storage* of an artesian aquifer is the number of cubic feet of water released from storage in each column of the aquifer having a base area of 1 sq ft and a height equal to the thickness of the aquifer, when the artesian head is lowered 1 ft.

The size of the sand grain in an aquifer has no relation to the amount of available water stored, but coarse-grained sand delivers water to a well with less trouble than fine-grained material.   Sandstones are used as sources of large water supplies, particularly in artesian areas, where the deep-lying sandstones contain water under pressure.   Water tables are fairly easy to locate in comparatively unaltered stratified rocks but they are by no means so easy to locate in those impervious or relatively impervious metamorphic rocks such as schists and those possessing a slaty cleavage.   If the rocks of this type are highly jointed, however, the water

---

[1] See also Ven Te Chow, *Trans. Am. Geophys. Union*, June, 1952, p. 397.
[2] See also Max Suter, *Illinois Well Driller*, Vol. 15, pp. 4, 13, 1946.
[3] L. K. Wenzel, *U.S. Geol. Survey, Water Supply Paper* 887, 1942.

filling the fissures may rise to about the same general level over a wide area and so give an approximation to a water table. The most common material in which ground water is encountered is *till*, a mixture of clay, sand, gravel, and boulders. It may hold large quantities of water and serve as a satisfactory source of water supply. Clay, shale, granite, and gneiss are more or less impervious to water, and wells sunk in such material cannot be expected to yield large quantities. Limestone is not highly porous but it contains caverns and channels which may hold appreciable

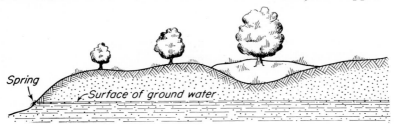

FIG. 4-2. A spring resulting from an overflow of the ground-water table.

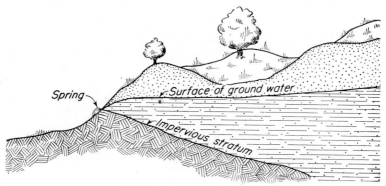

FIG. 4-3. A spring resulting from an outcropping of an impervious material.

quantities of water. Water in fissured rocks may carry pollution great distances through cracks and channels too large to serve as filters.

4-3. Springs. Ground water reappears at the ground surface in the form of springs, as indicated in Figs. 4-2 to 4-4. The greatest amount of water and the greatest certainty of continuous flow from springs of the type shown in Fig. 4-2 can be assured by constructing a cutoff trench along a contour at or near the point of appearance of the spring. The deeper the trench the greater the certainty of continuous flow because the saturated ground above the elevation of the trench bottom will act as an impounding reservoir to compensate for the fluctuations of the ground-water table. One form of construction is shown in Figs. 4-5, 4-5A, and 4-6, and a diagram of the hydraulics of an infiltration gallery is shown in Fig. 4-14.

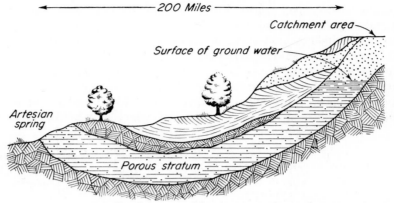

FIG. 4-4. Conditions resulting in an artesian spring.

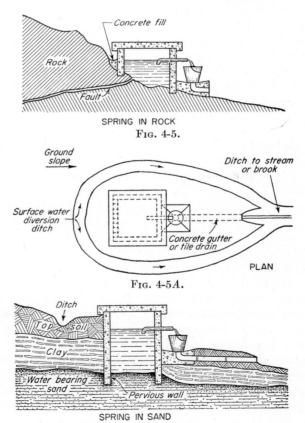

SPRING IN ROCK

FIG. 4-5.

FIG. 4-5A.

SPRING IN SAND

FIG. 4-6.

FIGS. 4-5, 4-5A, and 4-6. Methods for protection of springs. (From *Protection and Chlorination of Public Water Supplies*, New York State Health Dept., Bull. 21, 1942.)

Springs of the type shown in Fig. 4-3 are the most common. They may, however, be transitory, and because of the relatively small amount of underground storage available above the elevation of the overflow crest, the flow from them is uncertain and is likely to cease after a drought. Such springs are best developed by the construction of a cutoff trench. A method for the development of such a spring is shown in Fig. 4-6.

Artesian springs usually have a large tributary watershed at some distance from the spring, and the water may appear at the ground surface under pressure. The amount of water available in such a spring may be large, and the flow may be slightly increased by the removal of obstructions from the mouth of the spring.

The reverse action to the appearance of a spring is the disappearance into the ground of a river. This phenomenon appears most commonly in limestone regions and in arid sandy areas. For example, a large part of the Colorado River disappears into the sands of its delta.

4-4. Velocity of Underground Flow. The speed and direction of underground flow can be measured by the use of dyes, soluble salts, electrical methods, and other means. In determining the direction of flow, dyes or salts are most suitable. The tracing reagent is placed in a central well at equal distances from which test wells have been sunk. The direction of flow is the direction from the central well to the well in which the reagent is first detected.

Fluorescein, uranine, and eosine are the dyes best suited to the purpose. Powdered fluorescein has a reddish-brown color when dry. When dissolved in water, it appears, by reflected light, a brilliant green. One part in 40 million can be detected by the unaided eye. One part in 10 billion can be detected by colorimetric analysis. The dye has the advantage that it is unaffected by clay and will travel a long distance without change of properties.

Sodium chloride is used by placing it in the central well of a group encircling it and making chemical analyses to determine the chloride content of the water in the wells to which it is suspected the chloride is flowing. The method is not altogether satisfactory because, in long distances, the salt solution, whose specific gravity is higher than that of fresh water, sinks rapidly and may not reach the downgrade points, and also because of diffusion of the salt solution.[1]

The electrical method is used mainly for the determination of the speed of flow of underground water. It is operated as follows: In Fig. 4-7, A is the casing of the upper well which acts as an electrode, B is an electrode in the lower well that is insulated from the casing, and C and D, respectively, are a battery and an ammeter. E is a connection to the casing of the lower well. When connected for the test, a feeble current may be shown by the ammeter. A strong solution of an electrolyte is placed in

[1] See also L. K. Wenzel, *U.S. Geol. Survey, Water Supply Paper* 679A, p. 7, 1936.

the upper well, and the time is noted. Periodic observations of the ammeter and of the time are made and plotted. The appearance of the graph will be somewhat as shown in Fig. 4-8. In this figure, distance AB

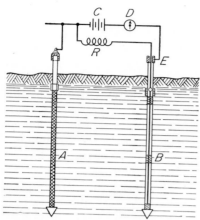

represents the time of passage of the ground water from the upper to the lower well. The sudden deflection at B shows the arrival of the electrolyte at the lower well. Point B should be taken at the point of inflection of the curve and not at the highest or maximum point. If the point of inflection is taken, the effect of diffusion of the electrolyte will be nullified.

4-5. Types of Wells. The following may be included among the types of wells in use for water-supply sources:

FIG. 4-7. Diagram illustrating Slichter's method of determining the velocity of flow of underground water.

Gravity Well. A vertical, or approximately vertical, hole from the surface of the earth, penetrating saturated underground material in which the surface of the water outside of and surrounding the well is at atmospheric pressure.

Pressure Well. A pressure well, sometimes called an artesian well, is a vertical or approximately vertical hole from the surface of the earth pass-

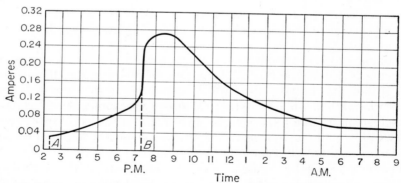

FIG. 4-8. Curve obtained by Slichter's electrical method for determining the velocity of flow of underground water.

ing through an impervious stratum to penetrate an aquifer holding water under pressure greater than atmospheric. Hence, when the hole, or well, penetrates the aquifer, water rises in the hole. If the pressure is sufficient, the water will rise to the ground surface and water will flow from the well.

It is to be noted that a flowing well is a pressure or artesian well, but an artesian or pressure well is not, necessarily, a flowing well.

Gallery.   A gallery is a horizontal, or approximately horizontal, tunnel or open ditch constructed through water-bearing material in a direction approximately normal to the direction of flow of the underground water. The tunnel type of gallery is sometimes called a horizontal well.

4-6. Conditions of Flow into Gravity Wells.   Hypothetical underground conditions surrounding a gravity well, in which the entire length of the well exposed to the aquifer will admit water into the well, are illustrated in Fig. 4-9.   If a test hole is bored into the ground at any point in the same aquifer as the gravity well, before water is withdrawn from the well, the water in the borehole and in the well stand at line AD, marked

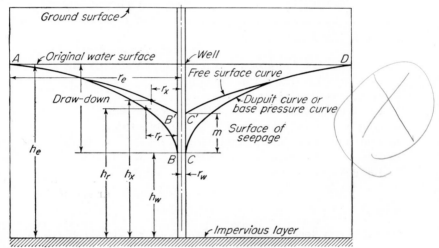

Fig. 4-9. Underground conditions in gravity well.

"original water surface," which is approximately horizontal. After water has been pumped from the well, water will stand for some time in the test boreholes, driven in a vertical plane passing through the axis of the well, at elevations along the line $AB'C'D$, marked "free-surface curve," provided the boreholes were only just deep enough to reach the free surface.   It is to be expected that moisture would probably be found in the ground above the "original water surface" and above the free surface, because of capillarity, retention, or other forces.   The original water surface and the free surface mark only elevations at which water would be encountered in the well and in the boreholes.

The free surface marks the boundaries of the "cone of depression." This is the space in the aquifer from which water has been removed.   The radius of the base of this cone, r_e in Fig. 4-9, is known as the *radius of the circle of influence.*   This radius is constant only when the rate of withdrawal from the well is equal to the rate of replenishment, unless the circle of influence reaches a fixed limit. This condition is illustrated in Fig. 4-10. The distance from the original water surface to the lowered surface in the well is known as the *drawdown*. When replenishment of the ground water surrounding a well is at a rate less than the rate of withdrawing water from the well, the drawdown will increase with time.

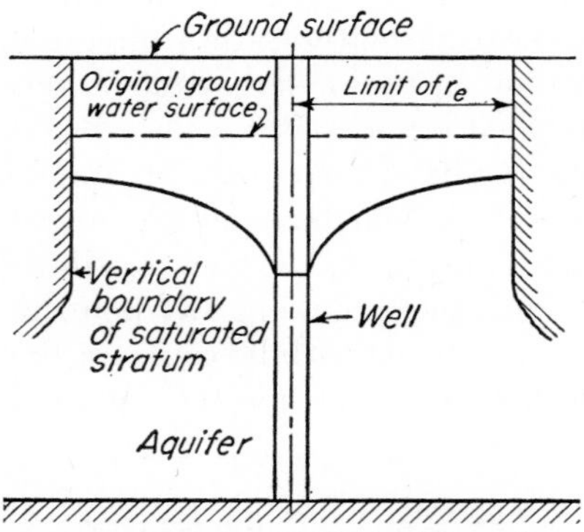

FIG. 4-10. Well with limited boundary.

It is to be noted in Fig. 4-9 that the elevation of the water surface in the well while it is being pumped lies at some distance below the free surface outside of and immediately adjacent to the well. The vertical surface, or face, of the ground forming the outside of the wellhole that is exposed between the surface of water in the well and the free surface is known as the *surface of seepage*.

4-7. Formulation of Rate of Underground Flow. The flow of underground waters through aquifers is usually so slow, in the order of a few feet per day, that it occurs under the hydraulic conditions of nonturbulent or straight-line flow in which the head loss due to friction varies directly as the velocity of flow. Under these conditions

$$V = ks \tag{4-1}$$

and
$$Q = kAsp \tag{4-2}$$

where V = velocity of flow, ft per day

s = slope of the hydraulic grade line, *i.e.*, slope of the ground-water table

k = a constant determined by the conditions of flow and the units used. Where the units are in feet and days, values of k are shown in the second column in Table 4-1

A = cross-sectional area of aquifer, sq ft

p = porosity of water-bearing medium, it being assumed that the product of Ap represents the area of the channels through which flow is taking place

4-8. Flow into a Gravity Well. Under the conditions of flow illustrated in Fig. 4-9, characteristics or dimensions that can be measured in the field are h_e, h_w, r_w, and Q, where Q is the rate of pumping from the well and other nomenclature is shown in the figure. Characteristics of flow that cannot be measured under most field conditions include the porosity and permeability of the aquifer,[1] the slope of the hydraulic grade line,

[1] See also L. K. Wenzel, *U.S. Geol. Survey, Water Supply Paper* 887, 1942.

TABLE 4-1. Velocity of Flow of Water in Sands of Various Effective Sizes of Grains and the Maximum Flow or Transmission Constant for Each Sand*

(Porosity, 32%; temperature, 50°F)

Diameter of soil grain, mm	Velocity, ft per day for a pressure gradient of		Kind of soil	Diameter of soil grain, mm	Velocity, ft per day for a pressure gradient of		Kind of soil
	1:1	100 ft per mile			1:1	100 ft per mile	
0.01	0.163	0.0038⎫	Silt	0.25	102	2.31⎫	Medium
0.04	2.62	0.0605⎭		0.45	331	7.47⎭	sand
0.05	4.08	0.0922⎫	Very fine	0.50	408	9.21⎫	
0.09	13.2	0.298 ⎭	sand	0.95	1,470	33.2 ⎭	Coarse sand
0.10	16.3	0.369 ⎫		1.00	1,630	36.8 ⎫	
0.20	65.4	2.09 ⎭	Fine sand	5.00	40,800	921. ⎭	Fine gravel

* C. S. Slichter, *U.S. Geol. Survey, Water Supply Papers* 67, p. 27; 140, p. 1.

the size of the particles composing the aquifer, and the magnitude of r_e.

A formula has been developed, involving all the measurable conditions, in addition to the value of r_e, by which it is possible to obtain approximate solutions to problems in connection with the flow from some wells. This is known as the Dupuit formula. It was devised by Jules Dupuit,[1] a French philosopher. His formula is based on assumptions of the conditions of underground flow that are only approximately correct. Hence, results given by the formula cannot be exact, but experience with the formula has shown that under most conditions its results are of practical value. An understanding of its development is desirable in an understanding of the mathematics of underground flow.

Dupuit's formula for the flow into a gravity well is based on Eq. (4-2). It is assumed that the direction of the flow of ground water is horizontal and that it flows radially toward the center of the well shown in Fig. 4-9. Hence, it flows through the surface of a right, vertical cylinder so that

$$A = 2\pi r_r h_r$$

and,
$$Q = 2\pi k r_r h_r s p$$

But
$$s = \frac{dh_r}{dr_r}$$

Hence
$$Q = 2\pi k r_r h_r p \frac{dh_r}{dr_r}$$

or
$$Q \frac{dr_r}{r_r} = 2\pi k p h_r \, dh_r$$

[1] J. Dupuit, "Etudes théoretiques et pratiques sur les mouvements des eaux," Dunod, Paris, 1863.

Integrating both sides of the equation,

$$Q \log_e r_r = \pi k p h_r^2 + C$$

Now, when $\qquad r_r = r_e \qquad$ then $\qquad h_r = h_e$

whence $\qquad\qquad C = Q \log_e r_e - k p h_e^2$

and $\qquad\qquad Q \log_e r_r = \pi k p h_r^2 + Q \log_e r_e - \pi k p h_e^2$

transposing $\qquad\qquad Q = \pi k p \dfrac{h_e^2 - h_r^2}{\log_e (r_e/r_r)}$ $\qquad\qquad$ (4-3)

but when $\qquad r_r = r_w \qquad$ then $\qquad h_r = h_w$

then $\qquad\qquad Q = \pi k p \dfrac{h_e^2 - h_w^2}{\log_e (r_e/r_w)}$ $\qquad\qquad$ (4-4)

If $K = 7.5\pi k p/(2.3 \times 1{,}440)$ and values of k, in ft per day, are taken from Table 4-1 and Q is expressed in gallons per minute, then

$$Q = K \frac{h_e^2 - h_w^2}{\log_{10} (r_e/r_w)} \qquad\qquad (4\text{-}5)$$

The numerical value of K or of k usually cannot be determined practicably by the measurement of any characteristic of the well. The values of the constants are more commonly determined by substituting measured values of other characteristics into Eq. (4-5) and solving for K.

The graph resulting from the plotting of the Dupuit formula produces the "base-pressure curve," line $ABCD$ in Fig. 4-9. It has been found in practice that the approximations involved in the use of the Dupuit formula give results of practical value, the results being most nearly correct when the ratio of the drawdown to the depth of water in the well when not being pumped is low.

4-9. The Free-surface Curve. The *free surface* of the water in the cone of depression surrounding a well that is being pumped is the surface of the water that is under atmospheric pressure. It is to be emphasized that the free surface does not coincide with Dupuit's base-pressure curve. The free surface has been formulated[1] as

$$Q = \frac{k(h_e - h_x)h_e}{C_x \log_{10} (r_e/0.1h_e)} \qquad\qquad (4\text{-}6)$$

where k is a constant for the well depending on the units used and the permeability of the soil, and other nomenclature is as shown in Fig. 4-9.[2] Values of C_x are to be taken from Fig. 4-11.

[1] See H. E. Babbitt and D. H. Caldwell, *Univ. Illinois Eng. Expt. Sta. Bull.* 374, 1948.

[2] See also D. F. Peterson and others, *Utah State Agr. College, Agr. Expt. Sta., Tech. Bull.* 351, March, 1952.

4-10. Drawdown vs. Rate of Flow, and Specific Capacity.

The rate of flow Q, from a well, the drawdown $(h_e - h_w)$, and the radius of the circle of influence r_e are related as indicated in Eq. (4-5). In order that the value r_e may be constant the rate of replenishment of underground

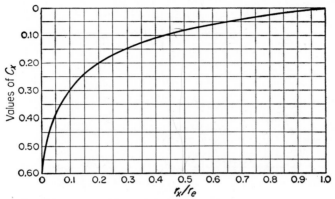

FIG. 4-11. Values of C_x to be used in Eq. (4-6).

flow must be equal to Q. Hence, for the purposes of approximate computation in the solution of well problems with the Dupuit formula it will be assumed that

$$r_e = CQ \tag{4-7}$$

or, substituting in Eq. (4-5),

$$Q = k\ \frac{(h_e - h_w)(h_e + h_w)}{\log_{10} (CQ/r_w)} \tag{4-8}$$

Values of C and of k for a well can be determined by measurements of Q and of h_w under two or more different rates of flow and values of drawdown, and substituting in Eq. (4-8).

It is evident from Eq. (4-8) that where the drawdown $(h_e - h_w)$ is small compared with $(h_e + h_w)$ the value of Q varies approximately as $(h_e - h_w)$. This straight-line relationship between rate of flow and drawdown leads to the definition of the *specific capacity* of a well as the rate of flow per unit of drawdown, usually expressed in gallons per minute per foot of drawdown.

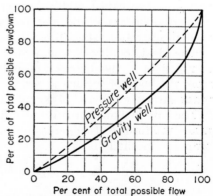

FIG. 4-12. Relation between drawdown and the flow from a well.

Since the relationship is not the same for all drawdowns it should be determined for the first foot of drawdown. The relationship is shown graphically for both gravity and pressure wells, in Fig. 4-12.

4-11. The Dupuit Formula for Flow into a Pressure Well. The hypothetical conditions of flow into a pressure or artesian well are illustrated in Fig. 4-13. The formula for the rate of flow into a pressure well can be

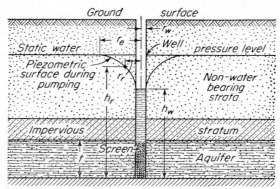

FIG. 4-13. Underground conditions of flow into a pressure well.

derived similarly to Eq. (4-5), starting with the expression $Q = kAsp$ and[1] $A = 2\pi r_r t$. The expression is

$$Q = k \frac{h_e - h_w}{\log_{10}(r_e/r_w)} \tag{4-9}$$

4-12. Infiltration Galleries and Wells. An infiltration gallery may be an open trench, a buried porous conduit, or a line of wells closely spaced, placed across or normal to the direction of underground flow in an aquifer. Such galleries are commonly placed close to the bank of a river or lake to intercept the underground flow toward the body of surface water. Wells so placed are called infiltration wells. It may be more economical to draw potable water from beneath a river by such means than to purify the surface water taken directly from the river.[2]

The ideal conditions of flow into an infiltration gallery are illustrated in Fig. 4-14. The direction of underground flow, either toward or away from the body of surface water, is determined by the relative elevations of the surface water and of the free-water surface in the infiltration gallery.

The rate of flow into an infiltration gallery, the direction of flow, and other conditions of underground flow can be formulated according to Dupuit's method[3] as

$$Q = k \frac{h_e^2 - h_w^2}{2r_e} \tag{4-10}$$

[1] See also: C. E. Jacob, *Proc. Am. Soc. Civil Engrs.*, May, 1946, p. 629; Ven Te Chow, *Civil Eng.*, October, 1951, p. 48.

[2] See also *Eng. News-Record*, Dec. 10, 1953, p. 52.

[3] See also: R. G. Kazmann, *Trans. Am. Geophys. Union*, February, 1948, p. 85; *Proc. Am. Soc. Civil Engrs.*, June, 1947, p. 837.

where Q is the rate of flow per unit length into one side of the gallery. This assumption is based on the expression $Q = kAsp$ and on the fact that A, per unit length of one side of the gallery, is h_r, k and p being absorbed in a single constant.

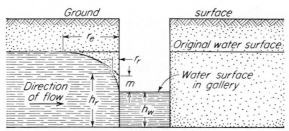

FIG. 4-14. Flow into one side of a gallery.

4-13. Partial Penetration of an Aquifer by a Well. If the gravity well does not penetrate to the bottom of the aquifer the Dupuit formula for full penetration is not applicable. Kozeny[1] has found that the expression for flow into a partially penetrating gravity well is

$$Q = \frac{k(h_e^2 - h_w^2)}{\log_{10}(r_e/r_w)} \left(1 + 7 \sqrt{\frac{r_w}{2h_e}} \cos \frac{\pi P}{2} \right) \qquad (4\text{-}11)$$

where $P = h_e/h$

h = thickness of the aquifer, $h_e \gtrless h$

In using this expression the degree of penetration must be known. It may be found by test borings or from logs of adjacent wells. If the penetration is small even a rough estimate of it introduces but little error into

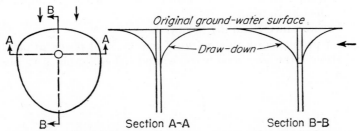

FIG. 4-15. Conditions when well is not in middle of field of influence.

the corrected value of Q, since for small values of P the term $\cos \pi P/2$ is very nearly equal to unity.

4-14. Area of Influence. The area of influence surrounding a gravity well in a sloping water table is not necessarily circular, and the well is not in the center of the area, as indicated in Fig. 4-15. It has been shown by

[1] J. Kozeny, *Wasserkraft u. Wasserwirtsch.*, Vol. 28, p. 101, 1933.

Muskat[1] that for an appreciably noncircular area the expression

$$Q = \frac{k(h_e^2 - h_w^2)}{\log (C/r_w)} \tag{4-12}$$

may be used to compute the flow into such a well, using for C an approximate average of the distance of the well from the boundary. The effect of the displacement of the well from the center of the area of influence may be neglected for displacements up to 50 per cent of the value of r_e.

4-15. Nonequilibrium Conditions. If a gravity or pressure well is pumped at a constant rate the drawdown in the well and the area of influence will continue to increase until the rate of replenishment is equal to the rate of pumping, *i.e.*, until equilibrium has been established. Theis[2] has expressed the nonequilibrium conditions as

$$S = \frac{114.6Q}{T} \int_\nu^\infty \frac{e^{-\nu}}{\nu} \, d\nu \tag{4-13}$$

where S = drawdown of the water level in the observation well, ft
   Q = constant rate of pumping, gpm
   T = coefficient of transmissibility, gal per day per ft under a unit hydraulic gradient
   e = base of natural logarithms, 2.7183
   ν = $1.87r_x^2 s/Tt$
   r_x = distance from observation well to center of pumped well, ft
   s = coefficient of storage, as a fraction, indicating yield of water from storage in the water-bearing material under a unit decline in head
   t = time since pumping began, days

Solutions of problems by this method[3] require field observations for the determination of the constants involved and either a table of values of the expression

$$\int_\nu^\infty \frac{e^{-\nu}}{\nu} \, d\nu$$

as given by Wenzel,[4] or a nomograph given by Chow.[5] A simple method

[1] M. Muskat, "The Flow of Homogeneous Fluids through Porous Media," McGraw-Hill Book Company, Inc., New York, 1937.

[2] C. V. Theis, *Trans. Am. Geophys. Union*, 1935, p. 519; *Econ. Geol.*, Vol. 33, p. 889, 1938.

[3] See also C. E. Jacob, *Trans. Am. Geophys. Union*, 1940, p. 574.

[4] L. K. Wenzel, *U.S. Geol. Survey, Water Supply Paper* 887, 1942.

[5] Ven Te Chow, *Civil Eng.*, October, 1951, p. 48.

for the solution of nonequilibrium problems has been presented by Caldwell.[1] The method is described in the following section.

4-16. Drawdown and Recovery Curves in Gravity Wells. The *drawdown curve* is a curve whose coordinates are drawdown in the well and time of pumping, as shown in Fig. 4-16. A *recovery curve* shows the recovery of the water level in the well after pumping has stopped, also

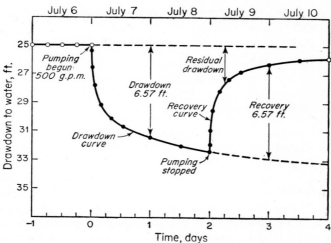

Fig. 4-16. Drawdown-recovery curve. (*From R. H. Brown, J.A.W.W.A., August, 1953, p. 849.*)

indicated in Fig. 4-16. A typical drawdown-recovery curve is based on the application of the expression[1]

$$T = \frac{0.184 r_e^2 f}{Q} \left(h_e - \sqrt{h_e^2 - 1.7 \frac{Q}{k}} \right) \qquad (4\text{-}14)$$

where T = time to develop radius r_e, hr

f = specific yield of the material, *i.e.*, the ratio of the amount of fluid that will drain from a saturated material to the volume of the material

other nomenclature is as in Eq. (4-5)

and on the expression $\quad d_o = \frac{1}{2.3} \log \frac{r_o}{r_w} \left(h_e - \sqrt{h_e^2 - 1.7 \frac{Q}{k}} \right) \qquad (4\text{-}15)$

where d_o = drawdown in well, ft

r_o = radius of circle of influence, ft, corresponding to value of d_o

[1] D. H. Caldwell, "The Hydraulics of Gravity Flow of Water Wells," Thesis, University of Illinois, 1943.

The drawdown of the base-pressure curve at any other point, expressed as d'_o, may be determined by replacing r_w by r_r, where r_r is the distance from the well center to the point in question.

4-17. Rate of Recovery in a Pressure Well. The rate of recovery is so much faster in a pressure well than in a gravity well that the fact may be used as one of the easily observed characteristics to identify the type of well. The rate of recovery is faster in a pressure well than in a gravity well because there is no cone of depression around a pressure well to be filled with water.

To express the rate of recovery in a pressure well Slichter[1] devised the expression

$$T = K \log \frac{y_o}{y_1} \qquad (4\text{-}16)$$

where T = time for water level to rise from y_o to y_1
K = constant for well and units used
y_o = drawdown in well at any time T after observation of the depth y_o

This is an approximate expression only, as it is based on the assumption that the radius of the circle of influence remains constant during the period of recovery. For the relatively small drawdowns in pressure wells, as compared with the depth of the well, solutions obtained by the use of the formula are practically applicable. It is undesirable to use the formula where the drawdown is a large proportion of the total depth of the well.

4-18. Interference among Wells. If two or more wells are located so that their cones of depression intersect, they are said to interfere, the amount of interference in any well being represented by the ratio of the diminution of flow from the well without interference. Muskat[2] has proposed formulas for the computation of interference effects that are based on logical analysis.[3] Tests made on a laboratory scale at the University of Illinois[4] have indicated that the results from Muskat's formulas are in close agreement with the laboratory observations.

Some formulas for interference among gravity wells are:

For two wells a distance W apart

$$Q_1 = Q_2 = \frac{k(h_e{}^2 - h_w{}^2)}{\log (r_e{}^2/r_w W)} \qquad (4\text{-}17)$$

where the nomenclature is as in Eq. (4-5) and Fig. 4-9.

[1] *U.S. Geol. Survey, Water Supply Paper* 10, 1905.

[2] *Loc. cit.*

[3] See also V. E. Hansen, *Proc. Am. Soc. Civil Engrs.*, August, 1952; *Trans. Am. Soc. Civil Engrs.*, Vol. 118, p. 1098, 1953.

[4] Babbitt and Caldwell, *loc. cit.*

For three wells equally spaced in a straight line, a distance W apart

$$Q_1 = Q_3 = \frac{k(h_e^2 - h_w^2) \log (W/r_w)}{[2 \log (r_e/W) \log (W/r_w)] + [\log (W/2r_w) \log (r_e/r_w)]} \quad (4\text{-}18)$$

$$Q_2 = \frac{k(h_e^2 - h_w^2) \log (W/2r_w)}{[2 \log (r_e/W) \log (W/r_w)] + [\log (W/2r_w) \log (r_e/r_w)]} \quad (4\text{-}19)$$

where Q_1 and Q_3 are the flows into the outer wells, and Q_2 is the flow into the middle well.

Hansen[1] describes the application of the "membrane anology" which greatly simplifies the solution of problems involving interfering wells, whether gravity or pressure, by means of measurements taken on a thin rubber membrane.

Interference between two pressure wells a distance W apart, based on work by Slichter,[2] can be formulated as

$$Q_1 = Q_2 = \frac{2k(h_e - h_w)}{\log [r_e^2(W + r_e)^2] - \log (2Wr_e^3 + W^2r_w^2)} \quad (4\text{-}20)$$

The flow from the middle well in a group of three wells in a line, a distance W apart, all pumped with the same drawdown, can be expressed as

$$Q_3 = \frac{k(h_e - h_w)}{\log [(r_e^2 + W^2)r_e] - \log (W^2r_w)} \quad (4\text{-}21)$$

4-19. Examples. *Problem* 1. A gravity-type well is 24 in. in diameter. When it is being pumped at 500 gpm the drawdown in a well 50 ft away is 10 ft, and in another well 100 ft away it is 3 ft. The well penetrates the aquifer giving a depth of water in the well, when not being pumped, of 100 ft. *a*. What is the drawdown in the well? *b*. What is the specific capacity of the well? *c*. What is the maximum rate at which water can be pumped from the well? *d*. What would be the drawdown for a discharge of 300 gpm? Solve by the use of the Dupuit formula.

Solution. 1. Solve for r_e.

$$Q = \frac{k(h_e^2 - h_w^2)}{\log (r_e/r_r)} = \frac{k(100^2 - 90^2)}{\log (r_e/50)} = \frac{k(100^2 - 97^2)}{\log (r_e/100)}$$

then $(10)(190)(\log r_e - 2) = (3)(197)(\log r_e - 1.7)$

and $3.21 \log r_e - 6.42 = \log r_e - 1.7$

3.21 log r_e − 4.72 = log r_e

and $\log r_e = 4.72/2.21 = 2.14$ and $r_e = 137$ ft.
2. Solve for C in the expression $r_e = CQ$. $C = {}^{137}\!/_{500} = 0.278$.
3. Solve for k.

$$k = \frac{(500)(\log 2.74)}{(10)(190)} = \frac{(500)(\log 1.37)}{(3)(197)} = 0.115$$

[1] V. E. Hansen, *Trans. Am. Geophys. Union*, December, 1952, p. 912.
[2] C. S. Slichter, *U.S. Geol. Survey*, 19th Ann. Rept., Part II, p. 295, 1897–1898.

4. Solve question a.

$$500 = 0.115 \frac{(100^2 - h_w^2)}{\log 137/1} \quad \text{and} \quad 10,000 - h_w^2 = \frac{(500)(2.136)}{0.115} = 9.27$$

$$h_w = \sqrt{730} = 27 \text{ ft}$$

Hence, the drawdown is $100 - 27 = 73$ ft.

5. Solve question b.

$$Q = 0.115 \frac{(1)(199)}{\log 0.278Q/1} \qquad Q = k \frac{CQ}{\log \frac{CQ}{r}}$$

By trial and error $Q = 27$ gpm.

6. Solve question c.

$$Q = 0.115 \frac{100^2}{\log 0.278Q/1}$$

By trial and error $Q = 535$ gpm.

7. Solve question d.

$$300 = 0.115 \frac{100^2 - h_w^2}{\log (83.4)}$$

Hence $h_w = 71$ ft and drawdown $= 100 - 71 = 29$ ft.

Problem 2. An 18-in.-diameter gravity-type well is being pumped at a rate of 350 gpm with a drawdown of 30 ft. The static depth of water in the well is 200 ft. During pumping the depth of water in a similar well, not being pumped, at a distance of 24 ft is 185 ft. If the elevation of the ground-water table is at 100 ft above datum, at what elevation would the free surface of water be encountered in the construction of a test hole 50 ft from the well being pumped?

Solution. 1. Solve for r_e. From Dupuit

$$\frac{200^2 - 170^2}{\log (r_e/0.75)} = \frac{200^2 - 185^2}{\log (r_e/24)}$$
$$(30)(370)[\log r_e - 1.380] = (15)(385)[\log r_e + 0.1248]$$
$$1.922 \log r_e - 2.655 = \log r_e + 1.248$$
$$0.922 \log r_e = 2.78 \quad \text{and} \quad r_e = 1,025 \text{ ft}$$

2. Solve for k.

$$350 = k \frac{200^2 - 170^2}{\log 1,025/0.75} = k \frac{200^2 - 185^2}{\log 1,025/24} \quad \text{and} \quad k = 0.099$$

3. From the free-surface curve

$$350 = \frac{(0.099)(200)(200 - h_x)}{(0.4) \log 1,025/20}$$
$$\frac{r_x}{r_e} = \frac{50}{125} = 0.49$$

hence $C_x = 0.4 \quad \text{and} \quad h_x = 180.8 \text{ ft}$

The water is at elevation 80.8 ft.

Problem 3. A gravity-type well is 12 in. in diameter and is discharging 150 gpm with a drawdown of 10 ft. It discharges 500 gpm at a drawdown of 50 ft. **The** static depth of water in the well is 150 ft. What will be the discharge from the well at a drawdown of 20 ft?

Solution. By the Dupuit formula

$$150 = k\,\frac{(10)(290)}{\log\,(150C/0.5)} \qquad \text{and} \qquad 500 = k\,\frac{(50)(25)}{\log\,(500C/0.5)}$$

hence $\qquad C = 0.12 \qquad$ and $\qquad k = \dfrac{(500)(\log\,120)}{12,500} = 0.085$

then $$Q = 0.085\,\frac{(20)(280)}{\log\,(0.12Q/0.5)}$$

By trial and error $Q = 264$ gpm.

Problem 4. At what rate could water be pumped from the two wells in Prob. 2, if both wells were being pumped together with a drawdown in each well of 30 ft? Answer in gallons per minute.

Solution. 1. Find r_e and k, as in the solution of Prob. 2. Then substitute in Eq. (4-17)

$$Q_1 = Q_2 = \frac{(0.099)(200^2 - 170^2)}{\log\,1,025^2/(1)(24)} = \frac{(0.099)(30)(370)}{\log\,43,750} = 237 \text{ gpm}$$

Hence, the combined rate of flow from the two wells is $2 \times 237 = 474$ gpm.

LOCATION, CONSTRUCTION, AND MAINTENANCE OF WELLS

5-1. Location of Wells.[1]   In a region where the ground-water table is high and the underground strata are pervious, shallow wells of moderate capacity may be located at almost any convenient site.   Such conditions exist in most regions of plentiful rainfall.   However, the location of a deep, high-capacity well, such as is required for a public water supply, may require exploratory prospecting in the region, including a study of the characteristics of existing wells.   By exploratory prospecting is meant the drilling and pumping of test wells to determine the direction of the underground flow and possibly the limits of the field of underground water, as a supplement to other scientific methods for the location of such water.

The existence of water in porous material at or above the level of a nearby surface stream can usually be depended on.   The farther the point is from the surface stream the higher the elevation at which water will probably be found.   The porous stratum may rise and fall in an unexpected and inexplicable fashion; there may be faults in the substrata so that a dry well will be located close to a well in the aquifer giving a good yield.   When a well is located near a surface stream, the water will enter the well from the surrounding ground if the circle of influence is too small to include the stream.   Underground percolation of water is *from* the stream if the circle of influence includes the stream.[2]

Where the information on geology and existing wells is meager, helpful information may be obtained through scientific instruments applied in underground surveys and in geophysical prospecting.[3]   Such prospecting[4] depends on the speed and manner in which underground strata of different characteristics convey sound waves or electrical currents.

[1] See also E. W. Bennison, "Ground Water," E. E. Johnson, Inc., St. Paul, Minn., 1947.

[2] See also E. B. Meier, *J.A.W.W.A.*, January, 1954, p. 19.

[3] See also: S. F. Kelly, *Civil Eng.*, October, 1932, p. 628; C. A. Bays, *Water Well J.*, May–June, 1949, p. 8.

[4] See also J. McG. Bruckshaw, *Water and Water Eng.*, September, 1946, p. 507.

In the seismic method of geophysical prospecting, sound waves, or stress waves, are propagated at or slightly below the ground surface by means of an explosion, usually of a few sticks of dynamite. These waves spread through the earth from the explosion as a center. The greater the density of the underground strata, the greater the speed of the waves. Some waves are reflected when encountering denser strata and return to the surface where sensitive instruments, attuned to detect only certain reflected waves, supply a record from which profiles of underground strata can be drawn. These profiles may be used in indicating the location of water-bearing strata.

The resistivity method of geophysical prospecting depends on the resistance of underground strata to the flow of electric current through them. The presence of water in the ground may reduce its electrical resistance. Hence, a study of the electric currents flowing underground may indicate the location of a water-bearing stratum.

Care should be taken not to locate wells in a region where the quality of the water will be endangered by surface drainage or by the existence of drainage wells, or in a region in which the top of the well may be flooded by impure surface water. All wells, particularly shallow dug wells, should be located at a safe distance from sources of pollution. In homogeneous material, such as sand or gravel, a minimum distance of 250 ft is recommended between the well and a source of pollution. In some jurisdictions 100 ft is permitted. Local conditions must control. No fixed distance for all situations can be *safe*.

5-2. Grouping of Wells. The grouping of a number of wells in a field depends on the type of aquifer from which the water is drawn, the area of the land under control of the water works, the rate at which the wells are to be pumped, and other conditions. In order to obtain, economically, the greatest amount of water available from a limited area in which the wells penetrate an underground reservoir from which the water may be drawn from all directions, some interference between wells is necessary. The minimum amount of interference that is economical is fixed by the cost of piping to bring the water from the wells to a central point, by the cost of power transmission to the wells, and other conditions. A number of wells penetrating an underground stream with distinct channel and direction of flow should be placed in a line transverse to the stream. Successive rows of wells can be placed downstream to increase the volume of water available from the underground stream, but the specific capacity of such wells will decrease downstream when upstream wells are being pumped.

In general, wells pumped by suction should be close together, and the suction line should be free from turns and obstructions to minimize head losses, since the available suction head is usually low. Air leaking into the suction line, combined with gases released from solution by the reduced pressure, causes trouble in drawing water from the wells.

When locating wells near property lines it should be borne in mind that, if water is taken from beneath neighboring property to the injury of the owner, damages may be recovered therefor.   The wells should be pumped so that the circle of influence does not pass beyond the water-works property.

5-3. Legal Restrictions on Well Construction.   Some states require the licensing of well drillers and require that certain information be furnished concerning the construction of all wells.   Legal restrictions on the use of ground water seem necessary to conserve the diminishing supply in many areas.[1]   Legal bases for such restrictions are discussed in Sec. 1-7.

5-4. Types of Well Construction.[2]   Wells may classified according to the method of construction as dug, bored, driven, jetted, or drilled.   The first three are commonly confined to relatively shallow wells not ordinarily used for large water supplies, although in a few instances large dug wells[3] have been constructed for large users.   Some methods for the protection of small wells against surface contamination are illustrated in Fig. 5-1. Drilling is used almost exclusively for the sinking of the deepest wells.

Specifications for the construction of deep wells were adopted by the American Water Works Association in 1945.[4]   One of the eleven types of wells described in the specifications is illustrated in Fig. 5-2A.

Some essentials that should probably be included in a well-construction contract[5] are:

1. Base production volume or specific capacity on a 96-hr test, or a minimum period of 30 hr
2. Construction materials
3. Sampling of water for quality
4. State minimum permissible sand content of water
5. Straight-hole survey—straightness and plumbness
6. Driller to furnish well data—log, electric log, material list
7. Type of well—gravel, single or double string
8. Finished well to meet state department's standards
9. Survey and cementing to be done by disinterested parties
10. Purchaser to provide facilities for waste of test water
11. Provision by purchaser to provide for ingress to, and egress from, drilling site
12. Performance bond and maintenance bond for 1 year

5-5. Dug, Bored, and Driven Wells.   Dug wells are commonly excavated by hand tools, the excavator descending into the well as the excavation progresses.   Where the walls of the well will not stand without

---

[1] See also C. F. Tolman and A. C. Stipp, *Trans. Am. Soc. Civil Engrs.*, Vol. 106, p. 882, 1941.

[2] See also H. A. Mylander, *J.A.W.W.A.*, July, 1953, p. 764.

[3] See also C. B. Coe, *Eng. News-Record*, Vol. 79, p. 460, 1917.

[4] See Standard Specifications A100-46, *J.A.W.W.A.*, September, 1945.

[5] From 32d *Texas Water Works Short School*, 1950, p. 64.

support, they are lined, or "curbed," usually with a watertight lining near the surface to exclude polluted surface water and with a pervious lining near the bottom to admit ground water. Dug wells are commonly constructed 3 to 4 ft in diameter and to depths of 30 to 100 ft, although deeper wells are in existence.[1]

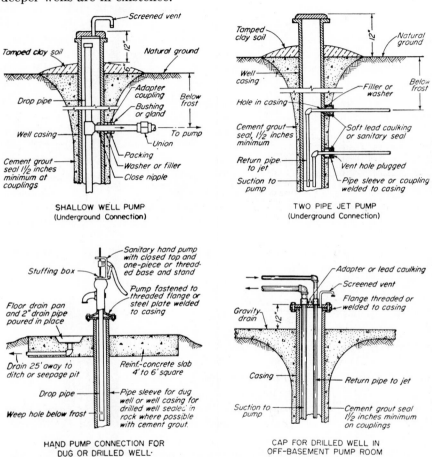

FIG. 5-1. Sanitary methods for protecting tops of wells. (*From J. A. Salvator, Jr., Modern Sanitation, July,* 1951, *p.* 30.)

Wells are sometimes constructed by driving into the aquifer a well point of the type shown in Fig. 5-3. They are constructed also by driving, or pulling, an open-end casing into the ground and removing the material by boring, drilling, sand bucket or bailer, orange-peel bucket, or other means, depending, to some extent, on the diameter of the well hole. In such wells, the casing is either driven down with hammer blows,

[1] See also J. A. Logan and J. L. Hummel, *Eng. News-Record*, June 13, 1946, p. 98.

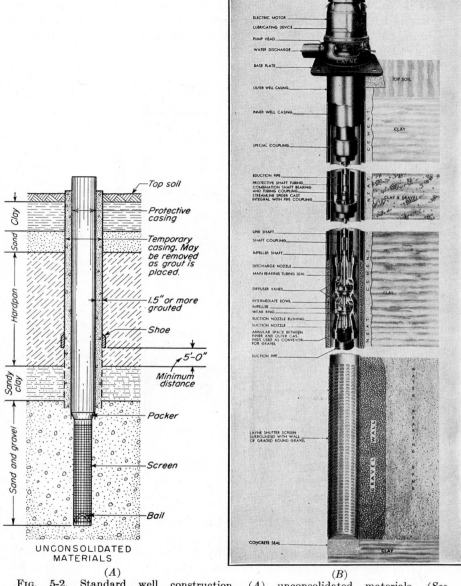

FIG. 5-2. Standard well construction. (A) unconsolidated materials. (See J.A.W.W.A., September, 1945, p. 913.) (B) typical deep-well equipment.

pulled down by jacks attached to deeply buried anchors or deadmen or to other objects, or allowed to sink of its own weight. In the last method, excavation proceeds slightly in advance of the casing. This method is known as the caisson method. It is used for holes from 4 to 6 ft and up to 50 or more feet in diameter.

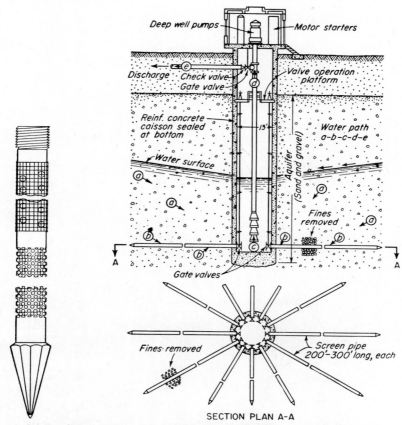

FIG. 5-3. Well point.

Fig. 5-4. Radial well or Ranney water collector. (*From R. Nebolsine, J. New Engl. Water Works Assoc., Vol. 57, p. 191, 1943.*)

The Ranney water collector is a dug well about 13 ft in diameter that has been sunk as a caisson. Screens are driven radially and approximately horizontally from this well, as indicated in Fig. 5-4.[1] The length of these horizontal screens varies from 100 to 300 ft, lengths up to 200 ft being most common. Such wells have great capacities, some up to

[1] See The Ranney System of Underground Water Collection, *Engineering*, Dec. 12, 1941, p. 461.

25 mgd, and have been found especially adapted as infiltration wells on river banks.[1]

5-6. Drilled Wells. The successful sinking of deep drilled wells requires special training, experience, tools, and equipment. Among the

Fig. 5-5. Percussion well-drilling rig. (*Courtesy of Stardrill-Keystone Co.*)

various methods of drilling wells may be included (1) the standard method, with or without modifications; (2) the jetting method; (3) the core-drill method; and (4) the hydraulic rotary method.

5-7. The Standard Method. The standard method involves percussion drilling in which a drill is alternately raised and dropped in the

---

[1] See also: R. G. Kazmann, *Proc. Am. Soc. Civil Engrs.*, June, 1947, p. 837, with discussion; J. Kruegel, *Am. City*, October, 1948, p. 108.

descending borehole. It is suited to the drilling of wells in any material from soft clay to the hardest rock. Other methods, such as the hydraulic rotary and core-drill methods, may advance more rapidly through hard rock. Modifications of the standard method include the "pole-tool" method, in which wooden rods are used instead of rope, and the "hollow-rod" method, in which a hollow rod replaces the rope to support the boring bit. Water is pumped into the top of the well between the casing and the hollow rod. The water leaves at a relatively high velocity through holes in the bit and rises through the hollow rod carrying the cuttings with it and permitting continuous advance of the well without the withdrawal of the bit to remove cuttings.

A light percussion drill rig adapted to the standard method is illustrated in Fig. 5-5, and a set of tools and accessories used with the rig is shown in Fig. 5-6.

The procedure in drilling with a standard rig is as follows:[1]

1. The rig is raised and a mud sill is placed under it to give the mast a solid foundation. Jacks are placed between the rig frame and the mud sill to level the rig and take the weight off the springs. Guys are led from the mast to deadmen or other holdfasts.

2. A wooden platform is built at the rear of the rig, surrounding the hole that is to be drilled. The platform should be at a height to make the control levers accessible to the driller. A sluice box and drain are built to receive and carry off bit cuttings and water as they are bailed from the well.

3. The string of tools, as illustrated in Fig. 5-7, is assembled and inserted in the drill-stem guide. The latter may be used in starting the hole and until its depth is equal to the length of the drill bit. However, it may be better to start the hole with an earth auger. As the hole deepens, the string of tools may be lengthened by increasing the length of the auger stem, to aid in keeping the hole straight, and by the addition of "jars." The jars are a loose link which gives a sharp upward blow to lessen the tendency of the drill bit to stick.

4. The rig is started and the drill is alternately raised and dropped to chip, crush, ream, and otherwise penetrate the strata.[2]

At the start of the hole, the full weight of the drilling tools is allowed to strike the ground to be penetrated. When the penetration is sufficient, the stretch of the rope is used to aid in causing the tools to rise after the blow has been delivered by the drill. Water is run into the hole during drilling to carry off some excavated material and to facilitate the bailing of the hole. When the bit has penetrated a short distance, it is withdrawn from the hole, and the bailer, operated on a separate cable, is lowered into the hole to remove the cuttings.

[1] Taken mainly from *War Dept. Tech. Manual* TM5-295, 1945.

[2] See also: J. R. Thoenen and E. J. Lintner, *U.S. Bur. Mines, Rept. Invest.* 4058, January, 1947; *Water Well J.*, Vol. 1, No. 3, p. 14, 1947.

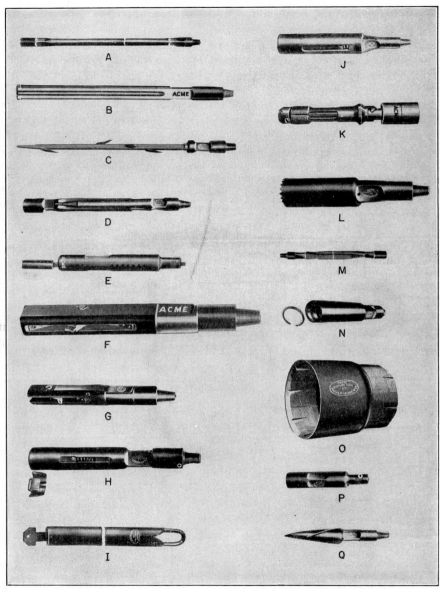

FIG. 5-6. Well-drilling tools. (A) drilling stem, (B) drilling bit, (C) fishing spear, (D) drilling jar, (E) Prosser swivel socket, (F) casing cutter, (G) collar buster, (H) side-slot combination socket slips, (I) bailer, (J) full-circle slip socket, (K) hollow spear, (L) drill mill, (M) fishing jar, (N) ring collar socket, (O) die nipple, (P) rope socket, (Q) mandrel or swage. (*Courtesy of Acme Fishing Tool Co.*)

If the hole is to be cased, the first length of casing, to the lower end of which a drive shoe may be attached, is lowered into the hole when it

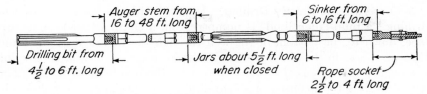

Fig. 5-7. String of tools used with standard drilling outfit.

reaches a sufficient depth. The drilling continues inside the casing, lengths of casing being added as progress is made. Drilling inside the casing is possible since the bit drills a hole 1 to 2 in. in diameter larger than the body of the drill inside the casing.

5-8. Jetting Methods. In the jetting method, the tools consist of a hollow drill, drill pipe, and water swivel. The equipment includes a derrick from which the pipe is supported, a force pump, and necessary water and power. Casing and a drive weight must be provided also. The hole is advanced by pumping water under pressure through the drill bit while it is churned up and down. The casing follows the bit very closely, and the water rising through the casing lifts the finely divided cuttings from the well.

This method of drilling is suitable in soft, unconsolidated, alluvial deposits and in a well of one diameter for depths up to 400 to 500 ft. If a greater depth is desired, the diameter of the hole must be decreased as the depth of the bore increases. In suitable materials, a well can be sunk by this method faster than by any other.

5-9. Core-drill Method. Core drills consist of a hollow bit armed with abrasive teeth on the annular circumference of the bit. The bit is rotated; it is not advanced by percussion. The parts of a diamond core drill are illustrated in Fig. 5-8. As the drill advances in solid material, a core rises in the

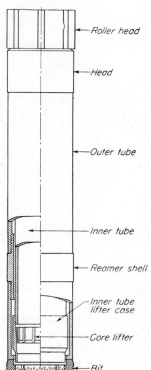

Fig. 5-8. Diamond coring bit. (*Courtesy of Sprague and Henwood, Inc.*)

center. This is broken off, raised, and should be preserved to furnish a record of the material penetrated.

Another method of advancing a borehole by a rotary abrasive method is by the use of steel shot poured into the hole and held beneath a revolving annular steel shoe. This method is known as the "chilled-shot" method.

5-10. Hydraulic Rotary Drilling. In the hydraulic rotary method of drilling,[1] a mud-laden fluid[2] is pumped from a sump at the ground surface, down to the bottom of the well through the hollow drill stem and through a hole in the cutting bit. The fluid returns up the well carrying with it the cuttings as they are loosened by the revolving drill bit. The actual drilling tools consist of a fishtail, disk, or special rock bit shown in Figs. 5-9 and 5-10. These are connected to a hollow drill stem, made up

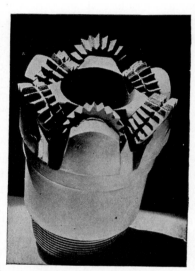

Fig. 5-9. Fishtail drill bit, showing hollow stem. (*Courtesy of National Supply Co.*)   Fig. 5-10. Hard-rock cutter head. (*Courtesy of Huges Tool Co.*)

in 20-ft lengths, which are connected at the top to a square rod, known as the "Kelly," which receives its rotary motion from a table similar to that shown in Fig. 5-11*A*.

Among the advantages of this method of drilling are the speed at which the hole can be advanced, particularly in soft materials, and the plastering effect of the mud-laden fluid as it rises through the core hole. The hydraulic head thus developed aids in preventing the caving of the walls of the hole before the casing has been set and simplifies the setting of the screen and casing in the hole before the completion of the well. The rotary core barrel makes it possible to determine the characteristics of the

[1] See L. P. Timmins, *Water and Water Eng.*, Apr. 19, 1930, p. 161.
[2] See also Drilling Fluids Conference, *Texas Eng. Expt. Sta. Bull.* 96, 1946.

formation being drilled, and the use of the rock bit now makes it possible to advance through hard rock without the use of a combination of the rotary- and cable-tool outfits.

5-11. Difficulties in Drilling. Difficulties in well drilling are the result of the loss of tools, bad alignment of the borehole, boulders, movements of plastic clay, quicksand, and other causes. Tools are lost through the breaking of the rope, which may be caused by defective material or by the jamming or "freezing" of the tools in the well. A bit may become wedged in the material being cut, as a result of striking too often in the same place,

Fig. 5-11. (*A*) Drilling a water well. (*Courtesy of National Supply Co.*) (*B*) Oil-well rig for depths to 10,000 ft. (*Courtesy of Power Rig and Equipment Co.*)

or tools may freeze because of rising sand or the sedimentation of cuttings if the pumps are stopped. Lost tools may be recovered by a number of ingenious devices, some of which are illustrated in Fig. 5-6. The position of the lost tool may be determined with accuracy by direct observation, by photography,[1] or by a wax impression. The fishing tool must be used with skill and care so as not to make conditions worse. The alignment of a well is maintained by the use of a long auger or drill stem.

5-12. Deviation from the Vertical. During construction, and before a well is accepted or the pumping equipment is installed, the plumbness and alignment should be tested. Relatively slight deviations from the

[1] Borehole Surveying, *Water and Water Eng.*, March, 1935, p. 112.

vertical can be measured by lowering a plumb bob into the well and noting the distance between the plumb-bob string and the edge of the top of the casing as the bob strikes the side of the casing at various depths. If the deviation from the vertical is greater than the diameter of the casing, two methods are available for making the necessary observations. In one, a glass bottle containing about a 50 per cent water dilution of hydrofluoric acid is lowered into the well and allowed to stand for about 15 min to permit the acid to etch the glass. The line of the surface of the acid shows the angle of deviation from the vertical. Both the direction and the angle of deviation can be detected by lowering into the well a compass floating in liquefied gelatin. The gelatin solidifies and fixes the compass in position and the surface of the gelatin shows the angle of deviation from the vertical. The alignment of the well can be tested by lowering into it a "dummy" consisting of a length of pipe slightly smaller in diameter than the well casing. The length of the dummy should be sufficient to detect undesirable deviations from a straight line. In general, a well should not deviate more than half its diameter for each 100 ft of its length.[1]

5-13. Depth of Well. The depth-capacity relation of a well is shown in Eq. (4-5). The well must be deep enough to penetrate the aquifer from which water is to be drawn so as to permit the installation of an adequate length of screen and the installation of the desired pumping equipment. Water wells are seldom more than a few hundred feet deep. Oil wells have been sunk to depths of many miles.

5-14. Diameter of Well. The diameter to be chosen for a well is affected by the method of construction, the amount of water to be drawn from the well, and other conditions. Theoretically the capacity of a well increases as the logarithm of its diameter, other conditions being unchanged. In practice, wells up to 6 in. in diameter may be expected to deliver about 50 gpm, and 24 in. and over in diameter may deliver more than 3,000 gpm. In deep drilled wells the minimum size of hole may be affected by the equipment necessary to reach the required depth. In general, the increase of the diameter of a well for the purpose of increasing its specific capacity is not economical. However, an increase in the diameter of the well screen may be justified in order to decrease the velocity of flow into the screen and thus increase the life of the well.

Deep wells may decrease in diameter at various stages of increasing depth, mainly for convenience in sinking the well. However, wells to be pumped by air lift should be smaller in diameter at the bottom than at the top to allow for the increasing volume of air at the lower pressures near the top of the well.

5-15. Log of a Well. The log of a well is a record of the underground materials penetrated at various depths and of the diameter and other

[1] See also W. C. Imbt, *Illinois Well Driller*, February, 1933, p. 10.

characteristics of the well. In most states, the keeping of a log is required by law, the log being filed for record with the U.S. Geological Survey or a similar bureau.

The logging of existing wells whose capacity has diminished has sometimes been found economically justifiable in a study of the best procedure in redeveloping the well. Results of such logging may include the location of lost tools, broken casing, cave-ins, strata that are taking water away from the well, and misplaced or broken seals. The results of acidizing or blasting wells and of the placing of gravel may be studied. Water horizons, detected behind casings by logging the well, have been recovered by punching or shooting holes in the casing.

Methods of logging wells include (1) seismic, (2) acoustic, (3) chemical, (4) mud analysis, (5) electrical,[1] (6) mechanical, (7) caliper, (8) optical, (9) thermal, (10) photographic, and (11) radioactive.[2] Seismic and acoustic waves are similar, except that the latter are of higher frequency and are absorbed differently. The characteristics of such waves propagated at the surface of the ground are detected by suitable instruments at various depths in the well. Obstructions in, and other features of, a well may be located by the detection of echoes from them resulting from the firing of a blank cartridge at the top of the well.

Chemical methods involve the determination of the characteristics of the formations penetrated by the well. There is a variety of electrical methods depending, in the main, on the measurement of the resistivities of the underground strata. The magnetic method depends on the fact that most rocks retain magnetic properties when placed in a magnetic field. The length of time of retention, called the "retentivity," gives a clue to the characteristics of the rock. Mechanical methods include hole calipering and, during construction, a record of drilling rate and drill reaction. Optical methods include the taking of photographs, the measurement of the intensity of light reflected from the walls of the well, or the measurement of fluorescence induced by irradiation of the well, usually with ultraviolet light. Thermal methods involve the measurement of the temperature gradient down the well or the direct measurement of the heat conductivity of the rocks. Artificial radioactivity can be induced in the rocks by a bombardment of neutrons, even through the casing.[3] The induced radiations can be picked up subsequently in the hole by suitable instruments. Mechanical and optical methods of logging of water wells are most commonly used.

---

[1] See also: F. L. Bryan, *Water Well J.*, Vol. 4, No. 2, p. 17, 1950, with references; T. S. Morris, *ibid.*, Vol. 6, No. 3, p. 12, 1952.

[2] See also: C. A. Bays and S. H. Folk, *J. Western Soc. Engrs.*, September, 1944, p. 248; Well Logging Methods Conference, *Texas Eng. Expt. Sta. Bull.* 93, 1946, with extensive bibliography.

[3] See also J. J. Baffa, *J. New Engl. Water Works Assoc.*, September, 1948, p. 207.

5-16. Well Casing.[1]   The well casing, as shown in Fig. 5-2, forms the lining of the well.   Near the top of wells of large diameter, it may be called the "curbing."   Among the purposes of well casing are the prevention of (1) collapse of the hole, (2) entrance of undesirable water into the well, (3) escape of good water from the well, and (4) material from falling into the well.   It is frequently necessary to case wells for the entire length

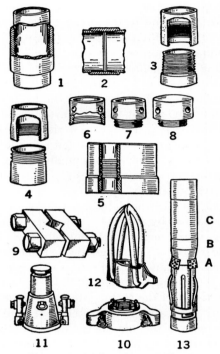

Fig. 5-12. Well-casing couplings.

of the hole; in some instances, however, casing has been omitted through strata that will not crumble, such as dry solid rock.

Materials[2] most commonly used for well casings are wrought iron, alloyed or unalloyed steel, and ingot iron.   The use of cast iron is increasing.   Cement-lined and enamel-lined pipes of the above materials are available and are suitable in some wells.   Other materials that have been used include copper, asbestos cement, plastics,[3] and vitrified clay.

Joints must be strong enough to withstand the stresses of driving and pulling.   Some types of joint are illustrated in Fig. 5-12.   Joints between

[1] See also *Johnson Natl. Well Drillers J.*, July–August, 1948.

[2] See Standard Specifications A100-46, *J.A.W.W.A.*, September, 1945.

[3] See also *Petroleum Engr.*, October, 1949, p. B-46.

casings of different diameters may be made tight by rubber or expanding lead gaskets.

5-17. Screens.[1]   A screen is required at the bottom of a well to prevent the walls of the aquifer from caving into the hole, to exclude fine sand, and to permit the entrance of water.   Some types of screens are illustrated in Figs. 5-13 and 5-14.   A common method of placing a screen in a cased well is to drive the casing to the full depth of the well.   The screen is lowered inside the casing until it rests on the bottom of the well.   The casing is then raised to expose the screen, and the joint between the screen

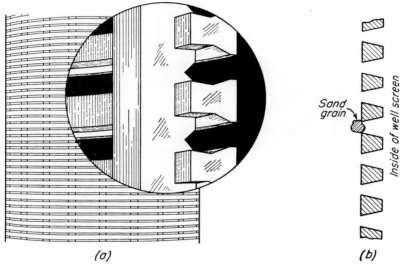

(a)   *(b)*

Fɪɢ. 5-13. Sections through well screens.   [*Section (a) courtesy of Layne and Bowler, Inc.*]

and the casing is closed with a rubber packer or a lead packing ring which is expanded against the casing.

The selection of the well screen is important in affecting the capacity and the life of the well.[2]   The size of the openings may be determined, after a study of a mechanical analysis of the aquifer, to permit the passage of all fine particles representing a certain percentage, by weight, of the water-bearing material.   It is common practice to use openings that will pass about 70 per cent, or more, of the sand grains in the aquifer, where the uniformity coefficient is high.   The shape of the openings should prevent clogging and bridging.   These can be diminished by the use of openings that are larger on the inside of the well, as shown in Fig. 5-13*b*.

[1] See also: E. W. Bennison, *J.A.W.W.A.*, June, 1939, p. 939; *Johnson Natl. Well Drillers J.*, September–October, 1948.

[2] See also J. S. Peterson and others, *Proc. Am. Soc. Civil Engrs.*, *Separate* 365, December, 1953.

Long, narrow, horizontal-slotted openings, as shown in Figs. 5-13 and 5-14, are satisfactory. The openings should be placed as close together as the strength of the screen will permit. This distance usually allows five to six openings per vertical inch. Screens formed by punching holes in the metal in order to leave a raised portion of the metal over the hole with a slot at the bottom, as shown in Fig. 5-14, are known as "shutter screens." They may be suitable as inside screens in gravel-packed wells, but because of the varying size and irregularity of openings they are not suitable in sandy material.

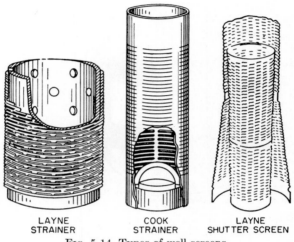

LAYNE   COOK   LAYNE
STRAINER   STRAINER   SHUTTER SCREEN

FIG. 5-14. Types of well screens.

The total area of the openings in a screen should be such as to maintain an entrance velocity less than necessary to carry the finest particle of sand that is to be excluded by the screen. In general, it should be less than about 0.125 to 0.2 fps. Lifting velocities of sand grains, with a specific gravity of about 2.65, are shown in Table 5-1. It is generally desirable,

TABLE 5-1. Lifting Velocities of Water

Diameter of grains, mm	Velocity of water, fps
Up to 0.25	0.0 –0.10
0.25–0.50	0.12–0.22
0.50–1.00	0.25–0.33
1.00–2.00	0.37–0.56
2.00–4.00	0.60–2.60

but not essential, that the length of the screen be equal to the thickness of the aquifer penetrated. The length, diameter, and total area are interdependent dimensions that must be adjusted to give the desired entering velocity. Some margin of safety in screen size is desirable to allow for incrustation and clogging and to prolong the life of the screen. The length of a screen should usually not be specified in advance of the construction of the well, in order that the length may be adjusted to the thickness of the aquifer penetrated.

Materials used for screens include iron or steel, either black or galvanized; corrosion-resistant alloys, some of which are listed in Table 5-2; concrete, wood; asbestos cement; and gravel. Since the useful life of the well is mainly dependent on the durability of the screen, emphasis is placed on the selection of the material of the screen.

TABLE 5-2. Some Alloys Used in Well Screens*

Alloy	% of each constituent
Monel metal..................	Nickel 70, copper 30
Super nickel.................	Nickel 30, copper 70
Everdur metal...............	Copper 96, silicon 3, manganese 1
Stainless steel...............	Steel 74, chromium 18, nickel 8
Silicon red brass............	Copper 83, silicon 1, zinc 16
Anaconda red brass..........	Copper 85, zinc 15
Armco iron†.................	Iron 99.84
Toncan iron†................	Iron 99.55, copper 0.40, molybdenum 0.05

* Maintaining Well Yields, *Water Works Eng.*, Aug. 27, 1941, p. 1061.
† Black or galvanized.

To remove a screen from a well without collapsing the screen, the sand-joint method may be used. In this method, sacking or similar material is fastened to the end of a pulling pipe that is lowered to the bottom of the screen. Sufficient clean sharp sand is poured into the well almost to fill the screen. Where the space between the pulling pipe and the screen is large, the sacking must be supported by a truncated cone or disk welded to the pulling pipe. The joint between the screen and casing is broken, and the pulling force is transmitted uniformly through the sand to the screen, usually lifting it without damage.

5-18. Corrosion of Screens. Corrosion of well screens may be classified as direct, selective, and electrolytic. It may include chemical action due to dissolved gases, such as carbon dioxide, hydrogen sulphide, or methane released as water enters the well through the screen. A uniform destruction of the surface, with enlarged openings, is typical of direct corrosion resulting from chemical reactions between the water and the screen. Selective corrosion is confined to alloys in which the corrosive water reacts mainly with one constituent of the alloy. Typical of this corrosion is dezincification and degraphitization. Electrolytic corrosion results from galvanic action set up by the presence of dissimilar metals in electrolytic solutions. This type of corrosion is discussed in Sec. 19-2. Direct and selective corrosion may be diminished by choosing other metals close to each other on the electrolytic scale.

5-19. Incrustation of Screens. Incrustation may be caused by the direct deposition of suspended matter from the water onto the screen, by the release of dissolved minerals from solution due either to the change in pressure at the screen or to chemical reactions, and by biological activities resulting in the deposition of a gelatinous zoogloeal material on the screen. The principal incrustant is calcium carbonate, which both forms a scale on the screen and cements deposited particles. Carbon dioxide in solution under the high pressure in the aquifer may be released at the screen surface, resulting in the deposition of calcium carbonate. Sometimes aluminum silicates, iron, and sulphates are found in the incrustations.

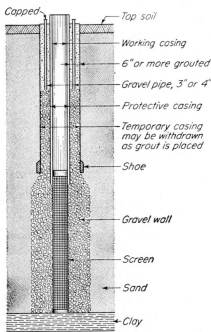

Fig. 5-15. Gravel-wall well. (*From J.A.W.W.A., Vol. 37, p. 938, 1945.*)

Incrustations can be minimized by allowing a low head loss through the screen, thus preventing the escape of dissolved gases and the precipitation of incrustants. The removal of incrustations from screens is discussed in Sec. 5-32.

5-20. Gravel-wall Wells.[1] Gravel-wall wells with interior screens, as illustrated in Fig. 5-15, are used to increase the area of contact between the aquifer and the well, thus diminishing the velocity of the entering water and increasing the specific capacity of the well. The gravel wall is placed during the construction of the well, various methods for placing the gravel being used.

Gravel should be selected of a size that will prevent the entrance of particles of sand greater than is desired. For example, Gerber[2] states: "If the natural sand grains have a diameter of 0.04 in. the pack gravel could have a diameter of 0.25 in., or if the sand were very fine, say 0.005 in., two sizes of pack gravel might be used: 0.03 and 0.02 in., approximately." The openings in the inner metallic screen should be as large as possible without permitting the entrance of gravel into the well.

The cost of gravel-wall wells is usually greater than that of typically screened wells, but the resulting increase in capacity and prolonged life justify the cost.

5-21. Finishing a Well. After the screen has been set or the casing has been perforated to admit water when no screen is to be placed, the

[1] See also *Johnson Natl. Well Drillers J.*, May–June, 1949.

[2] W. D. Gerber, *J.A.W.W.A.*, April, 1937, p. 486.

well should be protected against contamination and undesirable aquifers should be sealed off. The well is now ready for the installation of the drop pipe and pump, as shown in Fig. 5-2*B*.

5-22. Protection from Contamination. Wells may be contaminated either by surface water entering at the top or following outside the casing, or by interchange of waters between aquifers. Much attention has been given to the prevention of such contamination, and exhaustive specifications for the protection of wells have been published by the U.S. Public Health Service in a Sanitation Manual for Public Water Supplies.[1] Some items in the manual are as follows:

1. *Exclusion of Surface Water from Site.* The top of the well must be so constructed that no water from the well can drop back into it, the ground surface must slope away from the well or the site otherwise drained, and flood waters should not approach within 50 ft.

2. *Earth Formations above Water-bearing Stratum.* Earth formations above aquifer should provide sufficient filtration to prevent contamination from surface sources.

3. *Distance to Source of Contamination.* The minimum permissible horizontal distance to a source of contamination is 50 ft, with 300 ft preferred.

4. *Depth of Casing and Curbings.* It must extend at least 10 ft below the ground surface and preferably 10 ft below the ground-water table.

5. *Construction and Use of Casing and Curbing.* For drilled wells, the space between casing and well hole is to be filled with not less than $1\frac{1}{2}$ in. of cement grout to a depth of 10 ft or more. Casing is not to be used as suction pipe.

6. *Gravel-treated Wells.* Gravel surface must terminate not less than 10 ft below ground surface. Remaining space above gravel is to be filled with impervious clay, mortar, or cement grout. Gravel must have been disinfected before placing in the well.

. . . . .

8. *Well Seals or Covers.* There must be a watertight seal or cover at the top of the casing.

9. *Well Vents.* These are necessary to retain atmospheric pressure in casing, preventing suction of contaminated water into the well. Such vents should extend above the floor bend and should terminate in a covered or screened return bend facing downward.

10. *Well Pits.* Pumping machinery is not to be located below ground in pits.

11. *Construction and Installation of Pumps.* Among the details included are: pumps must not be primed by unsafe water; there must be a watertight connection between casing and power unit, or casing must extend 6 in. or more above surface.

12. *Pump House.* Adequately drained and protected against flooding.

5-23. Sealing a Well. Wells are sealed both during and after construction to prevent surface or underground contamination from entering the well, to prevent the passage of good water underground from one aquifer to another, to prevent the escape of gas from the well, and for other reasons. The sealing of the annular space near the ground surface is particularly important in creviced rock formations with connections to

[1] See *J.A.W.W.A.*, May, 1944, p. 501.

the ground surface.   Abandoned wells should always be sealed to prevent many possible subsequent difficulities, and to comply with the law in many jurisdictions.[1]

A satisfactory method of sealing a well below the surface of the ground[2] requires that the outside casing be driven to the point at which the well is to be sealed.   Drilling is continued below the casing to the full depth of the stratum that is to be sealed off, but in no case is the length of the hole below the casing to be less than the length of the string of tools.   The hole is then filled with sand to the level at which the end of the inner casing is to be set, and the remainder of the hole is filled with neat cement, either dry or as a soupy grout.   The inner casing, with a flat plate welded over its lower end, is lowered into the hole, pushing aside the grout until its lower end reaches the sand.   The cement grout is thus pushed into the annular space between the casings.   After the cement has set, the welded plate at the bottom of the inner casing is punched through, the sand is bailed out, and the drilling of the hole is continued.   The sand is used so that the cement will not be cracked when drilling is resumed.   A similar procedure may be followed in sealing an existing well.[3]   Pressure cement grouting can also be used to seal out undesirable water.

5-24. Chlorinating a Well.[4]   Well tools are sometimes disinfected during construction and all new wells should be chlorinated, as a sanitary precaution, before being turned into production.   A well can be chlorinated by filling it with a solution containing at least 50 to 100 ppm of available chlorine and allowing the solution to stand in the well about 24 hr.   A stock solution of chlorine containing about 15,000 ppm may be applied at different levels, after which the water in the well may be agitated to diffuse and distribute the chlorine.

5-25. Performance Requirements.   Specifications for the construction of a well sometimes include a statement of the required performance of the well under test conditions.   The usual guarantee covers the quality and quantity of water to be delivered for a particular drawdown.   Payment for the well may be in direct proportion to the specific capacity.

5-26. Well Tests.[5]   New wells may be subjected to acceptance tests, and existing wells may be tested to determine their condition and capacity.   The test usually requires the determination of the rate of flow from the well, while the drawdown *remains constant*, for a number of hours in the case of a gravity well.   The maximum rate at which water can be

[1] See Committee Report, *J.A.W.W.A.*, October, 1952, pp. 961, 965.

[2] See also J. A. Carr, *Water Works & Sewerage*, March, 1937, p. 94.

[3] See also F. Holland, *Illinois Well Driller*, Vol. 16, No. 1, p. 7, 1947.

[4] See also: Sanitation Manual for Public Ground Water Supplies, *Public Health Repts.* 59, No. 5; *J.A.W.W.A.*, May, 1944, p. 501.

[5] See also Standard Specifications for Deep Wells, A100-46, *J.A.W.W.A.*, September, 1945.

drawn from a well for a short period of time, without regard to the draw-down, bears no relation to the long-time capacity of the well. Careful observation of the movement of the water level in a gravity well is of greater importance than in a pressure or artesian well because of the relatively slow recession of the water level in a gravity well penetrating highly pervious water-bearing material.

5-27. Measurement of Water Level in a Well. The depth of water in a well while it is being pumped can be measured by any one of a number of methods. A simple method[1] requires an ordinary steel tape to the lower end of which a magnesium strip is attached so that one end protrudes about $\frac{1}{8}$ in. beyond the lower end of the tape. The strip is about $\frac{1}{8}$ in. thick, as wide as the tape, and $\frac{1}{2}$ in. long. The tape reel at the surface is electrically grounded through a d-c milliammeter. When the tape is lowered to allow the magnesium point to touch water, an electromotive force is set up to cause the milliammeter hand to move abruptly.

The depth of water in a well between the drop pipe and the casing can be observed and recorded continuously, even while the well is being pumped, by the arrangement shown in Fig. 5-16. In this method, before the pumping of the well is started, air is pumped into the tube D until all the water has been expelled from the tube at C. As soon as air escapes at C, the pressure shown on the gage will cease to rise. The pressure on the gage will show the depth of water AC before pumping. As pumping continues, the water in the well will drop to some such position as BC. The maximum pressure that can be developed on the pressure gage will be the measure of this depth BC.

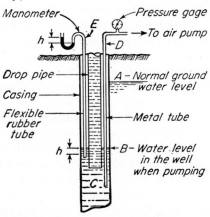

FIG. 5-16. Air-pressure method for measuring depth to water in a well.

The drawdown will be the difference between AC and BC. By pumping air slowly and continuously into tube D and recording the change in air pressure on the gage, in terms of depth of water in the well, a continuous record of the drawdown can be made.

In using the device shown at E, a measured length of the rubber tube is lowered into the well until the level in the manometer changes. The length of the tube let down the well, less the head h in the manometer, is the distance to water in the well.

5-28. Maintenance of Wells. Among the causes of well failures that must be guarded against are (1) overpumping, (2) lowering of the water

[1] See S. E. Norris, *Johnson Natl. Well Drillers J.*, November–December, 1952, p. 7.

table, (3) clogging or collapse of screen, (4) leaky casing, (5) clogging of the sand or crevices of the aquifer, (6) leaky drop pipe, (7) corrosion,[1] and (8) worn pump. The clogging and incrustation of screens, frequently caused by overpumping, are probably the cause of most well failures in sand and gravel.[2] Overpumping is difficult to specify, but if a screen is clogging, the well is being overpumped. Overpumping results also in pumping of sand, lowering the water level in the well, and lowering the ground-water table surrounding the well. Pumping of sand may result also from, or may be the cause of, collapse of the screen or the casing.

The lowering of the ground-water table by overdraft on the well field cannot always be avoided. As the water level is lowered, the specific capacity of the well is decreased. It may be necessary to increase the length of the drop pipe in the well, to increase the depth of the well, or both, in order to maintain the same rate of discharge from the well.

Clogging of the screen may be detected by a drop of the water level in the well during pumping without proportionate drop in the ground-water table. Collapse of the screen may be indicated by the pumping of sand, either with or without symptoms caused by the clogging of the screen.

Leaky casings may admit undesirable water, or they may allow good water to escape from the well into "thieving" strata. A leaky drop pipe or a worn pump will be indicated by a loss of capacity of the pump at known speeds of operation. "Thieving" strata may be detected by logging the well. Leaky drop pipes and worn pumps can be observed by pulling them from the well periodically for inspection.

5-29. Developing Wells.[3] By the development of a well is meant the restoration or increase of its capacity. An attempt to restore the failing capacity of a well should be made only after a study of the costs involved and the probable results. It may be less costly to construct a new well. A well may be developed by (1) removing, cleaning, and replacing the screen; (2) removing the screen and blasting, reaming, or otherwise reconstructing the well, and replacing the screen; or (3) without removing the screen, surging, acidizing, chlorinating, overpumping, or blasting and reconstructing. Where water-bearing aquifers that have been cased off are discovered, the casing may be cut or perforated opposite them and a screen placed in proper position. In wells larger than 6 in. in diameter or greater than 100 ft in depth, it is usually more economical to attempt to restore the well without removing the screen. Screens that have been removed may be cleaned on the surface of the ground with acid or by brushing, and repairs may be made to the screen.

[1] See also T. E. Larson, *Water Well J.*, September–October, 1949, p. 19.

[2] See also J. C. Harding and others, *J.A.W.W.A.*, January, 1947, p. 32.

[3] See also: *Johnson Natl. Well Drillers J.*, Vol. 21, Nos. 1, 2, 1949; R. B. Diehl, *Public Works*, April, 1950, p. 48.

5-30. Blasting Wells.[1]   The development of wells by blasting is most successful in consolidated material in which crevices are opened and interconnected by the shock of the blast.   In unconsolidated materials, sand grains may be more densely packed by the blast, resulting in a diminution of flow from the ground into the well.

Speed, high power, low bulk, and certain detonation are desired characteristics of the explosive to be used.   Speed and power are required to overcome the tremendous pressures underground and to shatter the rock; a dense explosive is needed because of the small space available to hold it; and certainty of detonation is essential, as a misfire deep in a well hole cannot be safely rectified.   The explosives that are most commonly used are 80 per cent high-velocity gelatin and nitroglycerin.   Where small charges can be used, 40 per cent and 60 per cent dynamites are sometimes used.   The size of the shots varies from 50 to 200 lb.   It is customary to begin with the lighter charges, progressively increasing them until the desired result has been obtained.   The size of the charge is affected also by the water pressure to be overcome; the greater the pressure the heavier the charge.[2]   The "Strata-Jet"[3] involves the firing of a penetrating shell horizontally into the stratum which it is desired to open up.   It is claimed that it makes possible the location of the explosive accurately at any desired spot.

In developing a well by means of "vibratory explosives,"[4] an oversize bubble of gas is created in the well with a relatively small explosive charge. Rapid expansion and contraction of this bubble through 10 or more cycles before coming to rest surge the well and clean the screen.

5-31. Surging.   To surge a well is to cause water to flow rapidly from the well into the ground, or alternately to overpump the well and to force water into the ground.   The principal purpose of surging a well is to dislodge clogging and incrusting material from the screen.   Immediately after a well has been surged, it should be strongly and continuously pumped until all dislodged material has been removed.   Otherwise the improvement resulting from surging will be only temporary.   Surging is not always successful, occasionally causing loss of the well.[5]

In surging with a plunger, the drop pipe is removed from the well, and a solid plunger, fitting the walls of the casing, is lowered beneath the water in the well.   The plunger is attached to a well rig and is moved violently up and down, as in spudding, causing water to rush into and out

[1] See also R. M. Ebaugh, *J.A.W.W.A.*, February, 1950, p. 171.

[2] See also K. P. Doerr, *Illinois Well Driller*, February, 1941, p. 8.

[3] See *Water Well J.*, Vol. 5, No. 2, p. 9, 1951.

[4] See also: H. A. Mylander, *ibid.*, January–February, 1951, p. 13; *J.A.W.W.A.*, January, 1952, p. 39.

[5] See also A. D. H. Henderson, *Water Works Eng.*, August, 1943, p. 882.

of the well through the screen.   By placing a check valve in the plunger, water can be forced through the screen in one direction only.   If the top of the well casing is sealed, compressed air can be discharged into it to force water violently back through the screen.   If air is permitted to follow through into the aquifer, it may cause "air logging" or clogging of the aquifer with pockets of air.

Dry ice, or solidified carbon dioxide, when dropped into a well, quickly turns to a gas, generating a strong pressure if the gas is confined.   In surging a well with dry ice, a charge of 50 to 500 lb should be inserted and supported near the top of the casing, which is then *quickly* and tightly closed.   The charge is suddenly released to fall into the well and vaporize. Pressures up to 90 psi have been generated in this manner.   Although the method has been successful, there are dangers in its use such as frozen hands, suffocation of the operators due to fumes of carbon dioxide, and rupture or lifting of the casing or collapse of the screen.[1]

5-32. Chemical Treatment.   Chemicals such as acids, chlorine, and sodium hexametaphosphate may be added to a well for the purpose of dissolving or dislodging clogging material or incrustation on the screen or in the sand surrounding the screen.   Acids[2] may be used only where the metal of the screen will not be attacked by them.   Brass or bronze may be treated with muriatic acid, while iron requires nitric acid.[3]   Inhibited acids[4] contain chemicals that inhibit the reaction between the acid and certain metals but not between the acid and the incrustants.   Many inhibitors are proprietary compounds, some of which contain arsenic or other toxic substances that must be used with caution, if used at all. Stabilizers in acids retain in solution certain materials that would otherwise be reprecipitated as the acid weakens through dilution and neutralization.   Acids should be applied in the highest concentration possible in the expectation that the acid concentration will reach at least 25 per cent in the screen.   In some cases, progressively stronger doses of acid have been applied to the well.   Acid is sometimes added by pouring it down a hose, with the lower end of the hose at the bottom of the well, and slowly raising the hose as the volume of the acid displaces the water in the well.

Muriatic acid is most commonly used because it is effective in dissolving calcium carbonate, the most common incrustant.   The addition of about 3 per cent citric or acetic acid to the muriatic acid eliminates some trouble in iron-bearing water.   Calcium sulphate incrustant may be dissolved by ammonium salts.   Acid with a content of about 27 per cent

[1] See also R. H. Porter, *Water Works Eng.*, Apr. 23, 1941, p. 446.

[2] See also: M. M. de Witt, *Water Well J.*, November–December, 1949, p. 11; C. H. Groom and J. T. Browning, *ibid.*, Vol. 1, No. 1, p. 9, summer, 1947.

[3] See also J. R. Goetz and F. L. Coventry, *Water & Sewage Works*, April, 1946, p. R-23.

[4] See also Sec. 22-8.

muriatic acid is a commercial strength commonly used. If results are not satisfactory, the use of the muriatic acid may be followed by the application of sulphuric acid, or the temperature of the muriatic acid may be raised by placing magnesium rods in the well. This is called the "hot-acid" treatment.[1] The acid may be allowed to stand in the well for 1 to 24 hr during which time the well may be gently surged intermittently for short periods of time. The well should be bailed clean of all dislodged material and the acid removed by flushing the well with water or neutralizing with lime, soda ash, or other chemical followed by thorough flushing with water until all traces of chemicals are removed.

Among the dangers to be guarded against in handling acids, besides burns, are the acid fumes, carbon dioxide which is generated in quantities large enough to be suffocating, or the release of explosive hydrogen.

Chlorine has been added to wells to remove incrustants resulting from the activity of so-called "iron bacteria." It serves also to produce hypochlorous acid, which will attack calcareous deposits.[2] In some cases, it has been applied successfully ahead of acidizing.

Treatment of porous concrete screens with sodium hexametaphosphate requiring the development of a concentration of the chemical in the order of 2,000 ppm[3] together with slime-removing substances has proved successful. The chemicals are added daily, or at other convenient intervals, and are allowed to concentrate for 7 to 10 days. "Meanwhile the well is surged several times daily to promote effective action inside the casing. Final flushing of the well clears it."[3]

5-33. Pumping Sand. Sand should be removed from well water before it passes through pumps or into the distribution system.[4] Various types of sand-removing equipment are available, including the Brassert strainer,[5] and a centrifugal device described by Jessup.[6] Bunker[7] describes a quick method for the detection of sand in well water based on visual comparison with the amount of sand in known standards. Sand may be pumped so rapidly from a well as to cause underground cavities which, extending to the surface, undermine the foundations of surface structures.

[1] See also Groom and Browning, *loc. cit.*

[2] See also: E. D. Brown, *J.A.W.W.A.*, May, 1942, p. 698; H. L. White, *Civil Eng.*, May, 1942, p. 263.

[3] See also G. N. Andrews, *J.A.W.W.A.*, August, 1947, p. 729.

[4] See also J. R. Rossum, *J.A.W.W.A.*, February, 1954, p. 123.

[5] See also G. L. Frigate, *Water Works & Sewerage*, April, 1942, p. 161.

[6] A. H. Jessup, *Water Works Eng.*, Sept. 11, 1940, p. 1156.

[7] G. C. Bunker, *Water Works & Sewerage*, June, 1943, p. 228.

CHAPTER 6

METEOROLOGY AND HYDROLOGY

6-1. Meteorology.[1] Meteorology, hydrology, and hydrography are related sciences dealing with the cycle of water in nature. When rain starts to fall upon the surface of the earth, that part which is not immediately evaporated is absorbed into or passes into the soil. When the rate of rainfall exceeds the capacity of the soil to absorb it water may collect in puddles or pools formed by surface irregularities and vegetable cover. As the supply exceeds the capacity of the pools they begin to overflow and runoff occurs into the drainage system of the area. The capacity of the soil to take moisture is known as its *infiltration capacity*. The effect of the pools is known as *surface detention*.

The infiltration capacity of a given soil is affected by its physical characteristics, the amount of soil moisture present, the prevailing plant-root structure, and other conditions. In general, the infiltration capacity becomes less and less as rainfall continues.

6-2. Source of Water Supply. Rain, snow, hail, and sleet are precipitated upon the surface of the earth as meteorological water and may be considered as the original source of all water supplied. The ultimate return of this water to the air by evaporation and transpiration completes what is known as the *hydrological cycle*. A part of the precipitated water becomes available for direct use in stream flow and in ground water, and part is evaporated, transpired, or percolates into the ground. It is axiomatic that the amount of water available for direct use will be the difference between total precipitation and the losses. It is to be emphasized that there is no easy solution for the determination of the amount of water available and that, until an engineer becomes thoroughly competent, formulas and charts may be used only as a guide to experience and knowledge of this interrelation of the various conditions.

6-3. Precipitation. Precipitation occurs when moisture is transferred from the atmosphere to the earth. The capacity of the atmosphere to retain water vapor is a function of the temperature; therefore, when the temperature of the atmosphere falls below the dew point, *i.e.*, the tem-

[1] See also "Hydrology Handbook," Manual of Engineering Practice, No. 28, American Society of Civil Engineers, 1949.

perature at which the atmosphere becomes saturated with moisture, precipitation results.[1]   Some of the conditions involved are temperature, barometric pressure, prevailing winds, mountain barriers, relative position of land and water areas, altitude, precipitation nuclei, and cyclonic storms.

6-4. Measurements and Records.   The measurement and recording of precipitation in the United States is done officially by the Weather Bureau.   The data are published as: a *daily weather map* for each of several principal stations; *climatological data* published monthly for 45 climatological sections and yearly in the form of a summary; *The Monthly*

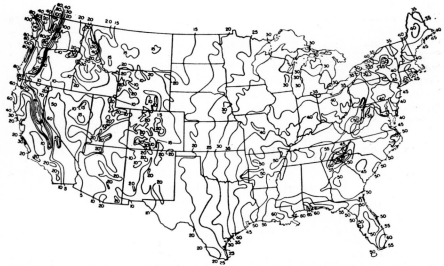

FIG. 6-1. Lines showing equal annual rainfall, or isohyetal, lines, in the United States. (*Courtesy of the U.S. Weather Bureau.*)

Weather Review, and an *Annual Report*.   Measurement of precipitation is made with standard instruments of the manual or automatic-recording type.   A description of the instruments, together with instructions for placement and manipulation, may be found in *Circular* E, Instrument Division, U.S. Weather Bureau.   Measurements of snowfall[2] are made in the mountains along the West Coast by municipal water departments and others.

6-5. Amount of Rainfall.   Topographic and climatic conditions in the United States are widely variant.   These factors, together with others, cause a large variation in the amount and distribution of rainfall.   The mean annual precipitation, as shown in Fig. 6-1, varies from less than 2 in. in sections of the Southwest to 100 or more in the extreme Northwest.

[1] See also T. H. Evans, *Public Works*, July, 1951, p. 36.
[2] See also B. S. Grant, *Water Works Eng.*, December, 1950, p. 1102.

TABLE 6-1. Precipitation at Long-time Weather Bureau Stations

Station	Period of record	Average annual, in.	Max		Min	
			Year	% of avg	Year	% of avg
Mobile, Ala..........	1871–1945	61.2	1881	151	1938	60
Yuma, Ariz..........	1870–1945	3.5	1905	326	1938	8.3
Los Angeles, Calif....	1878–1945	15.7	1884	257	1898	31
Denver, Colo........	1872–1945	14.0	1909	164	1939	54
Peoria, Ill...........	1856–1945	35.0	1858	152	1910	66
Indianapolis, Ind.....	1867–1945	39.6	1876	146	1934	63
Muscatine, Iowa.....	1846–1945	38.9	1851	192	1901	56
Boston, Mass........	1818–1945	40.0	1863	170	1822	68
St. Paul, Minn.......	1837–1945	27.3	1849	182	1910	37
St. Louis, Mo........	1837–1945	37.3	1858	184	1930	62
New York, N.Y......	1826–1945	43.0	1859	139	1835	67
Portland, Ore........	1872–1945	42.5	1882	159	1929	62
Yankton, S.D........	1874–1945	25.0	1881	164	1894	58
Austin, Tex..........	1856–1945	34.4	1919	188	1917	46
Milwaukee, Wis......	1844–1945	30.1	1876	167	1901	62

TABLE 6-2. Mean Annual Rainfall and Average Deviation from Mean

Region	Mean annual rainfall, in.	Average deviation, %
New England....................	40–45	11–14
Atlantic Coast..................	45–50	11–17
Florida........................	50–55	14–20
Tennessee River.................	45–55	11–14
North Gulf Coast...............	55–60	14–17
Texas Coast....................	25–45	17–23
Ohio River.....................	35–40	11–20
Missouri River..................	20–30	14–30
Eastern Rocky Mountain.........	10–15	17–26
New Mexico....................	10–15	17–41
North Plateau..................	10–20	17–26
South Plateau..................	10–15	17–50
North Pacific Coast.............	40–50	11–26
South Pacific Coast.............	10–15	23–32

Precipitation records at a few long-time Weather Bureau stations are given in Table 6-1.

The mean annual rainfall may be used as an index of the probable availability of water supply in a region. The actual rainfall in any one year may, however, deviate widely from the mean. The annual rainfall for each of a number of consecutive years may be continuously above or below the average. A long-continued period below the average **may** prove disastrous to a water supply. Many failures occurred during the drought periods of 1930–1934 and 1952–1954. Variations of seasonal rainfalls in a region, before recorded history, may be estimated by the development of a relation between the width of tree rings and the rain-fall.[1] An interesting analysis of studies to determine possible climatic

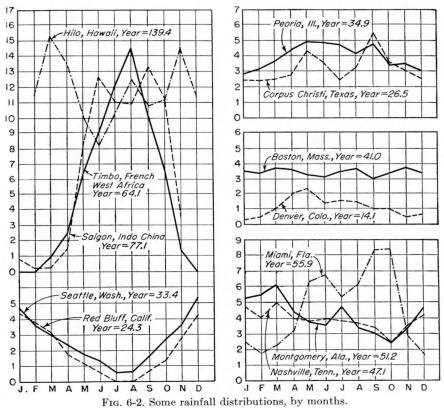

FIG. 6-2. Some rainfall distributions, by months.

changes in the United States is given in *U.S. Geological Survey, Water Supply Paper* 772, 1936. Annual deviations from the mean annual rain-fall in some regions are shown in Table 6-2.

6-6. Distribution of Rainfall. The distribution of the annual rainfall of a region seems to be determined by climatic conditions peculiar to the location, somewhat as is shown in Fig. 6-2. These patterns illustrate in a general way the amount and occurrence of rainfall in different regions. There is often a relation between rainfall distribution and seasonal demand for water, particularly in cases where storage problems are involved and where domestic supplies are used for irrigation purposes.

[1] See A. E. Douglas, *Sci. Monthly*, Vol. 37, p. 481, 1933.

Hydrological considerations make it convenient to divide the year into three seasons or periods: (1) replenishment, September through November; (2) storage, December through April; and (3) growing, May through August.

TABLE 6-3. Rainfall-intensity Formulas

Name of originator or compiler	Conditions for which formula was devised	Rate of rainfall, in. per hr. t is duration of rainfall, min	$R*$ when t is 1 hr	Source of information
A. N. Talbot	Ordinary storms in Eastern U.S.	$105/(t + 15)$	1.4	*The Technograph*, Univ. Illinois, 1891–1892, p. 103
A. N. Talbot	Maximum storms in Eastern U.S.	$150/(t + 30)$	1.7	*The Technograph*, Univ. Illinois, 1891–1892, p. 103
L. J. Le Conte	San Francisco, Calif.	$7/t^{0.5}$	0.9	*Trans. Am. Soc. Civil Engrs.*, Vol. 54, p. 198, 1905
J. de Bruyn Kops	Savannah, Ga.	$163/(t + 27)$	1.88	
A. J. Schafmayer	Chicago, Ill.	$90/(t^{0.9} + 11)$	1.76	*J. Western Soc. Engrs.*, December, 1944, p. 300
R. A. Brackenbury	Spokane, Wash.	$[23.92/(t + 2.15)] + 0.154$	0.53	*Eng. News-Record*, Aug. 10, 1912, p. 156
E. W. Clarke	Expected annually Exceeded once in 15 years	$(54/t)^{1/2}$ $(324/t)^{1/2}$	0.95 2.3	*Eng. News*, Vol. 48, p. 386
C. E. Gregory	Ordinary severe storm Maximum storm	$12/t^{1/2}$ $32/t^{0.8}$	1.6 1.2	*Trans. Am. Soc. Civil Engrs.*, Vol. 58, p. 483, 1907
D. W. Mead			10.0	"Hydrology," 2d ed., p. 289, 1950

* R = inches of rainfall. t = duration of storm, or time of concentration, minutes.

6-7. Rate and Frequency of Intense Rainfall.[1]

The water-supply engineer is concerned with the rate at which rain falls in a single storm or series of storms and also with the frequency at which excessive precipitation occurs. Since he is charged with the safety and economical design of structures that he builds for the control of water, he must provide against damage or failure due to floods or excessive erosion. Many rainfall formulas have been devised. Some are shown in Table 6-3.

The maximum intensity of rainfall used in design increases with the length of the period during which the maximum storm occurs. This can be formulated as[1]

[1] From M. M. Bernard, *Trans. Am. Soc. Civil Engrs.*, Vol. 96, p. 592, 1932.

$$R = \frac{KT^x}{(a + t)^n} \qquad (6\text{-}1)$$

where T = period covered, years

t = duration of storm, min

R = maximum intensity of rainfall, in. per hr

n, x, a, and K are constants; some values are given in Table 6-4
Equation (6-1) is empirical and should be used with care in the determination of actual rainfall-runoff relations.

TABLE 6-4. Illustrative Values of Coefficients and Exponents in the Formula
$R = KT^x/t^n$ East of 103d Meridian

Region	K		x	n	
	$t = 5$ to 60 min	$t = 60$ to 1,440 min	$t = 5$ to 1,440 min	$t = 5$ to 60 min	$t = 60$ to 1,440 min
New England...........	5.5– 8.5	15–35	0.19–0.23	0.44–0.45	0.70–0.80
North Atlantic..........	8.5– 9.0	35–45	0.17–0.23	0.43–0.44	0.79–0.82
Middle Atlantic........	9.0– 9.5	45	0.19–0.21	0.41–0.42	0.79–0.82
Southeast..............	10.0–11.0	40–60	0.16–0.19	0.38–0.42	0.78–0.82
Ohio Basin.............	8.0– 9.0	45–60	0.16–0.19	0.41–0.42	0.78–0.88
Upper Mississippi.......	8.5– 9.5	40–45	0.17–0.20	0.43–0.47	0.78–0.85
Lower Mississippi.......	9.0–11.0	40–50	0.15–0.17	0.39–0.42	0.70–0.80
Missouri River.........	7.5–10.0	45–60	0.19–0.20	0.44–0.47	0.78–0.90
Southwest Mississippi....	7.5– 9.5	40–60	0.18–0.22	0.41–0.44	0.75–0.87
Western Gulf...........	7.0–11.0	40–65	0.17–0.23	0.38–0.40	0.70–0.83

6-8. Rate of Rainfall on a Drainage Area. The average rate of rainfall over a large drainage area is usually determined from observations at a number of widely separated stations. The reports from the stations are usually not in agreement. Thiessen[1] has devised an accepted method for averaging such observations into a general average applicable to the entire drainage area. The method is best explained by the solution of an example.

Let Fig. 6-3 represent a drainage area with rainfall-observation stations at A, B, C, and D. Lines are drawn joining the points of observation, and perpendicular lines are erected that bisect the bases of the triangles so formed. These lines intersect and form districts whose areas correspond to the rainfall observed at the observation station enclosed. The sum of the products of the area of each district and its corresponding rainfall, divided by the total area of the watershed, will give an approximate average of the rainfall over the watershed.

---

[1] A. H. Thiessen, *Monthly Weather Rev.*, July, 1911, p. 1082; see also R. E. Horton, *J. New Engl. Water Works Assoc.*, Vol. 38, p. 1, March, 1924; J. B. Belknap, *ibid.*, Vol. 46, p. 272, 1932.

6-9. Snow and Ice.[1]   Snow forms an important source of water supply in regions adjacent to snow-capped mountains.   The amount of water available from snow depends on many conditions, including its depth and quality. New snow fallen in subfreezing weather may have a density of around 0.1, but old snow subject to packing, warm rain, and other consolidating conditions may have a density as high as 0.5 to 0.6 that of water.   Some snows may contain free water.   It is necessary, therefore, in estimating the amount of water available from snow to measure the depth, the density, and the free water in the snow.

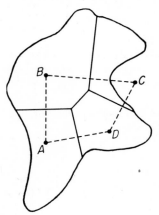

Snow melt may be computed from the empirical expression[2]

Fig. 6-3. Diagram of a drainage area with rainfall observation stations at *A, B, C,* and *D.*

$$D = K(T - 32) \qquad (6\text{-}2)$$

where D = average rate or snow melt over the basin, in. per day
$(T - 32)$ = number of degree-days above the Fahrenheit melting point
K = melting constant, or "degree-day factor"
Values of K lie between 0.02 and 0.11 in. per degree-day, with a maximum up to 0.3.

6-10. Disposal of Precipitation.   Precipitation that reaches the surface of the earth is disposed of in three ways, *viz.*, stream flow, percolation, and evaporation.   The stream-flow portion divides into surface flow and percolation.   Surface runoff derived from ground water is sometimes called *base flow* or *sustained flow*.   The characteristics of the flow in a stream are greatly affected by the relative amounts of water derived from surface flow and ground-water flow.   If the greater part is base flow, the runoff will tend to be regular and well sustained even through drought periods.[3]   Physical factors affecting precipitation and its disposal are listed in Table 6-5.   Evaporation includes direct evaporation from water and land surfaces, transpiration, and interception.   Deep seepage comprises the rainfall that is lost from a given drainage area to a deep underground reservoir, or by escape, through subterranean channels, to another drainage area.

[1] See also: Stream Flow Forecasting from Snow Surveys, *U.S. Soil Conservation Service, Circ.* 914, 1953; E. E. Foster, "Rainfall and Runoff," The Macmillan Company, New York, 1948; G. D. Clyde, *Monthly Weather Rev.*, Vol. 57, p. 326, 1929; F. A. Strauss, *J.A.W.W.A.*, September, 1954, p. 853.

[2] See "Hydrology Handbook," *op. cit.*, p. 30.

[3] See also *U.S. Geol. Survey, Water Supply Paper* 772, pp. 111*ff.*, 1936.

TABLE 6-5. Factors Affecting Stream Flow*

Factor	Remarks
Precipitation	The amount of rain or snow, its distribution throughout the year; the intensity and manner of its occurrence; the character, extent, direction, and duration of storms
Temperature	Variations. The relation of temperature variations to the occurrence of precipitation. The accumulation of snow and ice due to low temperature. The existence of frozen ground at the time of heavy rains
Topography	The slope and the character of the area, whether rough or smooth
Geology	Relative imperviousness and the depth, slope, and thickness of surface and substrata. The character of the outlet of pervious strata whether emptying into this or other watersheds. The relative imperviousness of the channel of the stream. The presence of sand and gravel in the bottom of the channel
Ground surface	Extent, character, and state of cultivation of vegetation
Natural storage	Lakes, ponds, swamps, marshes. Porosity of surface and substrata and ability to store water
Watershed	Its size and shape. Prevailing winds. Direction relative to path of storms. Relation to mountains. Proximity to ocean or large lake. Glaciers or snow-capped mountains
Character of stream and tributaries	Slope; falls and rapids; pondage; regimen of channel. Arrangement of tributaries—joining the main stream at various points along its course or concentrated in fanlike arrangement at a common point of discharge
Artificial control of the stream	Dams and storage reservoirs. Dikes, levees, piers, abutments, and other encroachments
Wind	Intensity, direction, and modification by mountains and forests
Ice evaporation	Winter conditions. Gorges and floods. Temperature, humidity, wind, and other factors

* Suggested by summary in D. W. Mead, *Univ. Wis., Bull.* 425.

6-11. Evaporation from Water Surface.[1] Direct evaporation from water surface is influenced by temperature, barometric pressure, mean wind velocity, vapor pressure of saturated vapor, and vapor pressure of saturated air. Several formulas have been developed to express the rate of evaporation from water surfaces. Among the most useful for general application is that proposed by Rohwer[2] which, in a slightly modified

---

[1] See also G. H. Hicox, *Trans. Am. Soc. Civil Engrs.*, Vol. 111, p. 1, 1946.

[2] See *U.S. Dept. Agr. Tech. Bull.* 271, 1931.

form, is

$$E = C(1.465 - 0.0186B)(0.44 + 0.118W)(e_s - e_d) \qquad (6\text{-}3)$$

A formula proposed by Cox[1] is

$$E = (e_s - e_d + 0.0016TD) \div \left(0.564 + 0.051TD + \frac{W}{7200}\right) \quad (6\text{-}4)$$

where, in the preceding formulas,

E = evaporation from open-water surface, in. per day

C = a coefficient, usually taken at about 0.75

B = mean barometric reading, in. mercury at 32°F

W = mean velocity of ground- or water-surface wind, mph

e_s = mean vapor pressure of saturated vapor at temperature of water surface, in. mercury.   See Table 6-6

e_d = mean vapor pressure of saturated air at dew point, in. mercury. See Table 6-6

TD = difference between mean temperature of air and of water, °F

TABLE 6-6. Pressure of Saturated Water Vapor at Different Temperatures*

Air temperature, °F	Vapor pressure, in. of mercury	Air temperature, °F	Vapor pressure, in. of mercury
0	0.0383	50	0.360
5	0.0491	55	0.432
10	0.0631	60	0.517
15	0.0810	65	0.616
20	0.103	70	0.732
25	0.130	75	0.866
30	0.164	80	0.926
35	0.203	85	1.201
40	0.247	90	1.408
45	0.298	95	1.645
		100	1.916

* *U.S. Weather Bureau, Bull.* 235.

Interpolations in this table do not give exact values but are sufficiently accurate for ordinary calculations.   Values of e_s in the Rohwer formula may be determined from this table.   Values of e_d are determined by multiplying tabular values by the relative humidity.

The Rohwer formula was derived from observations of the evaporation from pans which is known to exceed that from large open-water spaces by about 30 per cent.   The coefficient C is applied, therefore, to correct this discrepancy.   It is to be noted that the Rohwer formula makes no direct allowance for the difference between the temperature of air and water.

[1] G. N. Cox, *Bull. Louisiana State Univ.,* 1940.

Follansbee,[1] in his report on extensive studies of the evaporation from reservoir surfaces, shows the coefficient C to vary between 0.50 and 0.99.

Example. Find the daily evaporation from a reservoir water surface when the following conditions prevail: water temperature, 72°F; wind velocity, 2 mph; relative humidity, 0.68.

Solution. By Rohwer formula,

$$E = 0.75(1.465 - 0.0186 \times 29.51)(0.44 + 0.118 \times 2)(0.785 - 0.68 \times 0.685)$$
$$= 0.75 \times 0.916 \times 0.676 \times 0.319 = 0.148 \text{ in. per day}$$

6-12. Evaporation from Land Surface. The rate of evaporation from a land surface is affected by the same factors as evaporation from a water surface and, in addition, it is affected by the character of the land surface, the culture thereon, the topography, the amount of water in or on the watershed, soil moisture, and other conditions. The difficulty of expressing rates of evaporation from land surfaces with precision is, therefore, great. Thornthwaite[2] proposes as a formula the following:

$$E = \frac{17.1(e_1 - e_2)(u_1 - u_2)}{T + 459.4} \tag{6-5}$$

where E = evaporation, in. per hr
e_1 and e_2 = vapor pressures at lower and upper levels, respectively, in. mercury
u_1 and u_2 = wind velocities at lower and upper levels, respectively, mph
T = temperature, °F

A summary of some of the results of studies of evaporation from various land surfaces is presented in Table 6-7. Design conclusions must be based on data similar to those shown in the table. A diagram prepared

TABLE 6-7. Evaporation from Land Surfaces

Relative rates compared with bare ground*		Ratio of water returned to the atmosphere†·‡	
Bare ground§	1.00	Bare soil	60
Grain fields	0.80	Mixed crops	144
Grassland	0.70	Forest	151
Light forests	0.60	Small grass	173
Dense forests	0.2–0.4	Sod	192

* From A. F. Meyer, "Elements of Hydrology," p. 244, John Wiley & Sons, Inc., New York, 1928.

† As compared with evaporation from open-water surface as 100.

‡ See *Trans. Am. Soc. Civil Engrs.*, Vol. 99, p. 51, 1934.

§ For saturated soil the rate of evaporation may be taken the same as for free-water surface.

[1] See *Trans. Am. Soc. Civil Engrs.* Vol. 99, p. 708, 1934.
[2] See *Monthly Weather Rev.*, January, 1939, p. 6.

by Meyer[1] for the purpose of indicating the relation between evaporation from land surfaces and other conditions is shown in Fig. 6-4.

6-13. Transpiration, Consumptive Use, and Interception. Transpiration and consumptive use have been defined by the Committee on

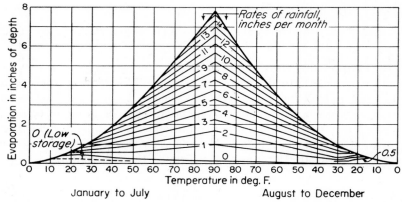

FIG. 6-4. Evaporation from land areas for various temperatures and rates of rainfall. *(From A. F. Meyer, Trans. Am. Soc. Civil Engrs., Vol. 79, p. 1099, 1915.)*

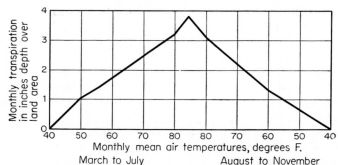

FIG. 6-5. Transpiration rates.   *(From A. F. Meyer, Civil Eng., June, 1951, p. 51.)*

Absorption and Transpiration of the American Geophysical Union[2] as follows:

Transpiration, the process by which water vapor leaves the living plant body and enters the atmosphere.

Consumptive use, the quantity of water per annum used by either cropped or natural vegetation in transpiration or building of plant tissues together with water evaporated from adjacent soil, snow, or intercepted precipitation.

Interception, the amount of water caught per annum by vegetation (or structures) which is evaporated before reaching the ground.

Some rates of transpiration are shown graphically in Fig. 6-5.

[1] A. F. Meyer, *Trans. Am. Soc. Civil Engrs.,* Vol. 79, p. 1099, 1915.
[2] See *Trans. Am. Geophys. Union,* Part II, p. 286, 1935.

Consumptive use[1] is sometimes expressed as the ratio of weight of water required to produce a unit weight of dry matter. Lee[2] has expressed some such ratios as: corn, 345; wheat, 375; potatoes, 426; cotton, 568; alfalfa, 829; buffalo grass, 308; sunflowers, 577; larch, 1,165; beach, 1,043; elm, 738; Norway spruce, 242; and fir, 86. Many factors, such as temperature, depth of water table, and kind of vegetation, influence the amount of consumptive use. Experiments[3] on cropped areas in the West show values of 1.2 to 3.0 acre-ft per year. Values as high as 9.63 acre-ft per acre per year have been found for the consumptive use of tules and cattails.

The use of water by vegetation is sometimes stated in terms of percentage of use compared with evaporation from open water. A few values are given in Table 6-7. The values are intended to indicate only a scale on the loss by consumptive use. They should not be used without consulting the references indicated in the table.[4]

6-14. Infiltration.[5] Runoff does not occur until the rate of rainfall exceeds the rate at which soil can absorb moisture. After a long dry period the infiltration capacity of a soil is at its maximum. This capacity is reduced during a single storm, and its recovery is rather slow between storms. Thus the effect of antecedent storms is important, especially when the time interval between storms is relatively short.

The phenomenon of infiltration is usually beneficial to water supplies because (1) reduction of immediate runoff tends to reduce flood flows, and (2) underground storage tends to increase base flow and hence dry-weather flow.

With adequate knowledge of the fluctuations of infiltration capacity of the ground under varying storm conditions, an engineer may arrive at close approximations of probable runoff for a particular storm or for a series of storms. The determination of infiltration involves a multitude of conditions found from a study of the watershed. For small watersheds the infiltration rates F_c for a number of storms should be computed from the expression

$$F_c = P - (Y_s - S_e - F_i) \tag{6-6}$$

and averaged. In this expression,

P = rainfall mass causing runoff

Y_s = mass of surface runoff attributable to P

[1] See also: O. Raber, *U.S. Dept. Agr., Misc. Publ.* 257, June, 1937; and a symposium in *Trans. Am. Soc. Civil Engrs.*, 1952, p. 949.

[2] C. H. Lee, *Trans. Am. Geophys. Union*, Part I, p. 50, 1941.

[3] See *Trans. Am. Soc. Civil Engrs.*, Vol. 94, p. 1399, 1930.

[4] See also bibliographies in *Trans. Am. Geophys. Union*, 1932–1946; *Trans. Am. Soc. Civil Engrs.*, Vol. 79, p. 1094; R. E. Horton, *Monthly Weather Rev.*, September, 1919.

[5] See also "Hydrology Handbook," Manual of Engineering Practice No. 28, American Society of Civil Engineers, 1949, with bibliography.

S_e = effective surface storage

F_i = estimated amount of infiltration occurring before rainfall exceeded infiltration rate

6-15. Rainfall-Runoff Relations. Statistical analyses[1] and empirical formulas are applicable to the solution of runoff problems. Both require a rational approach, and a solution by either method is no more accurate than the data on which it is based. There is no logical reason for a close and constant relation to exist between rainfall and runoff because the runoff from a watershed occurs only after all demands of storage and retention have been satisfied, and these demands vary with the season, preceding rainfall, and other conditions.

Two empirical relations are:

Vermuele formula:[2] $F = R - (11 + 0.29\,R)M$ (6-7)

where R = annual rainfall, in.

F = annual runoff, in.

M = factor depending on the mean temperature

Justin formula:[3] $C = 0.943\,\dfrac{R^2}{T}\,S^{0.155}$ (6-8)

where C = annual runoff, in.

R = annual rainfall, in.

T = mean annual temperature, °F

S = slope of the drainage area

Such formulas should be used with great caution; they may give reasonable values for conditions for which they were derived, but they are almost certain to give erroneous results when applied indiscriminately.

The *rational method* is useful, in the hands of an experienced engineer, for estimating peak flows from a watershed for which rainfall records are available. The method can be formulated as

$$Q = AIR$$ (6-9)

where Q = maximum runoff, cfs

A = area of the watershed, acres

I = a coefficient whose value depends on losses due to infiltration, evaporation, transpiration, soil characteristics, snow cover, and other conditions

R = intensity of average rainfall over the watershed during the time of concentration on the area, in in. per hr

Formulas for R are given in Table 6-3. The time t, in the table, is the *time of concentration.* It is the time elapsed from the start of a storm

[1] See also F. Law, *J. Inst. Water Engrs.*, May, 1953.

[2] C. C. Vermuele, *Geol. Survey, New Jersey*, Vol. 3, 1894.

[3] *Trans. Am. Soc. Civil Engrs.*, Vol. 77, p. 346, 1914.

until the flood crest reaches the point of observation below the watershed. Empirical formulas for t may be misleading if not used judiciously. Rational estimates of t can be properly based only on experience and judgment, supplemented by tests in the field.

The value of I represents the proportion of the rainfall that runs off in the surface stream. For example, if a rain having an average intensity of 2 in. per hr, falling on an area of 10 acres, produces a runoff of 10 cfs, I would have a value of 0.5.

It may be desirable to consider frequency in connection with the studies of peak flow. The following formula may be used:

$$I = I_{max}\left(\frac{T}{100}\right)^x \qquad (6\text{-}10)$$

where T = average number of years between occurrences of runoff of a given magnitude

x = an exponent depending on the locality. Some values of x are given in Table 6-4

Values of I_{max} may be greater than unity as a result of a warm rain falling on a snow-covered watershed. Values of 1.7 have been observed. In the United States, east of the 100th meridian, values of I_{max} will seldom go below 0.50.

Statistical methods for the computation of flood magnitude and frequency are given by E. E. Foster.[1]

Two analytical procedures,[2] "annual flood peaks" and "partial-duration series," are in use. In the former the highest observed flood peak in each water year is listed chronologically, showing calendar year dates. Only complete years of stream-flow records are included, but historical flood data can also be included, with limitations. The flood peaks should be numbered in the order of magnitude, beginning with 1 for the highest. The recurrence interval, in years, is computed from the expression

$$\frac{N + 1}{M} \qquad (6\text{-}11)$$

where N = number of years in the record

M = order of relative magnitude, as assigned

In the partial-duration series all peaks above a selected base are listed, regardless of the date of occurrence. Ordinarily this base should be chosen so that the number of peaks is at least equal to the years of record, but no more than three or four floods per year. The peaks should be arranged in order of magnitude and assigned numbers corresponding to their position in the array, beginning with the highest as 1. The next

[1] "Rainfall and Runoff," pp. 358*ff*., The Macmillan Company, New York, 1948.
[2] See "Hydrology Handbook," *op. cit.*, pp. 102*ff*.

step is to compute recurrence intervals by the ratio in (6-11). The data are plotted on a three-cycle semilog paper using discharge data as ordinates on the linear scale, and recurrence intervals as abscissas on the logarithmic scale. The curve passing through these points is used in the interpretation of the data.

6-16. Empirical Formulas for Peak Flows.[1] Empirical formulas for the estimation of peak flows are widely used. They generally take the form

$$Q = CM^q \tag{6-12}$$

where Q = discharge, cfs
    C = a coefficient
    q = an exponent
    M = drainage area, sq miles
The modified Myers formula[2] is

$$Q = 10,000pM^{1/2} \tag{6-13}$$

where p = variable percentage coefficient expressing the ratio of the maximum flood for a given stream to an assumed maximum for all streams
The percentage p that applies to any particular region is termed the "Myers rating" for the area. The maximum Myers rating for the Eastern part of the United States is rarely more than 60 per cent. Ratings for more than 900 streams are given by Jarvis.[3]

6-17. Runoff Records. Records of stream flow are available in certain Federal and state publications, generally of the Geological Survey. Reliable private records may sometimes be obtained from power companies and water companies. The *Water Supply Papers* of the U.S. Geological Survey are the chief sources of general information.

6-18. Droughts. Droughts are defined as[4] periods during which precipitation is less than 85 per cent of the mean. They are frequently of greater importance to the water-supply engineer than the effects of unusually heavy storms. Available amounts of both surface-water and ground-water supplies may be seriously curtailed by droughts. The effect of a drought on the available water supplies in an area having a low mean rainfall is apt to be much more serious than in an area having a high mean rainfall. Drought effects may continue long beyond the period of

---

[1] See also: Allen Hazen, "Flood Flows," John Wiley & Sons, Inc., New York, 1930; H. A. Foster, *Trans. Am. Soc. Civil Engrs.*, Vol. 88, p. 142, 1924; R. D. Goodrich, *ibid.*, Vol. 91, p. 1, 1927; W. E. Fuller, *ibid.*, Vol. 77, p. 564, 1914; C. R. Pettis, *Eng. News-Record*, Vol. 116, p. 871, 1936; Flood Flows in the U.S., *U.S. Geol. Survey, Water Supply Paper* 771, 1936.

[2] See C. S. Jarvis, *Trans. Am. Soc. Civil Engrs.*, Vol. 89, p. 994, 1926.

[3] *Loc. cit.*, pp. 1003ff.

[4] See also L. L. Harrold, *Eng. News-Record*, Vol. 114, p. 978, 1935.

deficient rainfall as a result of depletion of ground-water storage.   The severity of the drought is greatly increased when high temperatures prevail over the affected area.   The droughts of 1917 and of 1952–1954 have been severe in the United States.   In 1917 the rainfall over about 22 per cent of the country was less than 60 per cent of normal.[1]

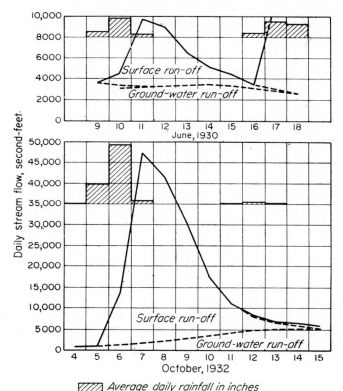

FIG. 6-6. Unit hydrographs for Susquehanna River at Towanda, Pa.   (*U.S. Geol. Survey, Water Supply Paper* 772.)

6-19. Low-flow Estimates.   In a study of the required capacity of an impounding reservoir it is frequently necessary to estimate the low rates of flow in a stream.   The "index of low flow," where it is known for a river, is useful in studies of low-flow conditions.   It is defined as the rate of runoff which is exceeded 90 per cent of the time.   For example, the index for the Hocking River at Athens, Ohio, is 0.088 cfs per sq mile, and for the Mad River at Springfield, Ohio, it is 0.340 cfs per sq mile.[2]

---

[1] See also *U.S. Geol. Survey, Water Supply Paper* 772, p. 255, 1936.
[2] See also R. Hazen, Conference on Water Resources, *Illinois State Water Survey, Bull.* **41**, 1952.

6-20. Graphical Presentation of Runoff Data. Graphical methods used in water-supply engineering for presenting runoff data include the hydrograph, the mass curve, the unit hydrograph, the distribution graph, and the flow-duration curve.

The hydrograph shows the rates of stream flow at various times. It is a curve whose abscissas are in units of time and whose ordinates are in units of rates of flow. The hydrograph may show also the base flow or that part of the stream flow derived from ground water. A hydrograph is shown in Fig. 11-1.

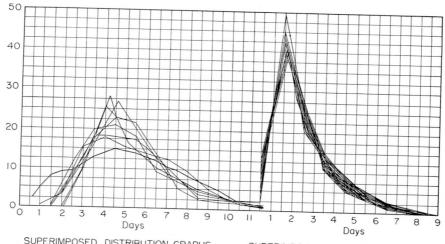

SUPERIMPOSED DISTRIBUTION GRAPHS
FOR THE RED RIVER BASIN
ABOVE DENISON, TEXAS

(A)

SUPERIMPOSED DISTRIBUTION GRAPHS
FOR THE DELAWARE RIVER BASIN
ABOVE PORT JERVIS, N.Y

(B)

Fig. 6-7. Distribution graphs. (*From G. W. Hoyt and others, U.S. Geol. Survey, Water Supply Paper 772.*)

The mass curve is the integral of the hydrograph. The abscissas are in units of time and the ordinates indicate the total volume of water that has passed the observation station since the starting time. A mass curve is shown in Fig. 11-1.

The unit hydrograph, such as the one shown in Fig. 6-6, was first defined by Sherman[1] as: " . . . the hydrograph of surface runoff (not including ground-water runoff) on a given basin due to an effective rain falling for a unit time. The term effective rain means producing surface runoff. The unit of time may be one day or preferably a fraction of a day. It must be less than the time of concentration." It is predicated on the hypothesis that in a given basin the runoff occurring in a unit of time will produce hydrographs of similar pattern. The unit graph may be used directly or as a basis for the construction of a distribution graph.

[1] L. K. Sherman, *Eng. News-Record*, 1932, p. 501.

The distribution graph is a graph whose ordinates represent the percentage of total surface runoff resulting from a unit rainfall, and whose abscissas are units of time, possibly hours, as indicated in Fig. 6-7. The distribution graph[1] may be computed from the unit hydrograph and both may be used, with a reasonable degree of approximation, to produce the unit hydrograph that would result from any unit rainfall on the corresponding watershed. For example, if the distribution graph for the runoff from a watershed shows 15 per cent runoff for a particular hour after the

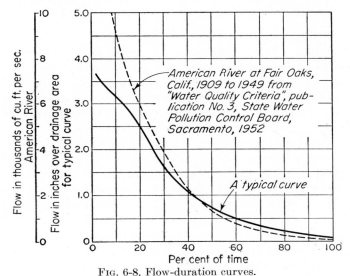

American River at Fair Oaks, Calif., 1909 to 1949 from "Water Quality Criteria", publication No. 3, State Water Pollution Control Board, Sacramento, 1952

A typical curve

FIG. 6-8. Flow-duration curves.

start of a unit storm, then for every unit storm on that watershed approximately 15 per cent of the total surface runoff should run off during the corresponding hour. On some rivers this agreement is close, as shown in Fig. 6-7B for the Delaware River. On others the agreement is less precise, as shown for the Red River in Fig. 6-7A.

A flow-duration curve is shown in Fig. 6-8. It is plotted to any convenient scale of rates of flow as ordinates and percentage of time during which these rates occurred, as abscissas. The area under the curve, when plotted on natural coordinate paper, with proper factor to care for the scale, is a measure of the volume of flow during the period represented.

[1] See also M. M. Bernard, *Trans. Am. Soc. Civil Engrs.*, Vol. 100, p. 347, 1935.

CHAPTER 7

DAMS

7-1. Purposes. Dams[1] may be used in water works to form impounding reservoirs or for the control of stream flow. Control dams, sometimes called "diversion dams," are used to raise the water level of a stream enough to provide gravity transportation of water to pumps or reservoirs, to maintain adequate submergence over intakes, or to provide a suitable depth of water in the suction well of a pumping station.

It is necessary to obtain a permit from the Federal government for the construction of a dam across a navigable stream and, in view of the New River Decision[2] by the United States Supreme Court, it is apparent that this stipulation includes any tributary to a navigable stream. In some states it may be necessary to obtain both a Federal and a state permit.

7-2. Types. Dams may be classified according to the materials of their construction, as earth, including rolled fill, hydraulic fill, and semi-hydraulic fill; rock fill; rock-filled timber crib; masonry, including stone, plain concrete, and reinforced concrete; timber; and steel. They may be classified also according to the basis on which they resist external stresses, as solid gravity, including straight, curved, and arched dams; hollow gravity, including slab and buttress, multiple arch, and multiple dome; and arch, including constant angle and constant radius.

7-3. Dam Sites. Topographically a dam to create a reservoir should be located where it can be constructed high enough to store the water needed. Methods for determining this height are discussed in Sec. 11-4.

The site must be carefully studied geologically. Foundation explorations are made by test pits and by drilling methods, some of which are explained in Chap. 5. The character of the material encountered is studied from the standpoint of its composition, structure, stratification, permeability, and bearing power. Guided by the result of subterranean explorations and by observation of surface conditions, a competent geologist may determine the presence of fault planes and the probability of movement on them. He will also give valuable advice concerning the

[1] See also W. P. Creager, J. D. Justin, and Julian Hinds, "Engineering for Dams," John Wiley & Sons, Inc., New York, 1944.

[2] See *J.A.W.W.A.*, February, 1941, p. 315.

suitability of the foundation materials in the matter of the effect on them of weathering, erosion, and immersion. Intelligent application of the principles of soil mechanics is indispensable to the proper design of many dams. Special care in the selection and preparation of the foundation is of vital importance to the safety of a dam.

7-4. Dam Foundations. Dam foundations must provide stable support for the structure and resistance to the passage of water through, beneath, or around the dam. Foundation failures have resulted from crushing, plastic flow, sliding, piping and scouring, and uplift. Prospective dam sites should be adequate to avoid failure from any of these causes.

Hard, unstratified, homogeneous igneous rock is universally considered to be *the* desirable foundation material, but no rock should be selected without thorough exploration to obtain adequate information concerning

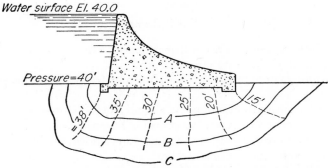

Fig. 7-1. Dam on porous foundations showing typical flow net.

its characteristics, as witnessed by failures of well-known dams.[1] Stratified rock, especially if there are intermediate strata of clay, shale, or similar material, is conducive to sliding, underflow, and leakage. Fissured limestone may lead to subterranean caverns and failure due to leakage and subsidence.

7-5. Porous Foundations. Dams may be safely founded on soft and on porous materials such as clay, shale, sand, and gravel provided adequate treatment is given to prevent dangerous seepage through the foundation or sliding or movement of the structure. Treatment to prevent seepage involves grouting with cement or asphalt, the construction of mechanical cutoffs, or the construction of a long downstream apron to increase the path of, and hence the frictional resistance to, underground flow. The weight of the structure and of the downstream apron must be sufficient to resist uplift indicated by the "flow net," and the imperviousness of the material must be sufficient to prevent "piping." This is a system of small channels permitting the flow of water beneath the dam.

[1] See L. A. Schmidt, Jr., *ibid.*, October, 1946, p. 1170.

The flow net is a diagram composed of lines of equal pressure in a porous medium. A typical flow net is shown in Fig. 7-1. Lines A, B, and C are lines along which the velocity of flow is constant. The rate of flow along each of such lines is fixed by the hydraulic gradient, or the distance between lines of equal pressure potential, and by the frictional resistance to flow. The rate of flow can be diminished by the construction of cutoff walls or by increasing the length of the apron. It is generally better to increase the length of the upstream apron since the weight of the water over it aids in reducing uplift pressure. If the velocity of flow is sufficiently great to move underground material, piping is taking place. This is most likely to occur along the "line of creep," *i.e.*, the line of contact between the dam and the foundation, because the resistance to flow is least along this line. The breaking of contact between the dam and its foundation is called "roofing."

Earth Dams

7-6. Safety in Design and in Construction. Some of the principles of safe design stated by Middlebrooks[1] are:

1. Provide adequate spillway capacity and freeboard to prevent overtopping.
2. Foundation and embankment should not be overstressed in shear.
3. Control seepage. Avoid pipe drains in embankment.
4. Use cutoff to bedrock and, if necessary, downstream drains.
5. Design conduits conservatively.
6. Provide slope protection where needed.
7. Compact embankment to avoid settling on saturation.
8. Avoid continuous seepage passages through embankment.
9. Avoid cracks due to settling of fill. Allow core to deform without cracking.

Earth dams can be designed and constructed safely if proper attention is paid to important details. Some causes of failure of earth dams are summarized in Table 7-1. Each failure may be attributed to lack of attention to a detail in design, construction, or maintenance.

Sections through typical earth dams are shown in Fig. 7-2. These sections illustrate some of the important details to be considered in their design. The features include (1) embankment slope; (2) slope protection; (3) top width; (4) freeboard; (5) berms; (6) quality and location of materials in the embankment, cutoff walls, and core wall; (7) drainage of downstream face and protection of upstream slope against sudden drop of water level in the reservoir; (8) prevention of piping; and (9) prevention of roofing.

[1] T. A. Middlebrooks, *Civil Eng.*, September, 1952, p. 118.

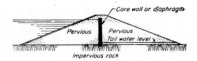

a. Core wall or diaphragm sealed in rock foundation.

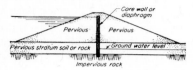

b. Core wall or diaphragm through pervious foundation to impervious rock.

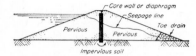

c. Dam with core wall or diaphragm sealed in relatively impervious soil.

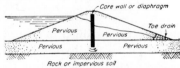

d. Dam with core wall or diaphragm extended into relatively impervious soil.

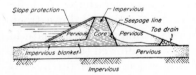

e. Earth-fill dam with impervious upstream blanket on pervious soil foundation.

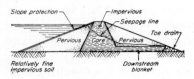

f. Earth-fill dam with impervious downstream blanket on relatively fine impervious foundation.

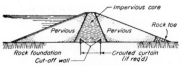

g. Earth-fill dam on rock foundation.

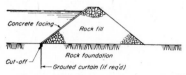

h. Rock-fill dam on rock foundation.

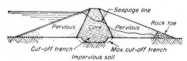

i. Earth-fill dam on impervious soil foundation.

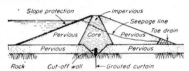

j. Earth-fill dam with cut-off trench extending to rock.

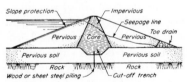

k. Earth-fill dam with sheet piling driven to rock.

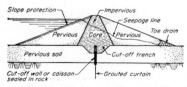

l. Earth-fill dam with cut-off wall or caisson sealed in rock.

Fig. 7-2. Typical sections of earth dams. (*From W. C. Huntington and G. A. Young, "Random Notes on Earth and Masonry Dams," 1953.*)

TABLE 7-1. Failures of Earth Dams*

Causes of failures, 1914–1950		Relation of failures to age of structure, % of total structures					Chronological distribution of failures, %					
Cause	% of total	Years after completion	Over-topping	Conduit leakage	Seep-age	Slides	Decade ending	Over-topping	Seep-age	Conduit leakage	Slides	Total†
Overtopping...	30	0–1	9	23	16	29	1860	0	0	0	0	0
Seepage.......	25	1–5	17	50	34	24	1870	0	0	7	0	1
Slides.........	15	5–10	9	9	13	12	1880	0	6	7	0	3
Conduit leakage							1890	6	4	11	3	5
	13	10–20	30	9	13	12	1900	12	11	21	3	13
Slope paving...							1910	23	14	16	18	17
	5	20–30	13	5	12	12	1920	22	25	18	23	21
Miscellaneous..	7	30–40	10	4	6	11	1930	14	13	18	26	16
Unknown......	5	40–50	9	0	6	0	1940	11	5	0	23	10
		50–100	3	0	0	0	1950	9	6	0	3	8
							1950‡	3	8	0	3	4

* From T. A. Middlebrooks, *Civil Eng.*, September, 1952, p. 118.

† Total number, not percentage. It includes all inadequate dams even though the cause of unsatisfactory performance was not determined.

‡ Year only, not for the decade.

7-7. Types of Construction. Earth dams may be classified in accordance with the methods of their construction as rolled fill, hydraulic fill, and semihydraulic fill. A rolled-fill dam is constructed by depositing the material in layers, 4 to 12 in. thick, and compacting each layer by rolling. The embankment material for hydraulic-fill dams is sluiced or transported from the borrow pit to the fill by means of a stream of water carried in a pipe or flume. A dike is maintained at the upstream and downstream faces, and the center is kept low, forming the central pool. The material is delivered from the sluices near the dikes and is allowed to flow toward the center. The heavier particles will be dropped first near the faces of the dam, and the finest will be carried into the central pool, thus procuring a gradation of materials. The finest materials form the core, or the impervious central portion, of the dam. Excess water from the central pool is carried away through controlled outlet pipes. Care is necessary to maintain the proper slopes from the outside toward the center in order to avoid high velocities or gullying, which might result in the coarse materials being carried into the center.

Slides occurring during construction or after completion, resulting from the high fluid pressures in the core due to inability of the core to drain, are a source of danger in hydraulic-fill dams. Hazen[1] states that:

To use the hydraulic method of dam construction successfully, it is necessary either to increase the toes until they are large and heavy enough to resist suc-

[1] Allen Hazen, *Trans. Am. Soc. Civil Engrs.*, Vol. 83, p. 1713, 1919–1920.

cessfully the fluid pressure of the core or else to handle the core material so that the finest particles are wasted, leaving only the large ones, and in that way increasing the grain size to the point where drainage can be secured, while on the other hand remaining sufficiently impervious for practical purposes.

Semihydraulic-fill dams differ from hydraulic-fill dams in the manner in which the filling material is brought to the embankment. Means other than water are used to transport the materials to the fill. Water, however, is used to classify and finally place the material. The same principles apply, in general, as for hydraulic-fill dams.

7-8. Embankment Slopes.[1] Embankment slopes may be governed by one or by all three of the following considerations: (1) stability of the material under all probable conditions of moisture content, (2) bearing power of the foundation material, and (3) the resistance of the soil to the percolation of water.

It is unsafe to make generalized statements in connection with safe slopes for earth dams. The character and properties of materials and of foundations vary so widely that each case must be considered separately. Ordinarily, for structures 25 ft or less in height, stable embankments may result if the upstream slope is built not steeper than $2\frac{1}{2}$ horizontal to 1 vertical and the downstream slope, 2 horizontal to 1 vertical. For higher dams, investigations should be made to determine:[2]

1. Stability of soil against sloughing when saturated
2. Watertightness or resistance to percolation
3. Workability for construction operations
4. Solubility of mineral constituents
5. Bearing power of foundations
6. Reasonable cost of handling, in excavation, transportation, spreading, and compacting

Intelligent interpretation of laboratory tests recommended by engineers, expert in this field, should form the basis of final designs for major structures and questionable minor ones.[3]

7-9. Slope Protection. The slopes of an earth dam may require protection against erosion from wave action and surface runoff and against burrowing animals. The effect of wave action may be eliminated or reduced by the placement of stone riprap, concrete slabs or blocks, or willow mattresses on the upstream slope. The protection should extend from the top of the dam to 5 ft below the lowest expected operating level. In important structures where riprap or concrete is used, a shoulder, or berm, should be provided at the base of the protection. Downstream

---

[1] See also Committee Report, *Proc. Am. Soc. Civil Engrs.*, June, 1948, p. 845.

[2] See also C. H. Lee, *ibid.*, September, 1936, p. 1025. See also *ibid.*, December, 1936, January, February, March, April, 1937.

[3] Laboratory Procedure in Testing Earth Dam Materials, *Bur. Reclamation, Tech. Mem.* 533, 1936.

slopes may be protected from erosion by loose rock fills or by planting with vines, shrubs, or grass. Plants that develop long root structures, which might penetrate too far into the dam, should be avoided. For long slopes, a berm wide enough to accommodate an intercepting gutter should be supplied. Loose rock fills, concrete, wood, or steel cores provide protection against burrowing animals. Fences may be necessary to keep grazing animals from destroying grass cover and making trails which become water channels during storms.

7-10. Top Width. The minimum top width W for a height H may be determined from the empirical formula $W = 2\sqrt{H} + 3$. If a roadway is to occupy the top of the dam, a width of at least 2 ft greater than the traveled way should be provided on each side of the road.

7-11. Freeboard. Freeboard is the vertical distance from the water surface to the top of the embankment. This distance must be sufficient to prevent overtopping of the dam during high water, frost penetration, and damage due to wave action. The height required to prevent overtopping is fixed by the height of water allowed over the spillway. The height required for safety against frost will vary from nothing in temperate climates up to 8 ft or more in cold climates. The freeboard necessary to prevent overtopping by waves should be measured from the highest water elevation anticipated. This freeboard may be computed from Stevenson's[1] formula $H = 1.5\sqrt{D} + (2.5 - \sqrt[4]{D})$ where H is the height of the waves, or the added freeboard required, and D is the horizontal length of water exposure, or "fetch" of the wind, in miles.

7-12. Berms. A berm is a horizontal break in the slope of the sides of an embankment. Submerged berms are used on the upstream side of earth dams to support pavement and to increase stability of the structure. They may be used on the downstream side to interrupt the flow of rain down the face of the dam and also to increase the stability of the structure. When placed with a gentle slope parallel to the axis of the dam, the berm may serve as a roadway up the dam.

7-13. Classification of Materials.[2] Materials most readily available for the construction of earth dams and embankments are clay, sand, and gravel. Clay is practically impervious but it is highly absorptive. When saturated, it tends to become fluid, it is slow to drain, and its cohesive and frictional resistances are greatly reduced. It shrinks in drying and is subject to cracking. Sand and gravel are pervious, drain easily, and their angle of repose, which is a measure of cohesive and frictional resistance, is not greatly affected by saturation. A mixture of gravel, sand, and clay, properly placed, forms a satisfactory material for an earth dam. Reduction in volume of materials due to settlement, shrinkage, com-

---

[1] Thomas, Stevenson, "Design and Construction of Harbors," 2d ed., Edinburgh, 1874.

[2] See also C. H. Lee, *Trans. Am. Soc. Civil Engrs.*, Vol. 103, p. 1, 1938.

paction, and consolidation is an important consideration in the preparation of designs and estimates. Compaction may reduce the volume of loose materials 25 to 20 per cent. An allowance of 5 per cent in height due to settlement is ample for dams in which ordinary care has been exercised in the placing of the materials.

In placing materials in the embankment, the most impervious, except possibly the core wall, should be placed at the upstream face of the dam. The material of the dam may grow progressively more pervious from the upstream to the downstream face of the dam. In fact, it may be desirable to drain the downstream part of an earth dam by placing drainage pipes in the embankment, thus preventing the accumulation of water in it with resulting danger to the structure. The seepage line, *i.e.*, the level of the water in the dam, should be kept low on the downstream side of the core wall. The classification of materials in some earth dams is shown in Fig. 7-2.

7-14. Core Walls and Cutoff Walls. A core wall, or core, is a partition placed in a dam, usually near the center or toward the upstream face, to prevent or impede the passage of water or of burrowing animals through the dam. An improperly placed core wall may endanger the safety of a dam by holding water in the structure, thus materially decreasing its resistance to shear and sliding, and increasing the danger of the overturning of the core wall.

Hollow, or cellular, cores have been used to assure the dryness of the embankment on the downstream side of the core wall, to prevent overtopping of the embankment during construction, and for other reasons. A cellular core wall is constructed with hollow vertical chambers as close together as practicable in the downstream portion of the wall. The vertical chambers terminate at the bottom in a drainage tunnel which conducts the leakage away. All percolation through the downstream portion of the embankment is thus prevented. The hollow cylinders and the tunnel should be made large enough to permit inspection of the condition of the dam.

Materials used in core walls include concrete, steel, wood and puddle or puddled earth. Since stresses on a core wall cannot be computed without making uncertain assumptions concerning movements of the dam, the determination of the core-wall thickness is a matter of judgment based on experience. Concrete core walls with a top thickness of 12 in. and sides battered 1 horizontal to 100 vertical have proved generally satisfactory. The core wall should be sufficiently high to extend above the frost line in the dam. Some cores extend above the top of the earth embankment to act as a parapet and factor of safety. During construction, the earth pressures on the sides of the core can be balanced by maintaining the rising fill at the same elevation on each side of the core.

Steel and wood are seldom used in core walls except for temporary installations since the alternate wetting and drying of the upper portion of the structure exposes the steel or wood to active corrosion.

Puddle is a definitely proportioned mixture of clay, sand, and water placed and tamped to form an almost impervious diaphragm. It may satisfactorily stop the flow of water, but it is not a deterrent to burrowing animals. Puddle cores, usually placed at or near the center of the dam, are formed by placing a mixture of selected materials by a hydraulic process. Puddle cores have the advantage of flexibility and are less subject than concrete to rupture by unbalanced forces within the fill. Care is necessary in placing the core to avoid undesirable stratification of materials within it.

A cutoff wall is a low core or wall extending from a short distance in the dam above the porous stratum on which the dam is founded, down into the porous stratum to cut through it. Such a wall is shown in Fig. 7-2.

7-15. Blankets. Blankets composed of a tough workable clay spread on the floor of the reservoir, under the fill or on the upstream slope, are often used to prevent or reduce seepage through or under an earth dam. For highly impervious material, the thickness of the blanket should be at least 2 ft. Blankets are used when the expense of a core, by reason of excessive depth, is too great and when they can be used advantageously instead of a core with material unsuitable because of its perviousness. To determine the thickness of blankets that extend upstream from the dam, the following formula may be used: $t = 2 + 0.02d$, where t is the thickness in feet, and d is the distance in feet from the upstream end of the blanket to the dam.

7-16. Drains. Drains on the surface of a dam may be used to carry off excess runoff and to prevent erosion of the surface. Such drains should be lined with vitrified clay tile, concrete, stones, or similar erosion-resistant material. Internal drains are sometimes used *only* in the downstream one-third of the embankment where seepage is anticipated that may cause soft spots in the embankment, or to prevent piping, roofing, or channeling. They should be installed only with full knowledge of their purpose and how they will function.

Masonry Dams

7-17. Masonry Dams.[1] Masonry dams may be classified according to type as:

Solid gravity: straight, curved, or arched
Hollow gravity: slab and buttress, multiple-arch dome, and flat slab
Arch: constant angle and constant radius

Types of masonry dams are shown in Fig. 7-3.

[1] See also Symposium, *Trans. Am. Soc. Civil Engrs.*, Vol. 106, p. 1113, 1941.

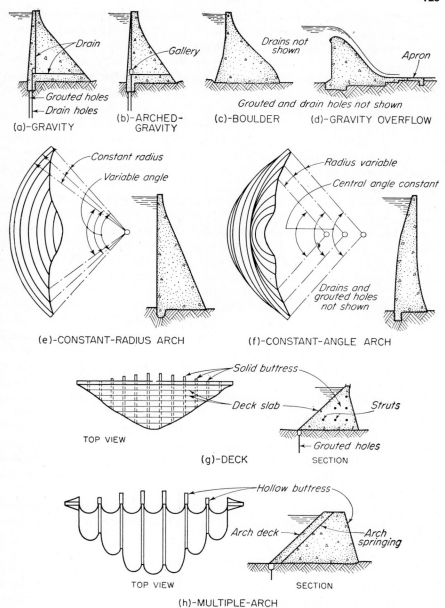

FIG. 7-3. Types of masonry dams. *(From W. C. Huntington and G. A. Young, "Random Notes on Earth and Masonry Dams," 1953.)*

The gravity dam receives its name from the fact that the weight of the structure plus the weight of water on it is sufficient to resist the forces acting to overturn, shear, or slide the structure. A straight gravity dam is a dam whose lines, in plan, particularly the axis of the dam, are straight. Curved, or arched, gravity dams are curved in plan, either upstream or downstream, but they resist overturning because of their weight and not as an arch. Hollow gravity dams when compared with solid gravity dams require less material,[1] offer effective drainage, relieve uplift pressure, and may slightly more than double the factors of safety against overturning, and the sliding factor is reduced not more than about 50 per cent. The serious objections to such dams are the difficulties and cost of construction.

An arch dam is curved in plan with its ends resting on abutments in the hills on either side of the valley. The dam acts as an arch with its haunches resting on the abutments and the dam structure under compression. In general, arch dams will have less material in them than a solid gravity dam. However, the cost of construction of the arch dam may be greater owing to form work and other difficulties.

7-18. Other Dams. A rock-fill dam[2] is an embankment of loose rock with a flow-retarding membrane somewhere in or on the embankment. Materials used for the membranes include concrete; earth, either paved or unprotected; timber; or steel.[3] There is a trend toward the placing of a layer of dry uncoursed rubble between the facing and the rock fill. The rubble furnishes a semirigid element subject to less settlement and provides good distribution of the water load to the rock fill. Settlement due to the consolidation of the fill and to the water load is an important factor in rock-fill dams.

A rock-fill dam is useful at sites for which transportation of other materials is difficult, concrete is expensive, and satisfactory earth materials are not available and where other conditions are favorable. If not properly designed and built, the frequent unwatering for repairs makes rock-fill dams undesirable for domestic water supplies.

Wood and steel dams have little application to water-works construction. They are generally short-lived and are suitable only for low dams.

Forces on Dams

7-19. Forces Acting on Dams. Forces that must be resisted by dams include (1) water pressure; (2) weight of dam and superimposed water, resulting in foundation reaction; (3) flotation; (4) uplift; (5) erosion; (6)

---

[1] See also J. W. Lewis, *Water and Water Eng.*, December, 1939, p. 569.

[2] See also: J. D. Galloway, *Trans. Am. Soc. Civil Engrs.*, Vol. 104, p. 1, 1939; L. L. Wise, *Eng. News-Record*, Jan. 22, 1953, p. 35.

[3] R. T. Logeman, *Civil Eng.*, January, 1939, p. 7.

ice pressure; (7) earthquake shocks; (8) wind pressure; (9) wave pressure; and (10) subatmospheric pressures.

7-20. Water Pressure. The horizontal component of the water pressure can be computed from the expression $P = wAh_o$, where P is the total horizontal pressure, w is the unit weight of water, A is the area of the horizontal projection of the face of the dam onto a vertical plane, and h_o is the vertical distance from the water surface to the center of gravity of the area A. The vertical component of the water pressure is equal to the weight of water vertically above any portion of the dam that is submerged. The direction and point of application of water pressure is normal to the face of the dam at the center of pressure.

7-21. Flotation and Uplift.[1] Flotation, uplift, and foundation reaction are forces with vertical components acting on the dam. Flotation and uplift cannot exist simultaneously at the same spot. The magnitude of flotation is equal to the volume of water displaced by any portion of the dam submerged in and completely surrounded by water, multiplied by the unit weight of water. Flotation will not come into play unless there is complete submergence of a part of the dam. Uplift is caused by the pressure of water confined within the interstices of the dam and connected by open channels, however small, to the water within the reservoir. The magnitude of the uplift can be expressed as $U = wAh$, where w is the unit weight of water, A is the area of the vertical projection on a horizontal plane of all surfaces subject to uplift, and h is the head, or pressure of water on such surfaces. It is measured as the distance from the point of pressure to the hydraulic grade line of the channel in which the water is confined. In the computation of uplift, the practice of the U.S. Bureau of Reclamation is to compute the uplift as varying linearly from full head water to full tail water, but acting over only the upstream two-thirds of the base.

7-22. Sliding and Shear. A tendency to slide is caused by the horizontal forces and is resisted by friction between assumed joints on horizontal planes, or between masonry and foundation. Sliding resistance, or shear, can be expressed as

$$f\Sigma W = f(W + V - U \pm X) \qquad (7\text{-}1)$$

where W = weight of the structure
V = weight of water on upstream face
U = uplift force
X = sum of all other vertical forces present
f = coefficient of friction

The value of f for rock is frequently used as 0.65. Values from 0.25 to 0.5 are used for earth. The factor of safety against sliding is the ratio

[1] See also Committee Report on Uplift in Masonry Dams, *Proc. Am. Soc. Civil Engrs.*, June, 1952; K. B. Keener, *Proc. Am. Soc. Civil Engrs.*, June, 1950.

between the sliding resistance and the total horizontal force ΣP_h, or $F = f(\Sigma W / \Sigma P_h)$. For masonry dams, values of F vary from 1.0 on rock foundations to 3.0 on earth foundations.

7-23. Ice Pressure.[1] Ice pressure against a dam is affected by such conditions as (1) rate of air-temperature rise at temperatures below freezing, (2) ice thickness, (3) restraint of ice sheet, (4) extent of exposure to

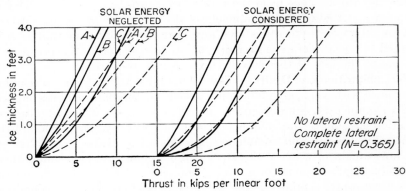

Fig. 7-4. Ice thrusts. (*From Edwin Rose, Proc. Am. Soc. Civil Engrs., May, 1946, p. 574.*) Conditions used in the figure:

1. Initial air temperature $-40°F$.
2. Initial ice temperature varies linearly from $-40°F$ at the air surface to $+32°F$ at lower surface.
3. Air temperature changes at rates of $+5°F$ (curve A), $+10°F$ (curve B), and $+15°F$ (curve C) per hour, from $-40°F$ to $+32°F$; then it remains constant at $+32°F$ until the temperature throughout the ice sheet has risen to about $+32°F$.
4. Emissivity effects are neglected, *i.e.*, temperature of ice at air surface is assumed same as air temperature itself.
5. Thickness of ice sheet remains constant.
6. Diffusivity constant of ice h^2 in square feet per hour equals 0.043.
7. Poisson's ratio equals 0.365.
8. Absorption of solar energy is neglected.

solar radiation, (5) currents under the ice, (6) snow on the ice acting as an insulator, (7) intensity and fetch of the wind, (8) buckling of ice, and (9) changes in reservoir level. The rate of rise of the temperature of the ice is probably the most effective condition in creating ice pressures. It should be recalled that ice expands as its temperature rises.

Rose[2] presents a diagram shown in Fig. 7-4 showing the effect of some of these conditions. Lofquist, Hogg, and Monfore[3] discuss pressures due to ice and conditions affecting them. Monfore reports pressures of 14 to 20 kips per lin ft. Gisiger[4] states that except in very confined spaces ice

[1] See also G. E. Monfore, *Proc. Am. Soc. Civil Engrs.*, December, 1952.
[2] E. Rose, *ibid.*, May, 1946, p. 571.
[3] See also B. Lofquist, A. D. Hogg, and G. E. Monfore, *ibid.*, Separates 160, 161, and 162, respectively, 1952.
[4] P. E. Gisiger, *Civil Eng.*, January, 1947, p. 24.

pressures will seldom exceed 10 kips per ft of dam.   Possibly a pressure
of 3,000 to 5,000 lb per sq ft of expected thickness of ice may be conserva-
tive in estimating the thrust against a dam.   Pressures due to broken
ice, *i.e.*, ice floes, are generally negligible[1] compared with the thrust of
sheet ice.

7-24. Foundation Reaction.   The vertical component of the foundation
reaction is equal to the weight of the structure and of the water vertically
above it.   If the dam acts as a homogeneous unit, as is often the case in a
masonry dam, the intensity of the foundation reaction will vary uniformly

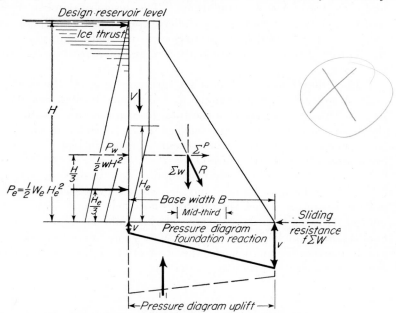

FIG. 7-5. Principal forces acting on gravity dams.

from toe to heel, as indicated in Fig. 7-5.   It is desirable that there shall
be no tension or upward pull at the upstream edge, or heel, of the dam.
To accomplish this, the resultant of the external forces on the dam should
pass through the edge of the middle third nearer to the downstream portion of the base.   The maximum compressive stress, or foundation reaction, will occur at the toe of the dam, as indicated in Fig. 7-5.   Allowable
pressures on primary rock vary from 30 tons per sq ft down to 10 for good
shale.   Earth is not suitable for high dams because of its relatively low
bearing power.   For preliminary designs and estimates for solid gravity
masonry dams, a triangular cross section or profile is often assumed.   The
ratio of base width to height may be taken as about 0.65 for no uplift
to 0.91 for full uplift.

[1] See also C. L. Harrison, *Trans. Am. Soc. Civil Engrs.*, Vol. 75, p. 142, 1912.

7-25. Earthquake Shocks.[1] Stresses[2] resulting from earthquake shocks may occur in a masonry dam because of the acceleration of the mass of the dam and changes in water pressure. The maximum horizontal acceleration due to an earthquake of intensity a is given by the formula

$$a = \alpha g \qquad\qquad (7\text{-}2)$$

in which g is the acceleration due to gravity (32.2 ft per sec²).[3] Vertical accelerations are usually neglected. In the United States, a value for α of 0.1 is generally considered adequate on sand and earth foundations, and up to 0.75 for rock foundations. The design of dams in regions subject to earthquakes requires specialized knowledge and experience. The committee report of the American Society of Civil Engineers[4] emphasizes the danger of too great simplification of assumed earthquake stresses for safe design.

7-26. Other Forces. Waves act not only to erode the face of a dam but also to create pressure against it. Molitor's[5] formula can be expressed as $P = 125h_w{}^2$, in which P is the total pressure, acting about $\frac{3}{8}h_w$ above the elevation of the still-water surface in the reservoir, in pounds; and h_w is the height of the wave from trough to crest, in feet, as computed by Stevenson's formula in Sec. 7-11.

Wind pressures are usually neglected in dam design.

Subatmospheric pressures may be caused by water falling over the crest of the dam. Since the pressures may become pulsating, their effect on the dam may be dangerous. They should be avoided rather than combatted in the design of the structure. They may be avoided by providing passage for air beneath the crest of the falling water. This procedure is called "aerating the crest."

Spillways

7-27. Capacity. In the design of a spillway, two things must be known: (1) its discharge capacity in terms of its dimensions and the depth of water on it, and (2) the maximum rate of discharge from the reservoir. The capacity of the spillway should be sufficient to pass the greatest flood to be expected from the watershed. Size of floods is discussed in Chap. 6.

7-28. Location. The spillway should be located, in general, at a low place in the rim of the reservoir where the distance of fall of water passing

---

[1] See also: H. M. Westergaard, *ibid.*, Vol. 98, p. 418, 1933; Committee Report, *Proc. Am. Soc. Civil Engrs.*, April, 1951.

[2] See Water Pressures on Dams during Earthquakes, *Bur. Reclamation, Tech. Mem.* 123, 1931; *Trans. Am. Soc. Civil Engrs.*, Vol. 98, p. 148, 1933.

[3] Water Pressures on Dams during Earthquakes, *op. cit.; Trans. Am. Soc. Civil Engrs.*, Vol. 98, p. 148, 1933.

[4] *Loc. cit.*

[5] D. A. Molitor, *Trans. Am. Soc. Civil Engrs.*, Vol. 100, p. 984, 1935.

the spillway is low.   If no suitable low point can be found in the reservoir rim, it may be possible to locate the spillway at the end of the dam and lead the water through a spillway channel on the hillside below the dam. If possible, the location of spillways in the body of a dam should be avoided, particularly in earth dams, because a spillway so located is conducive to erosion at the toe of the dam.

7-29. Types.   Spillways may be classified as uncontrolled, automatically controlled, and manually controlled.   Types of uncontrolled spillways include overflow, chute, and side-channel.

Manually controlled and automatically operated spillways make it possible to hold the surface of the water in the reservoir at any predetermined elevation for all designed rates of flow over the spillway.   The water surface in the reservoir can thus be held at the same elevation at low rates of stream flow and during floods.   Water may therefore be

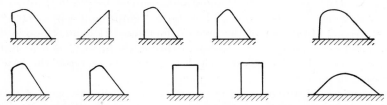

FIG. 7-6. Types of overflow spillways.   (*From Proc. Am. Soc. Civil Engrs., Vol.* 39, *pp.* 1513, 1913.)

stored in the reservoir near the flood level during both flood periods and during periods of low flow, thus increasing the available storage capacity of the reservoir as compared with one behind a dam of the same height but without a controlled spillway.   Types of automatically controlled spillways include siphon, shaft, flashboards, and float-controlled gates. Manually controlled spillways, more commonly called outlet works, control the upstream depth of water by the manipulation of gates or valves which determine the rate of flow of water through the control works.

7-30. Overflow Spillways.   These are uncontrolled spillways over the top of which water flows.   Types are shown in Fig. 7-6.   They are commonly shaped, in transverse section, in the form of an ogee curve or as a broad-crested weir.   The rate of discharge over them can be expressed as $Q = Clh^{3/2}$, in which Q is the rate of flow over the spillway for a length l along the spillway, h is the depth of water on the spillway measured vertically from the top of the spillway to the elevation of the surface of the water in the reservoir, and C is a coefficient, values of which are discussed in Sec. 2-9.[1]

The downstream face of the spillway must be designed to avoid scour. The production of turbulence in the stream before the water has left the

[1] See also A. S. Offitzeroff, *Civil Eng.,* August, 1940, p. 523.

apron serves to dissipate some of the scouring energy.[1]   Schemes for the dissipation of energy of water falling over a spillway include (1) the creation of a hydraulic jump at the foot of the dam, (2) indenting the spillway in plan to direct streams of falling water against each other, (3) obstructions in the face of the dam, (4) baffle piers, and (5) stilling pools. Spillways indented in plan, morning-glory patterns,[2] and other schemes for elongating the crest decrease fluctuations of water-surface elevation during discharge over the dam.

7-31. Spillway Channels.   Water may be conducted away from spillways to the main stream bed in spillway channels, or it may fall directly into the stream bed.   Types of spillway channels include flumes, tunnels, chutes, and side channels.   Flumes and tunnels may be constructed as in aqueducts.   Where local topography is favorable, it may be possible to construct a steeply sloping channel to carry the falling water at a higher, but less destructive, velocity than would result either from a direct fall or by following an ogee curve.   The term "chute spillway" refers, in general, to a spillway not in the face of the dam.   Instead, the overflow discharges to the water below the dam through a lined trench or flume. The bottom of the channel may be roughened to increase the rate of absorption of energy.

Where water falls over a spillway into a chute that is parallel to the length of the spillway, the chute may be known as a "side-flow channel." The hydraulics of side-flow channels have been analyzed by Camp,[3] who has formulated the flow in a rectangular flat-bottom channel with constant slope as

$$H_o = \sqrt{d^2 + \frac{2Q^2}{gb^2d} - Sx\bar{d} + \frac{fxQ^2}{12gb^2\bar{R}d}} \qquad (7\text{-}3)$$

where H_o = depth of water at upper end of spillway

d = depth at any point

Q = rate of flow

b = width of channel

S = bottom slope

x = distance from upper end of channel to point where depth is d

$\bar{d}$ = average depth throughout distance x

f = Weisbach-Darcy friction factor

$\bar{R}$ = average hydraulic radius throughout distance x

Where velocities are high in spillway channels or at their junction with the stream bed, special attention must be given to prevent erosion.

7-32. Siphon Spillways.   A section through a siphon spillway is shown in Fig. 7-7.   For the lowest flows, the spillway acts as a covered overflow

[1] See also *Eng. News-Record*, Dec. 12, 1946, p. 99.

[2] See also *ibid.*, June 28, 1951, p. 30.

[3] T. R. Camp, *Trans. Am. Soc. Civil Engrs.* Vol. 105, p. 606, 1940.

spillway, but when the rate of flow is sufficient to fill the channel a siphon is formed and the effective discharge head is measured vertically between the elevation of the water surface in the reservoir and either the center of the discharge opening below the spillway, or the surface of the water in the tailrace, whichever is higher.   Because of practical limitations, the effective value of this head h cannot exceed about 24 ft.[1]   The rate of discharge can be computed from the expression $Q = kA \sqrt{2gh}$, in which A is the cross-sectional area of the siphon at the throat or the narrowest portion and k is a constant usually taken at about 0.65.

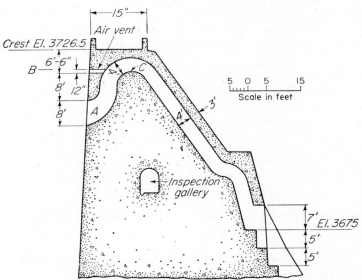

Fig. 7-7. Siphon spillway section, O'Shaughnessy Dam, city of San Francisco, Calif.

Advantages of siphon spillways include (1) close regulation of reservoir surface, (2) high capacity within relatively small space as compared with overflow spillways, (3) automatic action, (4) wide range or operating head, and (5) no moving parts.   On the other hand, their disadvantages include (1) serious danger due to clogging, (2) destructive vibrations due to alternate breaking and forming of siphonic action, and (3) relatively high cost of construction.

7-33. Shaft Spillways.[2]   A section through a shaft spillway is shown in Fig. 7-8.   Such spillways possess the advantages and disadvantages of the siphon spillway.   Where local topographical or other conditions are favorable, they may be the least expensive type of spillway to install.

[1] See also Elmer Rock, *ibid.*, Vol. 105, p. 1050, 1940.
[2] See also J. W. Trahern, *Eng. News-Record*, July 1, 1943, p. 77.

However, if the fall is high, erosion from cavitation and high velocities may be serious.

7-34. Flashboards and Automatic Gates. Flashboards are designed to collapse when the depth of water on them exceeds a predetermined maximum. Upon the collapse of the flashboard, the effective capacity of the spillway is increased without raising the elevation of the water in the reservoir. After the passage of the flood, the flashboard may be replaced manually or automatically. Modifications of the flashboard principle include counterbalanced or tilting gates that automatically tilt under high heads and restore themselves under low heads.[1]

Flashboards are infrequently used in water-works practice except as temporary expedients. They may be used to increase the capacity of an existing reservoir with an overflow spillway, without reconstructing the

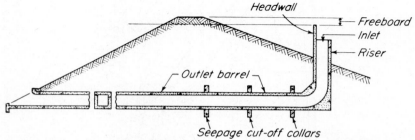

Fig. 7-8. Section through a shaft spillway. (*From "Low Dams," Natural Resources Committee,* 1938.)

dam. They are, however, not durable, offer obstruction to the passage of debris, and are uncertain in their action.

7-35. Outlet Works. Outlet devices are provided to control the release of water from a reservoir for any purposes. An intake, as discussed in Chap. 8, is an outlet from the reservoir. Outlet works may be used also for releasing excess water, for emptying the reservoir, or for control of water supplied to downstream owners of prior water rights.

The location, capacity, structural features, and safety of the outlet works are interrelated and may depend also on the purpose of the works. For most purposes, other than to supplement spillway capacity or to control maximum reservoir elevation, outlets are placed low in the reservoir so that its full capacity may be available, or it may be completely drained. Locations at intermediate elevations may be desirable in deep reservoirs to permit the withdrawal of water of the best quality in the reservoir.

Control devices and outlet works include overflow-spillway or crest-control devices and gates or valves. Types of crest-control gates, in

[1] See also *ibid.*, Aug. 10, 1950, p. 35; Sept. 14, 1950, p. 45.

addition to flashboards, include radial, or Tainter, gates, drum gates, and
sliding gates.

7-36. Radial, or Tainter, Gate.[1]   A section through the radial gate
at Watts Bar Project is shown in Fig. 7-9, and a diagram of the forces
acting on such a gate is shown in Probs. 2-2 and 2-3 in Appendix 2.   The
diagram of the forces acting on a radial gate, shown in Fig. 7-9, indicates

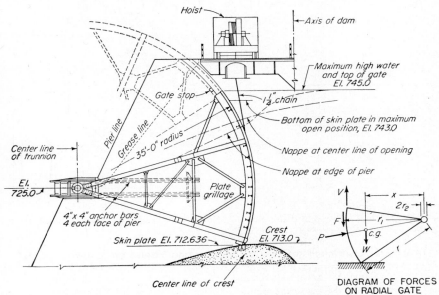

Fig. 7-9. Radial gate at Watts Bar Project, raised by traveling hoist.   (*From K. C.
Roberts, Civil Eng., January, 1946, p. 13.*)

how the gate operates.   When closed, the lower edge of the cylindrical
surface of the upstream face of the gate rests on the crest of the spillway.
The gate is opened by lifting it by means of gears along the edge of each
gate, or by an overhead hoist.   The vertical force in pounds required to
lift the gate can be formulated as

$$V = \frac{Wx + k_1 F r_1 + k_2 P r_2}{r} \tag{7-4}$$

where W = weight of gate, lb
k_1 = coefficient of starting friction of the sealing strips
k_2 = coefficient of friction of the trunnion bearing
Other nomenclature is shown in Fig. 7-9.   Values of coefficients of friction
are shown in Table 7-2.

7-37. Drum Gate.   The drum gate, a cross section of which is shown
in Fig. 7-10c, floats on water contained in the drum-gate chamber and

[1] See also D. A. Buzzell, *ibid.*, Apr. 1, 1948, p. 80.

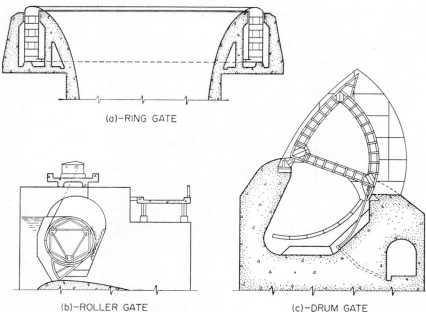

(a)–RING GATE

(b)–ROLLER GATE   (c)–DRUM GATE

Fig. 7-10. Ring, roller, and drum gates. (*From Water and Water Eng., August,* 1951, p. 282.)

TABLE 7-2. Coefficients of Friction and Bearing Values on Spillway Gates*

Values for gates that remain closed for a long period				Gate seal strips on wet surfaces	
Material	Friction coefficient k_2		Bearing pressure, psi	Bearing surfaces	k_1
	Starting	Sliding			
Timber on steel.............	0.62	0.31	...	New steel plates	0.64–0.73
Timber on bronze..........	0.60	0.30	...	Rusty steel plates	0.82–0.88
Bronze on bronze..........	0.70	0.35	500	Rough concrete	0.56–0.60
Steel on bronze (rustless)...	0.70	0.35	400	Smooth concrete	0.60–0.70
Cast iron on steel..........	0.75	0.38	400		

* From "Low Dams," p. 74, The National Resources Committee, 1938.

rotates about a hinge at the upstream edge. The level of the water in the chamber is controlled by a float which operates a balanced valve. When the water in the reservoir tends to rise above normal, the float opens the balanced valve which permits part of the water in the chamber to escape. The gate, floating on the water, lowers with it until the necessary additional spillway capacity is established. When the flow over the spillway becomes constant, the balanced valve is closed, and the water in the chamber and the gate are held at the required height. When the water in the reservoir drops below normal, the balanced valve admits water into the chamber, and the gate rises. The drum gate is used when close regulation of reservoir surface elevation is necessary.

7-38. Sliding, Leaf, and Roller Gates. Sliding gates consist of a deck or skin plate resting on a structural frame of beams and girders which slides in grooves or on tracks that are installed in piers or abutments. Unless provided with caterpillars or rollers to overcome friction, an excessive amount of power is required to operate them.

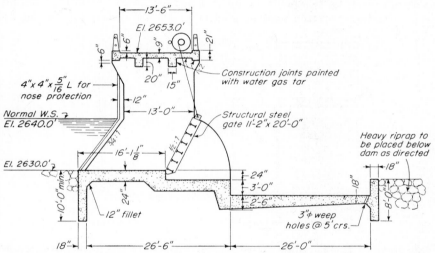

FIG. 7-11. Installation of a flap gate in the Harper diversion dam. (*Courtesy of U.S. Bureau of Reclamation.*)

Leaf or flap gates are hinged at the bottom and are raised and lowered by means of a crane. They are suitable for low diversion dams. A section of a flap gate is shown in Fig. 7-11.

The bear-trap gate consists of two hinged leaves which are raised and lowered by a difference of water pressure on the upper and lower surfaces of the leaves. They are seldom used in water-works practice.

The sector rolling gate consists of a steel drum the cross section of which is in the shape of a sector of a circle. At each end a circular casting having gear teeth on its outside face is fastened to the circular part of the drum. The gear teeth engage the teeth of a sloping rack fastened to the piers. The lifting force, applied by a hoist on a platform above the gate, causes the gate to roll on the gearing and lifts it from a concrete chamber provided in the top portion of the masonry. Sector rolling gates are adaptable for heights of 10 to 20 ft and in lengths from 50 to 100 ft.

7-39. Outlet Gates and Valves. The purpose of outlet gates and valves is to control the quantity of water drawn from the reservoir. They are, respectively, of two general types for water works, slide gates and needle valves.

A Stoney gate, as illustrated in Fig. 7-12, is a special form of large slide gate, usually provided with rollers or caterpillars to minimize friction and power for operation. A slide gate usually consists of a rectangular gate or leaf, properly mounted, which slides over an opening in a pipe or conduit. The leaf is moved by means of a screw or by hydraulic pressure against a piston contained in a cylinder, mounted over the leaf. Figure 7-13 shows a hydraulically operated slide gate. Slide gates are considered as low-pressure gates when they operate against heads of less than about 60 ft. Gates operating against greater heads are ordinarily classed as

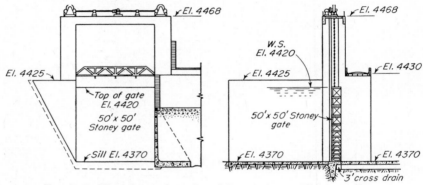

Fig. 7-12. Elevation and section of Stoney gate at Guernsey Dam.

high-pressure gates. Slide gates are not suitable for use for heads greater than about 250 ft, but types developed by the Bureau of Reclamation and known as ring-follower and Paradox may be used for heads up to 600 ft. High-pressure slide gates are equipped with air vents in order to eliminate pitting and erosive effects which are liable to occur in the outlet channel as a result of pressures less than atmospheric. Slide gates, if properly designed, manufactured, and installed, are satisfactory in operation and have little to get out of repair. They are slow in operation, especially under high heads.

A needle valve consists of a piston or needle that slides in an internal cylinder, closed at the upstream end, installed within a truncated ellipsoidal casting. The cylinder is held in place by ribs connecting it with the outside shell. Needle valves are useful for close control of the rate of flow, and in large sizes such as is shown in Fig. 7-14 can be controlled with hydraulic pressure.

Outlet-control devices should be placed on the upstream end of conduits leading through the dam. It is undesirable to pass conduits through

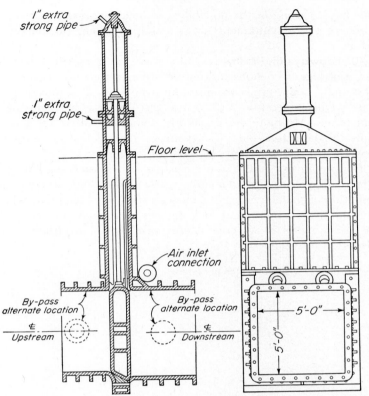

FIG. 7-13. High-pressure slide gate as built by the Bureau of Reclamation. (*From F. L. Boissonnault, Proc. Am. Soc. Civil Engrs., September, 1947, p. 1027.*)

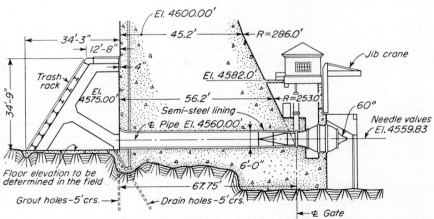

FIG. 7-14. Cross section through an outlet works showing needle-valve installation.

earth dams because of the possibility of breakage resulting from uneven settling of the embankment or to "piping" along the outside of the conduit.

7-40. Logways and Fishways. Logways are provided to facilitate the passage of logs over dams located on streams that are used for logging operations. Logways are usually built 6 to 30 ft wide and require 25 to 50 cfs for their operation. Flow into the logway is best controlled by a radial gate. Mechanical devices are sometimes used for passing the logs by the dams to avoid a loss of water. Logways may be used also to remove floating debris from the reservoir.

A fishway, or fish ladder, is a device to permit fish to pass upstream or downstream over or around a dam.[1] The laws of some states require the installation of such devices. Fishways vary from a simple low dam over which the fish may jump to such devices as a tank trap which is lifted with the contents of water and entrapped fish and either dumped or transported upstream.

[1] See also *Eng. News-Record*, Sept. 19, 1946, p. 106.

INTAKES

8-1. Types of Intakes.[1] A water-works intake is a device or structure placed in a surface water source to permit the withdrawal of water from this source and its discharge into an intake conduit through which it will flow into the water-works system. Types of intake structures consist of intake towers, submerged intakes, intake pipes or conduits, movable intakes, and shore intakes. Intake structures over the inlet ends of intake conduits are necessary to protect against wave action, floods, stoppage, navigation, ice, pollution, and other interference with the proper functioning of the intake.

Intake towers are used for large water works drawing water from lakes, reservoirs, and rivers in which there is either or both a wide fluctuation in water level or the desire to draw water at a depth that will give water of the best quality, to avoid clogging, or for other reasons. A wet intake tower is filled with water to the level of the source of supply. Sections through such towers are shown in Fig. 8-1. A dry intake tower has no water inside it other than in the intake pipes. Water is admitted through the ports connected to the intake pipes which convey it from the tower under pressure. The interior of the tower is thus made accessible for inspection and operation. Wet towers are less costly to construct. They are not subject to flotation, and certain other stresses need not be considered. Towers in lakes and in some rivers are usually located some distance from the shore line. An Australian reservoir tower is illustrated in Fig. 8-2.

Submerged intakes, an example of which is shown in Fig. 8-3, are constructed entirely under water and have such advantages over exposed structures as lower cost, no obstruction to navigation and but little obstruction to the flow of the river, little danger from floating material, and a minimum of trouble from ice. This type of structure is commonly used for intakes of moderate size on the Great Lakes and for the majority of other installations. An intake pipe of the type shown in Fig. 8-3 is usually satisfactory and should be used, where possible, to minimize cost.

[1] See also: C. B. Burdick, *J.A.W.W.A.*, March, 1946, p. 315; N. G. McDonald, *ibid.*, April, 1940, p. 661.

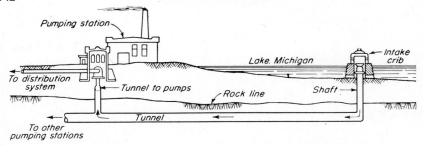

Water from Lake Michigan flows by gravity through intake cribs to suction wells whence pumps lift it directly into distribution mains. Cribs are located from two to four miles from shore in about 35 ft. of water.

(a)

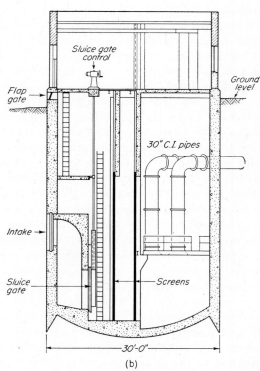

(b)

FIG. 8-1. Intake towers.   (a) Wet intake tower at Chicago.   (*From W. W. DeBerard, Civil Eng., 1950, p. 17.*)   (b) Dry intake tower.   (*From L. R. Howson, Water Works Eng., May, 1949, p. 415.*)

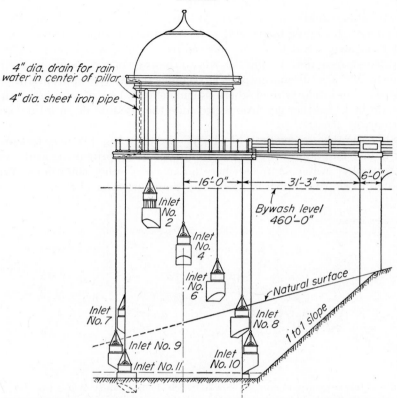

4" dia. drain for rain water in center of pillar

4" dia. sheet iron pipe

16'-0"

31'-3"

6'-0"

Inlet No. 2

Inlet No. 4

Inlet No. 6

Bywash level 460'-0"

Natural surface

Inlet No. 7

Inlet No. 8

1 to 1 slope

Inlet No. 9

Inlet No. 11

Inlet No. 10

FIG. 8-2. Outlet tower of Maroondah Reservoir, Australia. (*From G. E. Ritchie, Water Works Eng., Jan. 22, 1947, p. 72.*)

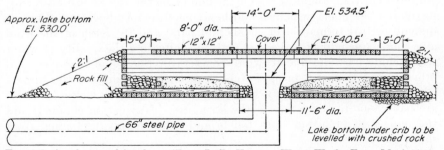

Approx. lake bottom El. 530.0'

14'-0"

El. 534.5'

8'-0" dia.

5'-0"

12"x12"

Cover

El. 540.5'

5'-0"

2:1

Rock fill

11'-6" dia.

66" steel pipe

Lake bottom under crib to be levelled with crushed rock

FIG. 8-3. A submerged intake. (*From L. R. Howson, Water Works Eng., May, 1949, p. 415.*)

Movable intakes,[1] such as the intake shown in Fig. 8-4, are used in streams with sloping banks and wide variations in surface elevation. As the river level changes the discharge pipe on the intake shown in Fig. 8-4 is disconnected and the pump is run to the edge of the water on the track shown, and the discharge pipe is reconnected at the appropriate level. This type of intake is used where shifting shoals, lack of foundation in the stream bed, or other conditions preclude the erection of an intake structure in the stream.

Shore intakes, an example of which is shown in Fig. 8-5, may be suitable for industrial plants where water quality is not a primary consideration, or for public water supplies where quality and other conditions permit. Shore intakes are probably less costly than towers or cribs.

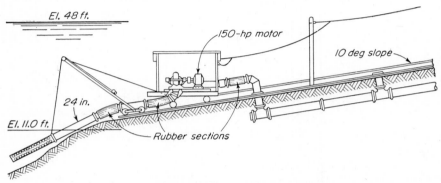

FIG. 8-4. Intake pump on movable carriage. St. Louis County Water Co. Plant on the Missouri River. The pump houses are built over railroad type wheels which roll upon a railroad track. (*From V. C. Lischer and H. O. Hartung, J.A.W.W.A., October, 1952, p. 873.*)

8-2. Location of Intakes. Conditions to be considered in the location of an intake include (1) the location of the best quality of water available; (2) currents that might threaten the safety of the intake structure; (3) navigation channels, which should be avoided; (4) ice floes and other ice difficulties; (5) formation of shoals and bars; and (6) fetch of the wind affecting the height of waves. Conditions affecting the quality of water will include currents due to wind, temperature, seasonal turnover, and other causes that will bring water of unsuitable quality to the intake. Channels with high-velocity currents carrying floating debris and ice are hazardous to the safety of the structure. Navigation channels add the danger of pollution from toilets and other refuse discharged from ships.

Ice floes are hazardous to the superstructure of an intake owing to the pressures exerted on it, and to intake ports both shallow and deep, since ice floes may push down surface ice to clog ports 20 to 30 ft below the

[1] See also V. C. Lischer and H. O. Hartung, *J.A.W.W.A.*, October, 1952, p. 873.

water surface.   Waves are hazardous to the superstructure of an intake, and they stir up mud and silt from the bottom in such quantity as to affect the quality of the water.

A study of the currents in a lake or river should be made before the location of an intake is selected in order to assure water of the best

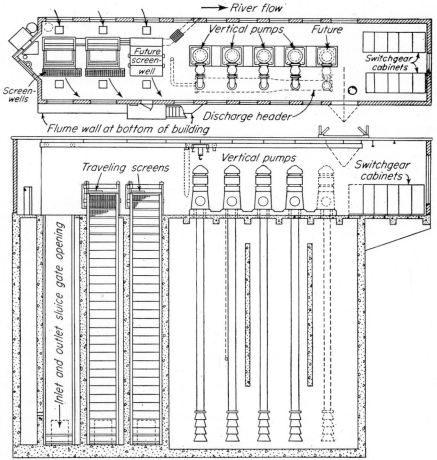

Fig. 8-5. A riverside or shore intake.   (*From Eng. News-Record, Mar.* 3, 1949, *p.* 52.)

quality and the avoidance of polluted water.   Such studies are made by observing the progress of both surface and submerged floats.

In bodies of water having wide fluctuations of surface level[1] the intake should be located so that, at the lowest water stage, one inlet is submerged.   An intake in an impounding reservoir is usually placed in the deepest part of the reservoir, which ordinarily is near the dam.   This will

[1] See also Lischer and Hartung, *loc. cit.*

render the full capacity of the reservoir available and will usually protect the intake from sediment in the reservoir. Intakes in streams with a steep bottom gradient should, where possible, be placed at sufficient distance upstream to supply water to the city by gravity.

8-3. Design of Intakes. External forces to be resisted by intakes include flotation, waves and currents, ice pressures, blows from floating and submerged objects, and shifting shoals. The magnitude of such forces is known only approximately; therefore, a generous factor of safety must be allowed.

Flotation can be computed on the basis of the weight of the volume of water displaced. Since air may be entrapped in intake conduits and in intake towers, and the towers may be pumped dry, a generous allowance should be made for flotation and to resist collapse caused by external hydrostatic pressure. Flotation is overcome by the construction of massive masonry structures; by weighting down submerged cribwork with broken stone; or by filling the annular space between two concentric cylindrical shells with stone or concrete, the cylinders being sunk to the bottom and supported thereon.

Little is known about pressures from waves and currents. Waves 10 ft high may cause pressures of 1,800 to 3,000 psf, with the maximum pressure at mean water level. Wind pressures up to 20 psf should be allowed against the portion of the tower exposed above low-water level.

The force of blows by floating or submerged objects should not exceed that of blows due to ice floes. Intakes in or near navigable channels should be protected by clusters of piles or other defense against blows from moving objects.

Undermining of foundations due to water currents or overturning pressures due to deposits of silt against one side of an intake structure are to be avoided rather than combated.

The entrance of large objects into the intake pipe is prevented by the use of a coarse screen or by the obstructions offered by the small openings in the cribwork or riprap placed around the intake pipe. Fine screens for the exclusion of small fish and other small objects should be placed at some accessible point, as at the suction or wet well at the pumping station where the screens can be easily inspected and cleaned. The location of the screens in an inaccessible position in a remote intake structure is undesirable. The area of the openings in the intake crib should be sufficient to prevent an entrance velocity greater than about 30 fpm, in order to avoid carrying settleable matter into the intake pipe.

Intake ports may be placed at various elevations in the tower[1] so that water of the best quality may be taken. They should also be placed so that if one or more of the ports is blocked another can be opened. Where the intake tower is in a river in which ice troubles may be encountered,

[1] See also S. B. Roberts, *Eng. News-Record*, Mar. 3, 1949, p. 52.

the upstream side of the tower should be protected and strengthened to resist ice pressure.   In general, the intake ports should be placed in the downstream face of the tower, and they should be protected against blocking by ice or other floating material.

Submerged ports should be designed and controlled to prevent air from entering the suction pipe.   The difficulty can be minimized by maintaining an entrance velocity not greater than 2 fps, preferably much less than this, and maintaining a depth of water over the port of at least three diameters of the port opening.

8-4. Screens and Strainers.   Screens or grids with parallel bars, preferably removable, may be placed over the intake ports.   Mesh screens are undesirable because of the difficulty of cleaning them.   Grids are used to prevent large floating objects from entering the intake or gaining access to the conduit.   Intake screens should not be used as a purification device for the mechanical straining of suspended matter.   Hence, the openings between bars may not be less than 1 to 2 in.   The velocity through a screen should not exceed about 30 fpm and is preferably much less than this.   In some installations screens are used only occasionally under suitable conditions; in others, automatically and mechanically cleaned screens are used.   An electrically charged screen has been devised to keep fish away.

8-5. Difficulties with Ice.[1]   Surface ice, anchor ice, frazil ice, and slush ice are forms in which ice may be troublesome at an intake.[2]   Anchor ice is formed beneath the surface on objects that radiate heat rapidly.   It forms most readily on dark metallic surfaces such as valves and gratings. It is usually formed at night in clear cold weather when opaque surface ice has not formed.   It may be possible to minimize troubles from anchor ice by locating the intake in a quiet locality where the surface will freeze readily, or by constructing some form of temporary surface protection around the proposed intake.

Frazil ice, sometimes called needle ice, consists of submerged ice crystals that have been formed as anchor ice and have broken loose, or are ice crystals that have been formed about small particles suspended in water which serve as nuclei.[3]   Slush ice is formed of a soft mushy mass of ice crystals ground from other forms of ice.

Expedients used for the removal of ice from intake ports include a vigorous reversal of the flow of water through the port, steam or electrical heating devices, compressed air, pike poles, chains, and explosives.   The maintenance of violent agitation at critical points, as by high-velocity

[1] See also: H. T. Barnes, "Ice Engineering," Renouf Publishing Co., Montreal, 1928; P. E. Gisiger, *Civil Eng.*, January, 1947, p. 24; J. R. Baylis and H. H. Gerstein, *Eng. News-Record*, Apr. 15, 1948, p. 80.

[2] See Burdick, *op. cit.*, p. 415; P. E. Gisiger, *Civil Eng.*, January, 1940, p. 24.

[3] See also Baylis and Gerstein, *loc. cit.*

jets, has been found effective, especially along reservoir walls.[1] Divers have been employed under urgent conditions, but the service is hazardous and should be avoided. Provision for vigorous reversal of flow should be made when the intake is installed. This can be done by draining an elevated storage tank into the intake conduit, or discharging the flow from the main pumps into it, the pumps drawing their water from storage on the distribution system. The height of the curb on the intake well above the elevation of the water in the intake must be sufficient to permit these expedients.

8-6. Intake Conduit and Intake Well. The conduit conveying water from the intake should lead to a suction well in or near the pumping station. Either a pipe lying on or buried in the bottom of the body of water or deep tunnels may be used as intake conduits. For conduits up to about 12 in. in diameter, standard bell-and-spigot cast-iron pipe may be used, occasionally with flexible joints. Larger conduits may be of steel or concrete. A tunnel, although more expensive, makes the safest and most satisfactory conduit.

The capacity of the conduit and the depth of the suction well should be such that the intake ports to the pumps will not draw air. A velocity of 2 to 3 fps in the intake conduit, with a lower velocity through the ports, will give satisfactory performance. The horizontal cross-sectional area of the suction well should be three to five times the vertical cross-sectional area of the intake conduit. Even with conduit and suction well of adequate capacity it might be possible, by starting the pumps too fast, to draw water from the suction well so fast as to expose the pump-suction ports. Pumps should be started gradually to avoid drawdown in the suction well, and they should be stopped gradually to prevent surge. The intake well acts as a surge tank on the intake conduit, thus minimizing surge.

The intake conduit should be laid on a continuously rising or falling grade to avoid accumulation of air or gas, pockets of which would otherwise restrict the capacity of the conduit. Where air traps are unavoidable, provision must be made to allow gas to be drawn off from them. Where pipes are used, they must be weighted down to avoid flotation.

It is desirable, in general, that most intake works be in duplicate because of the almost complete dependence of the water works on its intake, the intake conduit, and the suction pit. Two or more widely separated intakes are highly desirable where it is possible to have them.

---

[1] See also *Public Works*, May, 1948, p. 46.

CHAPTER 9

AQUEDUCTS

9-1. Definition.[1] An aqueduct is a conduit designed to convey water from a source to a point, usually a reservoir, where distribution begins. An aqueduct may include canals, flumes, pipe lines, siphons, tunnels, or other channels, either open or covered, flowing at atmospheric pressure or otherwise. A typical profile of an aqueduct is shown in Fig. 9-1. The choice between available types of conduits depends on such factors as topography, pressure head available, quality of water, conditions of construction, and economy.

An important consideration in the design of an aqueduct is the prevention of pollution of the water in the conduit. Among the most common sources of pollution to be guarded against may be infiltration or surface runoff from the surrounding ground and the direct pollution of water in uncovered conduits.

9-2. Diversion Works. It is sometimes necessary to divert water from a river or reservoir into a canal or aqueduct for water supply or other purposes. Two problems in the design of the diversion works involve their capacity and their location to permit the requisite capacity to be withdrawn at low flow or low surface elevation. It may be desirable to provide storage at the diversion works to care for minor fluctuations of surface level. Storage curves by Hazen[2] are shown in Fig. 9-2. The benefits of even a small amount of storage at the diversion works are apparent from the figure. The curves show also, *e.g.*, that a diversion capacity of about three times the mean flow will make it possible to obtain 80 per cent of the water without storage, and that further increases in diversion capacity show a lower return.

9-3. Canals. A canal is an open conduit, either covered or uncovered, designed to convey water. An open conduit is a channel conveying water in which the hydraulic grade line lies in the surface of the water. A canal supported on or above the surface of the ground may be called a flume. An underground canal is a tunnel. Conditions favorable to the

---

[1] See also J. D. Watson, *Engineer*, Vol. 168, pp. 344, 368, 1939.

[2] R. Hazen, Conference on Water Resources, *Illinois State Water Survey, Bull.* 41, 1952.

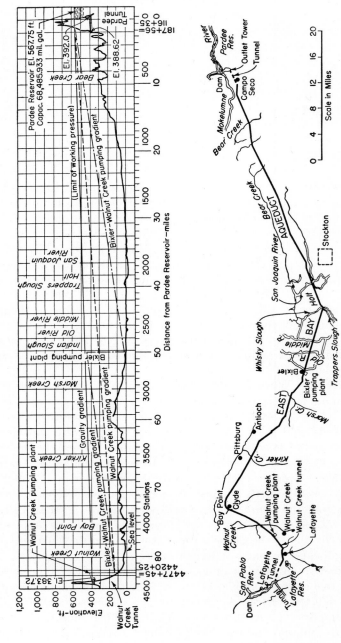

Fig. 9-1. Mokelumne River, East Bay Aqueduct, California. (*From H. A. Knudsen J.A.W.W.A., February, 1947, p. 134.*)

construction of a canal include topography permitting construction on the hydraulic grade line, impervious material easily excavated and not easily eroded or choked by plant growth, and surroundings free from pollution. A combination of all favorable conditions is unusual.   Objections to the use of canals for conveying public water supplies include the hazard of pollution of the water, high seepage and evaporation losses, difficulties of handling cross drainage, ice, danger from burrowing animals, and high maintenance costs.

The location of the route of a canal along a hydraulic grade line will require a study of a topographic map to balance cuts and fills, minimize crossings of streams, avoid tunnel construction, and avoid the objections previously listed.

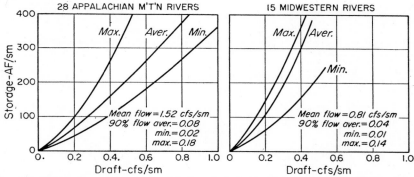

Fig. 9-2. Storage curves based on driest period of record and release of all flows below the 90 per cent flow.   (*From Richard Hazen, Conference on Water Resources, Illinois State Water Survey, Bull. 41, p. 87, 1951.*)

A semicircle is the most economical shape of cross section hydraulically, as it gives a maximum hydraulic radius for a given cross-sectional area. A trapezoidal channel is easier to construct and to maintain.   A trapezoid in which a semicircle, with its center in the water surface, can be inscribed gives the best hydraulic characteristics for a trapezoidal cross section. The steepness of the side slopes of the trapezoid, in unlined canals, depends on the angle of repose of the material that forms the banks.   In earth channels the slopes vary from $2\frac{1}{2}$ horizontal to 1 vertical in sand, to $1\frac{1}{4}:1$ in stiff clay.   In rock the sides may be vertical.

The use of lining in a canal has the effect of permitting higher velocities and thus reducing the required cross-sectional area.   The surface of the lining offers less resistance to flow.   Hence friction losses are reduced. Linings also reduce seepage losses and maintenance costs.   The general features of canal linings are similar to those of reservoir linings discussed in Sec. 20-13, except that construction joints are usually omitted in canals.   Figure 9-3 shows details of lined canals in earth and rock.   The figure shows also a method by which a number of cross sections may be shown on contract drawings. The location of a particular section may be shown on the profile, and a table is provided to show dimensions.

The need for basing the selection of the cross section of a channel on its hydraulic properties is, perhaps, overbalanced in many cases by other considerations, such as economy, facility of construction, structural characteristics, and practicability. Some typical cross sections of water-works canals are shown in Fig. 9-3.

Flumes are frequently constructed with walls of concrete, steel, or timber, either self-supporting or supported with the aid of other structural

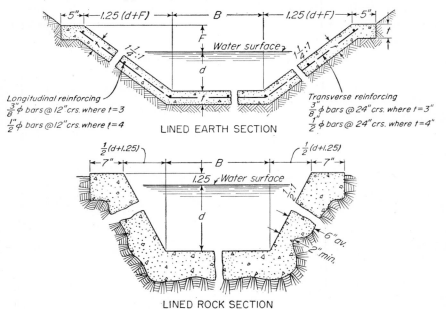

LINED EARTH SECTION

LINED ROCK SECTION

Fig. 9-3. Details of lined canals. (*Courtesy of U.S. Bureau of Reclamation.*)

members.[1] Sections of two concrete flumes are shown in Fig. 9-4. Metal flumes may consist of sheet-metal plates supported by stringers to reduce lateral stresses on the piers or bents.

Velocities of flow in canals and flumes should be high enough to consume the available head without eroding the banks or exceeding the critical velocity at which the energy (depth plus velocity head) is a minimum. At higher than critical velocity jumps, bores, standing waves, and other phenomena may occur and result in overtopping of the canal banks, or other undesirable features.

In general, flumes are a type of water-works aqueduct to be avoided. Difficulties met in their design and maintenance include prevention of leakage, provision for expansion and contraction, variations in the invert

---

[1] See also *Eng. News-Record*, Oct. 3, 1946, p. 86.

gradient caused by unequal settling of the supports, exposure to extremes of temperature and wind, and overflow due to clogging and to surge.

9-4. Pipe Lines. When rough topography or other conditions make the use of a canal impracticable, a pipe line with water flowing under pressure in it may be used. Since pipe lines can, in general, follow shorter

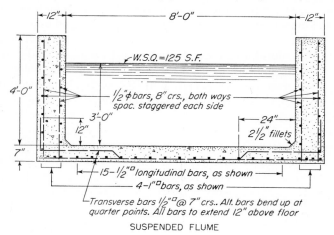

SUSPENDED FLUME

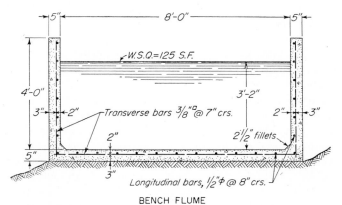

BENCH FLUME

FIG. 9-4. Rectangular reinforced-concrete flumes.

routes than canals, they may be cheaper to construct. A pipe line crossing a valley and lying on or under the ground surface with each end of the pipe line in or near the hydraulic grade line is called a siphon, although the pressures in it are normally greater than atmospheric. A true siphon is that part of a pipe line in which water flows above the hydraulic grade line. True siphons should be avoided because of difficulties to be expected from air leaks and from gases coming out of solution and accumulating at the top of the siphon, with resulting reduction in siphon capacity.   A force main is that portion of a pipe line through which water is pumped, usually to a higher elevation.   Booster pumps may be used to increase the pressure in long pipe lines.[1,2]   The discharge pipe from a booster pump would not necessarily be classified as a force main, unless the water were lifted to a higher elevation.

Materials used for pipe lines in aqueducts include concrete, cast iron, steel, wood, and asbestos cement.   The material selected depends on such conditions as (1) assurance that operation will not be interrupted; (2) annual cost; (3) suitability for conditions which include loads, pressures, and the corrosive characteristics of the water and the soil in contact with the pipe; (4) accessibility of the site and ease of transportation of materials, and (5) availability of skilled and other labor for construction.

Circular cross sections are most commonly used for pipe lines under high pressure, since the stresses can be economically carried under tension. Typical cross sections of concrete pipes and tunnels are illustrated in Figs. 9-5, 17-22, and 17-23.   However, large cross sections, either with or without cover, may be constructed of other shapes.   Such shapes are better suited to resisting heavy external loads and light internal pressures and are easier to construct.

To assure safety, to permit inspection, and to facilitate operation and maintenance, pipe lines should be provided with gate valves, check valves, drainage valves, air valves, and manholes.[3]   Surge tanks or other surge-control equipment may be necessary on some lines.   Gate valves may be placed about 1,000 to 1,500 ft apart, near manholes, with a drainage valve at a low point between the gate valves to permit emptying the pipe between valves for inspection and repair.   A check valve should be placed at the upstream side of the beginning of each rise in the pipe line to prevent reversal of flow in an emergency.   A gate valve may be placed near to and on a convenient side of the check valve to permit inspection and repair.   The check valve should be designed to close slowly enough to avoid dangerous water hammer.   Drainage valves should be placed at all low points to permit removal of deposited silt and the emptying of the pipe.   An air valve should be located at each high point to allow the escape of air and gases and to admit air sufficiently rapidly to prevent the creation of a partial vacuum in the pipe line.

Expansion joints may be required on long pipe lines, particularly on steel pipe exposed to marked changes of temperature.   Figure 9-6 shows a type of joint used by the Bureau of Reclamation.   When several expansion joints are used in a long line, it is necessary to construct anchors between them in order to force the movement into the pipe designed to take it.   Where piers are used to support the full weight of steel pipe and

[1] See also D. M. Radcliffe, *Eng. News-Record*, May 2, 1946, p. 107.

[2] See *Eng. News-Record*, May 29, 1947, p. 63.

[3] See also L. E. Goit, *J.A.W.W.A.*, January, 1949, p. 47.

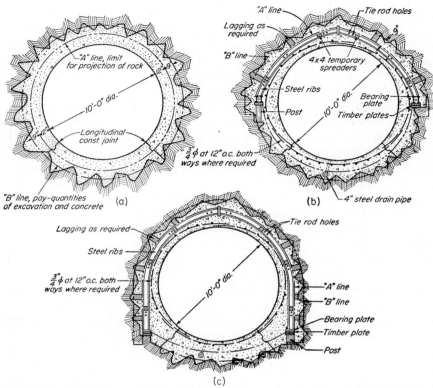

FIG. 9-5. Sections from aqueduct tunnel. (*From A. A. Burger, Eng. News-Record August 5, 1948, p. 79.*) Section *a* is the typical tunnel section. Roof support with lagged arch on bench is shown in Section *b*, and on post supports in Section *c*.

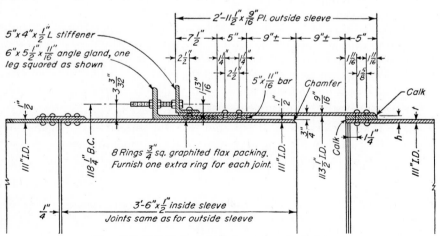

FIG. 9-6. Detail of a steel-pipe expansion joint.

water they should be spaced 20 to 40 ft apart and they should be constructed so that one-sixth to one-fourth, or more, of the pipe circumference will bear upon them. They should be constructed to resist the overturning forces resulting from friction due to longitudinal movements of the pipe. In general, a friction coefficient of not less than 0.5 between pipe and pier should be used in design.

9-5. Diameter of Pipe through Which Water Is Being Pumped.[1] The diameter of a pipe through which water is being pumped should be such as to give the lowest cost of the items of first cost; maintenance, including pumping; and renewal. The economical diameter of pipe can be determined by the procedure given below.[2] It is to be noted that this procedure is applicable to many problems involving economical dimensions or conditions to produce the lowest cost of an enterprise.

Procedure. 1. Formulate an expression for the capitalized cost, or total annual cost of the pipe line, assuming any convenient terms for the expression.

2. Express all the variables in the preceding expression in terms of any one of the variables.

3. Differentiate with respect to that variable, equate to zero, and solve. The result will be the economical value of the variable.

The above procedure will be applied to the determination of the economical diameter of a long cast-iron pipe line through which water is being pumped. The following nomenclature will be used:

a = cost of iron, cents per lb
$B = 0.00159L + 0.0006Y + (0.055 + 0.0145D)W$
C = coefficient in Hazen and Williams formula, taken here as 100
D = depth of trench, ft; d = diameter of pipe, in.
p = cost of pumping 1 million gal 1 ft high, cents
Q = rate of flow through pipe line, cfs
r = annual rate of interest plus sinking-fund rate of depreciation, plus rate of other annual charges
s = slope of hydraulic grade line
V = velocity of flow of water in pipe line, fps
W = wage rate for common labor, cents per hr
Y = cost of yarn (oakum), cents per lb

Now, to take the first step, it is found that the annual cost, per foot of length, of a cast-iron pipe, as shown by Maury,[3] including first cost and renewal and laying in trench, to be expressible in the form

$$\text{Cost} = Bdr + 2ard^{1.5} \tag{9-1}$$

[1] See also B. R. Sachet and A. P. Colburn, *Ind. Eng. Chem.*, September, 1940, p. 1240.

[2] See also W. E. Howland, *J.A.W.W.A.*, July, 1947, p. 630.

[3] D. H. Maury, *Eng. News-Record*, Vol. 88, p. 779, 1922.

The cost of pumping through the pipe line can be expressed as

$$\text{Pumping cost} = 236pQs \tag{9-2}$$

Hence the first step is completed and the total annual cost, for all charges, per foot of pipe is

$$\text{Total cost} = Bdr + 2ard^{1.5} + 236pQs \tag{9-3}$$

In taking the second step of the outlined procedure it is necessary to express the two variables d and s in terms of each other. This can be done by rearranging the Hazen and Williams formula into

$$s = 165 \frac{Q^{1.85}}{d^{4.86}} \tag{9-4}$$

Substituting this value of s in Eq. (9-3) there is obtained

$$\text{Total cost} = Bdr + 2ard^{1.5} + 39,000p \frac{Q^{2.85}}{d^{4.86}} \tag{9-5}$$

If the cost is now differentiated against the single variable d and the first differential is equated to zero it is found that

$$Brd^{5.86} + 3ard^{6.36} = 189,000pQ^{2.85} \tag{9-6}$$

which can be expressed approximately as

$$d = 7.25 \left(\frac{p}{r(B + 3a)}\right)^{0.167} Q^{0.476} \tag{9-7}$$

The economical velocity in a pipe can be determined from a combination of Eq. (9-7) and $Q = AV$, so that

$$V = 3.5Q^{0.05} \left[\frac{r(B + 3a)}{p}\right]^{0.33} \tag{9-8}$$

$$V = 3d^{0.1} \left[\frac{r(B + 3a)}{p}\right]^{0.35} \tag{9-9}$$

Economical values of the velocity of flow[1] are entered in Table 9-1. They have been computed from an approximate formula based on Flamant's formula of flow, as

$$V = 3.1d^{2/11} \left[\frac{r(B + 3a)}{p}\right]^{4/11} \tag{9-10}$$

9-6. Diameter of Pipe through Which Water Flows by Gravity. To secure the greatest economy, the diameter of a single pipe through which water flows by gravity should be such that all the head available to cause flow is consumed by friction.

---

[1] See also T. R. Camp, *Trans. Am. Soc. Civil Engrs.*, Vol. 104, p. 190, 1939.

TABLE 9-1. Economical Velocities for Different Diameters and Rates of Flow in Cast-iron Pipe*

Diam-eter, in.	Values of constants†			Quan-tity, sec-ft	Values of constants†		
	$L = 10$ $Y = 15$ $a = 4$ $r = 0.07$ $p = 4$ $W = 100$ $D = 6$ $B = 14.2$ $k = 0.441$	$L = 5$ $Y = 10$ $a = 3$ $r = 0.06$ $p = 6$ $W = 50$ $D = 4$ $B = 5.66$ $k = 0.1466$	$L = 3$ $Y = 4$ $a = 1.5$ $r = 0.04$ $p = 15$ $W = 30$ $D = 2$ $B = 2.33$ $k = 0.0182$		$L = 10$ $Y = 15$ $a = 4$ $r = 0.07$ $p = 4$ $W = 100$ $D = 6$ $B = 14.2$ $k = 0.441$	$L = 5$ $Y = 10$ $a = 3$ $r = 0.06$ $p = 6$ $W = 50$ $D = 4$ $B = 5.66$ $k = 0.1466$	$L = 3$ $Y = 4$ $a = 1.5$ $r = 0.04$ $p = 15$ $W = 30$ $D = 2$ $B = 2.33$ $k = 0.0182$
4	2.97	1.99	0.93	0.1	2.75	1.90	0.95
6	3.18	2.12	1.00	0.5	3.14	2.16	1.08
8	3.36	2.25	1.05	1.0	3.31	2.29	1.14
10	3.50	2.34	1.10	5	3.78	2.61	1.30
12	3.61	2.42	1.13	10	4.00	2.77	1.38
16	3.82	2.56	1.20	25	4.33	3.00	1.49
18	3.91	2.62	1.23	50	4.57	3.16	1.57
24	4.12	2.76	1.29	100	4.86	3.37	1.68
36	4.42	2.96	1.39				

* Velocities are given in feet per second.
† For nomenclature see p. (157) with the addition that $k = r(B + 3a)/p$.

9-7. Tunnels. Tunnels are constructed in aqueducts to pass through mountains and to cross under rivers and in situations in which surface lines or open-cut excavation would be impracticable. When a tunnel and a surface location are equally feasible, the tunnel will ordinarily involve a greater first cost, but the capitalized cost of the two may show the tunnel to be cheaper. The decision between them may lie in the availability of funds or in the consideration of safety and uninterrupted service.

In a grade tunnel the hydraulic grade line coincides with the surface of the flowing water in the tunnel. In a pressure tunnel the hydraulic grade line is above the tunnel. Both types of tunnel are in use, and both types may resist external forces due to surrounding ground pressures and ground-water pressures. Some tunnel sections designed to resist external forces are shown in Fig. 9-5.

Tunnels may or may not be lined, depending on the materials through which they are driven, the amount of head available, ground-water conditions, and other considerations. In earth and in crumbling rock, lining is essential. A reinforced concrete or metal lining must be provided in pressure tunnels at places where the weight of earth or rock cover is not sufficient to resist safely the bursting pressure in the tunnel. The hydraulic properties of a tunnel are greatly improved by lining; hence the loss of head due to friction for a given capacity is much smaller in a lined tunnel of a given cross-sectional area than in an unlined tunnel of the

same area.   The entrance of objectional ground water into a tunnel or
the escape of water from it may be prevented by a watertight lining of
brick, concrete, steel, cast iron, or concrete-protected metal or by grout,
placed under pressure, back of the lining.   When the tunnel is driven
through material not subject to caving or disintegration, and other considerations are not of sufficient weight to warrant the expense, the lining
is frequently omitted.

9-8. Cross Sections of Aqueducts.   The cross-sectional area of the
waterway of an aqueduct is determined by the head available, limiting
velocities, and other conditions.   When adequate head is available, the
area of waterway is determined by the maximum allowable velocity.
Table 9-2 gives maximum velocities recommended for various aqueduct
materials and types of structures.   The minimum velocity should be
sufficient to prevent the deposition of sediment in the channel.

TABLE 9-2. Maximum Velocities in Aqueducts

Type of structure	Max average velocity, fps
Cut-and-cover sections:	
Concrete lined......................	15.0
Brick lined.........................	18.0
Pipes:	
Steel and cast iron..................	12.0–20.0
Concrete...........................	10.0–15.0
Wood..............................	15.0
Tunnels:	
Unlined............................	12.0
Concrete lined.....................	10–15
Steel lined........................	12–20
Flumes—all types....................	Less than critical velocity
Canals:	
Earth:	
Ordinary.......................	2.5– 3.0
Sand...........................	1.0– 2.0
Hard gravel or firm clay...........	5.0– 6.0
Rock...............................	8.0–15.0
Concrete lined.....................	10.0–15.0

The sizes and shapes of cross sections in a long aqueduct are usually
varied to meet conditions of external loads and to provide the greatest
economy.   The shape should be designed to support the external loads,
and the area of waterway should give the least cost and consume the
available head in the most economical manner.   For example, where a
fixed amount of head loss is available between the upper and lower ends
of an aqueduct, part of which is to pass through a hard-rock tunnel and
the other to be constructed as a canal, it may be more economical to consume most of the available head in the tunnel, to permit the smallest

possible bore, than to divide the head loss between the two sections proportional to their length. The most economical distribution of head losses in an aqueduct passing through different materials, if the total head loss is fixed, can be determined by the following procedure:

1. Construct a set or curves whose abscissas are the total cost of the full length of each section of the aqueduct for the shape of cross section desired for that part of the aqueduct and whose ordinates are the head lost in that part of the aqueduct. A typical set of cost–head loss curves is shown in Fig. 9-7. Data for such curves must be obtained by designing various conduit shapes suitable for the materials through which each is

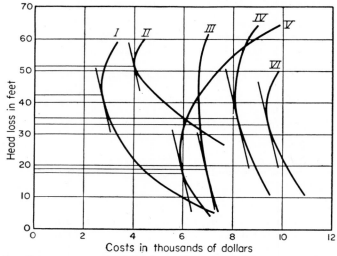

Fig. 9-7. Parallel tangent method for determining the minimum cost of an aqueduct.

passing and estimating the total cost of construction. The head loss is determined through the application of a suitable formula of flow.

2. Construct a series of parallel lines, by trial and error, each tangent to one curve, in a position such that the sum of the ordinates to all points of tangency is equal to the total available head. Then the sum of the abscissas to the points of tangency, *i.e.*, the total cost of the aqueduct, is a minimum. The aqueduct can be constructed for the least cost by adopting the head losses, shapes, and sizes in each section, as indicated in this study.

In the example illustrated in Fig. 9-7 the minimum cost for the six sections, for a total head loss of 200 ft, is $37,000. The head loss for each section of the aqueduct can be read from the figure. The shape and area of cross section that will give this head loss with the required rate of flow should be constructed.

9-9. Surge. Surge in closed aqueducts is similar to the phenomenon of water hammer discussed in Sec. 10-7, and in open channels it is similar to the traveling wave or bore. Both result from sudden changes in the velocity of flow in the conduit. Water hammer may create collapsing or bursting pressures in closed conduits or overflows in open channels. They may be controlled in closed conduits by the method discussed in Sec. 10-8, and in open channels by proper design under conditions of unsteady or nonuniform flow.[1]

[1] See also Delaware Aqueduct—V. Controlling the Flow, *Eng. News-Record*, July 18, 1940, p. 73.

CHAPTER 10

STRESSES IN PIPE

10-1. Loads and Stresses. Conduits carrying water under pressure develop stresses due to the following loads and conditions:

1. Internal bursting pressure produces circumferential tension and longitudinal tension at bends and dead ends.

2. Temperature changes produce longitudinal tension and compression.

3. Flow around bends produces longitudinal tension.

4. Weight of pipe, water, backfill, and other superimposed loads, and atmospheric pressure and reactions at foundations or other supports produce flexural tension and compression.

Shear may result under the application of any of the loads, depending on the manner of the load application and the construction of the conduit.

10-2. Internal Bursting Pressure. Internal pressures are caused by static pressure and water hammer. The tension T in a unit length of pipe, having a radius R and operating under an intensity of pressure p, is expressed by the formula

$$T = pR \tag{10-1}$$

The value of p for pressures due to static head is determined by the relation $p = wh$, in which w is the weight per unit volume of water and h is the maximum possible head to which the pipe may be subjected. The static head is measured from the highest possible position of the hydraulic grade line to a point in the pipe. If water hammer can occur, the head to which the pipe may be subjected is the sum of the static head and the head developed by the pressure rise due to water hammer.

10-3. Temperature Stresses. Longitudinal stresses due to changes in temperature can be computed from the expression

$$S = ETC \tag{10-2}$$

where S = intensity of stress due to change in temperature
E = modulus of elasticity of the metal
T = change in temperature
C = coefficient of expansion of the metal

If the pipe is to be allowed to expand and contract with changes in temperature, expansion joints must be provided. The movement of the pipe can be computed from the expression

$$M = LCT \qquad (10\text{-}3)$$

where M = change in length of the pipe
L = length of the pipe affected
C = coefficient of expansion of the metal
T = change in temperature

Temperature stresses and changes in length are usually not considered in the design of cast-iron distribution pipes underground. In the design of long steel conduits and of pipes conveying hot liquids, allowance should be made for temperature stresses unless adequate expansion joints are provided to reduce the effects of temperature change.

10-4. Flow around Bends. Longitudinal tension resulting from the flow of water around a bend in a closed pipe can be computed from the expression

$$T = \frac{WAV^2}{g} + pA \qquad (10\text{-}4)$$

where W = unit weight of water
A = cross-sectional area of the pipe
V = velocity of the flow of water
g = acceleration due to gravity
p = intensity of internal bursting pressure

The first term in Eq. (10-4) represents the stresses due to the flow of water around the bend. The load is produced by the centrifugal force resulting from the mass of water moving around the arc of the bend.

The force T may be carried as longitudinal tension in the shell and joints of the pipe, or it may be supported by a buttress placed at the bend. If a buttress is placed along the line of action of the resultant, *e.g.*, at E in Fig. 10-1, the buttress must resist the resultant force whose magnitude is

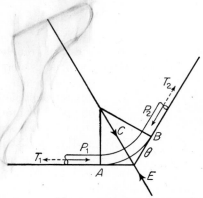

Fig. 10-1. Diagram of stresses in a pipe bend.

$$E = 2A\left(\frac{WV^2}{g} + p\right)\sin\frac{\theta}{2} \qquad (10\text{-}5)$$

Bends and tees that are not supported by a buttress must be adequately anchored. Anchors may consist of straps, tie rods, bolted flanges, or a combination of them.

10-5. Flexural Stresses. Flexural stresses result from the weight of the pipe, the weight of the water, from superimposed loads that tend to change the shape of the pipe, and from longitudinal loads that are resisted by the pipe acting as a beam, a column, or a tie rod. Combinations of transverse and longitudinal loads may result in combinations of arch, beam, column, and tie-rod actions in the pipe. Such loadings and conditions produce secondary flexural stresses resulting in transverse tension, compression, and shear that are difficult to compute because their magnitudes depend, to some extent, on the local deflections or strains produced in the pipe. Their computations must be based on the application of the principles of the theory of elasticity to the structural material of the conduit. Simple formulas are not available. When the external loads are known, the internal stresses and strains may be computed by reference to texts on structural analysis.

10-6. External Loads on Buried Pipes. Loads on buried pipe have been formulated by Marston[1] and discussed by Spangler.[2] Marston's formulas are expressed as:

For backfill load on ditch conduits

$$W = C_d w B^2 \qquad (10\text{-}6)$$

For superimposed dead loads along trench

$$W = C_{us} B U_{us} \qquad (10\text{-}7)$$

For moving short loads, across trench

$$W = \frac{I_c C_t T}{3} \qquad (10\text{-}8)$$

where B = width of trench slightly below top of pipe, ft

C_d, C_{us}, and C_t = coefficients depending on the conditions surrounding pipe in trench

I_c = impact coefficient, lying between 1.5 and 2.0, depending on speed of moving load

T = concentrated superimposed load, lb

U_{us} = uniformly distributed superimposed load, psf

W = load on pipe per ft length of trench, lb

w = unit weight of backfill material, lb per cu ft

A few representative values of the coefficients are shown in Table 10-1.

10-7. Water Hammer.[3] Water hammer is a pulsation of pressures above and below the operating pressure, resulting from rapid deceleration or acceleration of the velocity of flow of water in a closed conduit. The forces required to decelerate and to accelerate the confined column of

[1] Anson Marston, *Iowa Eng. Expt. Sta. Bulls.* 31, 47, 57, 76, 96, 108, 112.

[2] M. G. Spangler, *Proc. Am. Soc. Civil Engrs.*, June, 1947, p. 855.

[3] See also S. L. Kerr, *J.A.W.W.A.*, December, 1951, p. 985, with 11 references.

TABLE 10-1. Some Values of Coefficients in Marston's Formulas

Ratio $H/B*$	Damp top-soil and dry and wet sand		Saturated yellow clay		Depth of cover	Conduit breadth, ft				
						1	2	3	5	10
	C_d	C_{us}	C_d	C_{us}		Values of C_t				
1.0	0.85	0.72	0.90	0.80	1	0.52	0.78	0.86	0.90	0.92
2.5	1.70	0.44	1.91	0.57	3	0.125	0.25	0.34	0.44	0.53
5.0	2.45	0.19	3.02	0.33	5	0.045	0.10	0.15	0.23	0.31
10	2.92	0.04	4.01	0.11	7	0.02	0.05	0.08	0.12	0.20
15	3.01	....	4.34	....	10	.....	0.02	0.04	0.06	0.10
Inf	3.03	....	4.50							

* H is depth of cover over top of pipe, in feet.

water must be absorbed by or supplied by the elastic properties of the pipe and of the water. Such forces can be very great.[1]

The maximum internal bursting pressure produced in a conduit by water hammer can be expressed as

$$P = \frac{4,665WV}{144g} \sqrt{\frac{1}{1 + (Kd/Et)}} \qquad (10\text{-}9)$$

where P = water-hammer pressure above initial pressure, psi
W = weight of water per unit of volume, lb per cu ft
E = modulus of elasticity of the pipe material, psi
K = bulk modulus of elasticity of the fluid, 294,000 psi for water
d = diameter of pipe, in.
t = thickness of pipe shell, in.
g = acceleration of gravity, 32.2 ft per sec²

The velocity V_w at which the pressure wave travels through the pipe is

$$V_w = 4,665 \sqrt{\frac{1}{1 + (Kd/Et)}} \qquad (10\text{-}10)$$

Values of K/E for water and different pipe materials are given in Table 10-2.

If L is the length of the pipe from gate to point of relief, the time of closure of the gate must be less than or equal to $2L/V_w$ to develop maximum pressure.

An approximate value of the pressure rise that occurs when the actual time of closure T_a is greater than the critical time $T_c = 2L/V_w$ (greatest time that will produce maximum pressure rise) may be obtained by multiplying the maximum pressure rise from Eq. (10-9) by the ratio of T_c/T_a.

[1] See also C. Jaeger, *Civil Eng. (Br.)*, Vol. 43, February, May, 1948.

TABLE 10-2. Ratios of K/E in Eqs. (10-9) and (10-10)

Material	K/E
Plate steel.	0.01
Cast iron.	0.02–0.022
Concrete.	0.10
Wood.	0.20

The foregoing theory gives approximate values for single lines of pipe uncomplicated by interconnections with networks, branch pipes, dead ends, or multiple sources of input such as a combination of a pump and storage reservoir. A graphical solution for complex problems of water hammer has been developed by Angus.[1]

10-8. Causes and Prevention of Water Hammer.[2] Water hammer is frequently encountered in water-works practice. It may be caused by the quick opening or closing of valves or gates; the sudden starting, stopping, or variation in speed of pumps; breakage of pipe lines; and other conditions. Values for water hammer now used in practice[3] and the over-all factor of safety allowed provide for the occasional surge in excess of the working pressure for which the pipe is designed.

Some methods and devices used for the prevention or control of water hammer[4] include (1) relief valves, (2) air valves, (3) air chambers, (4) surge tanks or towers, (5) surge suppressors, (6) slowly closing valves, and (7) mechanically or spring-controlled valves or cushions.

Relief valves may be actuated by a slight change in pressure, of as little as 10 psi, to open wide in a few seconds to discharge water to waste if an increased pressure is to be relieved or to admit water or air if a decrease of pressure is to be relieved. Air-inlet valves are designed to open at a slight pressure below normal to admit air to avoid the creation of a partial vacuum. Closed air chambers may be used to relieve either a high pressure or a low pressure.[5] They are particularly useful near a valve or faucet on plumbing. Since closed air chambers must be filled with air at the time they are called on to function, the chamber should be set on a high point on the pipe line to permit the accumulation of air in the chamber.

A surge tower, in the form of an open tank "floating on the line," may be connected to a pipe line to take water from it or to deliver water to it as the conditions demand. The design of the capacity of such tanks is discussed in Sec. 10-9.

[1] See R. W. Angus, *Trans. Am. Soc. Civil Engrs.*, October, 1939, p. 340.

[2] See also: C. F. Lapworth, *Trans. Inst. Water Engrs.*, Vol. 49, p. 29, 1944; *Surveyor,* July 7, 1944, p. 321.

[3] See Standard Allowance for Water Hammer, *J.A.W.W.A.*, November, 1952, p. 977.

[4] See also R. Bennett, *Water & Sewage Works*, April, 1946, p. R-106; *ibid.*, April, 1951, p. 164.

[5] See also M. A. Libby, *Water & Sewage Works*, March, 1946, p. 98.

Surge suppressors are mechanical devices in which the energy of the surge or hammer is absorbed in springs, compressible fluids, such as air, or other suitable mediums, to be slowly returned to the water as the suppressor recovers from the shock. Suppressors are applicable particularly to small pipes and in plumbing, rather than to long lines in aqueducts.[1] The term suppressor is applied to other devices for the control of water hammer.

Water hammer resulting from the sudden cutting off of power from a pump may be diminished by increasing the inertia of the moving parts of the pump so that, acting as a flywheel, the pump is brought more slowly to a stop.[2] The use of check valves is discussed in Secs. 18-4 and 18-5. One type of valve designed to prevent water hammer is kept open by the velocity of the flowing water. When the velocity diminishes the valve closes before the direction of flow is reversed to build up the water pressure.

It is seldom that any two causes of water hammer are exactly alike. Each must be studied and one or more of the devices or methods available for its suppression must be used alone or in combination with others.

10-9. Surge-tower Design. Surge is a phenomenon closely related to water hammer, in which the force of the deceleration of the column of water in a pipe or conduit is expended in lifting a column of water in a surge tower. A method for the determination of the capacity of a surge tower and the rise and fall of water in it has been suggested by Halmos.[3] The following is an example of its application:

Example. Let it be desired to determine the rise of water level in the surge tower shown in Fig. 10-2 when the pump is suddenly stopped.

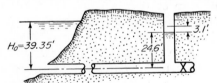

$H_0 = 39.35'$ $24.6'$ $3.1'$

FIG. 10-2. Surge tower on intake line.

Data. Length of conduit = 4,920 ft; velocity of flow in pipe line = 10.17 fps; velocity of pressure wave in conduit and in wet well computed from Eq. (10-10) = 2,950 fps; $A_a = A$.

Nomenclature

A = cross-sectional area
A_a = cross-sectional area of tunnel
A_b = cross-sectional area of surge tower
a = velocity of pressure wave

[1] See also J. M. White, *Water Works Eng.*, Mar. 25, 1942, p. 304.

[2] See also C. F. Lapworth, *J.A.W.W.A.*, October, 1945, p. 1036.

[3] E. E. Halmos, Symposium on Water Hammer, published jointly by the American Society of Civil Engineers and the American Society of Mechanical Engineers, 1933.

C = coefficient of discharge of opening into surge tower
g = acceleration due to gravity
H = head
H_b = head at base of surge tower
H_o = static head
L = length of pipe line
T = time of closing of valve or stopping of pump
V = linear velocity of water
μ_a = period of conduit = $2L/a$ = period of surge tower

Solution. 1. Determine H_b, where A_b = zero. The highest possible pressure, without a surge tower, is equal to $2K_aH_o$ where

$$K_a = aV/2gH_o = 2{,}950 \times 10.17/64.4 \times 39.35 = 11.85$$

Hence $H_b = 2 \times 11.85 \times 39.35 = 933.5$ ft.

2. Compute H_b where $A_a = A_b$. Under these conditions

$$H_b = \frac{(2K_aH_o)(A_b)}{(A_a + A_b)}$$

Hence
$$H_b = \frac{933.5 \times 1}{2} = 466.7 \text{ ft}$$

Because of the time required to close the valve, and because of the cushioning effect of the surge tower, the pressure rise will be less than that shown above. Under this condition

$$H_b = \frac{K_aH_oA_b\mu_b}{TA_a} + H_o$$

In this case $\mu_b = 2 \times 24.6/2{,}950 = 0.0167$. Then

$$H_b = 11.85 \times 39.35 \times 1 \times \frac{0.0167}{2.5} \times 1 = 3.12 + 39.35 \text{ ft}$$

where
$$T = 2.5 \text{ sec}$$

Enger[1] states that

$$H = \frac{aV}{g} - B_r{}^2 \left[\sqrt{\left(\frac{H_og^2}{B_r{}^2A^2} + \frac{Vg}{B_r{}^2a} + \frac{1}{4} \right)} - \frac{1}{2} \right] \qquad (10\text{-}11)$$

in which
$$B_r = \frac{CA_b}{A_a} \sqrt{2g}$$

---

[1] M. L. Enger, Symposium on Water Hammer, published jointly by the American Society of Civil Engineers and the American Society of Mechanical Engineers, 1933.

CHAPTER 11

IMPOUNDING RESERVOIRS

11-1. Function. An impounding reservoir is a basin constructed in the valley of a stream to store water during excess stream flow and to supply water when the flow of the stream is insufficient to meet the demand for water.

11-2. Site Characteristics. Certain site characteristics are desirable for an impounding reservoir. These, with the favorable features of each, are:

1. Geology
   a. Surface or immediately underlying soil or rock of such composition and structure that it will offer high resistance to the percolation of water through it
   b. The absence of objectionable soluble minerals or salts which would affect the quality of the stored water
2. Topography
   a. A narrow opening of the valley to reduce the length of the dam
   b. A rapid widening of the valley above the dam site to afford greater average volume per foot of height and length of dam
   c. Steep side slopes throughout the basin to reduce surface area per unit of volume so that undesirable shallow water and surface evaporation may be minimized
3. Real estate
   a. Inexpensive land to be submerged
   b. Absence of railways, highways, and water-power developments which might be submerged or injured
4. Cultural
   a. Freedom from trees and underbrush which may have to be removed
   b. Absence of objectionable vegetation and marshy land which might impart objectionable odor, color, or taste to the stored water

The selection of a site for an impounding reservoir is predicated on the fact that the yield of the stream will serve the intended purpose. Reservoirs possessing all the characteristics listed above are rarely found. It may be possible to remedy defects in a reservoir site by artificial means. This may be done, for example, by the use of cutoff walls and clay puddle or clay blankets at the dam site, or pressure grouting may be used to improve the dam foundation. Shore lines may be steepened by excavation and backfilling, and unsuitable material may be removed from the reservoir site or from the watershed.

Other features of reservoir sites, the maintenance of reservoirs, and their various uses are discussed in Sec. 23-5.

11-3. Preparation of Site.[1] The storage of water in contact with vegetation or decaying organic matter may be undesirable. Vegetation is removed from reservoir sites by cutting down and removing trees and undergrowth and by burning grass and weeds. Swampy areas are sometimes drained, scooped out, or filled in. In scooping, depressions in which organisms may grow should not be left in the reservoir. It may be considered necessary to remove highly organic surface soil such as peat, cultivated land, or boggy muck. Some authorities consider it desirable to strip all reservoir sites in this thorough manner, but the expense is usually a deterrent to the practice. Shallow areas should be avoided, as they are conducive to the growth of weeds and aquatic plants.

Experience shows[2] that the stripping of a reservoir site is an expedient which will obviate difficulties when the reservoir is first put in service, but in time there is little difference between a stripped and an unstripped reservoir. In general, the stripping of reservoir sites is not to be recommended because of the expense, which is not commensurate with the results. Trees, shrubs, and undergrowth which may protrude above the surface of the water at any stage should be removed. Human habitations, stables, barns, and other possible sources of pollution should be removed.

11-4. Storage Capacity Required.[3] The basic information needed to determine the required capacity of an impounding reservoir is a hydrograph of the flow of the stream for the longest and driest period known or predicted, and data on probable demand for water during that period. In some cases the storage requirements may be computed for the 95 per cent or the 98 per cent dry years. These are the years of such dryness that 5 per cent, or 2 per cent, respectively, of the years in a record of runoff are drier. With this information available the first step in the determination of the requisite capacity of an impounding reservoir is to construct a mass diagram of the flow of the stream. This is a curve whose abscissas are time and whose ordinates are total flow from the start of observations to the time observed. The information may be taken from a hydrograph such as shown in Fig. 11-1.

In the construction of a mass diagram, the length of any ordinate, such as *ab* or *cd*, is proportional to the area under the hydrograph and to the left of the ordinate extended. If the rate of demand is constant so that

[1] See also Allen Hazen and G. C. Whipple, *Eng. News*, Vol. 73, p. 858, 1915.

[2] See also *J.A.W.W.A.*, 1908, p. 195.

[3] See also C. S. Mallwood, Jr., *J.A.W.W.A.*, March, 1954, p. 251.

it can be represented by a horizontal line *ef* on the hydrograph, the mass diagram can be drawn as a straight line 0*g*.

Now draw lines parallel to 0*g* and tangent to the mass diagram of supply, as *hj*, *kl*, *mn*, and *pq*. The greatest vertical distance between tangents in a pair, when measured to the scale of the ordinates of the mass diagram, represents the requisite capacity of the impounding reservoir.

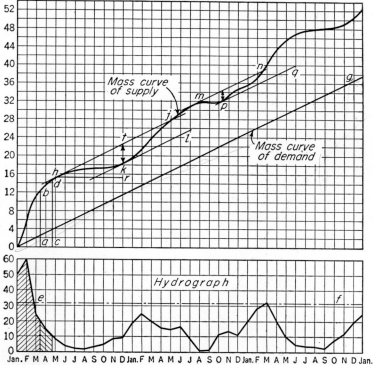

Fig. 11-1. Hydrograph and mass diagram for an impounding reservoir.

That the vertical distance between tangents in any pair represents the deficit of supply over demand for the particular deficit represented can be proved as follows:

At the point *h*, draw a horizontal line *hr*. At the point of tangency *k*, erect a vertical line *rkt*. The scalar distance *rt* represents the accumulated demand from the point *h*. The scalar distance *rk* represents the accumulated supply from the point *h*. The scalar distance *kt*, therefore, represents the accumulated deficit. Any other accumulated deficit from *h* to *j* will be less than *kt*. Hence, *kt* represents the requisite capacity of the impounding reservoir to supply the deficit during the period *h* to *j*.

Other information supplied by the mass diagram includes (1) the dates that the reservoir is full, points *h* and *m*; (2) the dates that the reservoir is empty, points k and p; (3) if the flow of the stream is insufficient to fill the reservoir, tangents to low points, such as kl and pq, if extended to the left will not intersect the mass diagram, and no reservoir can be constructed large enough to supply the deficit in the flow of the stream.

In the event that the rate of demand is not constant, the procedure should be to draw both the mass diagram of demand and the mass dia- gram of supply, as wavy curves. Then construct a third curve whose

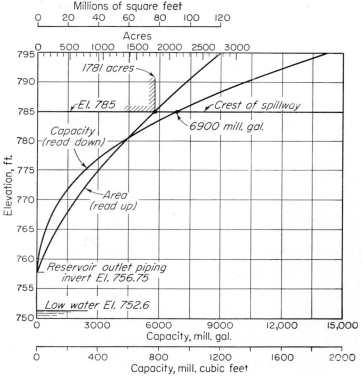

Fig. 11-2. Area and capacity curves, Geist Reservoir. (*From J.A.W.W.A., December, 1945, p. 1325.*)

abscissas are the same as for the other two curves and whose ordinates represent the difference between the two mass diagrams. If horizontal lines are drawn tangent to this third curve, the scalar distances between tangents in a pair of tangents will have a significance corresponding to the scalar distances between the sloping tangents where the rate of demand is constant. Other information can be obtained from this curve similar to that obtainable from the sloping tangents.

A storage curve, such as the curves shown in Fig. 11-2, may be constructed from the information obtained from the mass diagram. The storage curve shows graphically the volume of storage required for various conditions of stream flow.

11-5. Losses from Reservoirs. Evaporation, seepage, and compensation water represent losses from the stream and reservoir that may be considered as negative increments of stream flow. Compensation water is water that must be passed downstream from the dam to compensate water rights of persons below the reservoir. These increments may, at times, be greater than the flow of the stream so that it is possible for a mass diagram of supply, with allowance for losses, to have a negative slope. Another loss of capacity experienced by impounding reservoirs results from the partial filling of the reservoir by silt. This loss does not appear on the mass diagrams.

11-6. Measurement of Capacity. The volume of water that can be held in an impounding reservoir can be approximately determined by multiplying average surface areas between contours by the contour interval, or the prismoidal formula may be used, in which

$$V = \frac{h}{6}(A_1 + 4A_2 + A_3) \tag{11-1}$$

where V = volume between contours, corresponding to surface areas A_1 and A_3

A_1, A_2, A_3 = respective areas enclosed within a lower, a median, and an upper contour, where the contour interval is h

The summation of separate volumes determines the total volume. The capacity of the reservoir is usually expressed in gallons, cubic feet, or acre-feet, depending on local usage.

Curves showing the relation between depth and capacity, and depth and area of water surface, are known, respectively, as capacity and as area curves. Such curves for the Geist Reservoir at Indianapolis, Ind., are shown in Fig. 11-2.

11-7. The Elevation of the Spillway Crest. The elevation of the spillway crest is fixed by the depth necessary to give the requisite capacity and by the discharge capacity of the spillway to prevent the flooding of valuable property adjacent to the reservoir. An overflow spillway with a long crest, a siphon-shaft spillway, or controlled spillways will permit higher crest elevations and greater reservoir capacity without raising the maximum permissible water-surface elevation in the reservoir. Such spillways are costly, however, and their cost must be balanced against the value of the property protected.

11-8. Silting of Reservoirs. Loss of capacity of an impounding reservoir due to the deposition of silt in the reservoir may impair, if not destroy, the usefulness of the reservoir in a few years. Annual losses up to 7.34 per cent of capacity are reported by Brown[1] in New Lake Austin on

---

[1] C. B. Brown, *U.S. Dept. Agr., Misc. Publ.* 521, August, 1943, with bibliography; H. E. Hudson, Jr., and others, *J.A.W.W.A.*, October, 1949, p. 913.

the Colorado River at Austin, Tex.   Witzig[1] has formulated the silt-carry-ing capacity of streams as $G_s = C_s Q^x$, where G_s is the suspended sediment carried in the stream, in tons per second; C_s is a coefficient; Q is the rate of discharge of the stream, in cfs; and x is an exponent.   Although quite inaccurate, the formula may be useful in estimating the quantities of silt delivered to a reservoir, where values of C_s and of x have been determined by observation.   Witzig reports values of C_s of the order of 9.5×10^{-9} to 2.55×10^{-12}, and values of x from 1.78 to 2.77.   The average annual suspended silt load can be computed by a combination of the "silt-rating curve," as expressed by the above formula, and the discharge-frequency curve.   Silt-bearing water does not always discharge its silt in the reser-voir.   Because of greater specific gravity and lower temperature, it may pass through the reservoir as an underflow and be discharged over the dam with its burden of silt.   Such underflows are called "density flows." They have been experienced in many large reservoirs.[2]   If their control were understood the silting problem might be less of a menace.   One method of control might be to release silt-bearing waters before their silt is deposited.   Desilting works consisting of mechanically cleaned sedi-mentation basins may remove silt from water before it enters the reservoir.

After silt has been deposited in a reservoir there are no practicable methods, widely applicable, for removing it other than to operate gates in the dam to flush out the silt at times of high stream flow.   Dredging is expensive, and the disposal of the dredged material presents a serious problem.   The opening of sluices in the dam near the bottom of the reservoir is ineffective, as a negligible portion of the silt will be moved. Silting must be avoided; it is cured only infrequently.   It may be avoided by site selection, erosion control, and desilting works.   The reservoir site may be chosen on a non-silt-bearing stream, or the reservoir may be located in a basin off the main channel so that heavily silt-laden waters may be by-passed around the basin.   Reservoirs should be located on the smallest possible drainage areas, because it has been shown that the rate of silting increases directly as the ratio of drainage area to reser-voir capacity.   Witzig recommends a reservoir capacity of at least 75 acre-ft storage per sq mile of drainage area for 100-year life of typical reservoirs in Eastern United States, and Brown recommends a minimum of 25 acre-ft per sq mile in Texas.

11-9. Erosion Control.   Soil erosion and control are closely knit to the silting of reservoirs[3] since, without erosion[4] there would be no silting.

---

[1] B. J. Witzig, *Trans. Am. Soc. Civil Engrs.*, Vol. 109, p. 1047, 1944, with bibliography.

[2] See also *Eng. News-Record*, Dec. 17, 1953.

[3] See also: J. S. Longwell, *J.A.W.W.A.*, October, 1946, p. 1125; C. B. Brown, *ibid.*, p. 1127.

[4] See Task Group Report, *J.A.W.W.A.*, August, 1953, p. 790.

Erosion-prevention methods recommended for soil conservation include proper crop rotation, plowing on contours, terracing, strip cropping, protected drainage channels, check dams, reforestation and fire control, and grazing control.

11-10. Reservoir Problems. Among a few reservoir problems may be included (1) the effect of the reservoir on public health in the region,[1] (2) the area of land to be flooded, (3) the type and capacity of the spillway, and (4) the routing of floods through the reservoir. Problems affecting the health of the public may include (1) malaria control resulting from increased mosquito breeding, (2) recreational problems resulting from increased water surface, (3) fishing and hunting, (4) food supplies and agriculture, (5) industrial developments, (6) safety, and (7) drainage. In general, it is desirable to avoid shallow water and to avoid alternately exposing and inundating large areas along the shore. Steep-sided reservoirs are, therefore, ideal but are not always obtainable.

11-11. Routing of Floods.[2] By the routing of a flood through a reservoir is meant the determination of the rise of elevation of the water surface in respect to time. Posey suggests the following method:

Select a small increment of time t of such duration that the inflow may be assumed to be constant. Satisfactory accuracy may be obtained if there are 15 or 20 steps or increments during the time of a single flood peak.

Now if S_1 = storage in reservoir at beginning of time t

$\qquad S_2$ = storage in reservoir at end of time t

$\qquad i$ = average rate of inflow

Then
$$S_1 + it = S_2 + ot$$

and
$$it + \left(S_1 - \frac{o_1 t}{2} \right) = \left(S_2 + \frac{o_2 t}{2} \right)$$

where o_1 is the outflow corresponding to S_1, and o_2 is the outflow corresponding to S_2.

A timesaving computer for the solution of reservoir problems is described by Shepley and Walton.[3]

From these formulas, together with a depth-capacity curve and the calibration of the spillway, a time–surface-elevation curve can be plotted for the routing of a flood peak through a reservoir.

[1] See also S. L. Jones and Abel Wolman, *J.A.W.W.A.*, April, 1945, p. 327.

[2] See also C. J. Posey, *Bull. Assoc. State Eng. Socs.*, October, 1938, p. 155.

[3] *Civil Eng.*, March, 1942, p. 154.

CHAPTER 12

PUMPING STATIONS

12-1. Buildings.[1] The architecture and surroundings of a water-works pumping station can be made as attractive as desired, and the station can be operated without nuisance to the neighborhood. A building of attractive exterior and interior design, with the grounds attractively landscaped and well maintained, to which the public is made welcome,[2] will gain

Fig. 12-1. Thomas Jefferson Pumping Station, Evanston, Ill. (*Courtesy of L. D. Gayton.*)

public esteem, confidence, and good will. Fireproof materials should be used throughout the structure. An attractive pumping station at Evanston, Ill., is illustrated in Fig. 12-1. Possibilities for growth and expansion must be considered in the original design.

The design of the interior of the building includes consideration of such factors as space requirements for each piece of equipment; the proper location of the equipment; heating, lighting, ventilation, and drainage of

[1] See also Tentative Manual of Safe Practice in Water Distribution, *J.A.W.W.A.*, June, 1942, pp. 917, 926.

[2] With proper security measures.

the building; and the interior decoration. Space requirements of equipment must be determined from the design of the equipment or, in the case of "stock" equipment, from catalogue descriptions or similar information. The net space requirements will be determined in this manner. The total space allowed should provide for accessibility and convenience. Convenient interior arrangements of two pumping stations are shown in Figs. 12-2 and 12-3. Equipment placed in a small, dark, unpleasant location is more easily neglected than equipment accessible for observation, operation, and repairs. The location of a piece of equipment is

FIG. 12-2. Interior of pumping station at Moline, Ill. Designed by Beling Engineering Consultants. Four high-lift pumps are driven by 350-hp electric motors. Two units, in background of picture, are connected to 425-hp gasoline engines. Emergency gasoline-powered electric generator for small motors and for lighting stands in front of control panel.

more directly affected by the requirement of accessibility and convenience than it is by space requirements. Equipment should be located so as to provide short, well-laid-out steam piping, electric wiring, belt connections, or other methods of power transmission. Each piece of equipment should be accessible to an overhead crane or located so that it can be removed or replaced without disturbing other pieces of equipment.

Provision should be made for adequate heating for the comfort of the operators and for the safety of the equipment. The ventilation and lighting of all parts of the building should be generous so as to assure that no equipment will be neglected, to serve as an incentive to careful operation, and to create pride on the part of the operators in the appearance and maintenance of the equipment. A dark, dusty, gas-filled boiler room, or a damp, poorly lighted, noisy engine or pump room is unnecessary

and avoidable.   Plumbing in washrooms must be located and installed
to avoid possibilities of contamination of the public water supply.   All
surface drainage must be led away from the water intake or wet well.

The interior decoration should be simple, light-colored, and dignified,
in keeping with the important nature of the service being rendered.
Interior walls of white or light-colored glazed tile with dull colored floors
of tile or other ceramic or nonabsorbent material are frequently used and
are satisfactory.

Fig. 12-3. Pump room, Nottingham Filtration Plant, Cleveland, Ohio.   (*Courtesy of De Laval Steam Turbine Company.*)

12-2. Location.   Conditions to be considered in the location of a water-
works pumping station include (1) sanitary protection of the quality of
the water; (2) the hydraulics of the distribution system; (3) possibilities
of interruption by fire, flood, or other disaster; (4) the availability of
power or of fuel; (5) growth and expansion; and (6) the attitude of the
neighboring property owners.   Floods offer a hazard which may be
minimized by favorable location.   To obtain the greatest hydraulic
advantage the station should be located near the middle of the distribution system.   The danger of interruption of service by fire in the immediate neighborhood of the pumping station should be considered and a site

chosen to avoid or minimize this hazard. Where it is impossible to find such a protected site, the station should be protected by fire walls, fire-proofing, and a sprinkler system.

The use of electricity permits the location of the pumping station at any desired site insofar as electric power is concerned. If coal is to be used, the station should be located where coal can be easily transported to it. In general, pumping stations located in residential districts should be operated by electricity as it is difficult and expensive to suppress all the nuisances connected with the operation of a steam plant.

There should be no reasonable objection to the location of a water-works pumping station in any district, provided that pleasing architecture and the proper operation of the station are assured.

12-3. Choice of Power. Steam, electricity, water, wind, and fuels consumed within the engine are all used in driving pumping engines. Steam, electricity, and internally consumed fuels are commonly used in pumping public water supplies. The type of power selected should be the most reliable, the most available, and the least expensive. If all three conditions cannot be fulfilled they should be rated in the order stated, with the greatest reliability as the most important. "All main pumping stations should be provided with auxiliary sources of power source. . . ."[1]

The design of large pumping stations usually leads to the selection of steam power generated and applied at the pumping station. However, few steam water-works pumping stations have been built in the decade previous to 1950, and old steam plants are being converted to electric power transmitted to the pumping station. Electric power, which is not a prime mover, is commonly purchased from a utility supplying power to the region over interlocking electrical distribution systems that guarantee a high factor of safety for an uninterrupted supply of power. Neverthe-less, the availability of an independent source of power, such as diesel engines or other internal-combustion engines, is essential to good design. The use of electric power is advantageous for many reasons, among them being its low cost, reliability, and wide availability; the low load factor created by water works; the efficiency of electrically driven centrifugal pumps; and the possibility of labor savings with electric equipment, sometimes automatically controlled.

In cities under 50,000 to 100,000 population, and for auxiliary pumping stations in large cities, electrically driven pumps are frequently installed. The centralization of the generation of electric power is resulting in the availability of current at a low price—less than 1 cent per kilowatthour in some localities. Another saving in electrically driven equipment is the reduction in first cost compared with steam power, the fixed charges

---

[1] From Tentative Manual of Safe Practice in Water Distribution, *op. cit.*, pp. 917, 927.

thus being reduced compared with those required for the equipment and buildings needed for steam-power generation and application.

12-4. Classification of Pumps. Pumps may be classified as steam, electrical, water power, wind power, etc., in accordance with the kind of power used to actuate them. They may be classified as well pumps, low-service pumps, high-service pumps, etc., in accordance with the kind of service to which they are to be put. Low-service pumps discharge under relatively low pressures, and high-service pumps discharge under high pressures. Pumps may be classified also as displacement, centrifugal, impulse, or bucket pumps, in accordance with the mechanical principles of their operation.

12-5. Capacity of Pumps. A water-works pumping station should be designed to supply the peak demand without dangerously overloading the power and pumping equipment. It is not necessary that the pumping-station equipment should carry the peak demand at rated capacity. Practically all types of power and equipment will operate successfully for various periods of time under some overload. The percentage of over-load, the period of time this overload can be carried, and the rated capacity of the unit depend on the type of equipment. For example, a water-tube steam boiler may stand 250 per cent overload indefinitely with proper coal-burning equipment, but most types of electric motors would fail under half such a percentage of overload.

The highest efficiency and the greatest economy of operation require that the total load on all the units in the pumping station should be divided among them in such a manner that each can operate at its rated capacity. The operation of a pump or engine at other than rated capacity may be uneconomical because of the lower efficiency of the machine at other than full-load conditions.[1] Units are available that will operate efficiently when either underloaded or overloaded.

If electrical equipment is used in the pumping station and electric current is manufactured by the city, then sufficient capacity must be provided in the power plant to operate the pumps in an emergency and at their maximum capacity. The maintenance and fixed charges on this additional equipment are items properly charged to the water works. If electrical power is purchased from an independent manufacturer, such fixed charges are avoided, but the power company may be justified in levying a charge for readiness to serve if excess current is quickly available, whether or not such current is used. The ready-to-serve charge may be minimized or avoided by arranging a proper operation schedule for the pumping station so that much of the pumping can be done during off-peak periods of power requirements. Such off-peak pumping can be accomplished through the installation of reservoirs on the distribution system to supply the demand for water when the demand for electricity is high.

[1] See also E. R. Tull, *J.A.W.W.A.*, April, 1935, p. 454.

"Pumping station units and auxiliary equipment should be of ample capacity and in sufficient numbers of units to permit at least one unit being out for repairs without seriously reducing the station capacity."[1]

12-6. Selection of Pumps. In the selection of water-works pumping equipment considerations of capacity, lift, reliability, and economy are paramount and should be rated in the order indicated. Additional factors include conditions of suction lift, variations in load, floor-space requirements, flexibility of operation, starting and priming characteristics, type of drive most suitable, and other factors.[2]

The centrifugal pump, because of its outstanding advantages, has almost entirely displaced other types of pumps in water-works practice. The crank-and-flywheel steam pumping engine, which reigned supreme at one time, has now definitely been displaced. The centrifugal pump most satisfactorily fills the requirements of water-works service.

Considerations of operating efficiency are important economically. For example, assume that $1,300 will buy a motor and a 1,500 gpm centrifugal pump with a total lift of 150 ft operating with 70 per cent load factor and an over-all efficiency of 75 per cent. If the cost of electric power is 0.45 cent per horsepower-hour, life is 15 years, and interest is 3.5 per cent, an increase of 2 per cent in the over-all efficiency will be worth $1,420, slightly more than the first cost of the equipment. It is a rule of thumb that one can afford to pay 10 to 15 per cent more on the first cost of high-lift pumps for each 1 per cent increase in efficiency of operation. Since power is so great an item of cost in the operation of a pump it is generally more economical to scrap pumps that are smaller than about 3 mgd if they are operated continuously and consume more than about 500 kwhr per million gallons pumped 100 ft high. Similarly, in the range of 6 to 10 mgd the power consumption should not exceed about 475 kwhr. Units of low efficiency may be held for stand-by or for peak-load service.

12-7. Piping. The layout of the piping in a pumping station may be as important as the efficiency of operation in affecting the economy of the pumping station. Short, straight, well-supported pipe lines, devoid of traps either for sediment or for gas, sloping in one direction to drains, and with adequate cleanouts and valves should be the object of the designer. Desirable velocities may be estimated from a study of Table 9-1, with the knowledge that the economical velocity in pipes used infrequently is higher than the figures in the table. A few details to be observed in making pipe connections to centrifugal pumps are: (1) The elbow on the

---

[1] From Tentative Manual of Safe Practice in Water Distribution, *op. cit.*, pp. 917, 922.

[2] See also: H. P. Binder, *Bull. Assoc. State Eng. Socs.*, July, 1934, p. 33; W. H. Maxwell, "Water Supply Problems and Developments," Sir Isaac Pitman & Sons, Ltd., London, 1934.

suction side of a double-suction pump should be normal to the suction nozzle, or a special elbow with guide vane followed by a piece of straight pipe to the suction nozzle should be used, to equalize the flow on each side of the impeller. (2) On the pump discharge, where change of direction is necessary, use a constant-diameter bend, followed by a long, straight reducer or increaser. Such an installation will most effectively interchange velocity and pressure heads. Eccentric reducers with the top of the pipe and the top of the reducer at the same level should be used in horizontal suction piping to avoid the creation of an air pocket. An increaser whose length is ten times the difference in diameters may be considered "long."

12-8. Surge Control. Surge or water hammer in pumping stations and pipe lines results from starting or stopping a pump or pumps, the sudden opening or closing of a valve, the formation of a vacuum in a pipe and its sudden release, and from other causes. The effect of the phenomenon of surge or water hammer is to produce pressures either above or below normal that may rupture the pipe or draw in pollution. Methods of control[1] are discussed in Sec. 10-8, and in addition they include the use of (1) a flywheel on the pump which, by adding inertia, slows its starting or stopping speed; (2) motor-driven valves that control the rate of moving the valve mechanism; (3) electrical resistances in starting mechanisms of motors, slowing the rate at which the motor may be accelerated or decelerated; (4) a pressure-relief valve; (5) a surge suppressor, similar to the pressure-relief valve, except that the valve is opened by a partial vacuum instead of by a plenum; (6) an air chamber; (7) a surge tank, and (8) a surge buffer which consists of a closed vessel with an air valve on top. The vessel is normally filled with water. When a pressure below atmospheric is experienced, the air valve opens and admits air which acts as a cushion on the arrival of a pressure wave. When normal conditions are restored, the air is allowed to escape from the vessel which refills with water.

12-9. Suction Lift.[2] Suction lift should be avoided insofar as it is possible, by installing the pump either in a wet well or in a dry well below the level of the water in the intake. The location of pumps in inaccessible pits or dry wells subject to inundation is objectionable for reasons of sanitation and maintenance. Motors driving the pumps should be located above the water level in the intake.

Where suction lift cannot be avoided, provisions should be made for priming the pumps, or vacuum pumps may be installed to exhaust air from the suction lines. Care should be taken to assure the use of only potable water for priming.

---

[1] See also C. F. Lapworth, *J.A.W.W.A.*, October, 1945, p. 1036.

[2] See also Tentative Manual of Safe Practice in Water Distribution, *op. cit.*, pp. 917, 925.

Suction lines should be made as short and as straight as possible with a continuous upward slope from the foot valve to the pump in order to avoid air pockets. To minimize suction lift it is customary to design the suction pipe larger than the discharge pipe on the pump.

The height to which water can be raised by suction is limited by the pressure of the atmosphere, the temperature of the water, the velocity in the suction pipe, and the friction losses. It can be expressed as

$$\boxed{H} = A - (V_p + V_h + H_f)$$

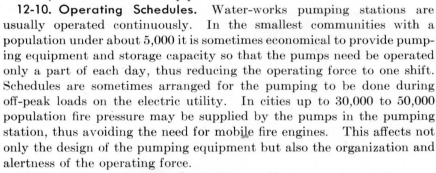

where H = suction lift

A = pressure of the atmosphere

V_p = vapor pressure of water

V_h = velocity head in suction line

H_f = friction losses in pipe

12-10. Operating Schedules. Water-works pumping stations are usually operated continuously. In the smallest communities with a population under about 5,000 it is sometimes economical to provide pumping equipment and storage capacity so that the pumps need be operated only a part of each day, thus reducing the operating force to one shift. Schedules are sometimes arranged for the pumping to be done during off-peak loads on the electric utility. In cities up to 30,000 to 50,000 population fire pressure may be supplied by the pumps in the pumping station, thus avoiding the need for mobile fire engines. This affects not only the design of the pumping equipment but also the organization and alertness of the operating force.

12-11. Auxiliary Pumping Stations. Auxiliary pumping stations are sometimes installed on large distribution systems to increase the pressure which otherwise might be too low. Low pressures in a district may be caused by inadequate sizes of pipe; a large local usage, as in an industrial region; or a high elevation above the main pumping station. Auxiliary pumping stations are sometimes equipped with automatically operated devices which may be remotely controlled at a central pumping station. Steam power is not suited to automatic control. An automatically controlled internal-combustion engine should not be left operating without attention. Electric motors and equipment are most suitable for unattended operation or remote control. Automatic or remote control is convenient, and it may be economical. No full-time operator is needed at the auxiliary station where electric equipment is installed. Daily or more frequent visits are desirable, however, and dependence on automatic apparatus may result in costly breakdowns due to neglect, improper lubrication, or other causes.

12-12. The Cost of Water and of Pumping. The cost of water is markedly different in different communities because of the various conditions under which it must be obtained. The least expensive supply is a potable surface supply which can be distributed without pumping and is available near the community. Ground waters at a remote distance, requiring purification, are among the most costly. Costs may be expected to lie between 5 and 30 to 40 cents per 1,000 gal delivered to the consumer. Capen[1] reports costs in 31 municipalities in New Jersey as between 7 and 30.5 cents per 1,000 gal, with an average of 11.35 cents.

The cost of pumping includes interest and depreciation on the building and equipment, sometimes called fixed charges; and the wages of labor, the cost of power, insurance, and taxes, sometimes called the operating charges. In addition to these items the cost will be affected by the efficiency of the pumps and the rate of interest allowed in amortizing the plant. For comparative purposes the cost should be expressed in cents per million gallons raised 1 ft. In practice it is customary to express the cost of water in cents per thousand gallons, regardless of the lift.

12-13. Maintenance of Pumping Equipment. Some basic principles in equipment maintenance[2] that may affect the selection of pumping equipment and avoid difficulties in operation include:

1. Investigate equipment for any unusual sound, change in appearance, or change in temperature.
2. Keep equipment clean.
3. Protect equipment against unfavorable external conditions.
4. Avoid excessive heat in surroundings, detrimental to equipment.
5. Minimize vibrations.
6. Lubricate.
7. Check excessive wear.
8. Make periodic checks and tests on a routine schedule.

12-14. Check List of Design Items. Some considerations in the design of a pumping station and the selection of equipment are:

1. *Load on the Pumping Station.* Data should include an analysis of the average, the maximum, and the minimum rates of pumping, possibly with hypothetical hydrographs on average and on critical days to be expected immediately and in the future.

2. *Lift.* Information should be available concerning the suction and discharge lifts, and the total lifts to be expected under different conditions and at various pumping rates. Such a study may be relatively extensive.

3. *Power Requirements.* Power requirements represent the product of loads and lifts under normal and under critical conditions.

4. *Location.* The topography, the surrounding district, the immediate neighborhood, and potential hazards such as fire, flood, wind, earthquake, and other disaster may affect the selection of the site and the character of the building and its equipment.

---

[1] C. H. Capen, *J.A.W.W.A.*, July, 1946, p. 846.
[2] See also H. O. Hartung and W. V. Weir, *J.A.W.W.A.*, August, 1946, p. 930.

5. *Power*. If electric power is to be purchased the nature of this power should be known. This includes cycle, phase, voltage, load limitations, permissible peak and ordinary loads, power factor, reliability, demand charge, and any other rate considerations.

6. *Auxiliary Power Sources*. What conditions demand auxiliary power units, and what type of power is to be selected.

7. *Types of Pumps*. Although centrifugal pumps are used almost exclusively, some consideration may be given to others.

8. *Centrifugal Pumps*. Type to be adopted and why. Number and size of units. Other conditions considered include horizontal or vertical shaft, single or double suction, number of stages, number of impellers, characteristics, speed, specific speed, cavitation.

9. *Pump Setting*. Wet or dry well; suction lift; access; illumination and ventilation.

10. *Wet or Dry Well*. Design, capacity, control, access, cleaning, drainage, overflow, illumination, and ventilation.

11. *Electric Motors*. Type, speed, power and overload characteristics; speed regulation and speed control; starting and operating current; efficiency with and without pump load.

12. *Piping and Valves*. Over-all economy; accessibility for operation and repairs; support; slopes; drainage; water hammer; insulation; condensation; color scheme; method of valve operation, manual, power, or remote-control, etc.; dangers of incorrect operation, *e.g.*, closing of gate valve on discharge line from a displacement pump; sizes should be standard; avoid air locks.

CHAPTER 13

ELECTRICAL EQUIPMENT

13-1. Equipment and Standards.[1] In the design of a water-works pumping station in which electric power is to be used, provision must be made for receiving, conveying, and utilizing the current. This involves such equipment as transformers, switchboards, motors, circuit breakers, relays, and safety devices. Knowledge of the nature of electric circuits is necessary in the application of such equipment. Valuable information in this field will be found in "National Electric Code Handbook" by A. L. Abbott (7th ed., McGraw-Hill Book Company, Inc., New York, 1952); "American Electricians' Handbook" by T. Croft and C. C. Carr (7th ed., McGraw-Hill Book Company, Inc., New York, 1953); and "Standard Handbook for Electrical Engineers" by A. E. Knowlton (8th ed., McGraw-Hill Book Company, Inc., New York, 1949).

Comprehensive standards of electrical equipment and methods of installation, approved by the National Board of Fire Underwriters and by the American Standards Association, were published in 1940, with subsequent supplements. These standards should serve as a guide in the design, purchase, and installation of electric equipment.

13-2. Electric Current. The type of electrical equipment used must be suited to the type of electric current available. Very little electric power equipment is interchangeable between types of electric current, and the pumping-station design is commonly limited to the kind of current available on the wires of the public-service company. Most power lines in the United States carry three-phase 60-cycle alternating current. In some communities, direct current and other combinations of phase and frequency in alternating currents are available such as single-phase, two-phase, 25-cycle, and 50-cycle currents. Advantages of alternating current include lower first cost and lower maintenance cost of induction equipment as compared with d-c equipment, and the ability to step the voltage up or down by the use of transformers.

Direct current is more costly in transmission and application because of the larger conductors needed and because of the greater first cost and

[1] See also N. L. Hadley and E. O. Potthoff, *Water Works Eng.*, September, 1952, p. 957.

maintenance cost of d-c motors. Direct-current wiring may be more simple than the wiring for polyphase alternating current; motors, batteries, and electrolytic equipment can be on the same circuit; the use of direct current allows better control of motor speeds; there is unit power factor under all conditions; and in certain applications, such as in electromagnetic devices, in starting synchronous motors, and in battery charging, its use may be either desirable or necessary. Where only alternating current is available, direct current can be produced in the pumping station by motor generators or current rectifiers.

In general, polyphase alternating current is used almost exclusively in water-works pumping stations because of the availability of simple, rugged, low-cost, constant-speed polyphase motors. Such motors can be operated at higher voltages than if direct current is used, thus decreasing the cost of the machine. Where electric current is generated within the pumping station and there are few motors or where the motors are to be operated at variable speed, the use of direct current may be advantageous.

13-3. Voltages. The voltages used in the transmission of electric power may be much higher than the voltage at which power is delivered in the pumping station. In general, it may be expected that the highest voltage coming into a pumping station will not exceed 13,800 volts; usually it is not over 2,200 volts. Such voltage can be stepped down by transformers to the standards for various applications shown in Table 13-1.

TABLE 13-1. Standard* Voltages Used for Pumping Equipment in Water-works Pumping Stations

D-c voltage	Uses	A-c voltage	Uses
110	Lighting, motors	110	Lighting, small motors, small appliances
220	Motors-all other purposes	110–120	Lighting, small appliances
		220	Motors, electric ranges
550	Motors-all other purposes	440	Motors
		550	Motors
		2,220 4,000	Motors larger than 60–100 hp
		6,600 11,000 13,200	Distribution lines and, sometimes, large motors

* ASA, National Electrical Manufacturing Association, and AIEE Standards.

Conditions affecting the voltage to be used include first cost of equipment, cost of maintenance, and danger to personnel. The higher the voltage the lower the cost of copper but the greater the cost of insulation, and the greater the hazard to personnel. A 100-hp 110-volt motor will cost more than a 100-hp 550-volt motor. In general, no special hazard exists and no objections are offered by personnel when the voltages are 440 or less. At and below this voltage, the cost of the equipment and its installation will usually control in the selection of the voltages to be used in the pumping station.

13-4. Frequencies. That frequency should be selected which is most suitable for all purposes in the pumping station because the use of different frequencies on different equipment is impractical. Sixty cycles has been found most satisfactory because it avoids noticeable flickering of lamps, which occurs at 25 cycles, and most motors and other induction equipment can be manufactured at less cost at the higher frequency. However, on the basis of power utilization alone, particularly on slow-speed induction motors, the lower frequency is advantageous because of less inductive effect, greater simplicity in design, and the better power factor obtained. Sixty cycles is used almost universally throughout the United States.

13-5. Phases and Circuit. The number of phases and the type of circuit to be used are of importance in power transmission. They are therefore important in power utilization because equipment must be suited to the type of current utilized. Systems of transmission in use include those listed in Table 13-2, which includes also a summary of the relative advantages of the various circuits. More than three phases are not commonly transmitted on public-service power lines. Single-phase two-wire, single-phase three-wire, and three-phase three-wire circuits are in common use. The change of motors, and some other equipment, from single-phase to three-phase involves rewinding. However, it is possible, by the use of transformers, to interchange between two-phase and three-phase currents, and between three-wire and four-wire circuits.

13-6. Power Factor. Power factor is the ratio of real power to apparent power in an electric circuit, apparent power being the product of the volts and amperes, or watts. It is important both for economy and for operation of equipment to maintain the rated power factor on electric equipment. If electric current is purchased, the economy of power-factor correction depends principally on the power rate structure. The equipment of water works manufacturing their own electric power is generally based on an 0.8 lagging power factor. Correction is desirable if the factor drops below this to avoid undue voltage drop in feeders, excessive current losses, and reduction in generating-plant capacity.

13-7. Characteristics of Electric Motors. In the selection of an electric motor, conditions to be considered, in addition to the type of current and of circuit available, include (1) first cost and maintenance cost; (2) suitability for the character of work to be done; (3) speed, speed regulation, and speed control; (4) ease in starting; (5) starting current in terms of full-load current; (6) starting torque in terms of full-load torque; (7) power factor; (8) rated power; (9) partial load characteristics; and (10)

TABLE 13-2. Relative Advantages of Circuits and Phases of Electrical Systems

System	Relative weight of copper, based on carrying capacity	Remarks
Single-phase alternating-current or two-wire direct current ⊢—110 V—⊣	115	Most simple of all forms
Single-phase alternating-current or three-wire direct-current ⊢————220 V————⊣ ● 110 V ● 110 V ●	All wires same size 87 Neutral 0.7 outside wire 77.5	Allows use of two voltages
Two-phase alternating current three-wire ● 110 V 155 V ● 110 V ●	Common wire $\sqrt{2}$ × outside wire 97.5	More simple than four-wire circuit
Two-phase alternating current four-wire ◐ 110 V ● 110 V ● 110 V ●	115	Requires only two transformers, and two phases are insulated from each other, independent in operation
Three-phase alternating current three-wire ● 110 V 110 V ● 110 V ●	100	Voltages between lines are equal and all wires are same size. Simple compared with four-wire circuit
Three-phase alternating current four-wire ● 190 V 110 V 190 V 110 V ● 110 V ○ 190 V ●	All wires same size 77 Neutral 0.7 × outside wires: 71.5	Principal savings in copper

whether enclosed, semienclosed, or open. Some characteristics of the more common types of electric motors are listed in Table 13-3. Motors with other characteristics may be manufactured by special windings, usually at a higher cost than for standard-type motors.

13-8. Induction Motors. An induction motor is an a-c motor similar to a transformer in which the core and the secondary winding are free to move. Induction motors consist of two concentric masses of laminated iron in the form of short hollow cylinders, of which the outer, called the "stator," is fixed, and the inner, called the "rotor," revolves.

There are two types of induction motors: the wound rotor and the squirrel cage. Each receives its name from the construction of the rotor and the stator. Single-phase and polyphase motors resemble each other structurally, but the single-phase is heavier, more costly, less efficient, and more difficult to start and has a lower power factor. A slip-ring wound-rotor motor is an induction motor with the rotor winding brought out to slip rings so that resistance can be introduced into the rotor circuit.

TABLE 13-3. Electric-motor Characteristics

Type of motor	Characteristics, advantages, and applications
Shunt-wound, d-c.....................	*Starting current:** normally about 1.5 times full load. *Starting torque:* normally about 1.5 times full-load torque. *Maximum torque:* twice full-load torque. *Speed regulation:* about 10% variation between no load and full load. *Speed control:* adjustable by means of rheostat, varies not more than 10% for any adjustment. *Sizes available:* up to 200 hp. *Suitable for* frequent starting and stopping with light or medium starting loads, shop machinery, conveyors, fans, centrifugal pumps
Series-wound d-c.....................	*Starting current:* same as for shunt-wound motor. *Starting torque:* 4.5 times full load but normally 2.25 to 3.0 times full-load torque. *Maximum torque:* four times full-load torque. *Speed regulation:* poor, increases dangerously with decrease of load, may "run away." *Speed control* is same as shunt-wound motor. Sizes available from 3 to 200 hp. *Suitable for* load that cannot be removed from motor such as cranes, fans, and railways, and for frequent stopping and starting. Not suitable for centrifugal pumps
Compound-wound, d-c................	Characteristics lie between shunt-wound and series-wound and depend on the character of the windings

TABLE 13-3. Electric-motor Characteristics. (Continued)

Type of motor	*Characteristics, advantages, and applications*
Induction a-c, polyphase squirrel-cage...	*Starting current:* 5 to 10 times full-load current. For sizes above 5 hp requires special starting devices. Where frequent starting is necessary, sizes below 5 hp may require special starting windings, condensers, or other starting aids. *Starting torque:* low in terms of full load. *Maximum torque:* 2 to 2.5 times running torque. *Speed regulation:* good, may diminish 5% between start and full load. *Speed control:* none, runs only at designed speed. *Sizes available:* 0.1 to 400 hp. *Power factor:* for split-phase, induction: fractional hp = 0.55 to 0.75; 1 to 10 hp = 0.75 to 0.85; and condenser type = 0.75 to 1.0. Squirrel-cage polyphase = 0.75 to 0.90. *Suitable for* constant load and continuous operation, excellent for fans and centrifugal pumps
Repulsion-induction, single-phase a-c....	*Starting current:* 1.75 to 2.5 times full load. *Speed regulation and control* at no load is above synchronism; at full load it is similar to that of an induction motor. *Sizes available:* $\frac{1}{8}$ to 15 hp. *Suitable for* heavy starting loads or frequent starting and stopping
Synchronous, a-c......................	*Starting current:* 4 to 8 times full load. Hard to start. Field must be excited with direct current. *Starting torque:* very low. *Maximum torque:* 1.5 to 1.75 running torque. *Speed regulation:* perfect, no variation in speed under varying load. *Speed control:* none. *Sizes available:* 20 to 5,000 hp. *Power factor:* up to 1.0. *Suitable for* steady load and constant operation. Excellent for pumps. Improves power factor

* Starting currents in this list are stated as 75 to 100% of the blocked-rotor values. The free-rotor value may be taken as 75 per cent of the blocked-rotor value.

The wound-rotor motor is sometimes known as the phase-wound or slipping motor.

13-9. Squirrel-cage Motors. The characteristics shown in Table 13-3 for the squirrel-cage induction motor make it the most widely used type of motor for driving water-works pumps. Its low starting torque and high starting current do not prevent its use for centrifugal pumps because the pump may be started with the discharge valve closed to minimize the starting load. Special forms of windings may be used to improve the starting conditions and provide motors suitable for any pumping load.

Ruggedness of construction, simplicity of design, low first cost, low maintenance cost, and other desirable features combine to make the squirrel-cage motor suitable for a wide variety of applications. These motors can be modified to provide high starting torque and rapid acceleration, which makes them available for frequent starting and stopping. The first cost may be increased, however, the efficiency lowered, and speed variation during operation increased by such modifications. The provision of a flywheel to equalize momentary fluctuations of load may make possible the use of squirrel-cage motors under conditions not otherwise suitable. Another method of increasing the starting torque is to provide a double squirrel-cage winding. This will give a starting torque 2 to 2.5 times full-load torque with a slip of less than 5 per cent.

The efficiency of induction motors at full load ranges from about 85 per cent for small motors to 92 per cent for large machines. The power factor is relatively low, particularly when starting, and is always lagging.

13-10. Phase-wound, or Slip-ring, Motors. This type of motor is especially adapted for large starting torque and hand control of speed. The speed is controlled through a rheostat which introduces resistance into the secondary windings in much the same manner as the starting rheostat. These motors are used in sizes above 50 hp where a high starting torque is required. Wound-rotor motors using starting resistance have a power factor at start of 0.60 to 0.65.

13-11. Synchronous Motors. A synchronous motor is an a-c generator running as a motor with its armature supplied with alternating current and its field excited with direct current. These motors require frequent attention and must be carefully selected and operated to assure adequate starting, pull-in torque, and efficient operating conditions. Direct current must be available for starting, unless specially wound for alternating current. They have satisfactory operating characteristics for continuous operation under steady load, particularly in large installations. Their outstanding advantage is their improvement of the power factor which can be brought to unity on any line by adjusting the synchronous motor to lag or lead the necessary amount. Among the advantages of such motors claimed by Moore[1] are (1) availability at low speeds, (2) low maintenance costs due to simplicity of construction, (3) wide range of torques is available to permit starting under heavy loads, and (4) dynamic braking brings loads to a smooth quick stop.

The cost of a small synchronous motor, its d-c exciter, and its control may sometimes be greater than the cost of a squirrel-cage motor of equal power; but where operating conditions are suitable, the higher efficiency, the leading power factor, and the more attractive rates for power some-

[1] J. C. Moore, *Water & Sewage Works*, May, 1952, p. 187.

times offered by power companies make the installation of a synchronous motor desirable.

13-12. Starting Alternating-current Motors. It is desirable, but not always possible, to start a motor under full line current in order to avoid the need for special starting equipment or motor winding. It is usually safe to start induction motors of less than 5 hp by connecting the full line operating voltage to the motor. Although the momentary current may be large, the motor quickly accelerates, if not too heavily loaded, thus reducing the current passing through the windings before heating occurs. Reduced voltage required in starting induction motors may be obtained by placing adjustable resistances in the starting circuit, thus by-passing the operating fuse or protecting relay. As such arrangements require a large line current, an autotransformer, or "autostarter," arranged for automatic or manual starting may be used. For smaller full-voltage-starting induction motors, the simple magnetic starter, with overload and undervoltage protection, operated by a push button, is widely used.

Wound-rotor motors are protected in starting by inserting resistance into the rotor winding. A thermal relay, or fuse, and a line switch protect the stator current, the starting circuit being protected with fuses permitting a current of 50 per cent of full-load current. As the motor gains speed, the starting resistance is reduced and finally cut out.

The starting characteristics of synchronous motors are varied to suit the load, but under any conditions the starting of a synchronous motor is difficult. For this reason frequent starts and stops are undesirable. Such motors are usually made self-starting by providing the rotor with an induction winding which permits the starting of the motor as an induction motor with the starting torque adapted to the load. Under such conditions, however, the motor draws a heavier starting current than an induction motor of the same rating, so that the application of other expedients may be necessary to get the motor started.

The line current required to start a centrifugal pump connected to an electric motor can be minimized by starting with the pump discharge valve closed. Under such conditions the torque at full speed will be about two-thirds of that under full load when the valve has been opened.

Starting switches and push-button relays may be assembled on a switchboard or placed separately near the motor. Under the latter arrangement the starting switch and fuses should be enclosed in a metal box, the equipment being called a safety switch.

13-13. Motor Speeds. High-speed motors cost less than slow-speed machines because more power is delivered per unit weight of machine. The limit of speed is fixed by the strength and durability of the parts and by the possibility of applying the speed to the load. Slow-speed motors are used for machines that revolve slowly and that cannot be connected through belts or reduction gears. Most motors operate with the highest efficiency at their rated speed.   This is not true of series-wound motors, which operate equally well at almost any speed.   Only a limited number of speeds is available in standard induction motors.   On 60-cycle current synchronous speeds available are 1,800 and 1,200 rpm.

13-14. Variable Speeds.   Where an electric motor is used to drive a centrifugal pump, some method of varying the speed of the pump is desirable, for economical operation, unless the load on the pump is constant.   Other applications of electric motors may require speed control. This may be obtained through varying the speed of the motor, or through mechanical devices in the motor or between the motor and the pump.

13-15. Speed Control.   Speed control for d-c motors is usually secured by the use of a rheostat connected in either the field or the armature circuit, or one in each circuit.   Multiple-voltage speed control is usually secured through the use of two voltages on a three-wire system, thus making possible a slow speed that bears the same relation to the high speed as the lower voltage bears to the higher voltage on the three-wire circuit.   Intermediate speeds are secured through the use of field or armature rheostats.

In general, the ordinary squirrel-cage induction motor is not suitable for close speed control giving uniform gradations of speed between limits. Where a few definite speeds will be satisfactory a so-called "multispeed motor," running at two, three, or four different speeds, may be used.

Wound-rotor motors should be used where close speed control is desired on polyphase alternating current.   The speed of these motors can be controlled by placing variable resistance in the rotor circuit.   Difficulties with speed control of wound-rotor motors are low efficiencies and relatively poor speed regulation which affects the speed with change in load.

Polyphase induction motors of the commutator brush-shifting type permit uniform gradation of speed from 40 per cent above to 60 per cent below synchronous speed.   The polyphase induction motor, with commutator and brushes, will give any speed from 0 to 50 per cent above synchronous without the introduction of resistance losses.

A gear motor is any type of electric motor which has built into it a speed-reduction gear that will give various shaft speeds.

In general, the highest efficiency of an a-c motor is obtained when the speed is nearest synchronism, *i.e.*, with the least slip.

13-16. Speed-reducing Devices.   Since the speed of most electric motors is too high for direct connection to centrifugal pumps, some form of speed-reduction device, other than variable-speed motors, may be used. Among these devices may be included (1) gear trains, (2) belts and pulleys, (3) hydraulic couplings, (4) mechanical couplings, and (5) magnetic drive.[1]   Drives depending on belts and cones are said to give any desired shaft speed from 1 to 10,000 rpm.

[1] See also C. W. Camp, *Water & Sewage Works*, Vol. 93, p. 243, 1946.

13-17. Special-duty Motors. There are many different types of motors, each of which is adapted to some special duty or operating conditions. Among those suitable for special conditions in water works may be included (1) dripproof, (2) splashproof, (3) waterproof, (4) submersible, (5) gear, and (6) brake. A dripproof motor is encased so that drops of water falling on the motor at an angle less than 15 deg from the vertical cannot enter the motor directly or by running along a horizontal or inclined surface. Similarly, a splashproof motor is safe against water approaching it at an angle less than 100 deg from the vertical. A waterproof motor is enclosed so that a stream of water from a hose 1 in. or larger in diameter under a head of 35 ft and from a distance of 10 ft can be played on the motor without leakage except possibly along the shaft, with provision for preventing this water from entering the oil reservoir and for automatically draining the motor. Water-works pumping stations offer many conditions where such motors are needed.

Since the enclosing of a motor limits its ventilation and cooling, open motors should be used where possible, as their ratings are higher and their costs comparatively lower. For similar reasons motors should be installed in cool well-ventilated surroundings.

Submersible motors can be operated when submerged in water. Their use is infrequent. Gear motors, as mentioned in Sec. 13-15, are variable-speed machines. Brake motors have a brake built into them which brings the motor, or motor and load, rapidly to a stop when the current is cut off.

13-18. Rating of Electrical Equipment. Electrical equipment, particularly motors, is rated in accordance with the power delivered with a limiting temperature rise under standardized time and conditions. The permissible temperature rise is in the neighborhood of 40 to 50°C, dependent on the construction of the motor or equipment. Since time is required to raise the temperature, it is possible for electrical equipment, particularly motors, to carry an appreciable overload for a short period of time, the greatest hazard under such conditions being sparking, or internal short-circuiting. Standard ratings for electrical equipment have been adopted and published by the American Institute of Electrical Engineers. These standards enter into detail concerning the requisite performance of electrical equipment and should be consulted by an engineer responsible for the selection of electrical equipment.

Where motors are to be operated in ambient temperatures above 40°C the construction of the motor, particularly its internal insulation, must be adapted to the higher temperatures, or the load on the motor must be reduced below the standard rating.

13-19. Operating Hazards for Polyphase Induction Motors. Hazards to which polyphase induction motors are subjected in operation may be classified as those due to (1) variations in characteristics of electric power delivered to the motor, (2) improper operation, and (3) improper care.

The current delivered to the motor may vary in phase, in frequency, and in voltage. If one or more phases are interrupted while the motor is idle, the motor will not start; but if it has been running at the time of the interruption or if it is started by the application of outside power, as by pulling on the belt, the motor will run at normal speed as a single-phase motor and will deliver about 60 per cent of normal-load torque, with a pull-out torque about two-thirds to one-half normal. The effect of operating a polyphase motor under full load and single-phase conditions will be to overload the motor and to lead to its probable destruction. The interruption of one or more phases of an a-c circuit is not unusual and must be guarded against in motor operation.

Voltage affects the torque of an induction motor. Both the starting and operating torque vary closely as the square of the voltage. Hence a drop in voltage may cause a motor to refuse to start, or to pull out if in operation. A motor thus stopped with current in its windings is open to destruction.

If a motor is operated above normal voltage, the core losses are increased approximately as the square of the voltage, and the copper losses are decreased. An excessive increase in voltage endangers the insulation of the windings as a result of the rise in temperature of the core. The slip of induction motors varies approximately inversely as the voltage.

The speed and torque of induction motors vary approximately as the frequency of the current. At normal operating load and with increased frequency the core losses are increased, the result being increased heating despite the lower speed. Since the horsepower required by a centrifugal pump varies as the cube of the speed, an increase in frequency might quickly result in overloading the motor.

In general, induction motors will not be seriously affected by variations of 10 per cent, more or less, in either voltage or frequency. Interruption of phase is, however, a serious hazard. The sudden interruption of power will have no serious effect on an induction motor unless it is connected to a reversible load, such as a centrifugal pump. Under such circumstances both the motor and the pump must be protected against reversal. This may be accomplished by the installation of check valves on the pump discharge line or other devices. Unless a motor is equipped for automatic self-starting under load, it must be protected against the resumption of power in the event of its interruption.

13-20. Protection of Motors and Operators. Electric motors should be protected against the hazards of over- and undervoltage, over- and underload, reverse current, reverse power, reverse phase, lightning, and other current surges. Protection against hazards are provided mainly by devices that break or ground the electric circuit when danger threatens.

Fuses, depending on the melting of a strip of metal carrying the current, are used to protect motors against overload. They are limited in capacity to 600 amp. Time-lag fuses are designed particularly for the protection of small motors. They are used to permit the momentary surge of current up to 500 per cent of rating, in starting the motor, but to interrupt the circuit if the temperature of the motor rises excessively. The thermal cutout is designed and functions similarly to a plug fuse and is used to protect small motors against overloads. They protect the motor against overload, whereas the time-lag fuse protects the motor against too high a temperature from any cause. Fuses and thermal cutouts do not protect against lightning or surges of current.

Circuit breakers, actuated either thermally or magnetically, are available to interrupt currents from 15 amp up, under all conditions of service and, if required, to close the circuit automatically when the current has returned to normal. Circuit breakers, actuated by magnetic devices or relays, are available for protection against all the hazards listed for motors, except to arrest lightning.

The lightning arrester is a device placed on an electric circuit to ground excess voltage in the circuit and to restore the circuit on the return to normal voltage limits. Since the energy grounded through a lightning arrester may be high, the arrester should be placed in a nonhazardous location away from other equipment or combustible materials, or outdoors.

Motor frames may become charged by leakage of current due to breakdown of insulation or by stray currents or induced current, all of which endanger the motor and the operator. This hazard can be eliminated by grounding all motor frames and carefully inspecting and maintaining this ground. Probably the most satisfactory ground is a connection to a water-supply pipe. The practice of making such grounds is widespread and is generally permitted.[1]

13-21. Setting of Motors. A foundation that is large enough on which to set the motor, is sufficiently massive to absorb vibrations of the motor without transmitting them to its surroundings, and will hold the motor in alignment under all the loads for which it is designed is required for a motor setting. Concrete, brick, or a combination of these two and, sometimes, wood or metal are used in satisfactory foundations, but no definite ratio of motor mass or speed to foundation mass can be set. Experience, based on a study of successful settings, must guide. Some typical motor foundations are illustrated in Figs. 12-2 and 12-3. Dimensions of motors may be approximated by a study of catalogues, or they may be obtained on request from manufacturers.

[1] See Sec. 19-11.

13-22. Transformers. It may be necessary to provide space for transformers in an electrically equipped pumping station, usually to step down the voltage from that carried on the transmission lines to the voltage to be used by the equipment in the pumping station. Because of the hazards of fire and high-voltage currents, transformers should be placed in a fireproof room or in a location protected from traffic in the pumping station. Rules for the safe installation of transformers are included in the National Electric Code.[1] Weights and dimensions of transformers for various purposes are listed in handbooks and in manufacturers' catalogues.

13-23. Relays and Circuit Breakers. Relays may be used for a multitude of services, but in an electrically operated pumping station, their principal use is to actuate circuit breakers in the protection of equipment and to start and stop motors, pumps, and other equipment. Relays are available that will actuate a circuit breaker under almost any condition such as change in voltage, phase, or cycle of current; overload, speed, or temperature of motor; or filling or emptying of a reservoir. Two types frequently used are the instantaneous or dashpot, and the induction. The latter is the most commonly used.

13-24. Switchboards. A switchboard is an essential part of the equipment of a pumping station or purification works using electrical equipment. The equipment placed on the switchboard includes starting devices, relays, meters, and recording and indicating devices. The equipment can be neatly arranged on the board with devices controlling separate circuits arranged on separate panels. A circuit breaker should be installed on the incoming line from the power plant, which will open all short circuits on the system. There should be smaller circuit breakers, with thermal-overload protection on each of the motor circuits. Knife switches should be used for direct current only with voltages below 250, and for alternating current with voltages below 500. At higher voltages, oil or air-gap switches, controlled by push-button relays, should be used. A drawing of the switchboard in the Thos. H. Allen Pumping Station at Memphis, Tenn., is shown in Fig. 13-1.

Types and space requirements of switchboards are listed in handbooks and catalogues. Rules for their installation are to be found in the National Electric Code.[1]

13-25. Installation of Electrical Equipment. Standard practice should be followed in the installation of electrical equipment. This constitutes the use of adequate-sized wire, supports, protection, and equipment for the loads and conditions contemplated. Details of this practice have been codified and published in the National Electric Code for Electric

[1] See A. L. Abbott, "National Electric Code Handbook," 7th ed., McGraw-Hill Book Company, Inc., New York, 1952.

Wiring and Apparatus. A copy should be in the hands of every designer, purchaser, and operator of electrical equipment.

13-26. Automatic Pumping Stations. Electrical equipment lends itself favorably to automatic operation and remote control of pumping stations, resulting in reliable, efficient, and economical operation.[1] Automatic stations are those in which the equipment is started and stopped through relays which are controlled by reservoir levels or system

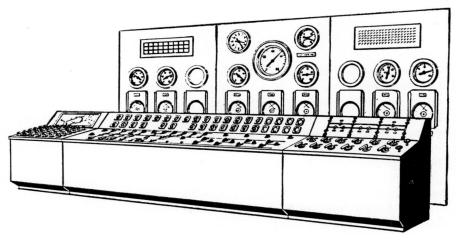

FIG. 13-1. Electrical benchboard and control panel, Thomas A. Allen Pumping Station, at Memphis, Tenn. (*From J. P. Kessler, Am. City, November,* 1952, *p.* 87.)

pressures or by faults in, or failure of, station equipment or connections. Remote-control stations are those in which all, or the major part, of the equipment in the pumping station is controlled by operators in a remote location. Such stations may be designed to operate for days at a time without attendance, reports of the conditions of station operation being telephoned, on demand, by robots. Automatic stations make possible the exercise of ingenuity in water-works design, resulting in economies of construction and of operation.

[1] S. A. Canariis, *J.A.W.W.A.,* May, 1936, p. 583.

CHAPTER 14

PUMPING ENGINES

14-1. Types of Engines. Almost all water-works pumps are driven by either steam engines, internal-combustion engines, or electric motors. Other types of engines such as the windmill, the hydraulic ram, and the hydraulic pump are not recognized as devices used for public water supplies. Practice is confined almost exclusively to the electric motor, the internal-combustion engine, and the steam-turbine-driven centrifugal pumping unit. The reciprocating steam pumping engine or steam-driven power pump may be suitable under such unusual local conditions as cheap steam, low first cost of steam pump, or other reasons.

14-2. Steam Pumping Engines. A steam pumping engine or, as more commonly known, a steam pump consists of one or more steam cylinders with pistons which are connected directly or by cranks and shafts to one or more water cylinders. The water end of a horizontal, outside, center-packed, plunger pump with a water-works type of surface condenser is illustrated in Fig. 14-1. Steam pumping engines are classified in accordance with the number of steam or water cylinders, the expansion of the steam, and other conditions. A pumping engine taking steam from the boiler under full boiler pressure for the full length of the stroke is known as a direct-acting steam pump. Since such a pumping engine cannot use the steam expansively, its economy is low. Pumping engines using steam expansively are equipped with a flywheel, or similar device, to carry the pump through a complete stroke after the steam has been cut off from the boiler and begins to act expansively, hence at reduced pressure, in the steam cylinder. Direct-acting steam pumps are relatively low in first cost but their high rate of steam consumption, known as the *water rate*, excludes them from selection in most pumping stations.

14-3. Steam Turbines. A steam turbine is a prime mover using the expansion and the velocity of steam to generate power. Its efficiency and simplicity are obtained, in part, through the absence of reciprocating parts, and ease in lubrication.[1] A steam turbine is more simple in con-

---

[1] See also E. F. Church, "Steam Turbines," 3d ed., McGraw-Hill Book Company, Inc., New York, 1950.

struction and is easier to operate than a high-duty, triple-expansion steam pumping engine. Turbines are adaptable to the use of steam at pressures below atmospheric to the highest pressures and degrees of superheat practicable in steam boilers. Over-all heat efficiencies of 18 per cent are not uncommon, and 22 per cent has been attained.[1] Water rates of 12 to 20 lb steam per indicated horsepower-hour can be anticipated by their use. The smaller water rates are obtained in the larger

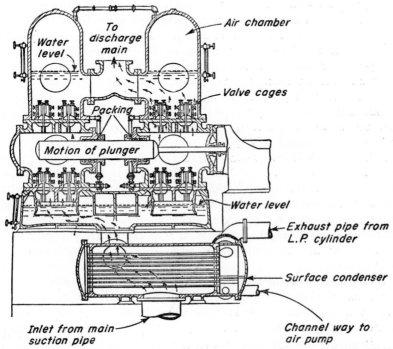

Fig. 14-1. Water end of a steam pumping engine. (*Courtesy of Allis-Chalmers Mfg. Co.*)

units. Owing to low first cost, relatively small space requirements, and efficient operation, the total charges on a steam-turbine, centrifugal-pump unit are usually lower than on a triple-expansion pumping engine. A result is that in the latest installations in large pumping stations there is a tendency to install the turbine-driven, centrifugal-pumping unit.

Steam turbines are suited particularly to the driving of centrifugal pumps or electric generators. Because the economical speed of steam turbines is much higher than that of centrifugal pumps, the two must be connected in such a manner that each may revolve at the proper speed. This is commonly accomplished by means of a speed-reduction gearing. Steam turbines require relatively small housing space compared with

[1] See also *J.A.W.W.A.*, Vol. 10, p. 758, 1923.

reciprocating pumping engines, and they can be constructed in any size. Units of 100,000 hp have been constructed, and there seems to be no limit to their capacity. An added advantage to their use is the extreme flatness of the rating curve. A test at Cleveland[1] showed a variation in power consumption of 7 per cent for a load variation of 100 per cent.

14-4. Internal-combustion Engines. An internal-combustion engine develops power by the explosion of fuel within the cylinder of the engine. Such engines are widely used in power development for all purposes and are advantageous for use in water-works pumping service either as main pumping units or as auxiliary stand-by units. They are particularly suited as stand-by equipment in pumping stations depending on electric power generated elsewhere than in the pumping station because, in the event of interruption of the electric power, the internal-combustion engine can be started quickly. Gas or gasoline engines operating on the otto cycle are more suitable for quick starting. Diesel-cycle engines are serviceable, and economical, for continuous duty at full load.

14-5. Gas or Gasoline Engines. An outstanding advantage of the otto-cycle engine is its quick-starting characteristics. The speeds of such engines are suited for direct drive of electric generators or centrifugal pumps. The first cost of such engines and their maintenance are usually lower than the corresponding costs of diesel engines of equal power. However, the fuel economy of otto-cycle engines, compared with other available power sources, is usually such that gas or gasoline engines are not often used as the main power-generating units in a water-works pumping station.

In a comparison of the features of two-cycle and four-cycle engines it is found that the latter can operate at a higher speed; the crankcase need not be enclosed; better lubrication is secured because of the lower temperatures; the economy and efficiency are higher; there is less loss of energy in exhausting old and inhaling new gases; and the power per unit volume of piston displacement is only about 52 to 58 per cent of that of a two-cycle motor, because there is only one power stroke in four rather than in two. In the two-cycle motor the exhaust gases are less completely expelled; there are fewer valves; and there is less weight per horsepower, which requires less space and lighter foundations.

High-speed gasoline engines are low in first cost but are relatively high in fuel cost compared with diesel engines. Large gas engines will develop 1 hp-hr on 0.7 lb fuel at full load. Units are available up to 585 hp, and, as they operate at speeds of 720 to 1,500 rpm, they are suitable for direct connection to centrifugal pumps or electrical generators.

14-6. Diesel Engines.[2] Diesel engines have high thermal efficiency; they can use any type of liquid or gaseous fuel; they are expensive in first

[1] See also A. L. Mullergren, *J.A.W.W.A.*, Vol. 18, pp. 180, 184, 1927.

[2] See also: W. S. Russell, *J.A.W.W.A.*, January, 1936, p. 119; A. M. Boehm, *J. New Engl. Water Works Assoc.*, Vol. 60, p. 27, 1946; *Public Works*, August, 1948, p. 25.

cost; they are difficult to start; and their speed is low, usually requiring a speed-increasing mechanism when driving an electric motor or a centrifugal pump. Common forms of power storage used for the purpose of starting diesel engines include electric storage batteries and compressed air. Where electric power is available it may be used to start the engine. In some installations starting may be made easier by operating the engine with an electric ignition system as a "semidiesel engine," shifting to the diesel cycle after the engine is started. Other difficulties with the diesel engine are caused by the relatively large number of moving parts and the experienced care required in their lubrication and maintenance.

Diesel engines have good partial-load characteristics and good speed regulation, *i.e.*, their speed is relatively constant under load variations. They will require slightly less than 0.5 lb crude oil per brake horsepower-hour[1] whereas a semidiesel engine will consume about 10 per cent more fuel. A supercharged diesel engine may supply 1 hp-hr for between 0.42 and 0.45 lb crude oil. The fuel efficiency is quite constant over a considerable variation of speed and head, and the economy of small units is almost equal to that of the largest sizes, making possible the use of a number of small units in a pumping station.

The diesel engine is approximately 135 per cent more economical at full load than the otto engine, on the basis of pounds of fuel per horsepower-hour developed, and 150 per cent more economical at light loads. In general terms the economy is in the ratio of 2:3. Fuel is sold by volume instead of by weight; therefore, the diesel effects a further saving compared with gasoline-driven engines in the ratio of approximately 7:8. The price of gasoline to the average user is about 3 or 2:1 compared with fuel oil. Therefore, the over-all operating cost of fuel for a diesel engine is 20 to 25 per cent of that for an equivalent otto gasoline unit. Lubricating costs are practically the same for the two types of engines. The fuel efficiency of a diesel engine is about 32 per cent as compared with the best steam-driven thermal efficiency of about 28 per cent.[2] It is therefore evident that the total annual hours of service, representing a definite saving, becomes a deciding factor in the selection of power.[3] Couch[4] has made a valuable comparison of steam, electric, and diesel power for waterworks pumping stations. The advantages of the diesel engine so outweigh its disadvantages that it has taken a permanent place in the waterworks field.[5]

Extracts from specifications for diesel engines used at Manchester, Mass.,[6] indicate features to be considered in planning for them in a waterworks pumping station, as follows:

[1] See also N. G. McDonald, *J.A.W.W.A.*, August, 1942, pp. 1241, 1243.

[2] See also E. Earl, *J. New Engl. Water Works Assoc.*, Vol. 47, p. 61, 1933.

[3] See also C. B. Jahnke, *Bull. Assoc. State Eng. Socs.*, April, 1934, p. 7.

[4] See *J. New Engl. Water Works Assoc.*, Vol. 44, p. 458, 1930.

[5] See also R. D. Hall, *J.A.W.W.A.*, Vol. 23, p. 337, 1931.

[6] See C. L. Ahlgren, *J. New Engl. Water Works Assoc.*, Vol. 63, p. 117, 1949.

1. *Intake Air.* Filtered, and an intake-air silencer is used.

2. *Exhaust.* Through a side-inlet maximum spark arrester-silencer.

3. *Fuel System.* Fuel flows by gravity through a 2-in. pipe to the pumping station from a 10,000-gal storage tank 400 ft from the engine room. Fuel flows into a 300-gal day tank in a concrete pit where it is picked up by a fuel pump and pushed through a Nugent filter to the Fairbanks injection pumps.

4. *Lubricating Oil.* Cooled to 165°F on coming from the engine, and filtered in either fuller's earth or cellulose cartridges.

5. *Cooling Water.* A gear-driven circulating pump forces water through the engine, out through a Ross heat exchanger, and back to the engine.

6. *Raw water* for the heat exchanger is piped through the force main.

7. *Starting air* capacity is provided for eight normal starts, at a pressure of 250 psi.

8. *Gage-board equipment* includes (*a*) pyrometer for readings on individual cylinders and on combined exhaust, (*b*) pressure and temperature of lubricating oil, temperature of circulating water, pressure of raw water, pressure of starting air, and scavenging-air pressure.

14-7. Dual-fuel Engines. A dual-fuel engine is an internal-combustion engine "which uses oil fuel on the diesel cycle, or predominantly gaseous fuel with oil fuel ignition, and is fully convertible from one fuel to another."[1] It is possible to switch from one fuel to another without stopping the engine. Since dual-fuel engines operate on the diesel cycle they are economical of fuel, delivering 1 bhp-hr per 11 cu ft of 650 Btu gas, compared with 15 to 15.5 cu ft of similar gas required by the four-cycle otto engine, with less than 5 per cent of total Btu input in pilot oil.[2] Supercharging will increase the power output of a dual-fuel engine about 50 per cent, but its heat efficiency will not be increased. The heat efficiency of a dual-fuel engine is about 24 to 35 per cent. The amount of recoverable heat, available for space heating or other purposes, from the dual-fuel engine is about 47 per cent of the total heat input. It is about 52.5 per cent from the low-compression otto-cycle engine.

14-8. Diesel Auxiliaries. The principal auxiliaries required in connection with a diesel engine have to do with the handling of fuel oil.[3] They include hand-operated and power-operated fuel-oil pump, cooling-water equipment, oil-storage equipment, equipment for warming the fuel oil, oil meters, and oil purifiers.

14-9. Fuel Oil. Although diesel engines will operate with many different kinds of liquid and gaseous fuels, the efficient operation of any

---

[1] Definition by Diesel Engine Manufacturers Association, quoted by W. R. Crooks, *Sewage Works J.*, Vol. 21, p. 957, 1949.

[2] See also N. Polakov, *Sewage and Ind. Wastes*, January, 1950, p. 24.

[3] See also Hall, *loc. cit.*

particular engine requires discriminating selection of the fuel. It is desirable that the type of engine installed shall be suited to the type of oil available in the locality. As a general guide in the purchase of fuel oil the following desirable characteristics may be considered: (1) minimum specific gravity, 24°Bé; (2) viscosity (Saybolt Universal at 100°F), minimum 40 sec, maximum 100 to 150 sec; (3) sulphur, maximum 1.5 per cent; (4) Conradson carbon (carbon residue), 1.0 per cent; (5) flash point, minimum 150°F; (6) water and sediment, by volume, 0.5 per cent; (7) pour point, less than the minimum temperature at which the oil is to be used. Gravity, flash point, and sulphur should, in general, be given the least consideration provided the flash point is above the legal limit.

14-10. Water Power and Wind Power. The development of hydraulic power for water-works purposes is a neglected field, because conditions are not usually favorable, other forms of power being less expensive.

For small installations for private estates and remote institutions the hydraulic ram may be used for raising water from a falling stream, or the windmill may be used for well pumping or surface-water pumping. A form of hot-air engine that has been used occasionally for small installations is now almost obsolete. Except for the hydraulic ram, which is manufactured with capacities up to 700 gpm, such devices are seldom used to raise more than a few gallons of water per minute and are not used for lifting public water supplies. Where water power is available, water turbines may be successfully connected directly to centrifugal pumps.[1]

[1] See also McDonald, *loc. cit.*, pp. 1241, 1253.

CHAPTER 15

CENTRIFUGAL, ROTARY, AND OTHER PUMPS

Centrifugal Pumps

15-1. Description. A centrifugal pump is a device that raises a liquid by centrifugal force created by a wheel, called an *impeller*, revolving in a tight casing. In operation the liquid enters the pump at the center of the impeller called the *eye*. It enters in a direction normal to the plane in which the impeller revolves and is thrown to the periphery by the centrifugal force resulting from the revolution of the impeller. The fluid

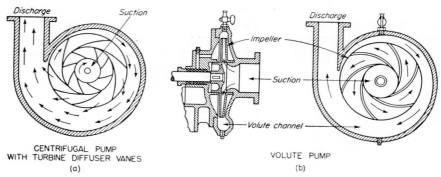

CENTRIFUGAL PUMP
WITH TURBINE DIFFUSER VANES
(a)

VOLUTE PUMP
(b)

FIG. 15-1. Centrifugal pumps.

passes through the channel between the rim of the impeller and the casing and issues at the discharge under pressure. Sections through centrifugal pumps are shown in Fig. 15-1.

15-2. Status and Performance. Centrifugal pumps are used almost exclusively in water-works practice except in the largest pumping stations, in a few of which triple-expansion reciprocating pumping engines are to be found. Centrifugal pumps are available commercially for almost any capacity that might normally be required, and for lifts up to 700 ft in one stage.[1] There is no theoretical limit to the number of stages that can be placed in series to increase the lift. Maximum lifts per stage

[1] See also: J. Burgess, *J.A.W.W.A.*, May, 1941, p. 837; H. R. Cady, *ibid.*, February, 1947, p. 139.

are commonly nearer 250 ft, however.   Efficiencies up to 93 per cent have
been attained by large pumps,[1] but, in general, the efficiencies of small
pumps are lower.   Speeds of 900, 1,200, 1,800 rpm, and even higher, are
used for water-works pumps.   Small pumps are manufactured with
speeds up to 6,000 rpm.[2]

Advantages of the centrifugal pump, particularly when compared with
other types of pumps, include (1) relatively small space for any given
capacity; (2) rotary rather than reciprocating motion; (3) adaptability
to high-speed driving mechanisms, such as electric motors, steam turbines,
and gas engines; (4) low first cost; (5) simple mechanism; (6) simple
operation and repair; and (7) safety against damage from high pressure
because of limited maximum pressure that can be developed.   The pump
is thus safe against damage if the discharge valve is suddenly closed,
although in a few low-lift pumps with special characteristics the motor
might be overloaded under these conditions.   Disadvantages include the
following: (1) Rate of flow cannot be efficiently regulated for wide ranges
of performance.   (2) Speed cannot always be adjusted to the prime mover
without the use of speed-reducing or speed-increasing gear.   (3) Pumps
are not self-priming without additional mechanism.   (4) Suction lift may
be restricted.   (5) Air leaks on the suction side easily affect pump performance.   (6) If stopped with the discharge valve open, the pump may
run backward.   (7) In general, high efficiency is maintained over only a
narrow range of head and discharge.

15-3. Cost.   The first cost of a centrifugal pump is, ordinarily, less than
the first cost of other types of pumps of the same capacity and lift.
Among the factors affecting first cost are included the discharge pressure,
speed, number of impellers in series, quality of material and construction,
market conditions, and capacity.   In general, it may be said that first
cost varies with capacity, other factors being equal.

The relative economy of centrifugal pumps should be compared with
that of other pumps on a capitalized cost basis, including first cost,
installation, space requirements, mechanical efficiency, lubrication, and
other maintenance costs, and durability or life.   Each of these items,
except possibly that of mechanical efficiency, will usually be found
favorable to the centrifugal pump.   Since the efficiency of the pump may
greatly affect its economy, careful attention should be paid to this factor
in the selection of a pump.

15-4. Theory.   The general physical laws applicable to a centrifugal
pump can be expressed as

$$F \,=\, Ma \,=\, \frac{MV^2}{r} \,=\, \frac{WV^2}{gr} \,=\, \frac{W\pi^2N^2r}{900g}$$

---

[1] Burgess, *loc. cit.*; R. W. Angus, *Eng. and Contract Record*, March, 1945, p. **72**.
[2] Burgess, *loc. cit.*

where F = centrifugal force
      a = radial acceleration
      g = acceleration due to gravity
      M = mass of moving body
      N = speed, rpm
      r = radius of path
      W = weight of moving body

The theoretical height to which a column of water will rise under the effect of centrifugal force produced by a revolving impeller is

$$h = \frac{V^2}{2g}$$

where V is the linear velocity of the tip of the impeller. V^2 is equal to $r^2\omega^2$, in which r is the radius of the impeller and ω is its angular velocity.

The equation of the surface curve of a body of water made to revolve in a cylindrical vessel, as shown in Fig. 15-2, is, therefore,

$$y = \frac{\omega^2 x^2}{2g} \tag{15-1}$$

This is known as the equation of a forced vortex. It is the shape of the pressure curve of the water in the casing of a centrifugal pump when the

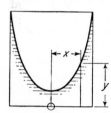

FIG. 15-2. A forced vortex.

discharge valve is closed and the impeller is revolving. It shows that the pressure exerted by a centrifugal pump varies as the square of the speed of the impeller. The value y when x is r is known as the pressure of impending delivery. In most pumps, since there is some leakage around the impeller blades into the casing, the pressure of impending delivery is seldom exactly as shown in the expression. It may be either higher or lower, depending upon the shape of the impeller blades, the rate of leakage, and other factors. It will usually be found that the actual pressure of impending delivery is within 10 to 15 per cent of the value of this expression.

If the impeller of a centrifugal pump is revolved while the discharge valve is closed and an orifice is opened at any point in the casing, water will flow from the orifice under a head of $\omega^2 x^2/2g$. Since the rate of discharge through an orifice is

$$Q = kA \sqrt{2gh}$$

where A is the area of the orifice, and h, the head on the orifice, is equal to $\omega^2 x^2/2g$, it follows, therefore, that

$$Q = kA\omega x \tag{15-2}$$

Hence, the rate of flow, or the discharge from a centrifugal pump, varies as the speed of revolution of the impeller.

The torque exerted by the impeller of a centrifugal pump is

$$T = \frac{Qwr_pV_w}{g} \qquad (15\text{-}3)$$

where T = torque
Q = rate of discharge past impeller blade
w = unit weight of water
r_p = radius of impeller
V_w = tangential velocity of the water at impeller tip

The power exerted by the impeller is equal to the torque multiplied by the angular velocity; therefore,

$$P = T\omega = \frac{Qwr_pV_w\omega}{g} = \frac{QwV_iV_w}{g} \qquad (15\text{-}4)$$

in which V_i is the linear velocity of the impeller tip, and other symbols are as in Eq. (15-3).

15-5. Relationships of Characteristics. Relationships between characteristics of centrifugal pumps, as developed from theoretical considerations, other conditions being unchanged, may be summarized as follows:

1. Q varies directly as the number of impellers in parallel.

2. H varies directly as the number of impellers in series, *i.e.*, the number of stages.

3. When N varies, Q varies directly as N; H varies directly as N^2; P, the power, varies as N^3; Q varies as $H^{1/2}$; and P varies as $H^{3/2}$.

These theoretical relationships do not hold exactly, because of errors in the hypotheses of the conditions of flow of water, but they are sufficiently accurate for rough approximations. It is found by test that for impending delivery the ratio $V_i/2gh$ varies between 0.95 and 1.09 and that for rated discharge or maximum efficiency this ratio lies between 0.10 and 0.30. If this ratio is called α and we allow $\beta = V_w/\sqrt{2gh}$, in which V_w is the velocity of the water relative to the impeller, then β is approximately equal to α for rated discharge or maximum efficiency. The important relationship between H and Q is shown by the characteristic of the pump discussed in Sec 15-7.

15-6. Centrifugal Pump Series. Centrifugal pumps when built in different sizes, but of the same proportions in every respect, constitute a series and are said to have homologous impellers. An advantage of series pumps is that knowledge of the characteristics of one pump of a series can be used as a basis of prediction of the performance of another pump of the same series. The outstanding relationships among pumps of the same series are that when the speed N is constant

Q varies directly as D^3

H varies directly as D^2

P varies directly as D^5

where Q is the rate of discharge, H is the total head, P is the power required, and D is the diameter of the impeller.

The specific speed of a pump is the speed at which the impeller of a series would run when discharging 1 gpm under a 1 ft head at the highest efficiency. Since the specific speed of all pumps of the same series is the same, then, if the head, discharge, and speed of a pump are known, the head, discharge, and speed of any pump of the same series *under different conditions* can be predicted.

Specific speed can be expressed algebraically as

$$N_s = \frac{\text{rpm } \sqrt{\text{gpm}}}{H^{3/4}} \qquad (15\text{-}5)$$

where N_s = specific speed, rpm

rpm = speed of revolution of pump

gpm = discharge from pump

H = discharge head, ft

The *type* of an impeller is the ratio of its diameter to its width. It is possible to obtain the same discharge pressures from a series of impellers of different diameters running at different speeds, but for the same discharge the type (width) of the impeller would be different. In order to reduce skin friction, it is desirable to operate the impeller at as slow a peripheral speed as possible, and impeller types should be designed to permit slow peripheral speeds.

15-7. Characteristic Curves.[1] The characteristic curves or, more commonly, the characteristics of a centrifugal pump are the relations between the various conditions affecting its performance. They are usually expressed graphically with the rate of discharge Q as the abscissas and the other factors plotted, at constant speeds, as ordinates, such as the head H, the power P, and the efficiency E. The *characteristic*, at any particular speed, is the graph showing the relation between H and Q, with values of H plotted as ordinates. Other methods of plotting characteristics are also used. Characteristic curves for a single pump at different speeds are shown in Fig. 15-3 and for different impellers are shown in Fig. 15-4.

A study of the characteristics of a centrifugal pump is necessary to determine the best conditions under which it should be operated. For example, Fig. 15-3 shows that, at 1,455 rpm, the pump will discharge 350 gpm against no other head than 200 ft. To reduce the discharge by closing the discharge valve will change the head, the power, and the

[1] See also R. Carter and I. J. Karassik, *Water & Sewage Works*, May, 1951, p. 212; August, 1951, p. 335.

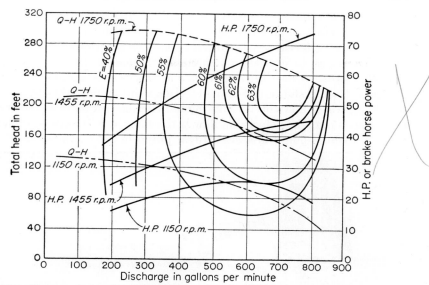

FIG. 15-3. Characteristics of a centrifugal pump at different speeds. (*Based on Eng. News-Record, Vol. 91, p. 564.*)

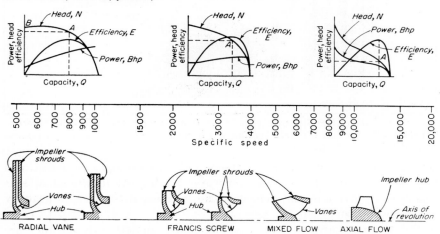

FIG. 15-4. Characteristic graphs and specific-speed scale for impellers of various design. (*From Roy Carter and I. J. Karassik, Water & Sewage Works, August, 1951, p. 335.*)

efficiency. The highest efficiency will occur at a discharge rate of about 720 gpm at a speed of 1,750 rpm. It is shown in Fig. 15-3 that where it is possible to vary the speed of the pump the range of N, Q, and H for highest efficiency can be obtained. It shows that this pump should be operated at 1,750 rpm, with discharge of about 720 gpm at a head of 244 ft. A pump with flat characteristics at all speeds and a wide plateau at the highest efficiency is most desirable.

Centrifugal pumps[1] should be selected on the basis of their characteristics and operated where the efficiency curve is as flat as possible. Scales to which characteristics are plotted should be scrutinized, as the shape of the curve can be changed by changing the scales.

15-8. Types. Centrifugal pumps are classed as volute or turbine pumps. Each is shown in Fig. 15-1. In a volute pump, the channel into which the water flows on leaving the impeller has a volute shape of such proportions that the velocity of flow is the same at all points in the channel. A turbine pump is a centrifugal pump in which the channel into

Fig. 15-5. Single-stage centrifugal pump. (*Courtesy of American Well Works.*) (1) shell, (2) impeller, (3) main bearing, (4) frame, (5) shaft, (6) shaft nut, (7) ball bearings, (8) packing gland.

which the water flows on leaving the impeller has the same cross-sectional area throughout. The velocity of water leaving the impeller blades is changed in direction, and velocity head is changed to pressure head by means of diffusion vanes.

Volute pumps are lower than turbine pumps in first cost, and they are more suitable to the handling of liquids containing grit and large particles of suspended matter. Higher efficiencies can be secured from turbine than from volute pumps, but their greater cost and the greater wear on diffusion vanes, combined with other reasons, are diminishing their use in water-works practice.

Centrifugal pumps are classed also as single-stage, two-stage, etc., in accordance with the number of stages of pressure developed by the impellers. A single-stage centrifugal pump is illustrated in Fig. 15-5. In the

[1] See also H. E. Beckwith, *Water Works & Sewerage*, April, 1940, p. 30.

development of discharge pressure, it may be inefficient to develop the entire pressure by a single impeller, as either the diameter or the speed, or both, may be undesirably great. Since the discharge pressure from a centrifugal pump is the sum of the initial pressure at the inlet and the pressure energy added by the impeller, increased pressure can be secured by leading the discharge from one impeller into the suction of another. The discharge pressure is directly proportional to the number of stages, other things being equal.

Another classification is as horizontal and as vertical pumps, depending on the position of the shaft. A horizontal pump is shown in Fig. 15-5. The deep-well pumps shown in Figs. 16-5 and 16-6 are vertical pumps. The use of vertical pumps for both low service and high service in lifting water from wet wells in pumping stations is increasing.[1]

15-9. Selection of Pump.[2] In the selection of a pump, it is better to specify required performance and to allow the manufacturer to determine speed and other operating details, some of which may subsequently be guaranteed. It will probably be more economical to provide a number of small pumps to operate at highest efficiency and, in addition, to provide a single unit that can be operated at different speeds, or to provide, in addition to the pump or pumps that are to run at constant speed, an equalizing reservoir to care for the fluctuations of demand. Another consideration mitigating against the use of large pumps operating at less than full capacity is the practice, used by some power companies, of basing the power-demand charge on the total capacity of the power units in the pumping station.

The designation of the size of a centrifugal pump is stated by giving the diameter, in inches, of the discharge opening. The capacity in gallons per minute may be roughly determined by multiplying the square of the size by 25. This rule is based on the fact that the velocity of the water through the discharge opening is about 10 fps. This velocity may vary between 5 and 15 fps.

15-10. Limiting Values of Specific Speed. Experience has shown[2] that the limiting values for specific speed above which unsatisfactory operation may be expected can be formulated as

$$N_s = (k/H)^n \tag{15-6}$$

where H is the total dynamic head and k and n are constants. The expression is applicable primarily to water at sea level and a temperature of 85°F. Some values of k and of n are given in Table 15-1.

---

[1] See O. A. Fabrin, *J.A.W.W.A.*, October, 1953, p. 1045.
[2] See also R. Carter and I. J. Karassik, *Water & Sewage Works*, May, 1953, pp. R-23 and R-50.

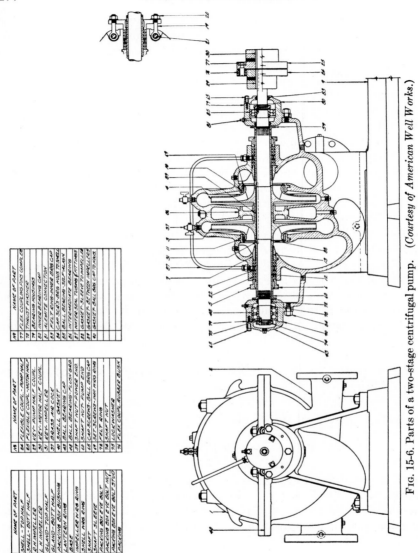

FIG. 15-6. Parts of a two-stage centrifugal pump. (*Courtesy of American Well Works.*)

TABLE 15-1. Constants in the Expression $N_s = (k/H)^n$

Suction head and lift, ft	Single-suction pumps with shaft through eye of the impeller ($n = 0.585$), $k \times 10^8$	Double-suction pumps ($n = 0.585$), $k \times 10^8$	Single-stage pumps of mixed-flow and axial-flow types ($n = 0.757$), $k \times 10^6$
Head:			
15	1.36	2.48	6.86
10	1.25	2.25	6.13
5	1.10	2.00	5.4
0	0.96	1.76	4.67
Lift:			
5	0.85	1.50	4.0
10	0.69	1.28	3.2
15	0.55	0.99	2.6
20	0.40	0.75	1.8
25	0.25	0.46	

15-11. Parts. The simplicity of a centrifugal pump is indicated by its parts, shown in Fig. 15-5 and in Fig. 15-6. Bronze or gun metal is desirable in parts in contact with water. It is especially desirable that the impeller be of bronze or gun metal in order to resist corrosion. The impeller

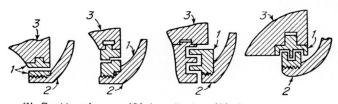

(1)-Packing ring   (2)-Impeller   (3)-Casing
FIG. 15-7. Packing rings.

should be machined and polished to reduce friction, and the sides of the impeller should be enclosed so as to avoid friction between the moving water and the pump casing. It is important that the impeller should be balanced both statically and when in rotation, as an unbalanced impeller may cause heating of the bearings and vibration and noise or the failure of the pump.

Special types of packing rings are illustrated in Fig. 15-7. They are called labyrinth packing rings and are used between the impeller and the casing to minimize leakage and maintain efficiency. Interior shaft bearings should be of hard bronze. They are placed between impellers and at bottoms of stuffing boxes that are designed for water lubrication only. Lignum vitae bearings are to be avoided in centrifugal pumps, regardless of lubrication or other conditions. Exterior bearings should be easily accessible. They should be designed for oil lubrication and should be provided with deep oil wells and ring oilers.

The casing of all but the smallest pumps is usually split horizontally along the center, as shown in Fig. 15-6, so that the top may be removed for inspection and repair of the pump.

Thrust bearings or thrust-balancing devices are used to take up the end thrust which occurs in even the best-designed pumps. To overcome end thrust, pumps are designed with opposed impellers, double suction; or two pumps with their impellers opposed may be placed on the same shaft. Because of inequalities in wear, workmanship, or other conditions, end thrust will occur and must be cared for. Various types of thrust bearings are in successful use, *e.g.*, the piston disk, roller, and marine types, illustrated in Fig. 15-8. Flexible-shaft couplings should be used

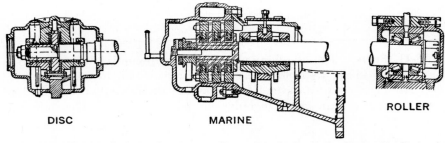

DISC   MARINE   ROLLER

Fig. 15-8. Types of thrust bearings. (*From Standards of the Hydraulic Society.*)

if the shaft of the driving motor and of the pump are in the same line, as direct alignment is difficult to attain and maintain. Where connected to steam turbines, reduction gearing and rigid couplings are usually used. Flexible couplings are of various types. One type is shown in Fig. 15-6. A rigid coupling would be formed by bolting the shaft flanges together.

The use of hydraulic or fluid-filled couplings and of magnetic couplings[1] between electric motors and centrifugal pumps overcomes many of the difficulties of friction or flexible couplings. In such couplings[2] there is no solid contact between the power unit and the driven unit, power being transmitted by the friction of a fluid, which occupies an enclosed space connecting the ends of the two shafts, or by means of an induced current.

The stuffing box shown at 22 in Fig. 15-6 is usually packed with metallic packing, hemp, or asbestos, between which is a lantern gland, in order to permit a small amount of leakage. A drip box is placed below this gland to catch the leakage and to return it to the pump. The leakage aids lubrication, and the tightening of the gland would cause binding of the shaft. The gland on the suction side of the pump should be connected by

[1] See also H. R. Cady, *J.A.W.W.A.*, February, 1947, p. 139.
[2] See also H. Sinclair, *Engineering*, Apr. 29, 1938, p. 487.

a small pipe to the discharge chamber in order to keep a constant supply of water for lubrication and to prevent the entrance of air to the suction end of the pump.

15-12. Setting.[1] Centrifugal pumps are driven by electric motors, steam turbines, internal-combustion engines, and other prime movers. Steam turbines are sometimes arranged to drive an electric generator and a centrifugal pump through a speed-reducing gear on the same shaft. The electric motor is usually considered to be the most satisfactory driving mechanism. The engine or motor may be connected to the pump by a belt, gearing, or shafting. The simplest and most efficient arrangement is the use of an electric motor and a pump mounted on the same shaft, as illustrated in Fig. 15-9. If a centrifugal pump and a motor are to be

Fig. 15-9. Centrifugal fire pump driven by either an electric motor or a gas engine. (*Courtesy of Fairbanks Morse Co.*)

operated on the same shaft, both the pump and the motor should be attached to the same rigid foundation so that the alignment of the shaft will remain true. Pumps with capacities up to about 2,500 gpm are available with the pump flange and motor frame cast as a unit, so that difficulties with shaft alignment are eliminated. Where rigid shaft alignment is not possible, flexible couplings are used on the shaft to allow some variation in alignment. Whatever the method of connecting the motor and the pump, it is highly desirable to provide for variable speed of operation in order to obtain the great possible efficiency. Hydraulic and magnetic couplings are useful also in allowing control of the pump speed without affecting the speed of the motor.[2]

Centrifugal pumps are not ordinarily self-priming. Hence, in setting and in operation, care must be taken to avoid the loss of suction and to permit its easy restoration. These conditions are best secured by setting

[1] See also Standards for the Installation of Centrifugal Pumps, National Board of Fire Underwriters, September, 1944.

[2] See also: A. Peterson, *Power*, July, September, 1940; C. W. Camp, *Water & Sewage Works*, June, 1946, p. 243.

the pump below the source of supply so that there is a positive pressure at all times on the suction line. It is undesirable to set the pump with the casing submerged, because of the difficulties of making necessary repairs and adjustments. If the pump is set higher than the level of the water in the suction pit, a foot valve may be required to permit priming of the pump or to prevent the pump from running backward in the event of shutdown with the discharge valve open. The suction pipe should be submerged sufficiently to prevent drawing air into it. This can be done by submerging it about four diameters and keeping the velocity of entrance low. Richardson[1] has given empirical relations between the entrance velocity V, in feet per second, into a circular bell, and the minimum submergence S, in feet, which can be formulated approximately as $V^2 - 17S + 10 = 0$. Where no strainer is used, the minimum distance from the face of the bell to the bottom of the reservoir should be $D/2$, where D is the diameter of the suction bell. The distance should be increased where a strainer is used.

The suction line to the pump should be (1) as short and as straight as possible; (2) at least one size larger than the pump suction nozzle; (3) connected by an eccentric reducer, with its top horizontal, to avoid the

TABLE 15-2. Permissible Suction Lift to Avoid Cavitation in Centrifugal Pumps
(Lift in feet)

Permissible suction lift, ft	Single-suction, mixed flow, $K = HN_s^{1.33}$			Single-suction, with shaft through impeller eye, $K = HN_s^{1.7}$			Double-suction pump, $K = HN_s^{1.7}$		
	Dynamic head, ft		K, millions	Dynamic head, ft		K, millions	Dynamic head, ft		K, millions
	N_s 15,000	N_s 5,000		N_s 3,520	N_s 1,760		N_s 5,000	N_s 2,500	
25	....	....	...	21.8	70	24	21.8	70	42.5
20	5.7	24.1	2.0	35	112	38	35	112	68.5
15	7.8	34	2.8	44	151	49	44	151	89
10	10.1	43	3.6	59	192	64	59	192	116
5	12.1	53	4.4	71	214	75	71	214	135
0	14.4	62	5.2	85	283	94	85	283	170
− 5*	16.6	72	6.0	93	305	102	93	305	184
−10	18.9	81	6.8	106	340	116	106	340	208
−15	20.5	91	7.5	115	370	126	115	370	225

* The negative sign indicates a depth of water in the suction pit over the top of the pump suction.

[1] C. A. Richardson, *Water & Sewage Works*, Vol. 95, p. R-51, 1948.

accumulation of an air pocket; and (4) free from "high points" conducive to the formation of air pockets.

15-13. Cavitation.[1] It has been found that cavitation may occur in a centrifugal pump as a result of too great speed or too high a suction lift.[2] The cavitation factor, usually expressed as Σ or σ, is equal to $(H_a - H_{vp} - H_s)/H_t$ where H_a = atmospheric pressure; H_{vp} = vapor pressure; H_s = suction lift; H_t = total dynamic head of the pump. Critical σ occurs when cavitation begins. Operating σ should be a safe margin above it, as determined by tests.[3] The permissible height of suction lift to avoid cavitation is related to the specific speed as indicated by the data in Table 15-2 which have been computed from information by the Hydraulic Institute.[4]

It is to be noted from this table that high-speed low-head pumps are restricted to lower suction lifts.

Example. Find the limiting suction lift for a single-suction pump with N = 2,070 rpm, H = 50 ft, and Q = 2,000 gpm

Solution. N_s the specific speed

$$N_s = \frac{2{,}070 \times 44.8}{18.8} = 4{,}930$$

K, from Table 15-2 = $HN_s{}^{1.7}$

$$K = 50 \times 4{,}930^{1.7} = 94{,}000{,}000$$

Reading in the table this value of K for a single-suction pump corresponds to a suction lift of zero.

If, however, the same pump is reduced to half the speed, or 1,035 rpm, the limiting head can be computed as above. It will be found to be 25 ft.

A noisy pump may indicate cavitation. The admission of a small amount of air into the suction pipe may stop the noise without materially affecting the efficiency of the pump.

15-14. Operation. In starting a centrifugal pump, knowledge of its characteristics may be desirable to avoid overloading of the motor. In general, all centrifugal pumps, except a few low-head pumps with special characteristics at low or no discharge, are best started with the discharge valve closed. Small pumps driven by squirrel-cage motors may be started on reduced voltage if torque is sufficient, and water hammer will not result from surges in the discharge pipe as full-line voltage is developed on the motor. It may be possible to bring the pump slowly up to full load, with the discharge valve closed, by a by-pass provided to return the

[1] See also G. F. Wislicensus and others, *Trans. Am. Soc. Civil Engrs.*, January, 1939, p. 170.

[2] See also R. W. Angus, *Water & Sewage Works*, April, 1946, p. 125.

[3] See also H. Ulmann, *Water and Sewage*, January, 1949, p. 24.

[4] See also *Water & Sewage Works*, April, 1946, p. R-80.

discharge from the pump to the suction pit. If the pump must be started with the discharge valve open, a wound-rotor induction motor developing adequate torque without excessive line current may be used.

Centrifugal pumps must have a submerged suction or must be primed before starting. They can be primed by the use of some form of vacuum pump, such as an ejector or a wet vacuum pump. If a dry vacuum pump is used, a barometric siphon must be provided on its suction to prevent water from getting into it. The pump may be primed also by closing the foot valve and filling the suction pipe and the pump with water. The installation of a typical "self-priming" centrifugal pump is illustrated in

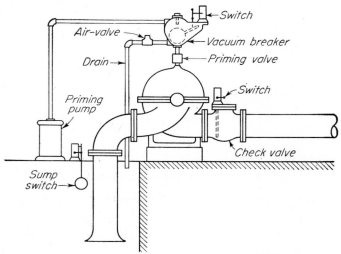

Fig. 15-10. Self-priming centrifugal pump and automatic control system.

Fig. 15-10. If the pump is noisy, as though filled with gravel, cavitation may be occurring. Where there is high suction lift and changes in the temperature of the water, "flashing" may occur in the suction line, producing the effects of cavitation or causing loss of prime.

Installations of centrifugal pumps involving automatic operation or remote control are successful.[1] A typical installation is shown in Fig. 15-9. Among the requirements for successful automatic operation are a priming device, a device to limit the number of false starts in the event priming fails, and a cutoff in the event the check valve closes while the pump is operating.

After the pump is started, if no water is delivered, the difficulty may be due to (1) the pump's not being primed, (2) too low a speed, (3) discharge head or suction head being too high, (4) a plugged impeller, or (5) mechanical difficulties. If the discharge is less than it should be, there may be, in

---

[1] See also W. D. Haentjens, *Water & Sewage Works*, April, 1946, p. R-78.

addition to the above difficulties, air leakage into the suction side or the suction pipe or the foot valve may be too small. If the motor heats, the speed may be too high, the operating conditions may be off the highest efficiency, or there may be mechanical defects, such as the bearings being too tight.

Owing to wear and other factors, the pump characteristics may change materially so that tests of the characteristics should be made periodically. The performance of the pump should be controlled by changing the speed rather than by manipulation of the discharge valve alone. Opening of the valve to decrease the discharge head or closing it to decrease the rate of discharge may increase the load on the motor or decrease the efficiency of the pump and the motor.

Other Types of Pumps

15-15. Power Pumps. A pump that is connected to the driving engine by means of gearing, belting, or shafting is called a power pump, provided that it is not integrally connected to the motive power as in a steam pump.

Fig. 15-11. Triplex power pump. (*Deming.*)

The triplex pump, illustrated in Fig. 15-11, consists of three water cylinders operated in parallel by means of some type of power drive. It is a frequently used type of power pump and gives satisfactory service. Such pumps are available in capacities up to about 6,000,000 gal per day and under about 200 hp. With first-class maintenance, they will develop efficiencies up to about 85 per cent. In the installation of a triplex pump, some form of pressure relief should be connected to the discharge pipe so that, in the event of a stoppage in the discharge line, bursting pressures will not be developed.   The rigid connection between the pump and the driving engine allows no pressure relief in the pump.

Types of power pumps, which may be used also as the water end of steam pumps, are illustrated in Fig. 15-12.   Two types of single-acting piston pump are available.   In the type illustrated in Fig. 15-12a, the water does not pass through the piston or cylinder, whereas in the type shown in Fig. 15-12b, the water flows through a port in the piston.   The latter is used mainly for well pumps.

In each of the single-acting pumps, the motion of the water is alternately started and stopped, resulting in vibration, shock, and loss of

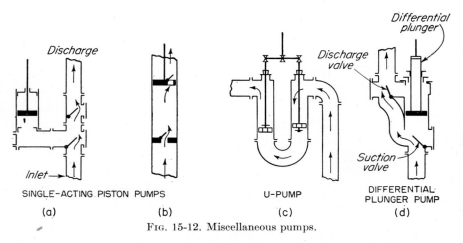

FIG. 15-12. Miscellaneous pumps.

energy.   This condition is partly overcome by the U pump shown in Fig. 15-11c in which the flow of water is always in the same direction.

When the discharge pipe and pump chamber of the differential-plunger pump shown in Fig. 15-11d are filled with water, the discharge valve closes as the plunger rises, and water is drawn into the pump through the suction valve.   At the same time, the water between the plunger and the walls of the cylinder is expelled through the discharge pipe.   There is therefore both suction and discharge on the upstroke of the plunger.   On the downstroke, the suction valve is closed, and water is expelled from the pump chamber through the discharge valve.   A portion of this water leaves through the discharge pipe, and another portion passes into the space between the plunger and the cylinder walls.

15-16. Jet Pumps.   The jet pump shown in Fig. 15-13 operates because the velocity of water passing through the jet is retarded by the expansion of the stream beyond the jet orifice.   The increase in the size of the stream creates a partial vacuum which raises water through the suction pipe. The velocity energy of the incoming high-pressure water is converted into pressure energy in the discharge pipe.   A jet pump is simple and reliable and requires no lubrication and little or no attention in operation.   Such pumps are suitable only where the mechanical equipment must be of the simplest kind and where high-pressure water is available at a low cost.

The discharge lift of the pump is limited to about 12 to 18 ft, and the discharge line should be arranged to prevent the backflow of air.   This can be done by submerging the end of the discharge pipe.   The operation of the pump requires about 4 to 5 psi pressure on the high-pressure line for each foot of lift on the discharge line and about 1 gal of high-pressure water for each gallon of water raised through the suction pipe for lifts up to about 8 ft.   In order to obtain the best efficiency, the pumps should be so set that all the lift is in the suction pipe.

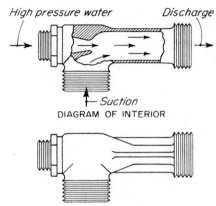

Fig. 15-13. Hydraulic ejector.

Jet pumps are used mainly as auxiliaries in pumping stations, particularly where steam is available.   Their discharge pressures and efficiencies are low.

15-17. Rotary Pumps.[1]   A rotary pump is a displacement pump, since the revolving blade fits close to the casing, thus pushing the water from the pump by displacement.   Sections through rotary pumps are shown in Fig. 15-14.   The blades revolve in a downward direction at the center, water being carried upward around the sides of the casing.   Water is thus pushed through the discharge pipe, and a partial vacuum is created on the suction side.   A relatively high vacuum is created because of the tight-fitting parts.

Rotary pumps are used in small water works and to some slight extent in larger units on public water supplies.   They are not suitable for handling liquids containing suspended matter because of the close fit of the rotors in the casing.   The pumps are self-priming.   They give

[1] Blakewell, W. E., Rotary Pumps, *Power*, November, 1934, p. 602.

operating efficiencies between 50 and 85 per cent, with a flat efficiency curve under partial loads.[1]

A rotary pump is necessarily power-driven and, because of its positive action, provision for pressure relief must be put on the discharge pipe.

15-18. Miscellaneous Pumps. The many devices used for pumping water testify to the ingenuity of man in their invention. Those devices which are used to some extent in pumping public water supplies are

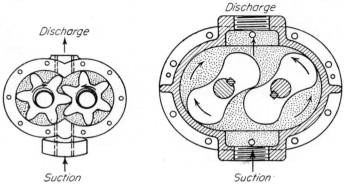

Fig. 15-14. Rotary pumps.

described in other sections of this book. Air-displacement pumps, hydraulically driven reciprocating pumps, Humphrey pumps, diaphragm pumps, and steam vacuum pumps are only a few of the types of machines used for moving water. They are useful primarily in other fields than that of public water supplies. Screw pumps are infrequently used in the pumping of public water supplies because of the low lift to which they are limited. One type of screw pump is similar to a ship's propeller. Another consists of a helix revolving in a closed cylinder open only at the top and bottom.

[1] Blakewell, W. E., *Ibid.*

CHAPTER 16

WELL PUMPS

16-1. Types. Pumps for removing water from wells may be classified as reciprocating, jet, revolving vertical-shaft, and air-lift. Reciprocating pumps may be classified as single-stroke, two-stroke, differential-plunger, and double-acting cylinder pumps. Small reciprocating pumps for private water supplies may be hand-driven or power-driven. Larger reciprocating pumps and all other types of pumps for public water sup-

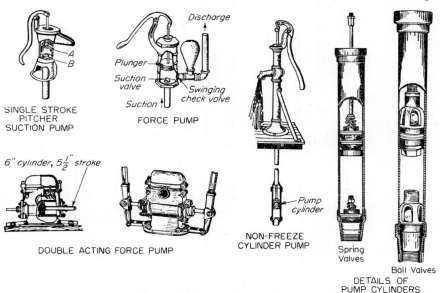

Fig. 16-1. Hand-operated well pumps.

plies are power-driven. Revolving vertical-shaft pumps may be classified as centrifugal or turbine, mixed-flow, angle-flow, and propeller or screw pumps. The centrifugal or turbine pumps dominate the field in deep wells, the use of reciprocating pumps being restricted to small and to old installations. Jet pumps are used in small and moderate-sized capacities. Air lifts are used, under conditions in which they alone are most suitable, in installations of any capacity desired.

16-2. Single-stroke Pumps. Two hand-operated single-stroke well pumps are illustrated in Fig. 16-1. The single-acting pump operates as follows: When the handle is pressed down, plunger *A* rises, valve *A* closes, and valve *B* opens. Water above plunger *A* is discharged from the pump, and water is sucked into it below piston *A* through valve *B*. As plunger *A* descends, valve *B* closes, holding water in the pump. In the force

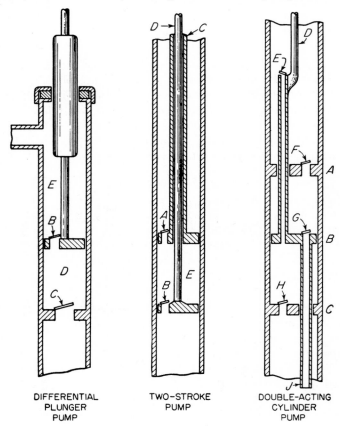

DIFFERENTIAL PLUNGER PUMP

TWO-STROKE PUMP

DOUBLE-ACTING CYLINDER PUMP

FIG. 16-2. Deep-well reciprocating pumps.

pump, water is sucked upward into the pump on the downstroke of the handle and is discharged upward through the discharge pipe on the upstroke. Capacities of hand-driven pumps cannot be expected to exceed about 5 gpm.

16-3. Two-stroke Pumps. A two-stroke pump is illustrated in Fig. 16-2. It operates as follows: The rods *C* and *D* move in opposite directions, one moving down as the other moves up. As *D* moves up, valve *B* is closed, and the water in chamber *E* is discharged through valve *A*, one-half of it being discharged from the pump. As rod *C* moves up, the water, which has previously passed through valve A, is discharged from the pump, and the chamber E is refilled through valve B.

16-4. Differential-plunger Pumps. A differential plunger pump is illustrated in Fig. 16-2. It operates as follows: As piston B moves up, water is sucked into chamber D through valve C and water is discharged from chamber E through the discharge pipe. The volume of water discharged is equal to the difference of the displacement of the piston B and of the differential plunger. On the downstroke, valve C closes and the water in chamber D passes through valve B into chamber E. Water is discharged through the discharge pipe, the volume of water discharged being equal to the displacement of the descending differential plunger.

The size of the piston and of the plunger can be proportioned to give equal volumes of discharge, or equal work, on the upstroke and on the downstroke.

16-5. Double-acting Cylinder Pumps. A section through a double-acting cylinder pump is shown in Fig. 16-2. A and C represent fixed partitions across the working barrel. F and H are check valves in these partitions. B is a moving partition or piston attached to the pump rod D. E and G are check valves over the channels through the pump rod. On the downstroke F and H are closed; E and G are open. Water is being drawn into the pump through J and is being discharged through E. On the upstroke E and G are closed; F and H are open. Water is being drawn into the pump through H

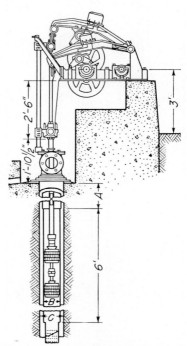

FIG. 16-3. Pomona deep-well pump. (*Courtesy of American Well Works.*)

and is being discharged at F. A disadvantage of the double-acting pump is evident when long rods are used. The thrust of the downstroke tends to bend the rods out of alignment and hence requires the use of guides.

16-6. Power Heads for Reciprocating Pumps. In reciprocating deep-well pumps the pump, or water, valves are in the well and the power head is at the ground surface, connected to the valves by long slender rods that rise and fall in the well. In some pumps the valves are actuated by rocker arms driven by the power head so that the valves may move in harmonic motion, may deliver equal volumes on the up and the down strokes, or may do equal work on both strokes. In an old type shown in Fig. 16-3 the cam shown slows the motion on the up stroke. The upward motion therefore lasts longer than the downward; when it is used to drive a two-stroke pump, one valve is always rising.   This action reduces the magnitude of velocity changes in water passing through the well.   The result is greater efficiency, smoothness of action, and longer life to the pump.

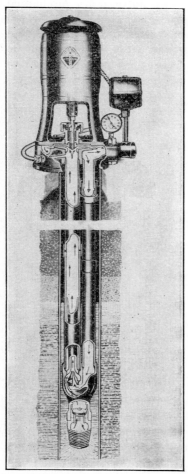

FIG. 16-4. Typical cross section of two-pipe jet pump with pump set directly over the well. (*Courtesy of Jacuzzi Bros., Inc.*)

16-7. Jet Pumps. A jet pump is illustrated in Fig. 16-4. It consists of a centrifugal pump and motor at the ground surface and a jet down in the well below the water level. The centrifugal pump has two discharge pipes. One leads water downward to the jet through which it is discharged at a high velocity which serves to lift water into the suction of the centrifugal pump. The other carries the water into the distribution system or storage tank. Jet pumps are available in capacities from 70 gpm at 30 ft lift to about 20 gpm at 150-ft lift. They are widely used in low-capacity installations, but they are too small for general use in public water supplies.

16-8. Revolving Vertical-shaft Pumps. There are four types of revolving vertical-shaft pumps illustrated in Fig. 16-5. A two stage turbine pump is shown in greater detail in Fig. 16-6, and a more complete installation is shown in Fig. 16-7. This type of pump is used almost exclusively in water-works practice. Six-inch wells are about the smallest in which such pumps can be used. They are available in all sizes above about 5½-in. impellers up to pumps with capacities above 1,000 gpm. Almost any reasonable head, or lift, required can be obtained by increasing the number of stages.[1] Efficiencies up to 90 per cent, and better, are reported, but only 75 to 80 per cent, or lower, should be anticipated in capacities less than about 200 gpm.

Thrust bearings at the bottom of the shaft carry the full weight of pump parts, shaft, and the unbalanced weight of the rising water.   The lubrica-

[1] See also D. J. Conant, *J.A.W.W.A.*, October, 1932, p. 1499.

tion of thrust bearings and of shaft bearings presents a difficult problem in the design and operation of the pump. Practice tends toward oil rather than water lubrication.[1]

Helical or axial-flow pumps are available in lifts up to 600 ft with capacities up to 50 gpm.

High-lift, revolving-vertical-shaft pumps are suitable for pumping directly from the well into the distribution system or into elevated tanks where their economy for this service exceeds that of pumps lifting water into a surface reservoir from which it is pumped to the distribution system by another type of pump.

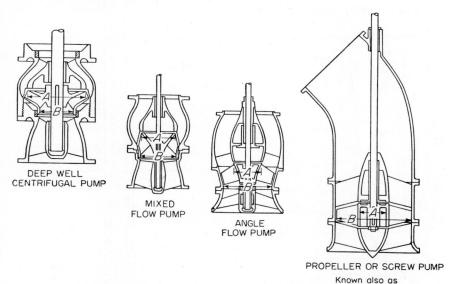

DEEP WELL
CENTRIFUGAL PUMP

MIXED
FLOW PUMP

ANGLE
FLOW PUMP

PROPELLER OR SCREW PUMP
Known also as
axial flow pump

FIG. 16-5. Types of deep-well centrifugal pumps.

16-9. Selection of Turbine Pumps.[2] Materials of construction, quality of water, relation between drawdown and discharge from the well, specific speed, and other conditions must be considered in the selection of a deep-well turbine pump. Where water is corrosive, corrosion-resistant materials should be selected.[3] For example, a corrosion-resistant installation would be represented by a stainless-steel shaft, bronze bowl or shell and impellers, stainless-steel line shaft from bowls to static water level, with a 5-ft section of bronze oil tubes, with coal-tar enamel on the inside and on the outside of the eduction or column pipe. No installation can long

---

[1] See also: C. N. Ward, *J.A.W.W.A.*, Vol. 28, p. 361, 1936; *Public Works*, January, 1936, p. 30.

[2] See also A. O. Fabrin, *Water & Sewage Works*, April, 1946, p. R-87.

[3] See also L. J. Alexander, *J.A.W.W.A.*, October, 1946, p. 1197.

resist erosion by sand-bearing water or by cavitation.   In general, the
higher the speed, the faster the
corrosion.

The pump characteristic must be
suited to the drawdown in the well
for the rate of discharge and lift
desired. The characteristic and
the draw-down may be coordinated
by constructing productivity curves
and characteristic curves of the well
and pumps under consideration, as

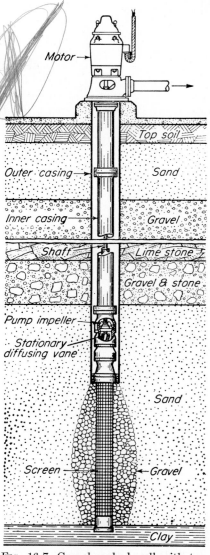

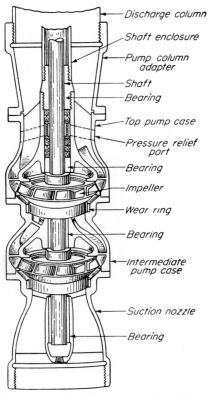

FIG. 16-6. Two-stage deep-well centrifugal pump. (*From Water & Sewage
Works, April, 1946, p. R-88.*)

FIG. 16-7. Gravel-packed well with turbine pump. (*From "The Sanitary Industry," by permission of Johns Manville,
Industrial Products Division.*)

illustrated in Fig. 16-8.[1]   The curves show that both pumps *D* and *E* are
best suited to draw 700 gpm from the well with a total lift of 145 ft but

[1] See also Alexander, *loc. cit.*

that pump D is better suited for all conditions since it more nearly follows the range of most economical production and has a higher capacity under low-water conditions during the summer when more water is needed.

Specific speed (N_s) is an important consideration in the selection of vertical rotating shaft pumps. Fabrin[1] has shown that where N_s is less than about 4,100 the deep-well centrifugal pump should be used; between 4,100 and 5,800 a mixed-flow pump, between 5,800 and 7,500 an angle-flow pump, and above 7,500 the propeller or screw pump should be used.

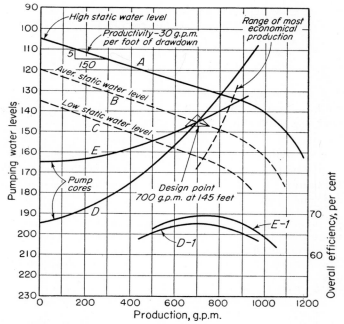

Fig. 16-8. Typical pump characteristics used in selection of deep-well pump. (*From L. J. Alexander, J.A.W.W.A., October, 1946, p. 1205.*)

The most favorable designs will be found at a specific speed of 2,500, with a favorable range between 1,500 and 4,100. Specific speed is related to the ratio of wheel diameter D and to inlet diameter B. This relationship has been formulated empirically as

$$\frac{D}{B} N_s^{0.53} = 10,600 \tag{16-1}$$

when N_s is less than 4,100 and D/B is more than 1.25, and

$$\frac{DN_s}{B} = 530,000 \tag{16-2}$$

[1] See also Fabrin, *loc. cit.*

when N_s is more than 4,100 and D/B is less than 1.25. It is to be noted that, when N_s is high, D/B is low and the condition is unfavorable to high suction lift.

An empirical formula, based on the recommendations of Fabrin, showing the relation between some controlling conditions in pump selection can be expressed as

$$D = \frac{236Q^{0.154}H^{0.256}}{N^{0.678}} \qquad (16\text{-}3)$$

where D = outside diameter of the pump casing, in.

H = total head, in feet of water, for one stage or wheel

N = speed of the wheel, rpm

N_s = specific speed = $\dfrac{N\sqrt{Q}}{H^{3/4}}$

Q = rate of discharge, gpm

The formula is limited to pumps of the highest efficiency, with specific speeds between 4,100 and 1,500.

If, in the selection of pump diameter, the computations show a diameter approximately midway between two available sizes, the larger size will probably give better life and efficiency than the smaller size. The following is an example of the computations required in the selection of pump size, speed, and stages.

Example. Let it be desired to select a deep-well turbine pump; when the well is to be constructed to fit the pump, the rate of discharge is to be 750 gpm and the total lift is to be 200 ft.

Solution. Assuming a convenient specific speed of 2,500, determine the speed of the pump.

$$N = \frac{N_s H^{3/4}}{\sqrt{Q}} = \frac{2,500 \times 51.6}{27.4} = 4,710 \text{ rpm}$$

This speed is too fast. To reduce it, assume four stages, reducing the head to 50 ft per stage. Then

$$N = \frac{2,500 \times 18.8}{27.4} = 1,715 \text{ rpm}$$

The speed is satisfactory.

From Eq. (16-3)

$$D = \frac{236 \times 750^{0.154} \times 50^{0.256}}{1,715^{0.678}} = 11\tfrac{1}{2} \text{ in.}$$

Hence, a four-stage turbine pump with an outside diameter of casing of $11\tfrac{1}{2}$ in. is probably the best for the conditions, provided its characteristics fit the drawdown in the well.

If a $10\tfrac{1}{2}$-in. outside-diameter casing is the nearest size available, or the diameter of the well restricts the pump to this size, then the problem will be to determine the speed at which the pump must run and its specific speed, to meet the conditions for a turbine pump.

To determine the new speed, transposing Eq. (16-3)

$$N = \left(\frac{236Q^{0.154}H^{0.256}}{D}\right)^{1/0.678} = \left(\frac{236 \times 750^{0.154} \times 50^{0.256}}{10.5}\right)^{1.476} = 2,000$$

and

$$N_s = \frac{2,000 \times 750^{0.5}}{50^{3/4}} = 2,910$$

Since the speed of 2,000 rpm is somewhat high, it must be reduced. This can be done by increasing the number of stages. At six stages, the speed becomes 1,660 rpm and the specific speed becomes 3,260. Both of these are within the desirable range for a turbine pump. Again, the characteristic of the pump selected must be coordinated with drawdown conditions in the well.

Characteristics of importance to be considered in pump selection include[1]

Bowls. Best-grade iron

Pump Shaft. Stainless steel

Line Shaft. Polished, cold-rolled steel

Pump Characteristics. Must be known from shutoff to cavitation

Motor. Of such size that rated horsepower is never exceeded

Impellers. Bronze, 85 to 88 per cent copper; 5 to 10 per cent tin; 2 to 5 per cent zinc; and 5 per cent lead if the same bronze is used for both the impellers and the line-shaft bearings

16-10. Turbine-pump Corrosion. "Turbine pumps will corrode"[2] with possibly disastrous results or will require costly repairs, or both. Corrosion may be due to galvanic action set up by the dissimilar metals commonly specified. Water-line corrosion of the well casing and eductor pipe is usually due to an electrolytic "oxygen concentration cell" near the water line. "Carbon dioxide corrosion takes place at the high-pressure points in the pump bowls and between the column pipe and shaft tube."[2] Stray currents may cause electrolysis of well casings. Corrosion prevention can be applied by the methods outlined in Secs. 19-12 to 19-23.

16-11. Submersible Pumps and Motors.[3] Well pumps are in successful use in which the electric motor and turbine pumps are attached as a unit and are lowered to the desired depth beneath the water in the well. The motor is protected in a watertight casing, the lubrication being such that the running period between servicing may be between 1,500 and 6,000 hr. Such an installation avoids difficulties from shaft alignment and lubrication but the inaccessibility of the motor for observation and servicing may result in difficulties in operation.[4] The usefulness of the unit becomes apparent for depths of well greater than about 100 ft.

[1] See also Alexander, *loc. cit.*

[2] Statement by T. E. Larson in discussion of article by Alexander, *loc. cit.*

[3] See also W. L. Gardiner, *Water and Water Eng.*, November, 1948, p. 530.

[4] See also *Water Works Eng.*, Nov. 24, 1937, p. 1684.

16-12. Air-lift Pumps. An arrangement of an air-lift pump is shown in Fig. 16-9. It operates as follows: Compressed air is released through a "foot piece," or air diffuser, at the bottom of the eductor pipe and, rising in small bubbles, a mixture of air and water is created that has a lower specific gravity than that of water alone. The weight of the column of

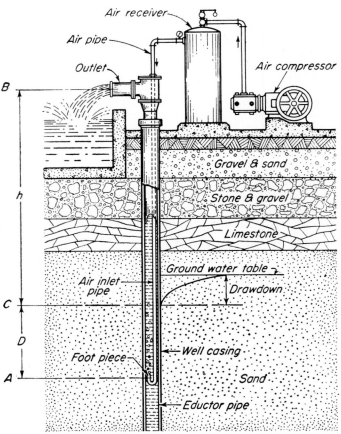

FIG. 16-9. Air-lift pump. (*From "The Sanitary Industry," by permission of Johns Manville, Industrial Products Division.*)

air and water from *A* to *B* in the figure equals the weight of the column of water from *A* to *C*. The rising air bubbles, if sufficiently small, exert no appreciable lifting force on the water. If the air bubbles are large enough to move upward more rapidly than the rising water, efficiency is lost. Unfortunately, there is a tendency for small air bubbles to coalesce and form larger bubbles that rise more rapidly than the water and result in intermittent gushing discharge. It is to be emphasized that water is not pushed from the well by rising pistons of air.

Air lifts have many unique features not possessed by other types of well pumps. They are the most simple and foolproof type of pump and, in operation, give the least trouble because there are no remote or submerged moving parts. Air lifts can be operated successfully in holes of any practicable size, and they can be used in crooked holes not suited to any other type of pump. If it were not for the air lift, crooked holes would be valueless. An air-lift pump can draw more water from a well, with sufficient capacity to deliver it, than any other type of pump that can be installed in the well. A number of wells in a group can be operated from a central control station where the air compressor is located.

The principal disadvantages to the universal adoption of air lifts as deep-well pumps are the necessity for making the well deeper than is required for other types of well pumps in order to secure adequate submergence of the air outlet; the intermittent nature of the flow from the well; and the relatively low efficiencies developed. As the efficiency is greatly affected by both the lift and the submergence, the dropping of the water level in the well without corresponding changes in the well equipment and construction is a common cause of gross inefficiency in the operation of air-lift pumps. Little is usually known of the efficiency of the average air-lift installation in small water works, but tests have revealed efficiencies in the neighborhood of 45 per cent for depths of 50 ft, down to 20 per cent for depths of 600 ft. The changes in the efficiencies of an air lift resulting from the use of different submergence ratios are shown in Table 16-1.

TABLE 16-1. Effect of Submergence on Efficiencies of Air Lift at Hattiesburg, Miss.

Ratio D/h	8.70	5.46	3.86	2.91	2.25
Submergence ratio $= D/(D + h)$	0.896	0.845	0.795	0.745	0.693
Percentage efficiency	26.5	31.0	35.0	36.6	37.7

Ratio of D/h	1.86	1.45	1.19	0.96
Submergence ratio $= D/(D + h)$	0.650	0.592	0.544	0.490
Percentage efficiency	36.8	34.5	31.0	26.5

16-13. Design of an Air Lift.[1] The factors entering into the design of an air lift include (1) Q_w, the rate at which water is to be raised, in cubic feet per second; (2) h, the effective lift from the "free" surface of water outside the well casing when pumping, in feet (see Fig. 16-9); (3) D, the depth of submergence, in feet (this is the depth at which air is liberated

---

[1] See also: Ward and Kessler, Experimental Study of Air-lift Pumps and Application of Results in Design, *Univ. Wis. Bull.*, 1924; E. M. Ivens, "Pumping by Compressed Air," 2d ed., John Wiley & Sons, Inc., New York, 1920; F. Pickert, *Engineering*, July 1, 1932, p. 19.

in the well below the "free" surface of water outside the eductor pipe);
(4) $l = D + h$, expressed in feet, represents the effective length of the
eductor pipe; (5) Q_a, the rate at which free air is forced into the well,
expressed in cubic feet per second; (6) H, the total head pumped against
(this is equal to the velocity head, plus static lift, plus all friction losses
expressed in feet); (7) r, the ratio of compression, which equals $(D + 34)/$
34.   The design of an air lift usually requires the determination of

1. The depth of the well
2. The capacity of the air compressor
3. The size of the air pipe
4. The starting and operating pressures
5. The size of the eductor pipe

These are all based upon the rate at which water is to be pumped and the
height to which it is to be lifted.

1. *The Depth of the Well.*   In order that water may be lifted from a
well, it is necessary that air be released at some depth below the surface of
the water.   It is evident in Fig. 16-9 that the weight of the column of
mixed air and water within the eductor pipe must equal the weight of the
column of water, of the same cross-sectional area, outside the eductor
pipe.   It is evident, therefore, that as h is increased D must be increased
and that there is some relation between them for impending delivery.
The magnitude of D can be greater than is necessary to cause delivery,
but the efficiency of the pump will be affected because of the increased
friction in the longer eductor pipe.   Because of the velocity imparted to
the water by the rising bubbles, D may be slightly less than the amount
necessary to cause perfect balance in order to lift water.   The value of
D is known as the *submergence*, and the expression $D/(D + h)$ is the
submergence ratio, or the percentage submergence, when multiplied by
100.

2. *The volume of free air* required can be expressed, approximately, as

$$Q_a = \frac{Q_w(h + h_1)}{75E \log r} \tag{16-4}$$

where h_1 = velocity head at discharge, usually taken as 6 ft for deep
        wells, down to 1 ft for shallow wells

    E = efficiency, usually about 45 to 50 per cent with submergence
        ratio of 50 to 65 per cent and submergence between 350 and
        500 ft

In any case some excess air capacity should be provided, because if the
free-water surface in the well should fall more than anticipated after
prolonged pumping, more air will be required to maintain the discharge.

3. *The Size of the Air Pipe.*   The size of the air pipe depends on the
rate at which air is to be transmitted and the velocity of flow permitted in
the pipe.   No acceptable formula for the economical velocity of flow in

an air pipe is available. The velocity assumed is usually between 1,000 and 2,000 fpm. The size of the air pipe can be computed from the expression $d = 13.6(q_1 \div V)^{1/2}$ and the loss of pressure computed from the following formula:[1]

$$P_1{}^2 - P_2{}^2 = \frac{0.0006Q_a{}^2l}{d^5} \qquad (16\text{-}5)$$

where P_1 = absolute initial pressure, psi
  P_2 = absolute terminal pressure, psi
  q_1 = volume of air, cfm, passing through pipe
  Q_a = free-air equivalent, cfm, volume passing through pipe
  l = length of pipe, ft
  d = diameter of pipe, in.
  V = velocity of flow, fpm

If the size of the pipe and the loss of head are reasonable, no furthur computations are necessary. If not, the size of the pipe must be recomputed.

4. *Starting and Operating Pressures.* The starting pressure is equal to the depth of water over the submerged end of the air pipe or foot piece. After the pump has been operating a sufficient length of time for the water in the well to reach constant conditions, the operating pressure will become constant and will be equal to the friction loss in the air pipe plus the depth of water outside the well casing and above the foot piece. The latter is the same as the difference between the depth of water in the well when not pumping and the drawdown for the particular rate of discharge.

5. *The Size of the Eductor Pipe.* It is desirable to have a high velocity in the eductor pipe in order to prevent the formation of slugs of air and water. The velocity of the mixture of air and water should increase in ascending the pipe in order to avoid, as much as possible, "slip" of the bubbles. The maximum efficiency has been found to occur near that velocity at the lower end of the eductor pipe at which the mixture first becomes complete. This velocity varies with the diameter of the eductor pipe only, so far as is now known. Experiments have shown the following velocities to be suitable:

Size of air pipe, in.	2¾	3	4	5
Velocity at entrance to educator pipe, fps	5.6	7.3	11.8	12.7

The velocity at discharge is assumed to be about 20 to 25 fps. The volume of the mixture must be computed as the volume of the water plus the volume of the air corrected for the proper pressure.

16-14. Air-lift Boosters. The inefficiency of air lifts renders them unsuitable for lifting water after it has been delivered from the well,

[1] J. E. Johnson, *Am. Machinist,* July 27, 1899.

particularly for moving the water in any direction but vertical. Because of the high velocity of the flowing water at the discharge, there is considerable kinetic energy that can be utilized for further lifting the water, thus recovering some energy that otherwise would be dissipated.

The device used for this purpose is known as a booster. It is illustrated in Fig. 16-10. The air and water escaping from the eductor pipe are separated by the umbrella, the water falling to the bottom of the con-

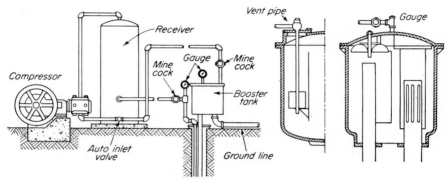

Fig. 16-10. Sullivan air-lift booster.

tainer, the air rising to the top. The entrapped air is compressed partially by the water discharging from the well. This forms a back pressure on the well and a pressure on the entrained water which forces it out through the slotted discharge pipe. Air escapes continuously through the air vent at the top. The air vent is throttled to maintain the desired pressure in the booster.

If the air from the booster is returned to the compressor, an advantage is gained in the use of cooler air and a slight increase in pressure of the air at the intake.

CHAPTER 17

MATERIALS FOR AND THE DESIGN OF PIPES

17-1. Materials and Specifications. Materials most commonly used for distribution pipes include iron, steel, cement, and asbestos cement. Lead, copper, zinc, aluminum, and alloys such as brass, bronze, and stainless steel are used, in addition to ferrous metals, in pumping machinery, small pipes, valves, and other appurtenances. Plastic materials are used in 6-in.-diameter, and smaller, pipes. Sulphur, sand, rubber, lead and lead substitutes, and oakum are used in pipe joints. Other substances such as nickel, aluminum, chromium, clay, and asbestos are used occasionally in alloys or in mixtures principally for the protection of metals against corrosion. Wood is occasionally used for large pipes and for small pipes in temporary locations.

Specifications for materials and equipment are prepared periodically by such authorities as the American Water Works Association, the American Society for Testing Materials, the American Standards Association, the American Society of Mechanical Engineers, the Division of Simplified Practice, U.S. Department of Commerce, and the Procurement Division, U.S. Treasury Department. Specifications prepared by the last-named authority are commonly referred to as Federal Specifications. In the introduction to the index of the Federal Specifications, revised to 1943, it is stated:

Commercial Standards: 1. Outstanding examples of commercial specifications voluntarily proposed and supported as a basis for marketing by the industries concerned are the Commercial Standards established through the procedure of the Division of Trade Standards of the National Bureau of Standards.

Simplified Practice Recommendations: Closely allied with the commercial types, grades, sizes, etc., . . . are the Simplified Practice Recommendations proposed by industry and established under the auspices of the Division of Simplified Practice of the National Bureau of Standards.

While Simplified Practice Recommendations differ from Federal Specifications in that they originate with, and are voluntarily supported by, industry itself, nevertheless the programs of simplification should serve as helpful guides to procurement officers.

References are made in this text to various standard specifications, but because of the state of flux of such specifications, any final design should be checked against the latest publication or revision of pertinent standards. Possibly the best source of information concerning the existence of such standards and revisions is the American Water Works Association, either by direct inquiry or through its journal.

17-2. Cast Iron. Cast iron is used, in water-works practice, most commonly in the manufacture of pipe. The material is highly resistant to corrosion and has other desirable properties. Its use has endured through the centuries, some of the earliest pipe that is still in use being laid in Versailles, France, in 1664. Specifications for the quality of cast iron for pipes vary with the method of manufacture, as indicated in Sec. 17-3. American Society for Testing Materials (ASTM) Specifications A126-42 were prepared for valves and fittings. Modifications intended to improve corrosion resistance show the following composition:

Total carbon.......	3.00 ± 0.15*	Chromium and molybdenum..	0.35 ± 0.05
Silicon.............	2.00 ± 0.25	Phosphorus, maximum........	0.3
Manganese........	0.75 ± 0.15	Sulphur, maximum...........	0.12
Nickel.............	1.05 ± 0.15	Tensile strength.............	$40,000$ psi

* Percentages unless otherwise indicated.

Ductile iron,[1] introduced to the water-works industry about 1949, is attractive for use in pipes because of its high bursting strength combined with some ductility. Experience with it is limited.

17-3. Manufacture of Cast-iron Pipe. There are four recognized methods for the manufacture of cast-iron pipe, only three of which are in common use. The four methods are: (1) horizontally cast or McWane pipe, (2) vertical or pit cast in sand molds,[2] (3) centrifugally cast in sand-lined molds,[3] and (4) centrifugally cast in metal molds.[4] Vertically cast or pit-cast pipe is stronger, heavier, and more costly than centrifugally cast pipe. Horizontally cast pipe is not widely used, practice being almost confined to the use of centrifugally cast pipe.[5] Standard specials continue to be manufactured in sand molds with the axis of the special horizontal, according to specifications adopted by the American Water Works Association in 1908.

In both methods of centrifugal casting, the mold is spun rapidly on a horizontal axis while molten metal is run into the mold. Close regulation of the rate of pouring and of spinning makes possible the production of dense, smooth walls of uniform thickness. After the desired amount of

[1] See also C. T. Haller, *J.A.W.W.A.*, October, 1952, p. 912.

[2] See American Water Works Association Standard Specifications, adopted May 12, 1908.

[3] For Standard Specifications, see *J.A.W.W.A.*, February, 1953, p. 209.

[4] *Ibid.*, p. 189.

[5] For other Standard Specifications for Cast-iron Pipe, see ASA A21.2-1939 in *J.A.W.W.A.*, December, 1939; and Federal Specifications WW-P-421, amended to April, 1940, available from Superintendent of Documents, Washington, D.C.

metal has been poured into it, the mold continues to spin until the temperature has dropped to about 1500°F. The pipe is then removed from the mold and inserted in a heat-treating furnace where it slowly cools to about 1200°F. The molds continue to cool slowly to assure annealing. After cooling, the flasks are stripped and the pipes are cleaned, tested, and coated.

17-4. Thickness of Cast-iron Pipe.[1] Iron pipes are cast in 14 classes or thicknesses designed for various conditions of loading. The following procedure in the determination of pipe-wall thickness is taken mainly from the Manual for the Computation of Strength and Thickness of Cast Iron Pipe.[2]

The load that will just cause breakage of pipe is

$$w = \frac{W}{\sqrt{P}} \sqrt{P - p} \tag{17-1}$$

where w = external load per unit length
p = intensity of internal bursting pressure
W = external load per unit length that will crush pipe
P = intensity of internal pressure that will burst pipe

For a pipe supported on a standard three-edge bearing

$$W = \frac{t^2 R}{0.0795(d + t)} \tag{17-2}$$

where t = net thickness of pipe wall, in.
d = internal diameter of pipe, in.
R = modulus of rupture, psi, of metal in pipe, as determined by crushing tests, usually taken as 31,000

Values of the ratio W'/W are given in Table 17-1, in which W' is external load per unit length that will crush the pipe under the field conditions shown and W is the corresponding load under three-point bearing.

Net wall thickness is computed to resist external loads, as discussed in Sec. 10-6. Gross thickness is computed as the sum of net thickness to care for all loads, with allowance for factory tolerance, corrosion, beam conditions, and a factor of safety, usually about 2.5. The allowance for beam conditions is particularly important for small pipes.

The empirical procedure in the determination of net thickness is as follows:

1. Assume two thicknesses, one slightly larger and the other slightly smaller than the true thickness, and compute the corresponding values of W and P from Eq. (17-2) and from the expression

$$P = \frac{2ts}{d} \tag{17-3}$$

where s = strength of iron in bursting tension, psi, usually taken at 11,000.

[1] For Standard Specifications, see ASA A21.1-1939 in *J.A.W.W.A.*, December, 1939.
[2] *Ibid.*

2. With the computed values of W and of P plot a graph for Eq. (17-1), as a straight line on specially prepared coordinate paper with the abscissas for P plotted to a natural scale and with the ordinates for W varying as W^2. Such a plot is shown in Fig. 17-1.

3. The net value of t is found by interpolation, using the values of p and of w to be resisted.

TABLE 17-1. Ratio of Trench Load to Equivalent Three-edge Bearing Load

Field condition*	Pipe diameter, in.															
	4	6	8	10	12	14	16	18	20	24	30	36	42	48	54	60
A	1.15	1.15	1.15	1.15	1.15	1.15	1.15	1.15	1.15	1.15	1.15	1.15	1.15	1.15	1.15	1.15
B	1.29	1.32	1.34	1.36	1.38	1.41	1.43	1.45	1.47	1.52	1.58	1.64	1.69	1.72	1.75	1.77
C	0.22	0.31	0.40	0.50	0.60	0.67	0.73	0.78	0.81	0.87	0.93	0.96	0.98	0.99	0.99	1.00
D	0.82	0.83	0.84	0.86	0.88	0.91	0.95	0.98	1.01	1.07	1.14	1.19	1.23	1.25	1.28	1.31
E	1.50	1.50	1.50	1.50	1.50	1.50	1.50	1.50	1.50	1.50	1.50	1.50	1.50	1.50	1.50	1.50
F	1.75	1.78	1.80	1.83	1.85	1.88	1.90	1.93	1.95	2.00	2.08	2.14	2.20	2.25	2.29	2.31

* See following descriptions:
A = flat-bottom trench, not tamped.
B = flat-bottom trench, tamped.
C = pipe on blocks, not tamped.
D = pipe on blocks, tamped.
E = bottom of trench shaped to 90 deg of pipe, not tamped.
F = bottom of trench shaped to 90 deg of pipe, tamped.

The following is an example of the procedure:

Example. Let it be desired to determine the thickness of a cast-iron pipe for the following conditions: $d = 48$ in.; $s = 11,000$ psi; $R = 31,000$ psi; water-hammer allowance = 70 psi; static pressure = 100 psi; external load due to backfill = 2,925 lb per ft; external load due to trucks = 1,400 lb per ft, to be neglected in this example; factor of safety = 2.5; and field condition B, Table 17-1, prevails.

Solution. The three-edge bearing load equivalent to fill load plus truck load, with value 1.72, from Table 17-1, = 2,925/1.72 = 1,700 lb per ft length of pipe. Hence

$$w = 1,700 \times 2.5 = 4,250$$
$$p = (100 + 70)2.5 = 425$$

Now assume that $t_1 = 1.10$ and $t_2 = 1.20$
Then

$$P = \frac{2ts}{d} = \frac{2 \times 1.1 \times 11,000}{48} \quad \text{or} \quad \frac{2 \times 1.20 \times 11,000}{48}$$
$$= 504 \text{ or } 550$$
$$W = \frac{t^2 R}{0.0795(d + t)} = \frac{1.10^2 \times 31,000}{0.0795 \times 49.1} \quad \text{or} \quad \frac{1.20^2 \times 31,000}{0.0795 \times 49.2} = 9,610 \quad \text{or} \quad 11,420$$

The curves, or graphs, for these values of P and of W are shown in Fig. 17-1. By interpolation, using $p = 425$ and $w = 4,250$, the value of $t = 1.15$ in. is found.

This value of t must be increased by the necessary foundry tolerance and corrosion allowance. The maximum foundry tolerances allowed by standard specifications are as follows: for pipes 3 to 8 in. in diameter, 0.07 in.; 10 to 24 in. in

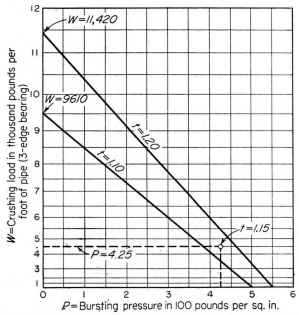

FIG. 17-1. Determining thickness of cast-iron pipe by load-pressure parabolas drawn as straight lines; 48-in. pipe used as sample. (*From Manual for the Computation of Strength and Thickness of Cast-iron Pipe, J.A.W.W.A., December, 1939, p. 19.*)

diameter, 0.08 in.; and 30 to 60 in. in diameter, 0.10 in. Corrosion allowance is 0.08 in. No thickness should be made less than a certain minimum permitted for the particular diameter and kind of iron.

TABLE 17-2. Some Standard Thicknesses for Pit-cast Iron Pipe*
(Thickness in inches)

Diam, in.	Standard thickness classes							
	1	2	4	6	8	10	12	14
4	0.40	0.43	0.50	0.58	0.68	0.79	0.92	1.07
8	0.46	0.50	0.58	0.68	0.79	0.92	1.07	1.25
12	0.54	0.58	0.68	0.79	0.92	1.07	1.25	1.46
18	0.63	0.68	0.79	0.92	1.07	1.25	1.46	1.71
24	0.74	0.80	0.93	1.08	1.26	1.47	1.72	2.01
36	0.97	1.05	1.22	1.43	1.66	1.93	2.25	2.62
48	1.18	1.27	1.48	1.73	2.02	2.35	2.74	3.20
60	1.39	1.50	1.75	2.04	2.38	2.78	3.24	3.78

* Manual for Computation of Thickness, *J.A.W.W.A.*, December, 1939, p .3.

Calculated thicknesses are not used exactly, but the standard thickness, or the next thicker standard thickness, is used. A few standard thicknesses for some of the 14 classes of pit-cast pipe are shown in Table 17-2. The figures in this table emphasize the necessity of proper bedding of the pipe when laid in a trench.

Centrifugally cast pipe for equal thicknesses are stronger than pit-cast pipe, since the permissible value of R, the modulus of rupture, is 40,000 psi. Some standard thicknesses of pit-cast and of centrifugally cast pipes are shown in Table 17-3.

TABLE 17-3. Some Standard Thicknesses and Weights of Pit-cast and
Centrifugally Cast Iron Pipe*

Nominal diam, in.	Pit-cast				Centrifugally cast in metal molds			
	Thickness, in.		Lb per 12-ft length with bell		Thickness, in.		Lb per 12-ft length with bell	
	50 psi	350 psi	50 psi	350 psi	50 psi	350 psi	50 psi	350 psi
4	0.40	0.40	230	230	0.35	0.35	200	200
6	0.43	0.50	360	410	0.38	0.38	315	415
8	0.46	0.58	515	645	0.41	0.41	455	455
10	0.50	0.73	635	980	0.44	0.52	605	900
12	0.54	0.79	880	1,260	0.48	0.56	785	900
14	0.54	0.92	1,025	1,780	0.48	0.64	915	1,210
16	0.58	0.99	1,265	2,180	0.54	0.68	1,165	1,465
18	0.63	1.07	1,535	2,560	0.54	0.79	1,320	1,920
20	0.66	1.22	1,785	3,325	0.57	0.84	1,545	2,265
24	0.74	1.36	2,385	4,440	0.63	0.92	2,045	2,975
30	0.87	1.62	3,460	6,695				
36	0.97	1.93	4,610	9,530				
42	1.07		5,970					
48	1.18		7,510					
54	1.30		9,325					
60	1.39		11,070					

* Pit-cast pipe are ASA Specifications A21.6-1953, and centrifugally cast pipe are ASA Specifications A21.6-1952.

17-5. Lengths of Cast-iron Pipes. Pit-cast iron pipe is manufactured in standard lengths of 12 ft, 16 ft, and 5 m. Centrifugally cast pipe, according to Federal Specifications WW-P-421, is available in standard lengths of 12, 16, 16½, 18, and 20 ft. Advantages in the use of the greater lengths are the smaller number of joints to be made and the smaller amount of leakage to be expected. Shorter lengths are, however, lighter and easier to handle. The cutting of cast-iron pipes[1] to a desired length in the field is slow and difficult and endangers the pipe because of

[1] See also O. G. Goldman, *J.A.W.W.A.*, March, 1954, p. 231.

cracking in the cutting process.   Power-driven and hand-driven cutting tools[1] are available which remove much of the danger inherent in cutting with hammer and chisel.[2]   An electric-arc–oxygen method of cutting has proved quick, safe, and economical.[3]

17-6. Cast-iron Pipe Fittings.[4]   Some bell-and-spigot pressure fittings for cast-iron water pipes, standardized under AWWA C100-52T Specifications and standardized also by the New England Water Works Association, are illustrated in Fig. 17-2.   The various branches shown and

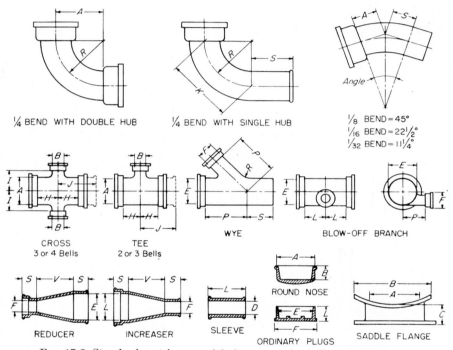

FIG. 17-2. Standard cast-iron specials for water-pipe bell-and-spigot ends.

certain other specials are cast with all ends bell or with one end bell and the other end spigot.   The casting of fittings not included among those considered "standard" is expensive.   It is to be avoided where the use of standard specials can be devised in a satisfactory manner.

Standards for flanged cast-iron pipe and for cast-iron fittings have been adopted by the American Water Works Association in 1908 and by

[1] See also *Water Works Eng.*, August, 1949, p. 721.

[2] See also *ibid.*, August, 1952, p. 753; November, 1952, p. 1051.

[3] See also *Eng. News-Record*, Sept. 28, 1950, p. 38.

[4] See AWWA Standard Specifications 7C.1, 1908; A21.10-1952 in *J.A.W.W.A.*, November, 1952, p. 1065; pressure fittings C100-52T in *J.A.W.W.A.*, March, 1953, p. 321; also ASA B16.1-1948, B16.b-1944, and AWWA C102-39.

the American Standards Association in Specifications A21.2-1939, ASA B16.1-1948, and ASA B16b-1944. The American standard flanged fittings for steam pipe[1] give smaller radii and permit work in more confined space than the manufacturers' standards for water-works fittings. Standard steam fittings are used in water-works practice when the occasion demands.

17-7. Repair Clamps and Sleeves.[2] Repair clamps and sleeves of the type shown in Fig. 17-3, either with or without the packing gland, are

SPLIT SLEEVE   DOUBLE UNIVERSAL PIPE   PHILBROOK TYPE
                          REPAIR CLAMP   REPAIR CLAMP

Fig. 17-3. Repair clamps and sleeves.

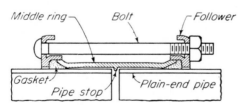

DRESSER COUPLING   VICTAULIC COUPLING

Fig. 17-4. Couplings for steel pipe.

used in emergencies to repair or to hold together parts of a cracked pipe. The couplings shown in Fig. 17-4 may be used for a similar purpose.[3]

17-8. Joints for Cast-iron Pipe.[4] Joints used for cast-iron water pipe include bell-and-spigot, mechanical, flanged, and threaded. Other types are used under special conditions.

Bell-and-spigot joints are used principally for buried pipes. Sections through typical joints are shown in Fig. 17-5. The bell-and-spigot joint is made by slipping the spigot end of the pipe into the bell end of the adjacent pipe until contact is made at the base of the bell. If a lead

[1] Adopted by American Society of Mechanical Engineers, Mar. 20, 1914.

[2] See also *Water Works Eng.*, June, 1951, p. 571.

[3] See also *ibid.*, July, 1951, p. 673.

[4] See also *ibid.*, September, 1952, p. 859.

joint is to be made, the space between the bell and the spigot is packed with hemp to a depth of 2 or 2½ in. The remaining space is filled with molten lead or lead substitute. In making the bell-and-spigot joint, it is not necessary for the pipes to fit with exactness in order to hold the joint tight, and a slight variation in alignment is permissible, so that the

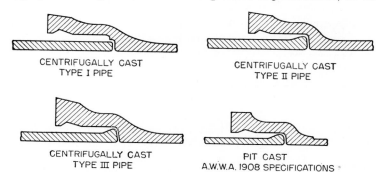

CENTRIFUGALLY CAST
TYPE I PIPE

CENTRIFUGALLY CAST
TYPE II PIPE

CENTRIFUGALLY CAST
TYPE III PIPE

PIT CAST
A.W.W.A. 1908 SPECIFICATIONS

FIG. 17-5. Bell-and-spigot cast-iron pipe joints. Centrifugally cast pipe by Federal Specifications WW-P-421, 1931.

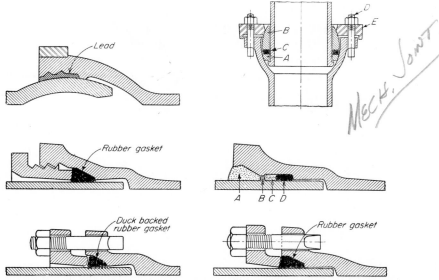

FIG. 17-6. Miscellaneous cast-iron pipe joints. (*From Water Works Eng., September,* 1952, *pp.* 859*ff.*)

pipe line can be laid around a long-radius curve. The joints require some skill in finishing, and they do not make a neat appearance when compared with some other types of joints.

There is a tendency for the joints to pull apart under tension. Prior[1]

[1] J. C. Prior, *Ohio State Univ. Bull.* 87, January, 1935.

expressed this tendency as

$$P = \frac{3,800}{D + 6} - 40 \qquad (17\text{-}4)$$

where P = pressure in pipe at pull out or failure, psi

D = diameter of pipe, in.

The pulling apart of pipes may be prevented by the use of tie rods

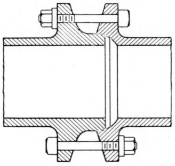

FIG. 17-7. Universal pipe joint.

embedded in concrete "anchors," the use of bolted joints, and by other expedients.

Mechanical joints[1] and rubber-packed or filled joints have been more commonly used during and since the Second World War, primarily because of the scarcity of lead. Types of mechanical joints are shown in Figs. 17-6 and 17-7.[2] A rubber-gasket joint is shown in Fig. 17-8. Synthetic-rubber rings are said to be better than those made of natural rubber.[3] The sleeve coupling, shown in Fig. 17-4, sometimes called a Dresser coupling, is a mechanical joint frequently used for emergencies and repairs. The complete joint consists of the sleeve, two gasket rings, and two following rings connected by bolts. The sleeve is slipped over or around the plain-end pipes, and the rubber packing rings are pushed home

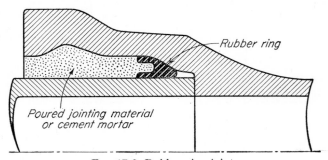

Rubber ring

Poured jointing material or cement mortar

FIG. 17-8. Rubber ring joint.

by tightening the bolts. The slipping of the coupling or joint on the pipe, as a result of expansion and contraction, can be prevented by placing a middle lug, cast on the sleeve, between the ends of the pipes at the joint. In these gland-packed joints, the rubber is held firmly under com-

[1] See ASA A21.11-1953 in *J.A.W.W.A.*, April, 1943, p. 431; and Federal Specifications WW-P-423 for bolted joints.

[2] See also *Water Works Eng.*, December, 1949, p. 1105.

[3] See also W. L. White, *J.A.W.W.A.*, November, 1951, p. 872.

pression—a requisite for long service. Sleeve and gland-packed joints are flexible, watertight, durable, and do not require special skill or tools.

Flanged joints are used extensively on pipes within pumping stations, filter plants, and other close quarters. They require close fitting and perfect alignment. The joints are neat in appearance, rigid, and are easily made if the pipes are in alignment. Some fittings with flanged joints, and some companion flanges, are illustrated in Fig. 17-9.

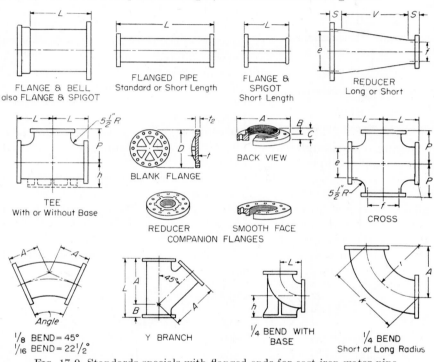

Fig. 17-9. Standards specials with flanged ends for cast-iron water pipe.

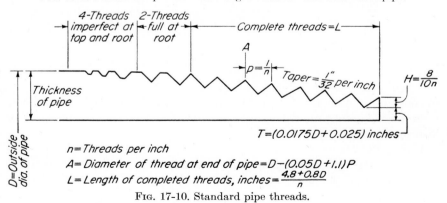

Fig. 17-10. Standard pipe threads.

Threaded joints are rarely used on cast-iron water pipes and never on pipes over 12 in. in diameter. They are relatively costly and offer no general advantages over flanged joints. American Standard Pipe Threads are shown in Fig. 17-10. These standard threads were devised for wrought-iron steam pipe, but they have been adopted for use on cast iron, brass, copper, and other materials capable of being threaded.

Other types of joints used on cast-iron pipes include expansion, a simple

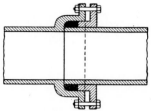

type of which is shown in Fig. 17-11; and a flexible joint, such as is illustrated in Fig. 17-12. The expansion joint is used on pipes exposed to considerable differences of temperature. Such joints are not commonly used on buried cast-iron pipe carrying cold water. Flexible joints are used for pipes to be laid submerged under water where the bottom of the trench or of the body of water may be uneven, around bends,

Fig. 17-11. Expansion joint.

in joining pipes of different materials, and under conditions where rigid joints would preclude the laying of pipe.

Most joints, except machined joints, require some material to fill the spaces in the joint to assure watertightness. Materials may be packed, calked, or poured into joints. In a packed joint, the material is pushed into the joint and is held in place by a follower ring and bolts. Calking comprises the pounding of a compressible material into the spaces in the joint in which it is held by friction and shear. Poured joints are formed

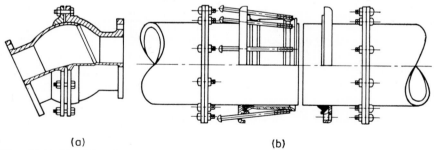

(a)　　　　　　　　　　　　　　　(b)

Fig. 17-12. Flexible joints.　[(b) *from E. T. Killam, J.A.W.W.A., November, 1943, p.* 1457.]

by pouring molten material into the joint where it cools and solidifies. Poured lead joints must be subsequently calked owing to shrinkage of lead on cooling.

17-9. Joint Materials. Desirable features in joint compounds[1] include elasticity, strength, durability, adhesiveness, workability, availability, and economy; if the material is to be poured, no special skill is required in

[1] See C. R. Payne, *J. Penna. Water Works Operators' Assoc.*, Vol. 8. p. 85, 1936.

pouring.   Materials used for joints in water pipes include lead,[1] sulphur-and-sand mixtures, poured bituminous compounds, cement, rubber, and various proprietary substances with asbestos, hemp, jute, and other substances used as packing in poured joints.   "Sulphur cements should not be used in cast-iron pipe under conditions that are corrosive to cast iron itself nor should they be used if the pH of the water or the surrounding soil is greater than 9.0."[2]   In some jurisdictions, the use of jute and oakum is forbidden.[3]

Lead, either poured or calked cold, is probably the oldest material used and continues to be the most widely used material for filling bell-and-spigot joints.   Cement joints are being used with satisfaction.[4]

The use of rubber for jointing materials is not uncommon.   As a joint-filling substance, rubber possesses many of the desirable features of an ideal joint material.   When used in place of hemp, a rubber packing ring may harbor no bacteria, and once sterilized, is less easily contaminated than hemp or jute.   Rubber packing makes watertight joints, expands and contracts but little with temperature changes, is easy to use, and produces a flexible joint.   Among its disadvantages, however, is its deterioration when exposed to gasoline or other petroleum products and its susceptibility to microbial attack.[5]   Among other types of elastic joints is one that utilizes round rubber rings deformed and adjusted in the joint as the spigot is pushed into the bell.[6]

Other joint materials, some of which may be proprietary, include Sinterite,[7] a war-developed substitute made by heating iron powder or iron oxides to form a spongy mass that can be calked like lead; and Fibrex, a sanitary paper packing with twisted pulp core and braided jacket.

17-10. Poured Joints.   Lead has been considered to be the standard material for filling the space in a bell-and-spigot joint, but so many satisfactory and economical substitutes are available that its use for this purpose is diminishing.   An important objection to lead is its lack of elasticity and its tendency to work loose under vibration.   Lead substitutes include Leadite, Hydrotite, lead wool, Metalium, Tegul, and others.[8]

---

[1] See also R. B. Seymour and others, *J.A.W.W.A.*, March, 1954, p. 237.

[2] *Ibid.*, December, 1951, p. 1101.

[3] *Ibid.*, May, 1952, p. 378.

[4] See also K. F. Hoefle, *Eng. News-Record*, May 2, 1946, p. 108.

[5] See also C. E. ZoBell and J. D. Beckwith, *J.A.W.W.A.*, April, 1944, p. 439.

[6] See also R. H. Hyde, *Water Works & Sewerage*, September, 1940, p. 410.

[7] See also Hans Vogt, *Gesundh.-Ing.*, Vol. 59, p. 631, abstracted in *J.A.W.W.A.*, June, 1939, p. 1071.

[8] See also: R. J. Thomas, Lead Wool, *J.A.W.W.A.*, Vol. 5, p. 10, 1918; T. Healey, Substitutes for Lead Joints, *J.A.W.W.A.*, Vol. 7, p. 234, 1920; H. V. Knowles, Metalium, *J.A.W.W.A.*, Vol. 5, p. 174, 1918; C. R. Payne, Tegul, *Water Works & Sewerage*, September, 1935, p. 317; R. B. Seymour and D. F. Deakin, *Public Works*, July, 1952, p. 50.

Lead wool is shredded lead. It is packed into the joints in strands about ½ in. in diameter and 1 to 3 ft long, depending on the size of the pipe. Calking is best done with a pneumatic tool, using a calking iron of the type shown in Fig. 17-13. Sulphur compounds which include such proprietary products as Leadite, Tegul, Hydrotite, and Metalium, are composed principally of sulphur mixed with such substances as iron, slag, and salt. They are lighter than lead and possess some advantages over it. Sulphur and sand compounds melt at about 240°F, become liquid at 248°F, and ignite at 280°F.

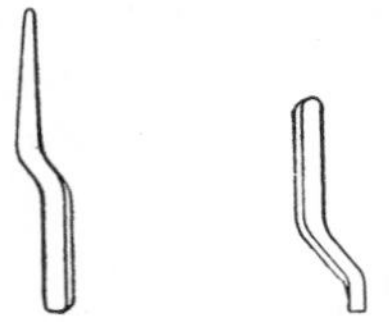

YARNING   CALKING
TOOL   TOOL

Fig. 17-13. Calking tools.

Sulphur-compound[1] joints tend to become tighter with time, whereas where lead joints leak, the condition tends to become progressively worse. Specifications for newly laid pipe may provide that the leakage should not exceed 100 gal per day per mile of pipe per inch nominal diameter for pipe in 12-ft lengths, 75 gal for 16-ft lengths, and corresponding amounts for other lengths of pipe. The test for leakage is to be made under a pressure of 150 psi. "Tests made immediately after the completion of a pipe laid with sulphur-compound joints showing a relatively high rate of leakage are not at all indicative of the ultimate tightness of that line . . . (because) sulphur-compound joints will seep in the early stages of their life, but will take-up as they age."[2] Difficulties have been experienced with the bursting of cast-iron pipes in which sulphur compounds have been used.[3] These difficulties are not general but seem to be confined to specific local areas.

Cement is used successfully for bell-and-spigot joints in both concrete pipes and metal pipes. The material may be either packed into place as a stiff mortar or poured into the joint space as cement grout.[4]

17-11. Wrought Pipe and Fittings. There is some confusion about the quality of materials known as wrought iron and that of wrought steel for pipe. This is due partly to the similarity of methods of manufacture and of the quality of the materials in the two kinds of pipe. The term "wrought pipe" partly overcomes the difficulty. Wrought pipe is manufactured by rolling flat plates of the metal to the proper diameter and welding the edges. It is used principally for installations within buildings where it is protected against the agents of corrosion that are more active in exposed locations. The material is used in pipes from ⅛ to about 20 in. in diameter. Compared with cast iron, the pipe is lighter; is more easily cut, threaded, and worked; and, for interior work, presents a

---

[1] See also R. B. Seymour and others, *J.A.W.W.A.*, March, 1954, p. 237.

[2] Tentative Standard Specifications for Laying Cast-iron Pipe, C600-49T, *J.A.-W.W.A.*, December, 1949, p. 1079.

[3] See *Eng. News-Record*, Mar. 15, 1952, p. 62.

[4] See also J. L. Alexander and R. M. Ebaugh, *J.A.W.W.A.*, April, 1941, p. 769.

neater appearance. It is less durable and is more expensive than cast-iron pipe.

Couplings and nipples are the only fittings made of wrought iron or steel. Other ferrous metal fittings are made of cast or malleable iron.

TABLE 17-4. Dimensions of Standard Malleable Iron Fittings
(Crane Company)

(Dimensions in inches)

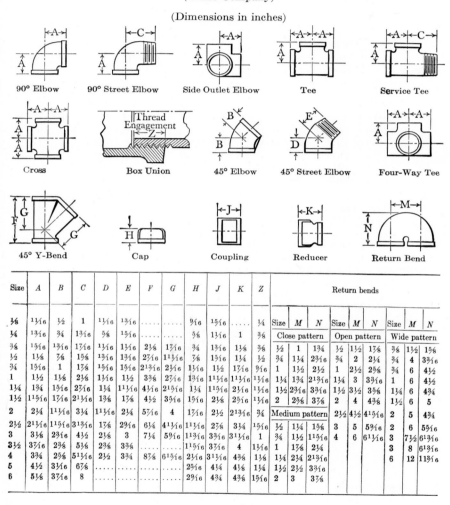

90° Elbow   90° Street Elbow   Side Outlet Elbow   Tee   Service Tee

Cross   Box Union   45° Elbow   45° Street Elbow   Four-Way Tee

45° Y-Bend   Cap   Coupling   Reducer   Return Bend

Size	A	B	C	D	E	F	G	H	J	K	Z	Return bends								
1/8	1 1/16	1/2	1	1 1/16	13/16	....	....	9/16	15/16	....	1/4	Size	M	N	Size	M	N	Size	M	N
1/4	1 3/16	3/4	1 3/16	5/8	15/16	....	....	5/8	1 1/16	1	3/8	Close pattern			Open pattern			Wide pattern		
3/8	1 5/16	1 3/16	1 7/16	1 1/16	1 1/16	2 1/8	1 7/16	3/4	1 3/16	1 1/8	3/8	1/2	1	1 3/4	1/2	1 1/2	1 7/8	3/8	1 1/2	1 5/8
1/2	1 1/8	7/8	1 5/8	1 3/16	1 3/16	2 7/16	1 11/16	7/8	1 5/16	1 1/4	1/2	3/4	1 1/4	2 3/16	3/4	2	2 1/4	3/4	3 3/16	
3/4	1 5/16	1	1 7/8	1 5/16	1 5/16	2 13/16	2 1/16	1 1/16	1 1/2	1 7/16	9/16	1	1 1/2	2 1/2	1	2 1/2	2 5/8	3/4	6	4 1/2
1	1 1/2	1 1/8	2 1/8	1 1/16	1 1/2	3 3/8	2 7/16	1 3/16	1 11/16	1 11/16	1 1/16	1 1/4	1 3/4	2 13/16	1 1/4	3	3 3/16	1	6	4 1/2
1 1/4	1 3/4	1 5/16	2 7/16	1 1/4	1 11/16	4 1/16	2 15/16	1 1/4	1 15/16	2 1/16	1 1/16	1 1/2	2 3/16	3 3/16	1 1/2	3 1/2	3 5/8	1 1/4	6	4 3/4
1 1/2	1 15/16	1 7/16	2 11/16	1 3/8	1 7/8	4 1/2	3 5/16	1 5/16	2 1/8	2 3/16	1 1/16	2	2 5/8	3 7/8	2	4	4 3/8	1 1/2	6	5
2	2 1/4	1 11/16	3 1/4	1 11/16	2 1/4	5 7/16	4	1 7/16	2 1/2	2 13/16	3/4	Medium pattern			2 1/2	4 1/2	4 15/16	2	5	4 3/4
2 1/2	2 11/16	1 15/16	3 13/16	1 7/8	2 9/16	6 1/4	4 11/16	1 11/16	2 7/8	3 1/4	15/16	1/2	1 1/4	1 5/8	3	5	5 9/16	2	6	5 5/16
3	3 1/8	2 3/16	4 1/2	2 1/8	3	7 1/4	5 9/16	1 13/16	3 3/16	3 11/16	1	3/4	1 1/2	1 15/16	4	6	6 11/16	3	7 1/2	6 13/16
3 1/2	3 7/16	2 3/8	5 1/8	2 3/8	3 3/8	....	....	1 15/16	3 7/16	4	1 1/16	1	1 7/8	2 1/4				3	8	6 13/16
4	3 3/4	2 5/8	5 11/16	2 1/2	3 3/4	8 7/8	6 15/16	2 1/16	3 11/16	4 3/8	1 1/8	1 1/4	2 1/4	2 13/16				6	12	11 13/16
5	4 1/2	3 1/16	6 7/8	....	....	....	....	2 5/16	4 1/4	4 1/2	1 1/4	1 1/2	2 1/2	3 3/16						
6	5 1/8	3 7/16	8	....	....	....	....	2 9/16	4 3/4	4 3/8	1 5/16	2	3	3 7/8						

Malleable iron is cast iron of such quality that it has some toughness which permits its being bent or pounded to some extent. It cannot be forged, and it can be broken by a hammer blow. Some dimensions of standard fittings are shown in Table 17-4.

17-12. Steel Pipe.[1] Specifications for various forms of steel pipe have been published from time to time by the American Water Works Association.[2] Seamless steel tubing or mill pipe is made in sizes from $\frac{1}{8}$ to 24 in. Thickness, weights, and working pressures for nine sizes of pipe are shown in Table 17-5.

TABLE 17-5. Data on Small-diameter Steel Pipe[a]

Nominal diam, in.	Weight per ft, lb	Working internal pressure, psi[b]	Collapsing pressure, psi[c]	Deflection under external load in trenches, in.				Saddle loads[d]	
				5-ft cover		10 ft cover		Values P for $S_l = 1,000$ psi A = 120°	l^e ft for $S_f = 12,500$
				No truck	With truck	No truck	With truck		
6	12.89	710	1,510	0	0.01	0.01	0.01	1,730	46
8	16.90	550	650	0.01	0.02	0.02	0.02	1,580	47
10	21.15	440	330	0.03	0.06	0.05	0.07	1,480	49
12	25.15	370	190	0.06	0.12	0.10	0.12	1,410	50
14	27.65	340	120	0.09	0.21	0.19	0.24	1,370	50
18	35.67	260	60	0.21	0.41	0.39	0.47	1,280	52
20	39.67	240	40	0.28	0.53	0.49	0.59	1,250	54
24	47.68	200	25	0.44	0.75	0.71	0.83	1,190	56
24	125.49[f]	520[f]	190[g]	0.14[g]	0.24[g]	0.23[g]	0.27[g]	5,700[g]	69[g]
30	......	310[g]	230[f]	0.23[g]	0.40[g]	0.40[g]	0.48[g]	5,350[g]	71[g]

[a] Adapted from Design Standards for Steel Pipe, *J.A.W.W.A.*, January, 1948, p. 24.

[b] Wall thickness for all pipes in this table is 0.188 in. except as noted. Pipes are made with eight different wall thicknesses, up to 0.5 in.

[c] Due to concentrically applied uniformly distributed external pressure.

[d] Pipe is full of water. Saddle load is transmitted to pipe support as shown in Fig. 17-14, thus:

$$S_l = k \frac{P}{t^2} \log \left(\frac{R}{t} \right)$$

where S_l = localized saddle stress, psi
P = total saddle reaction, lb
R = pipe radius, in.
t = pipe wall thickness, in.
$k = 0.02 - 0.00012 (A - 90)$
A = degrees in central angle subtended by saddle
[e] l = distance from center to center of saddles, ft, and S_f = flexure stress, psi.
[f] Wall thickness 0.5 in.
[g] Wall thickness 0.375 in.

FIG. 17-14. Saddle pipe support.

[1] See also: R. E. Barnard, *J.A.W.W.A.*, January, 1948, p. 24; W. H. Cates, *J.A.W.W.A.*, September, 1950, p. 860, with 43 references.

[2] See *J.A.W.W.A.*, January, 1940; April, 1943; January, March, and August, 1950; October, 1952.

Information on properties of welded steel pipe 24 in. in diameter is given in *Journal of the American Water Works Association,* September, 1950, on page 862. Pipes made of rolled steel are used mainly on long pipe lines with diameters greater than 3 or 4 ft. They are particularly suitable on bridges or under similar conditions where strength and low weight are desired. Steel pipe cannot be easily made to resist high external pressure. Hence, a steel pipe should be placed under favorable conditions in which high external loads are not expected to fall on the pipe unless the pipe is corrugated or otherwise reinforced. Since buried steel pipe may deteriorate rapidly, it should be exposed and accessible to inspection and repair.

The life of steel pipe under ordinary conditions is greatly dependent on the quality of the protective coating.[1] Steel pipes have been found in good condition after 50 years, and they have depreciated materially in 20 years.

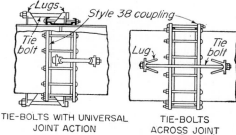

TIE-BOLTS WITH UNIVERSAL JOINT ACTION   TIE-BOLTS ACROSS JOINT

Fig. 17-15. Mechanical joint harness to take longitudinal pull. (*From W. J. Hurlbut, J.A.W.W.A., October, 1943, p. 1284.*)

Joints in steel pipe are made by riveting or welding.[2] The joints may be either transverse and longitudinal, or transverse and spiral. Spiral-welded steel pipe is available in sizes from 6 to 36 in. in diameter, and in lengths up to 40 ft. Couplings or joints of the Dresser type, shown in Figs. 17-4 and 17-15, depend on rubber rings or lips for watertightness; they provide flexibility not to be found in riveted or in welded joints. The couplings are prevented from working off the joint by a rib on the inside of the sleeve which goes between the ends of the pipes being connected. Joints for service connections for water consumers cannot be made by tapping, as they are in cast-iron pipe, unless the steel is $\frac{1}{4}$ in. or more in thickness. Pipe saddles, with the proper size hole tapped in them, may be clamped to the steel pipe, or a plate may be welded directly to the steel pipe and then drilled and tapped. Tees, crosses, ells, and other specials[3] made of welded steel, with flanged ends, are available for working pressures up to 125 psi.

[1] See Sec. 19-16.

[2] See also Specifications C206-50T, formerly 7A.8-50, *J.A.W.W.A.,* March, 1946; March, 1950, p. 315.

[3] See also R. E. Barnard, *op. cit.,* October, 1941, p. 1751.

17-13. Design of Plate-steel Pipe.[1] The plate thickness t, of a steel pipe, required to resist internal bursting pressure is given by the formula

$$t = \frac{pR}{f_t e} \tag{17-5}$$

where p = internal bursting pressure, psi
  R = radius, in.
  f_t = allowable unit stress, psi
  e = joint efficiency

The joint efficiency is taken as the smaller of the two values, efficiency of plate and efficiency of rivets. The efficiency of the plate is $e = (r - d)/r$ and of the rivets $e = (ns/rtf_t)$ in which r is the pitch and d is the diameter of the rivets. s is the smaller of the two values, shearing or bearing value, of the rivet, t is the plate thickness, and n is the number of rivets in a lap joint or on either side of a double-strap butt joint. Welded pipe is ordinarily considered to have a joint efficiency of unity.

Longitudinal stresses are not so important in buried pipes but are considered in uncovered pipes. In the latter case, longitudinal forces may occur because of (1) the inclination of the pipe from the horizontal, (2) changes in length due to temperature which tend to cause the pipe to develop frictional resistance at the supports, (3) the frictional resistance of expansion joints, and (4) pressures acting on reducers in the pipe line. The unit stresses f_c or f_t in the pipe shell may be determined by the formulas

$$\text{Compression, } f_c = \frac{\Sigma F}{a} \qquad \text{or} \qquad \text{tension, } f_t = \frac{\Sigma F}{ae} \tag{17-6}$$

where ΣF = summation of longitudinal loads
  a = cross-sectional area of pipe shell
  e = efficiency of girth joints

Stress intensities due to changes in temperature computed from Eq. (10-3) may also be considered.

The design of plate-steel pipe to resist combined direct and flexural stresses is a specialized problem, particularly for pipes having diameters greater than about 3 ft. The magnitude of the stresses is governed by the loads and conditions stated in Sec. 10-1 and by the manner in which the pipe is supported and stiffened. Design methods may be found in standard books and professional papers.[2]

[1] See also Cates, *loc. cit.*; R. E. Bernard, *J.A.W.W.A.*, January, 1948, p. 24.

[2] Report of Hydraulic Power Committee, National Electric Light Association, 1923; W. P. Creager and J. Justin, "Hydroelectric Handbook," Chap. 20, John Wiley & Sons, Inc., New York, 1927; Peter Bier, *Eng. News-Record*, Vol. 99, p. 629, 1927; H. Schorer, *Trans. Am. Soc. Civil Engrs.*, Vol. 98, p. 101, 1933; A. Schoklitsch, "Hydraulic Structures," translated by Samuel Shulits, American Society of Mechanical Engineers, 1937.

The critical external pressure that will cause buckling in a pipe without stiffening rings is given approximately by the formula[1]

$$P_{cr} = 20 \frac{EI}{d^3} = \frac{5E(t)^3}{3(d)} \qquad (17\text{-}7)$$

where P_{cr} = external pressure per unit of length

E = modulus of elasticity of the metal

I = moment of inertia ($t^3/12$ for a unit length)

t = thickness of pipe

d = diameter of pipe

Methods for the design of steel-pipe spans stiffened by circumferential girders at the supports are given by Schorer,[2] and formulas to facilitate the design of ring-girder-supported pipes are given by Foster.[3]

FIG. 17-16. An 11-ft continuous wood-stave pipe line. (*Courtesy of Continental Pipe Manufacturing Co.*)

17-14. Wood Pipe.[4]   Wood-stave pipes are of two types: continuous stave, as illustrated in Fig. 17-16, and machine-banded, as illustrated in Fig. 17-17. They are made in any diameter up to about 20 ft, and for

---

[1] *Univ. Illinois Eng. Expt. Sta. Bull.* 5, 1906.

[2] H. Schorer, *Trans. Am. Soc. Civil Engrs.*, Vol. 98, p. 101, 1933.

[3] H. A. Foster, *Civil Eng.*, September, 1949, p. 55; October, 1949, p. 45.

[4] See also: A. L. Adams, *Trans. Am. Soc. Civil Engrs.*, Vol. 41, p. 25, 1899; A. L. Adams, *ibid.*, Vol. 58, p. 65, 1907; J. W. Ledoux, *Eng. News-Record*, Vol. 85, p. 932, 1920; "Wood Pipe Handbook," National Tank and Pipe Co., 1938.

internal pressures up to about 150 psi, or even higher. Pine, fir, redwood, red cedar, and cypress are used for making wood pipe. Among the advantages of the use of wood pipe may be included light weight, fairly long life under favorable conditions, high carrying capacity or value of C in Hazen and Williams formula, freedom from electrolysis, and easy transportation when knocked down. Wood pipe is not suitable for high

FIG. 17-17. 24-in. uncoated machine-banded wood pipe. (*Courtesy of Continental Pipe Manufacturing Co.*)

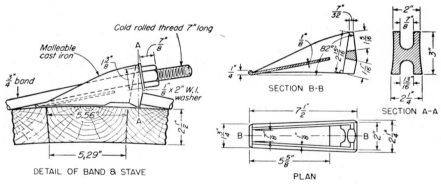

FIG. 17-18. Cast-iron shoe for holding bands on wood-stave pipe.

external loads, and wood should not be used where the wood is alternately wet and dry, or in dry regions where the moisture in the air is continuously low, as in deserts and in the Arctic.

Continuous-stave pipe is usually manufactured in cradles at the point of installation. The staves are laid together in such a manner that the joints between the ends of the staves do not come at the same transverse section. The joints between the sides of the staves are planed radially. A copper or zinc plate is sometimes fitted between end joints to secure watertightness, because of the slight longitudinal expansion of wood on swelling due to moisture. The staves are held in place by wire bands.

The ends of the wires are held firmly in cast-iron shoes, such as are shown in Fig. 17-18, and the bands are drawn tightly by turning the nuts, also shown in the figure. Continuous-stave pipe which is fabricated at the site of installation can be made of one continuous length, and the flexibility of the wood is such that the pipe can be laid on curves with a minimum radius about fifty times the diameter of the pipe.

Machine-banded pipes are usually made in the factory and are shipped to the site of installation. The staves are held together by spirally wound steel bands. The pipes are made in almost any length, up to 20 ft. Adjacent sections of pipes are joined by collars that are placed around the outside of the pipe as shown in Fig. 17-19, or by means of recessed or tenon joints. The former are suitable only for low pressures. The collars may be made of wood staves, cast iron, or steel. Where

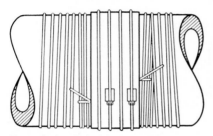

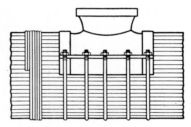

Fig. 17-19. Joint for machine-banded wood-stave pipe.

Fig. 17-20. Typical cast-iron connection for wood-stave pipe.

collars are used, it is necessary to leave an unbanded space at the end of each pipe over which the collar fits. The collars, when made of wood, are usually machine-banded, and they should receive particular protection against rot, because they are not protected by the moisture in the pipe.

The backfilling of wood-stave pipe should be done with great care, particular attention being taken to tamp the backfill firmly under and around the pipe to the height of the horizontal diameter. Failure to do this results in high leakage or failure of the pipe, owing to the weight of the backfill over the top of the pipe. Dry sand constitutes the best material for backfill next to the pipe. It must, however, be restrained. Loam and rich soil should not be placed in close proximity to wood pipe. If the pipe is not placed in a trench, it is supported by cradles at suitable intervals.

The pipe should be slowly filled with water to allow the staves to swell and close leaks before the full water pressure is placed in it. Large leaks might cause erosion of the backfill and endanger the safety of the pipe.

Connections to wood pipe are made by special iron castings which are fastened to the wood pipe in a manner similar to that shown in Fig. 17-20.

17-15. Design of Wood Pipe. Wood-stave pipe is designed to resist internal bursting pressures. Flexural stresses are usually neglected in design, but their effects may cause failure of the pipe if proper measures to resist them are not provided for in construction and backfilling.   Adequate tamping to the height of the horizontal diameter is essential for the safety of buried pipe.

In designing a wooden pipe made up of staves held together by metal bands, two factors are to be considered in the design of the bands: their diameter and the spacing between them.   As these factors are dependent upon each other, one must be fixed before the other can be determined. It is customary to fix the diameter first, so as to develop the full crushing

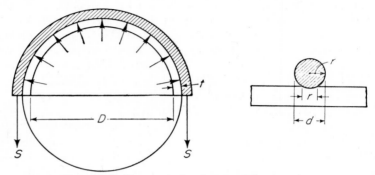

Fig. 17-21. Stresses in bands on wood-stave pipe.

strength of the wood.   Under such circumstances, the diameter of the band is independent of the internal bursting pressure.   The distribution of stresses on a band around a wood-stave pipe is illustrated in Fig. 17-21. In this figure

$$2S = (D + 2t)ae \qquad (17\text{-}8)$$

where S = total stress in band
D = internal diameter of pipe
t = thickness of wood stave
e = crushing strength of wood across grain (sometimes taken as about 650 psi)
a = width of band in contact with wood

It is common practice to assume that $a = r$ per unit length of the band. Then

$$r = \frac{(R + t)e}{\pi f_t} \qquad (17\text{-}9)$$

where R = internal radius of pipe
r = radius of band
f_t = strength of steel in band in tension (sometimes taken between 15,000 and 20,000 psi)

The full strength of each band is $S = \pi r^2 f_t$, and this must equal the total internal pressure between the bands.   The internal pressure per unit length of pipe is

$$2pR + 2tW \qquad (17\text{-}10)$$

where p = intensity of internal bursting pressure

W = swelling strength of wood, often assumed to be about 100 psi
Then if B represents the distance between bands, *i.e.*, the pitch of the bands,

$$B(2pR + 2tW) = 2\pi r^2 f_t \qquad (17\text{-}11)$$

Therefore
$$B = \frac{\pi r^2 f_t}{(pR + tW)} \qquad (17\text{-}12)$$

It is possible to determine the diameter and spacing of steel bands on wood-stave pipe by the use of Eqs. (17-9) and (17-12). The maximum spacing between bands is dependent upon the strength of the staves to resist bending and the allowable deflection. A spacing greater than 10 to 12 in. is unusual. The minimum limit of band spacing is fixed by the size of the band shoe and the possibility of turning up the nut.

The assumption that, for circular bands, the width of the contact surface is equal to the radius of the band is approximate only. Actually, the smaller the band, the greater the relative area in contact.[1] Circular or oval bands are preferable to flat bands, as the former expose relatively less surface to the atmosphere to be corroded, and the condition of the bands can be more easily inspected. In general, the wood outlasts the bands, particularly if both are constantly wet.

17-16. Concrete Pipe. Concrete pipe is used on long conduits and aqueducts but is not commonly used in distribution systems. Among the advantages of concrete pipe may be included:

1. Suitability to resist loads due to backfilling and due to collapsing external pressures.

2. Low cost of maintenance.

3. The weight tends to decrease the liability of the pipe to float when empty.

4. Transportation of cement and reinforcing steel only is required when local aggregates and water can be used in making the pipe.

5. It is not subject to corrosion when buried in ordinary soil or when carrying normal potable water.

6. Expansion joints are not normally required.

7. Specially skilled labor is not required for its construction.

Among the disadvantages may be included:

1. Tendency to leak as a result of porosity and shrinkage cracks

2. Corrosion in presence of alkali or acid

3. Difficulty to repair

Concrete pipe may be poured in place, or it may be precast and shipped to the job. Because of better control of the concrete mix and tamping

[1] See also D. C. Henny, *Trans. Am. Soc. Civil Engrs.*, Vol. 41, p. 71, 1899.

facilities afforded in the casting yard, precast pipe can be made thinner than monolithic pipe cast in place. Monolithic pipe is desirable for diameters greater than 60 in., although precast pipe of larger diameters have been used. A saving in form costs and a better distribution of the foundation reaction may be had by the use of a section similar to that shown in Fig. 17-22, instead of the hollow-ring type shown in Figs.

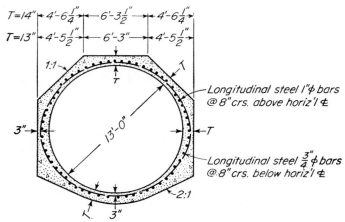

FIG. 17-22. Typical siphon barrel of reinforced concrete.

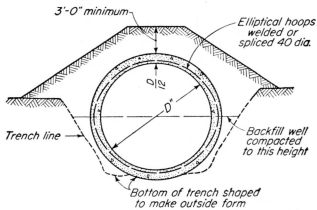

FIG. 17-23. Typical hollow-ring type of reinforced-concrete pipe.

17-23 and 17-24. Steel-cylinder reinforced-concrete pipe, not prestressed, should fulfill American Water Works Association Specifications C300, and prestressed should fulfill Specifications C301. Noncylinder type, not prestressed, should fulfill Specifications C302-51T.[1]

Watertightness is obtained in low-pressure concrete pipe by providing sufficient thickness of good concrete and longitudinal reinforcement equal

[1] See *J.A.W.W.A.*, October, 1951, p. 85; December, 1951, p. 1000.

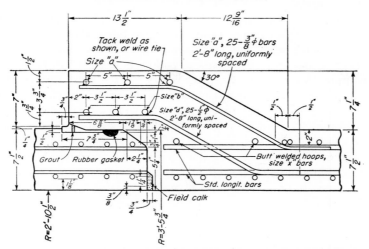

JOINT FOR REINFORCED SIXTY-NINE-INCH CONCRETE PIPE FOR SALT LAKE AQUEDUCT
From Water Works Eng., Oct., 1951, p. 966

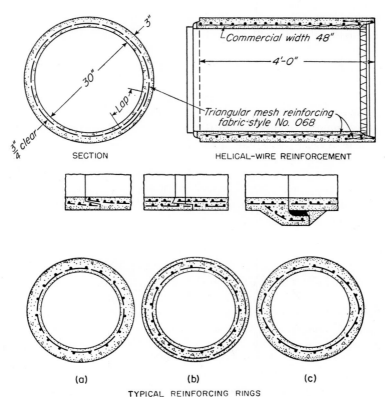

TYPICAL REINFORCING RINGS

FIG. 17-24. Methods for reinforcing concrete pipe.

to at least 0.25 per cent of the cross-sectional area of the concrete and by reducing allowable unit stress in the steel as the internal pressure increases. For large-diameter pipes, a minimum wall thickness of 1 in. for each foot in diameter of pipe is a good rule to follow in design. Surface washes may be applied to the concrete, after it has set, to assure watertightness.

Watertightness of high-pressure concrete pipe may be obtained by the insertion of a thin steel cylinder in the pipe walls either with or without prestressed reinforcement.[1] Lighter-weight pipes may be used when the reinforcement is prestressed because the concrete is kept under compression at higher internal pressures than when not prestressed.[2]

Reinforcement may be placed in concrete pipe to enable it to withstand the shock of handling and of external pressure. For ordinary conditions, reinforcement is placed in precast pipe, as experience has indicated will be satisfactory, no attempt being made to compute the indeterminate stresses that may be encountered after the pipes are in place. Methods for the reinforcing of concrete pipe are shown in Figs. 17-22 to 17-25. Reinforcement, as shown in Fig. 17-24, is most efficient if the pipe is placed in the position shown. If, however, the pipe is turned 90 deg, the reinforcement is almost useless. In monolithic pipes of diameters over 60 in., elliptical hoops are usually used as reinforcement except for the higher internal pressures. These should be placed as shown in Fig. 17-23. Welded hoops have an advantage in that they eliminate laps and thus effect a saving of steel and permit a closer spacing of hoops where necessary. A double layer of circular hoops is used as reinforcement for resisting stress due to high heads.

Precast concrete is manufactured also under proprietary rights by various processes. Lock-joint pipe is a pipe that may be so manufactured either as precast or as cast-in-place pipe. This pipe receives its name from the type of joint used, details of which are shown in Fig. 17-24.[3]

Concrete pipe is subject to corrosion[4] when exposed to moist acid soils or to ground impregnated with magnesium or calcium sulphates. This corrosion is a result of bacterial activity, as explained in Sec. 19-7. Most failures due to corrosion are traceable to inferior materials or to poor workmanship.

Since the coefficient of expansion of concrete is nearly the same as that of steel, similar allowance for expansion and contraction must be made in each kind of pipe. Usually, however, concrete pipe is buried so that wide changes of temperature are not experienced, and more commonly, expansion and contraction are taken up in the joints in the concrete pipe.

[1] See also: F. F. Longley, *J. New Engl. Water Works Assoc.*, December, 1945, p. 335; D. B. Gumensky, *Civil Eng.*, November, 1948, p. 42.

[2] See also *Water Works Eng.*, Mar. 20, 1946, p. 291.

[3] See F. F. Longley, *J. New Engl. Water Works Assoc.*, Vol. 49, p. 212, 1926.

[4] See also Corrosion of Cement and Concrete, *Surveyor*, Mar. 2, 1945, p. 123.

17-17. Design of Reinforced-concrete Pipe. Reinforcing steel is placed in concrete water pipe to resist the tensile stresses due to bursting pressure and flexure. The concrete carries the compressive stresses in pipe subject to flexural stresses. When bursting pressure alone is considered, the area of steel per foot of pipe is computed by the formula

$$A_s = \frac{pr}{f_t} \times 12 \qquad (17\text{-}13)$$

where p = internal pressure, psi

r = radius of pipe, in.

f_t = allowable tensile stress, psi

When flexural stresses are considered, the moments and tensions due to the loads causing bending are calculated for critical points by an elastic analysis or from known coefficients, such as are given in Table I of Fig. 17-25. To the tension thus determined is added that due to internal pressure. The section is then designed by usual methods for reinforced concrete for the combined stress due to tension and bending. Distribution of cracks that might cause leakage is controlled by the proper selection of bar sizes and allowable working stresses. Longitudinal reinforcement is usually used to distribute cracks due to temperature effects and contraction due to setting. The total area of longitudinal steel usually placed is $\frac{1}{4}$ to $\frac{1}{2}$ per cent of the cross-sectional area of the concrete in the pipe.

17-18. Design of Prestressed-concrete Pipe. Prestressed-concrete pipes are constructed with tension in the reinforcing steel such that there is compression in the concrete even when under full working internal bursting pressure. The amount of steel must be such that its maximum stress is below the elastic limit. Pipes may be constructed with a steel cylinder surrounding a concrete shell, as described in Sec. 17-16, or the steel cylinder may be spirally bound with a spirally wound high-tensile wire as shown in Fig. 17-26. The wire is covered, in turn, with a protective, but unstressed, layer of concrete which forms the outer skin of the pipe. An economical design results by prestressing to such an extent that the elastic limits of the steel cylinder and the wire will be reached simultaneously. Both Gumensky[1] and Kennison[2] give a method for the design of such pipes.

17-19. Asbestos-cement Pipe.[3] Asbestos-cement pipe is composed of asbestos fiber and portland cement combined under pressure into a dense homogeneous structure in which a strong bond is effected between the cement and the asbestos fiber. Among its advantages may be included

[1] D. B. Gumensky, *Civil Eng.*, November, 1948, p. 42.

[2] H. F. Kennison, *J.A.W.W.A.*, November, 1950, p. 1049.

[3] See Federal Specifications SS-P-351; AWWA Specifications in *J.A.W.W.A.*, July, 1953, p. 773.

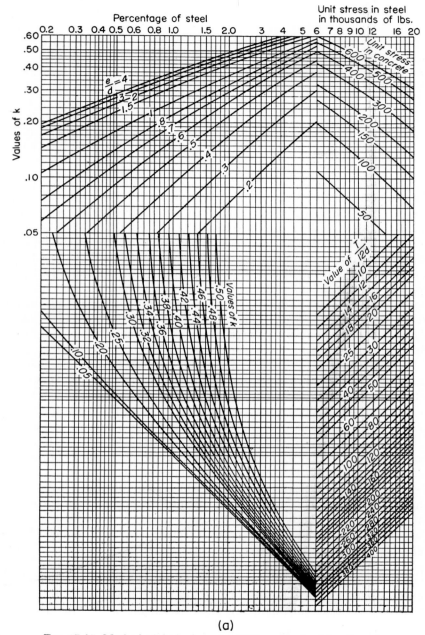

(a)

FIG. 17-25. Method of designing monolithic concrete siphon barrels.

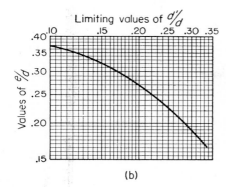

Limiting values of d''/d

(b)

TABLE I
Coefficients for Moment and Thrust

	Thrust in pounds per lin. ft		Moment in foot pounds per lin. ft	
	Top	Bottom	Top	Bottom
Water.....	$-37.41\ r^2$	$-87.59\ r^2$	$+12.19\ r^3$	$+10.65\ r^3$
Pipe.......	$-7.79\ r^2$	$+7.79\ r^2$	$+13.27\ r^3$	$+12.00\ r^3$
Horizontal earth reaction .	$+10.70\ r^2$	$+36.87\ r^2$	$-4.64\ r^3$	$-5.39\ r^3$
Sum.......	$-34.50\ r^2$	$-42.93\ r^2$	$+20.82\ r^3$	$+17.26\ r^3$
Earth cover	0	0	$+.128\ Pr$	$+.077\ Pr$

P = total load on top of pipe in pounds per linear ft

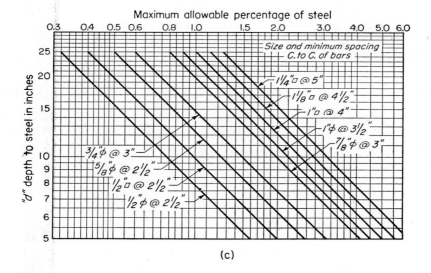

Maximum allowable percentage of steel

Size and minimum spacing C. to C. of bars

$1\frac{1}{4}"\square @ 5"$
$1\frac{1}{8}"\square @ 4\frac{1}{2}"$
$1"\square @ 4"$
$1"\phi @ 3\frac{1}{2}"$
$\frac{7}{8}"\phi @ 3"$
$\frac{3}{4}"\phi @ 3"$
$\frac{5}{8}"\phi @ 2\frac{1}{2}"$
$\frac{1}{2}"\square @ 2\frac{1}{2}"$
$\frac{1}{2}"\phi @ 2\frac{1}{2}"$

"d" depth to steel in inches

(c)

TABLE II
Thickness of Pipe "t"

Head in Ft	Inches to Nearest In.
0–40.....................	$D/12''$
40–80....................	$D/12 + 1''$
80–100...................	$D/12 + 2''$
100–120..................	$D/12 + 3''$
120–140..................	$D/12 + 4''$
140–160..................	$D/12 + 5''$

D = Inside diameter of pipe in inches.
Minimum 6''.

TABLE III
Allowable Stress in Reinforcing

Head in Ft	Pounds per Sq In.
0–20..........................	14,000
20–40.........................	13,000
40–60.........................	12,000
60–80.........................	11,000
80–100........................	10,000
100–120.......................	9,000
120 and over..................	8,000

TABLE IV
Effective Depth to Steel

Diam. less than 8'' total thickness—2''
Diam. from 8' to 12' "   "   —$2\frac{1}{2}$''
Diam. 12' or more   "   "   —3''

Note: Longitudinal reinforcement
For covered pipe.............. 0.25 of 1 %
For exposed pipe............. 0.50 of 1 %
Allowable stress in concrete 600 lb per sq in.

FIG. 17-25. (*Continued.*)

EXPLANATION

1. From coefficients in Table I determine for each linear foot of pipe total moment M in foot pounds and thrust T_1 in pounds due to all loads other than hydrostatic pressure.

2. Determine thrust T_2 due to head measured from hydraulic gradient to inside top of pipe $T_2 = 62.5 \times$ hd. in ft. $\times$ inside radius of pipe in ft.

3. Determine total thrust T from $T = T_1 + T_2$.

4. Determine eccentricity e in inches from $e = \dfrac{M}{T} \times 12$.

5. Determine relation e/d when d equals depth to steel in inches.

6. Determine $\dfrac{T}{12d}$.

7. Enter diagram a at top with an assumed percentage of steel, proceed vertically downward to value of e/d determined in 5, read value of k at left.

8. Continue vertically downward on percentage first assumed to line corresponding to value of k determined in 7, thence to the right to intersection with line corresponding to value $\dfrac{T}{12d}$ determined in 6, thence vertically upward to value of k determined in 7 and read the stress in concrete, continue vertically upward and read the stress in steel. If above or below allowable stresses, assume new percentage and repeat.

9. When hydrostatic pressure is sufficient to require two layers of steel, determine relation d'/d where d' equals depth to steel in inches from nearest face of concrete.

10. In diagram b determine limiting value of e/d for relation of d'/d determined in 9. This value of e/d indicates point at which the change from single to double layers of steel is made. Compute area of steel required for double layer reinforcement by hydrostatic head on center of pipe.

11. The required spacing of steel applies to shorter arc of vertical curves in pipe. Diagram c gives maximum allowable percentage for different sizes of bars for variable effective depths to steel.

12. Maximum spacing of bars $= 1.5d$ (maximum $12''$)

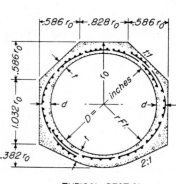

TYPICAL SECTION
Single Layer–Reinforcement

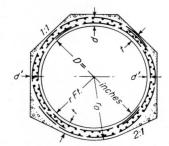

Note: *100 circumferential bars on 45° axis of pipe.*
Area of section $3.356\, r_0^2 - \pi r^2$

TYPICAL SECTION
Double Layer–Reinforcement

(d)

FIG. 17-25. (*Continued.*)

high resistance to most corrosive conditions; freedom from electrolysis; light weight, being about 25 per cent lighter than standard pit-cast iron pipe; easily cut and fitted; easily handled; not easily broken in handling; resistance to external loads properly applied; easily drilled and tapped for service connections; joints can be made without specially skilled labor; flexible joints; no expansion joints are needed; and the initially high Hazen and Williams coefficient of 140 does not reduce materially with age. Among its disadvantages may be included relatively low structural resistance to flexural stresses that cause breakage when the pipe is moved or undermined under pressure; the pipe is easily punctured by excavating tools; the durability of rubber in the joints is uncertain under all conditions, being attacked by gasoline and petroleum products; the material may be corroded by acids and by sulphates in the soil; and the fact that it will not conduct electricity prevents its being thawed electrically.

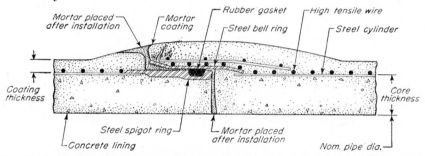

FIG. 17-26. Prestressed-concrete cylinder pipe, rubber and steel joint. (*From H. F. Kennison, J.A.W.W.A., November, 1950, p. 1049.*)

Asbestos-cement pipe is manufactured under such proprietary names as Century, Eternite, Roxite, and Transite.[1] The last named is manufactured in four different grades to withstand internal bursting pressures from 50 to 200 psi; in standard internal diameters from 2 to 36 in.; and in standard lengths of 5 and 10 ft for 2 to 3½ in. diameters and 13 ft for 4 in. and larger diameters. All pipes are finished with plain ends, the exterior of the barrel being machined to receive the coupling illustrated in Fig. 17-27. No special skill is required in completing the connection, as the coupling is pushed over the rubber gasket, which rolls up on the pipe, making a tight and flexible joint which can be completed either in a dry trench or under water. The pipe can be tapped and threaded for service connections in the same manner as iron pipe, and it can be cut to any desired length, shorter than standard, and at any angle, by means of a common wood saw and miter box. Standard cast-iron specials may be connected to the pipe with sulphur-base compounds or metallic lead.

[1] See also: Committee Report, *J.A.W.W.A.*, May, 1937, p. 607; G. W. Blakeley, *J. New Engl. Water Works Assoc.*, September, 1937, p. 317.

17-20. Service Pipes.[1]   The pipe leading from the distributing main of the public water supply to the plumbing system in a building is known as the "service pipe."   Materials most commonly used for service pipes include copper, brass, lead, cast iron, wrought iron, and steel.   These should fulfill the requirements contained in Collected Standard Specifications for Service Line Materials, an unofficial report of a committee of

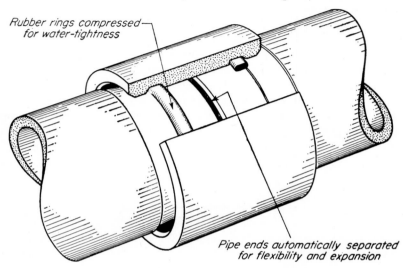

Rubber rings compressed— for water-tightness

Pipe ends automatically separated for flexibility and expansion

Coupling and pipe made of long-lived corrosion-resistant asbestos-cement Transite.

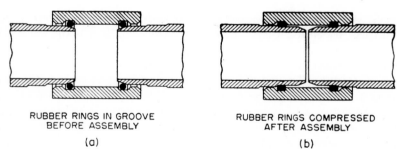

RUBBER RINGS IN GROOVE BEFORE ASSEMBLY

RUBBER RINGS COMPRESSED AFTER ASSEMBLY

(a)   (b)

Fig. 17-27. Ring-Tite coupling for Transite pipe.   (*Courtesy of Johns-Manville Co., Industrial Products Division.*)

the American Water Works Association, published with the AWWA Specifications C800 for threads for underground service fittings.   Other materials used for service pipes include pipes of the above materials lined with tin, lead, or portland cement, and plastic materials.

Copper tube is highly regarded because of its corrosion-resistant properties, its flexibility, the ease of its installation, and its relatively low resist-

[1] See also *J.A.W.W.A.*, November, 1952, p. 1021.

ance to flow. It can be attached to the main without the use of the conventional gooseneck, the flared end of the tubing being connected directly to the corporation cock without threading. The tubing can be pushed underground by first pushing a steel pipe and then pulling the copper tubing through the steel pipe. The steel pipe is withdrawn, leaving the copper tubing in place. Copper is insufficiently soluble in potable water to present a hazard to health.[1]

Lead possesses many of the advantages of copper tube in that it is highly resistant to corrosion, is flexible, and has a high hydraulic coefficient of flow. It is generally considered to be unsuitable where high pressures may be encountered, and the subtle physiological dangers from lead poisoning have created some prejudice against its use. Lead pipes that conform to all acceptable specifications sometimes fail,[2] either because of "creep" or as a result of intercrystalline cracking. The finer the grain of the lead, the greater the tendency to creep; too coarse a grain is conducive to intercrystalline cracking. The ability to resist intercrystalline cracking and, at the same time, secure coarse grains may be improved by alloying the lead with antimony, bismuth, tin, cadmium, and certain other metals.

Galvanized iron or steel pipe, connected to the water main by a lead gooseneck, is probably the least expensive material for a service pipe. As the material is not highly resistant to corrosion, it should be used only in temporary installations or where there will be no undue exposure to corrosive conditions.

Cast iron, brass, and other metallic alloys may be used to resist corrosion or for other reasons, but all alloys will not resist all corrosive attacks; e.g., brass is unsuitable in the presence of sea water. Cast iron is used only for services 2 in. in diameter or larger.

17-21. Service-pipe Connections. A service pipe is usually connected to the water main in the street by a valve called a corporation cock which should be threaded into a hole tapped into the water main. Such a connection can be made without interrupting the flow of water in the main.[3] Because of the movement that takes place between the water main and the service pipe, flexibility must be allowed at the junction. This is obtained by the use of a "gooseneck" connection of flexible material. A typical installation of a service pipe and of a gooseneck connection is shown in Figs. 17-28 and 17-29. La Due[4] improvised the curb box shown in Fig. 17-28. The service pipe leads from the gooseneck to the curb stop or corporation cock, which should be accessible from the service, as indicated.[5] The service pipe then leads to a stop-and-waste valve close

[1] See also F. E. Hale, *Water Works Eng.*, Vol. 95, pp. 84, 139, 187, 240, 1942.

[2] See also B. Jones, *Engineering*, Mar. 18, 1938, p. 285.

[3] See also *Water Works Eng.*, July, 1950, p. 638.

[4] W. R. La Due, *J.A.W.W.A.*, October, 1946, p. 1144.

[5] See also *Water Works Eng.*, March, 1951, p. 227; May, 1951, p. 482.

to the foundation wall inside the building. If a meter is installed, it may be placed close to and on the house side of the stop-and-waste valve. Sometimes meters are placed in a vault outside the building.

Sizes of service pipes and meters should be selected to supply water at a satisfactory rate to every plumbing fixture in the building. Conditions affecting these sizes include[1] (1) pressure in the water main, (2) length of service pipe, and (3) number and types of plumbing fixtures supplied.

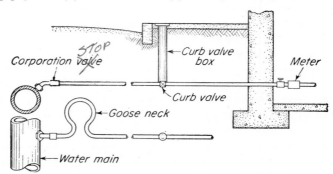

FIG. 17-28. Typical service-pipe installation.

FIG. 17-29. Lead gooseneck. (*Courtesy of Mueller.*)

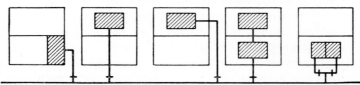

FIG. 17-30. Some forms of service-pipe connections. (*From M. P. Hatcher, J.A.W.W.A., December, 1947, p. 1165.*)

In general, the flow into a fixture will be adequate if the pressure on it is 5 to 10 psi with the faucet wide open. Common sizes of service pipes and meters in use for residences are $\frac{5}{8}$, $\frac{3}{4}$, and 1 in. Larger sizes are used for heavier demands. Some approximate figures for head losses in meters and services are given in Table 17-6.

In the making of service connections, many difficult problems are involved. Six undesirable, but sometimes unavoidable, service connections are illustrated in Fig. 17-30.[2] Recommended sizes of service pipes are given in Table 17-7.

[1] See also W. B. Bushway, *J. New Engl. Water Works Assoc.*, December, 1944, p. 317.

[2] From M. P. Hatcher, *J.A.W.W.A.*, December, 1947, p. 1165.

TABLE 17-6. Approximate Head Losses through Meters and Services
(Saint Paul Water Department Engineering Division)*

Rate of flow, gpm	Head losses, psi per 100 ft of service pipe											
	Meter size, in.						Size of pipe, in.					
	⅝	¾	1	1¼	1½	2	⅝	¾	1	1¼	1½	2
10	6	2.0	0.5	0.5	0.2	....	30.0	11.0	3.0	0.9	0.3	0.1
12	9	3.0	1.0	1.0	....	....	41.5	15.0	4.5	1.4	0.5	
14	11	4.0	1.5	1.5	....	....	55.5	19.5	6.0	2.0	0.7	
16	14	5.0	2.0	2.0	....	....	71.0	24.5	7.5	2.3	0.9	
20	22	8.0	3.5	3.0	1.0	0.4	....	37.5	11.5	3.7	1.4	0.4
24	..	11.0	5.0	4.0	....	....	....	53.5	16.5	5.0	2.2	
30	..	19.5	8.0	7.0	2.0	0.9	....	....	25.5	7.5	3.5	0.9
40	..	....	14.0	12.0	4.0	1.5	....	....	48.0	14.8	6.5	1.6
50	..	....	22.0	....	6.0	2.5	....	....	....	22.0	10.0	2.4
75	..	....	....	....	14.0	5.5	....	....	....	45.6	22.4	5.3
100	..	....	....	....	25.0	10.0	....	....	....	....	39.0	9.5

* G. Roden, Sizing and Installation of Service Pipes, *J.A.W.W.A.*, May, 1946, p. 637.

17-22. Plastics.[1] Plastics are, in general, synthetic resins of high molecular weight, polymerized from simple compounds by heat, pressure, and catalysis. Plastics used in the manufacture of pipes and tubes belong principally to polyvinylidine chloride and cellulose acetate–butyrate types.[2] The three plastics principally used for pipes and tubes are Saran, Tenite, and Plastitube.

Saran[3] is a flexible yellowish translucent polyvinylidine chloride plastic. It melts at 310°F, will withstand water temperature up to 170°F continuously, is hydraulically smooth, heat conductivity is 0.00022 times that of copper, coefficient of expansion is 0.000083, and its weight is about 125 lb per cu ft. Black Saran pipe is available in sizes from ½ to 4 in. It will withstand bursting pressures up to 1,500 psi, depending on the diameter and thickness. Joints may be threaded as for metallic pipe, or they may be made by autogeneous welding.

Plastitube and Plastiflex are plastic substances extruded from cellulose acetate butyrate. Plastitube is rigid and comes in 12-ft lengths. Plastiflex is flexible and comes in 60-ft coils in sizes from ⅛ to 2 in. outside diameter. Tenite is a similar substance but is not well suited for pipe as it offers a fire hazard about equal to that of bulk newsprint.

Advantages claimed for plastics, particularly for Saran, include freedom from corrosion; freedom from damage due to freezing and thawing of

[1] See also W. D. Tiedeman, *J.A.W.W.A.*, August, 1954, p. 775.

[2] For British standards for polythene tubing, see *Water and Water Eng.*, June, 1953, p. 244.

[3] See also F. M. Dawson and A. A. Kalinske, *J.A.W.W.A.*, August, 1943, p. 1058.

TABLE 17-7. Recommended Sizes of Service Pipes[a,b]

Class of building	Length of service pipe, main to meter, ft sizes of pipe, in.			
	100	50	25	10
A[c]	1¼	1	1	¾
B[d]	1½	1¼	1¼	1
C[e]	2	1½	1½	1¼
D[f]	2	2	1½	1¼

[a] From H. E. Babbitt, "Plumbing," 2d ed., p. 65, McGraw-Hill Book Company, Inc., New York, 1950.

[b] Computed on basis of 20-ft loss of head from main to meter.

[c] An ordinary single-family dwelling—2 to 2½ stories, and not more than 8 to 10 rooms, containing 1 bathroom, a kitchen sink, laundry trays, and garden hose.

[d] A 2-family house or larger dwelling, up to about 16 rooms, containing 2 bathrooms, 2 kitchen sinks, laundry trays, and 1 garden hose.

[e] A 4-apartment building, apartments not more than 6 rooms each. Building contains 4 bathrooms, 4 kitchen sinks, 4 sets of laundry trays, and 1 garden hose.

[f] A large apartment building containing not more than 25 apartments with a total of about 100 rooms; with full equipment of 1 bathroom and 1 kitchen, laundry trays for each apartment, and 2 hose connections for the building.

water in closed pipe; acid-resistant to solutions up to about 10 per cent concentration; light weight, about 11 per cent that of cast-iron pipe; easy to bend and to join; has adequate strength; unaffected by age, sunlight, or weather; resistant to shock; good electric insulator; resilient and flexible; and some may be transported in coils. Saran is not recommended for temperatures above 180°F. Taste and toxicity of plastic materials must be considered in their selection.[1]

17-23. Aluminum. Aluminum is used for water-works structures[2] such as tanks, towers for elevated tanks, ladders, floor plates, hand railings, doors, and in electrical circuits. It has the advantages over ferrous metals of higher resistance to corrosion, light weight for equal strength, freedom from need of painting, and it is relatively easily fabricated and erected.

17-24. Silicones. Silicones are materials produced by synthetic chemical processes in which silicon is used to replace carbon. Some such products are superior for such purposes as (1) insulation in electric motors to operate at temperatures up to 350°F; grease lubricants serviceable at −4°F; varnishes and lacquers that will not char at 350°F and are serviceable at higher temperatures, and fluids for hydraulic systems to operate at close to −70°F.

[1] See also: *Am. City*, January, 1952, p. 116; J. G. Carns, Jr., and M. E. Knight, *Water & Sewage Works*, November, 1952, p. 446; J. N. Spaulding, *J.A.W.W.A.*, May, 1953, p. 476; Panel Discussion, *ibid.*, July, 1953, p. 757.

[2] J. M. Perryman, *J.A.W.W.A.*, December, 1946, p. 1327.

CHAPTER 18

VALVES, GATES, HYDRANTS, AND METERS

18-1. Valves. Valves are used in water-works practice on pipes to control the flow of water, to regulate pressures, to release or admit air, and for other purposes. For each purpose some type of valve is best suited. Standard specifications for the most commonly used valves are published periodically by the American Water Works Association. It is possible, by means of a special tool, to insert a valve in a water main without shutting off the pressure.[1] Valves used in plumbing, in steam power plants, and for other specialized purposes are not standard in water-works practice. Losses of head in some valves and fittings are listed in Table 18-1.

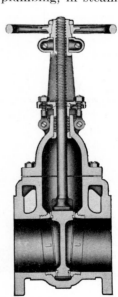

Fig. 18-1. Rising-stem gate valve. (*Courtesy of Crane Co.*)

18-2. Gate Valves.[2] Gate valves are the most common type of valve used in water works. They possess the advantage over most other valves, used for the same purpose, of combining relatively low cost and little resistance to flow when the valve is wide open.

Gate valves used in water-distribution systems are usually made of cast iron with brass mountings. They are usually of the solid-wedge type, illustrated in Fig. 18-1, or of the double-disk type shown in Fig. 18-2. Such valves are available with threaded, flanged, or bell-and-spigot ends. The valves shown in the figures cannot be used with complete satisfaction on sizes of pipe larger than about 16 in. when the pressures are greater than about 100 psi unless a by-pass is provided, as illustrated in Figs. 18-3 and 18-4, to reduce the force necessary to open or close the valve. Small-sized gate valves, buried underground, may be operated from the surface by the

[1] See also *Water Works Eng.*, December, 1950, p. 1119; April, 1951, p. 348.

[2] See also *ibid.*, December, 1950, p. 1115; January, 1951, p. 47; Standard Specifications C500-52T, *J.A.W.W.A.*, September, 1952, p. 857.

TABLE 18-1. Head Loss in Valves, Fittings, and Service Pipes

Computed from expressions

$$H = K \frac{V^2}{2g} \quad \text{or} \quad H = k \frac{Q^2}{d^5}$$

where

H = head loss, ft

V = velocity, fps, in a pipe whose nominal diameter is the same as that of the valve or fitting shown in the table

Q = flow, gpm, in a pipe whose diameter is d in inches

K and k = constants shown in the table

Valve, fitting, or pipe	K	Valve, fitting, or pipe	k^e
Gate valve:		Service pipe:[f]	
Open	0.19[a]	⅝-in. lead	0.00035
¾ open	1.15[a]	¾-in. lead	0.00036
½ open	5.6[a]	1-in. lead	0.00039
¼ open	24[a]	¾-in. copper	0.00033
Globe valve, open	10[b]	1-in. copper	0.00034
Angle valve, open	5[b]	½-in. gal. iron[g]	0.00036
90-deg. ell, short radius	0.9[c]	¾-in. gal. iron[g]	0.00036
Medium radius	0.75[b]	1-in. gal. iron[g]	0.00035
Long radius	0.6[b]	Corporation cocks:	
Return bend	2.2[b]	½-in. with tailpiece for lead	0.00127
45-deg. ell	0.42[b]	½-in. with ¾-in. copper adapter	0.00077
22½-deg. ell (18 in.)	0.13[d]	¾-in. with ¾-in copper adapter	0.0023
Tee	1.25[d]	¾-in. with tailpiece for lead	0.0020
Reducer (V at small end)	0.25[d]	1-in. with 1-in. copper adapter	0.0029
Increaser = 0.25 $(V_1{}^2 - V_2{}^2)/2g$[d]	.....	Curb stops:	
Bellmouth reducer	0.10[d]	¾-in., lead service	0.002
Shear gate, open (orifice)	1.80[d]	¾-in., copper service	0.0012
Sluice gate in 12-in. wall, submerged	2.35[d]	1-in., lead service	0.001
Passing branches or openings	0.03[d]	1-in., copper service	0.00059
		Yokes:	
		⅝-in. rams horn (new)	0.0035
		⅝-in. rams horn (old)	0.0135
		⅝-in. straight line	0.00106
		¾-in. rams horn	0.0029
		Stop-and-waste valves:	
		½ × ¾ in. compression valve	0.0021
		⅝ × ¾ in. compression valve	0.0030
		¾ × ¾-in. compression valve	0.0048
		1 × 1 in. compression valve	0.013

[a] *Univ. Wis., Bull.* 252.
[b] Crane Co., *Bull.* 405.
[c] *Univ. Texas, Bull.* 2712.
[d] Burns and McDonnell, *Water Works & Sewerage*, May, 1937, p. 196.
[e] Values of k are taken from *J.A.W.W.A.*, May, 1932, p. 631.
[f] The head losses in service pipes are per foot length of pipe.
[g] Presumably new pipe.

insertion of a "key" through a stop box with its opening at the ground surface above the valve, as shown in Fig. 18-5. Larger valves placed in underground valve chambers may be opened or closed through gearing, as shown in Fig. 18-6. Where high pressure is always available, whether or not the valve is open or closed, the use of a hydraulic cylinder is desirable, as illustrated in Fig. 18-3.

In opening the valve in Fig. 18-2 the disk is raised by a nut which climbs the stem as the latter is turned. This is known as a "nonrising stem," the threaded portion of the stem being protected within the bonnet of the valve, as shown in the figure. It is the most common form used in valves placed underground. In the rising-stem valve, illustrated in Fig. 18-1, the hub of the valve wheel is threaded, and as it is turned the stem moves, carrying the disk with it. This type of valve is used where the valve is accessible for inspection and the threads can be easily lubricated. In quick-opening valves the disk is moved by means of a handle, like a pump handle,

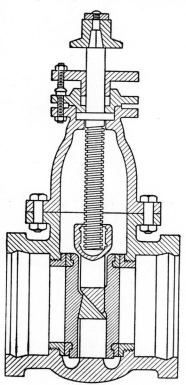

FIG. 18-2. Nonrising stem, double-disk gate valve.

FIG. 18-3. Hydraulically operated gate valve. (*Courtesy of Crane Co.*)

as illustrated in Fig. 18-7. It is suitable only for smaller sizes of pipe. Too quick opening of large valves may be undesirable because of the excessive water-hammer pressures created.

The area of the opening of a gate valve, or the rate of flow through it, does not vary directly as the percentage of the opening of the valve. The rate of discharge through the valve is affected by the velocity of flow through it, by the length of pipe on each side of the valve, by the loss of head through the valve, and possibly by other conditions. The percentage of opening of a valve is generally considered to be one hundred times the ratio of the number of turns that the valve has been opened, to the total number of turns required to open the valve fully.

FIG. 18-4. Low-pressure, wedge gate valve with by-pass and spur gearing.   (*Courtesy of Crane Co.*)

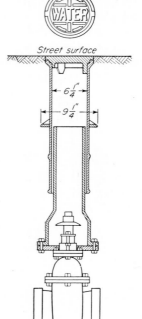

FIG. 18-5. Valve and valve box.

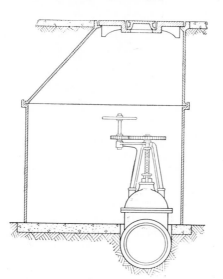

FIG. 18-6. Valve, with gearing, in cast-iron manhole.

FIG. 18-7. Quick-opening gate valve.   (*Courtesy of Crane Co.*)

18-3. Globe Valves. Globe valves are used almost exclusively on pipes 4 in. in diameter, or smaller, mainly for pipes in plumbing. They are rarely used on water-distribution systems. Globe valves have the advantage of being less expensive than gate valves of the same size, and they are less costly to repair. A disadvantage is the relatively high loss of pressure through the tortuous passage provided. A typical globe valve is illustrated in Fig. 18-8. A relatively inexpensive type of globe valve, called an angle valve, is shown in Fig. 18-9.

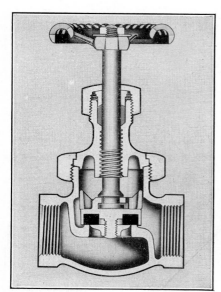

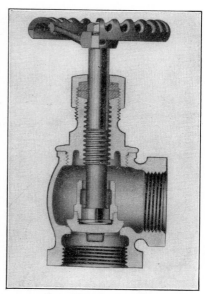

Fig. 18-8. Section through a globe valve. (*Courtesy of Crane Co.*)

Fig. 18-9. Angle valve.

18-4. Check Valves.[1] Check valves are used to permit the flow of water in one direction only. Flow in the reverse direction is automatically stopped by the valve. Four types of check valve are shown in Fig. 18-10.[2]

18-5. Check-valve Slam. When a check valve closes suddenly as a result of reversal of flow of water in a pipe, the force tending to stop the motion of the water is proportional to the head on the valve.[3] This force produces an acceleration in a direction opposite to the normal direction of the flow of water in the conduit. It can be shown that

$$hAw = \frac{AwaL}{g} \quad \text{and that} \quad a = \frac{hg}{L}$$

[1] See also H. J. Bartlett, *Water & Sewage Works*, April, 1948, p. 138.
[2] See also *Water Works Eng.*, February, 1953, p. 120.
[3] See also H. K. Palmer, *Water Works & Sewerage*, June, 1942, p. R58.

where h = static head at valve at instant of reversal of flow

A = cross-sectional area of pipe

w = unit weight of water

L = length of pipe

g = acceleration due to gravity

Check-valve slam is minimized by many devices, some of which provide air cushions, some mechanical springs, and some a slow-closing device.

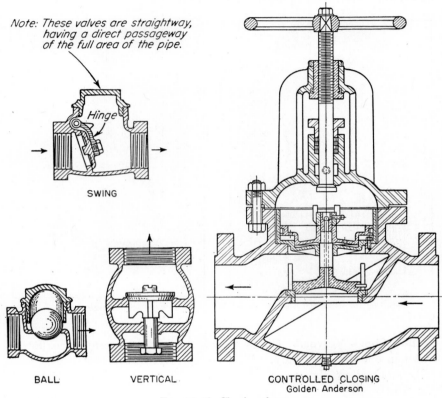

Fig. 18-10. Check valves.

A pump-control valve is available[1] to minimize surge in water mains. Its opening and closing are controlled by a solenoid-operated pilot valve actuated by pressures at the pump discharge. The intensity of pressure resulting, in part, from the sudden closing of a check valve is a function of the time of closing of the valve; the greater the time of closing the less the valve slam.

Two types of slow-closing check valves are shown in Figs. 18-11 and 18-12. In Fig. 18-11, when water is flowing through the valve, piston B

[1] See also S. B. Morris, *J.A.W.W.A.*, September, 1946, p. 993.

is off its seat.   When the flow of water is reversed, some water flows upward through port P and presses piston B down at the same time that water pressure is transmitted through port M into the annular channel around the edge of the piston, providing a brake and cushion effect on the descending piston.   Figure 18-12 shows a revolving-cone valve.   It provides an unrestricted passage for the water when the valve is fully open. It is closed by water pressure in the mechanism shown in the figure.   The mechanism can be set so that the rate of closing of the valve will prevent slam.

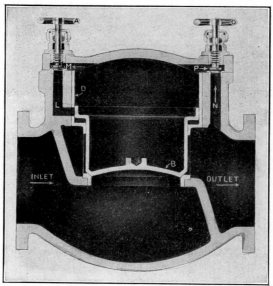

FIG. 18-11. Check valve designed to close slowly, without slam.   (*Courtesy of Golden-Anderson Valve Specialty Co.*)

The principle of the revolving-cone valve is used for quick-closing valves, for the control of the rate of flow, and in automatic devices.

18-6. Air-relief Valves.[1]   A valve that will allow air to escape from or to enter a pipe is called an air-relief valve, or sometimes if air is to be admitted only, an air-inlet valve.   An air-relief valve is shown in Fig. 18-13.   If such a valve is placed at the summit of a pipe line in which water is flowing under pressure greater than atmospheric, air collecting in the valve will allow the float to drop, thus opening a passage to the atmosphere for the escape of the confined air.   If the pressure in the pipe is lowered and water escapes from the lower end, the float will drop and admit air to replace the escaping water and the creation of a vacuum will be prevented.

[1] See also: *Water Works Eng.*, January, 1950, p. 46; J. Parmakian, *Proc. Am. Soc. Civil Engrs.*, Vol. 75, p. 789, 1949.

18-7. Balanced Valves. A section through a balanced valve is shown in the Simplex rate controller in Fig. 28-22. Since the upward and downward pressures against the valve disks can be balanced, together with the weight of the moving parts, only friction must be overcome in using the valve. The principle of the balanced valve is used in many automatic devices and in other special-use valves.

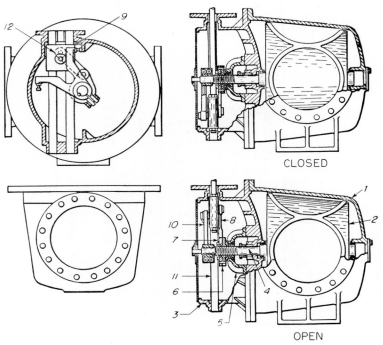

Fig. 18-12. Revolving-cone valve. Direction of flow in this view is either toward or away from the reader. (1) casing, (2) plug or cone, (3) cover, (4) stem, (5) yoke, (6) lifter nut, (7) lifter arm, (8) link, (9) crosshead, (10) rotator arm, (11) guides, (12) roller. (*Courtesy of Golden-Anderson Valve Specialty Co.*)

18-8. Pressure-regulating Valves.[1] Pressure-regulating valves are used to deliver water from a high-pressure to a low-pressure system. Types of such valves are shown in Figs. 18-14 and 18-15.

18-9. Pressure-relief Valves. A pressure-relief valve is intended to release excessive pressure that may build up in a closed container. One type of such valve is illustrated in Fig. 18-16.

18-10. Altitude Valves. Altitude valves are used principally on the supply lines to elevated tanks or standpipes, to close automatically when the tank is full and to open when the pressure on the pump side is less than that on the tank side of the valve. A section through such a valve is

[1] See also *Water Works Eng.*, September, 1949, p. 827.

FIG. 18-13. Air-relief valve. Picture on right shows collapse of an improperly equipped aqueduct. (*Courtesy of Simplex Valve and Meter Co.*)

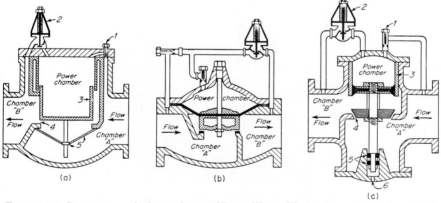

FIG. 18-14. Pressure-regulating valves. (*From Water Works Eng., September,* 1949, *p.* 827.) (*a*) Pressure-reducing pilot-controlled valve with hollow-piston operated main valve. (1) Needle valve, (2) pilot control valve, (3) hollow piston, (4) main valve and seat, (5) stem guide. (*b*) Pressure-reducing pilot-controlled valve with diaphragm-operated main valve. (*c*) Pressure-reducing pilot-controlled valve with piston-operated main valve. (1) Needle valve, (2) pilot control valve, (3) piston, (4) main valve and seat, (5) stem guides, (6) vent.

shown in Fig. 18-17. The valve shown is operated by the water pressure in the pipe line. Other valves are available that are operated by electric energy transmitted to a solenoid.

18-11. Water-level-control Devices. Devices to control the level of water in sedimentation basis, on filters, and in other containers include

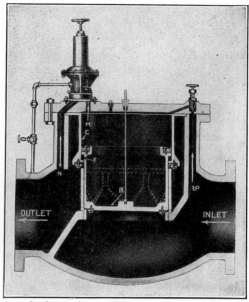

Fig. 18-15. Pressure-reducing valve. *(Courtesy of Golden-Anderson Valve Specialty Co.)*

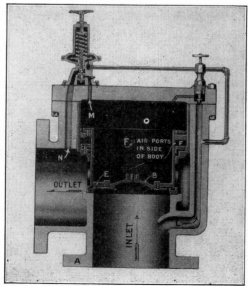

Fig. 18-16. Pressure-relief valve. When the pressure reaches the adjustment of the valve water passes through port *L* and acts on the diaphragm shown beneath the adjustment spring, thus opening the pilot valve. This allows the water which the initial pressure has forced through the main valve *B* to exhaust through ports *M* and *N*, thus relieving the excess pressure. The adjustment of the valve is controlled by the pressure on the adjusting spring shown in the upper left corner of the figure. *(Courtesy of Golden-Anderson Valve Specialty Co.)*

float-controlled valves, as shown in Fig. 18-18, and other devices which may actuate remote-control equipment pneumatically, hydraulically, or electrically.[1]

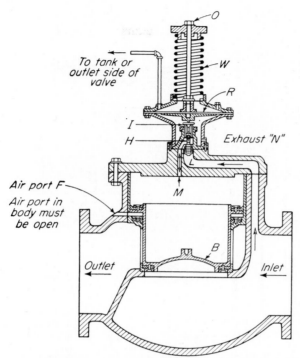

FIG. 18-17. Altitude-control valve.   In the position shown in the figure the valve is closed because the pressure above diaphragm R has overcome the adjustment of spring W.   This causes the spindle head to close the pilot exhaust valve I and to open pilot high-pressure valve H, thus permitting inflow of pressure above piston B through port L, the pilot valve, and port M.   Since the area of the top of piston B is larger than the area of the bottom, the larger total pressure above keeps piston B closed. When the static head in the tank lowers above diaphragm R, coil spring W lifts the spindle head away from exhaust valve I, allowing it to open.   This closes high-pressure valve H, thus opening port M, the pilot valve, and port N to atmospheric drain.   This reduces the pressure above piston B, allowing it to open to full area. There is only a slight momentary exhaust of water from above piston B each time the altitude-control valve opens.   The drainage is usually piped to a suitable outlet. (*Courtesy of Golden-Anderson Valve Specialty Co.*)

18-12. Needle Valves.   Needle valves such as those illustrated in Figs. 7-14 and 18-19 are used for the control of water into and from large reservoirs and in the close adjustment of the rate of flow in mechanical control devices.   Their principal advantage is the close control of the flow when the valve is partly open, because a large movement of the operating mechanism is required to make an appreciable change in the

[1] See also S. B. Morris and L. L. Camy, *J.A.W.W.A.*, September, 1946, p. 993.

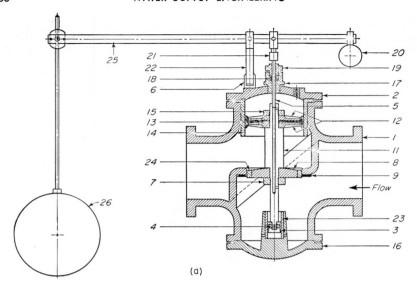

(a)

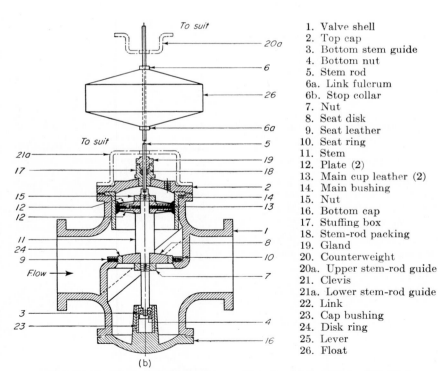

(b)

1. Valve shell
2. Top cap
3. Bottom stem guide
4. Bottom nut
5. Stem rod
6a. Link fulcrum
6b. Stop collar
7. Nut
8. Seat disk
9. Seat leather
10. Seat ring
11. Stem
12. Plate (2)
13. Main cup leather (2)
14. Main bushing
15. Nut
16. Bottom cap
17. Stuffing box
18. Stem-rod packing
19. Gland
20. Counterweight
20a. Upper stem-rod guide
21. Clevis
21a. Lower stem-rod guide
22. Link
23. Cap bushing
24. Disk ring
25. Lever
26. Float

FIG. 18-18. Float-controlled valves.   (*Courtesy of Ross Valve Mfg. Co.*)

flow through the valve, and it is difficult to close the valve so quickly as to cause surge or water hammer.

18-13. Ground-key Valves. Ground-key valves, as shown in Fig. 18-20, are used only on small pipes, principally as corporation cocks on

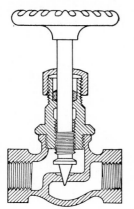 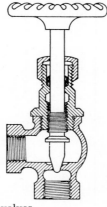

FIG. 18-19. Needle valves.

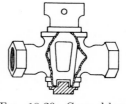

FIG. 18-20. Ground-key valve.

service pipes. They have the advantage of closing or opening to full flow in a 90-deg turn of the handle. Multiple-port ground-key valves, as shown in Fig. 18-21, are used to direct water from one channel to another without interrupting the flow of water through the valve. They are useful in filter-control devices, base-exchange water softeners, and similar equipment.

18-14. Mud Valves. Mud valves of the type shown in Fig. 18-22 are used for removing water and mud or sludge from the bottom of a reservoir.

18-15. Sluice Gates and Other Gates.[1] Sluice gates are used principally at the inlet or outlet pipes entering or leaving reservoirs, the pressure on the gate frequently being against

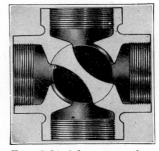

FIG. 18-21. A four-way valve.

one side and in one direction only. A 60-in. sluice gate with hydraulic cylinder lift is shown in Fig. 7-13.

Shear gates, of the type shown in Fig. 18-23, are used for quickly starting or stopping the flow of water in pipes. They are not suitable for use on pipes larger than 15 to 18 in. in diameter.

A tide gate or flap gate, as illustrated in Fig. 18-24, is used on the outlet end of a pipe to prevent backflow into the pipe.

[1] See also latest AWWA Standard Specifications and Specifications C501-41T in *J.A.W.W.A.*, October, 1941.

18-16. Butterfly Valves.[1]   Butterfly valves, as shown in Fig. 18-25, are usually unsuited for shutting off the flow of water completely, as the moving parts do not always fit closely enough to the seat to stop all flow of water.

18-17. Other Valves.   Other types of valves used in waterworks include pump-control valves, surge-relief valves, and sleeve valves.   Few involve principles not used in the valves described.

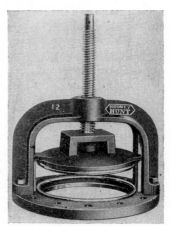

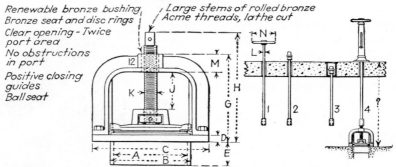

Fig. 18-22. Mud valve, showing method of installation.   (*Courtesy of Rodney Hunt Machine Co.*)

18-18. Operation of Valves.   Valves may be opened manually; by hydraulic, pneumatic, or other fluid pressure; or electrically.   In manual operation the turning of a handwheel actuates the mechanism, as shown in Fig. 18-1.   In valves controlled by hydraulic or other fluid pressure, the valve stem, passing through a packing ring, as shown in Fig. 18-3, is joined to a piston in a closed chamber.   To raise the valve gate, fluid under pressure is admitted to the chamber below the piston.   At the same time any fluid in the chamber above the piston is allowed to escape.   The

[1] See also Standard Specifications, *J.A.W.W.A.*, September, 1954, p. 943.

piston is thus lifted, and the valve is opened.   When the pressure and release are reversed, the valve closes.   Valves may be opened or closed by solenoids and by electric motors geared to the valve mechanism.

18-19. Hydrants.[1]   Standard specifications for fire hydrants, including specifications for fire-hose coupling screw threads,[2] and for uniform mark-

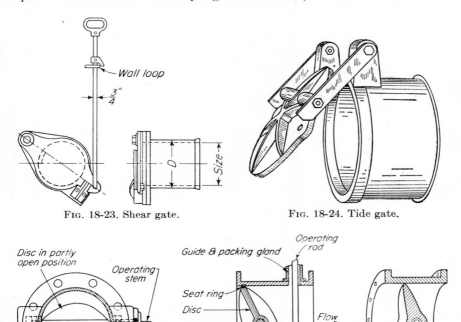

FIG. 18-23. Shear gate.   FIG. 18-24. Tide gate.

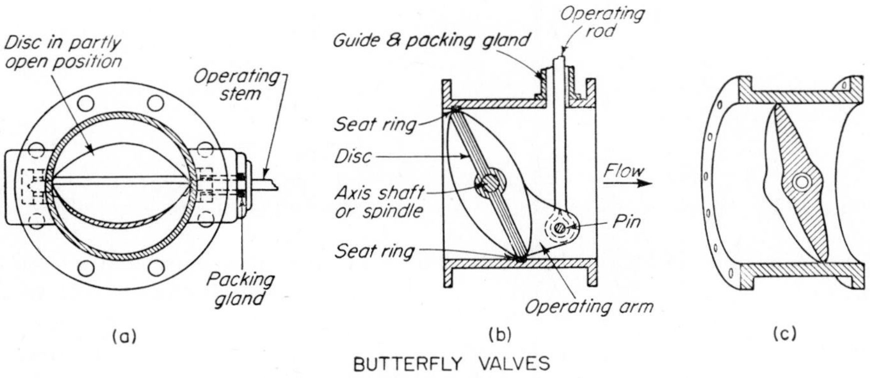

BUTTERFLY VALVES

FIG. 18-25. Butterfly valves.

ing of fire hydrants[3] have been adopted, from time to time, by the American Water Works Association.   The standard compression hydrant is shown in Fig. 18-26.

Fire hydrants are usually made of cast iron with bronze surfaces.   It is frequently desired that a gate valve be placed on the connection to the distribution system, in addition to the main valve on the hydrant.   In

---

[1] See also: *J.A.W.W.A.*, March, 1954, p. 263; May, 1953, p. 539; *Water Works Eng.*, September, 1950, p. 817; October, 1950, p. 927; November, 1950, p. 1009.

[2] See *J.A.W.W.A.*, April, 1937.

[3] See *ibid.*, May, 1953, p. 550.

high-risk districts the hydrants should have a pumper connection, as

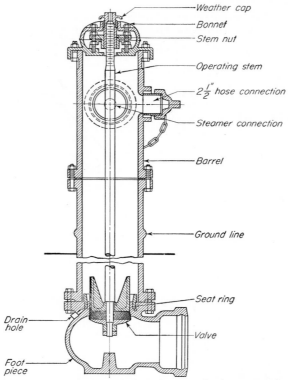

FIG. 18-26. American Water Works Association standard compression fire hydrant.

shown in Figs. 18-26 and 18-27, as well as the customary hose connections.

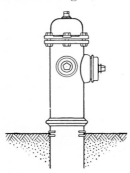

FIG. 18-27. Fire hydrant with two hose and one pumper outlets.

A drain for emptying the barrel of the hydrant when it is closed is essential in a cold climate to prevent the freezing of the hydrant. The drain should be connected to a drainage channel other than a sanitary or combined sewer or, when no channel is available, to a bed of crushed stone or other hard coarse material the volume of whose voids is more than three times the volume of the water held in the barrel of the hydrant. The discharge from hydrants has been formulated as shown below.

Threads for hose connections for fire hydrants have been standardized, the standard adopted by the National Board of Fire Underwriters being $7\frac{1}{2}$ threads per inch, $3\frac{1}{16}$ in. in diameter. The use of a standard thread makes possible mutual fire protection by neighboring cities; but where nonstandard threads are used, special adapters should be available which will make possible connections with any desired thread.

The National Board of Fire Underwriters requires that

. . . hydrants shall be able to deliver 600 gpm with a loss of not more than 2.5 psi in the hydrant and a total loss of not more than 5 psi between the street main and the outlet; they shall not have less than 2.5-in. outlets and also a large suction connection where engine service is necessary. They shall be of such design that when the hydrant barrel is broken off the hydrant will remain closed. Street connections shall not be less than 6 in. in diameter and shall be gated.

The size of a fire hydrant is designated in terms of the minimum opening of the seat ring of the main valve. It must be at least 4 in. for two 2½-in. nozzles, at least 5 in. for three 2½-in. nozzles, and at least 6 in. for four 2½-in. nozzles. The rate of discharge from a hydrant can be approximated by the expression[1]

$$Q = 27d^2p^{0.5}$$

where Q = flow, gpm

d = diameter of hydrant nozzle, in.

p = gage reading, psi

18-20. Meters. Meters used on water-distribution systems are of both the displacement[2] and the velocity[3] types. Displacement meters are used primarily for relatively small flows, such as those required by small and moderate consumers. A displacement meter measures the rate of flow by recording the number of times a container of known volume is filled and emptied. A velocity meter measures the velocity of flow past a cross section of known area. Types of displacement meters in use include reciprocating, rotary, oscillating, and nutating-disk meters, depending on the motion of the moving part in the measuring device. The nutating-disk meter, as illustrated in Fig. 18-28, is the type most commonly used on domestic services, almost to the exclusion of all other types, in the United States. There is some evidence[4] that a ⅝-in.-displacement meter will start registering at a rate of about 0.05 gpm. Turbine and venturi meters are examples of velocity meters.

Most nutating-disk meters may be severely damaged by passing hot water through the meter unless otherwise protected, since the disk is usually composed of a compound that softens at a high temperature. To prevent the backflow of hot water from a plumbing system through a meter, devices are available combining a check valve and a safety valve or by-pass.[5] Such devices must be of an approved type to prevent explosion

[1] See also P. S. Wilson, *Water & Sewage Works*, April, 1946, p. R61.

[2] See also *Water Works Eng.*, February, 1924, p. 127.

[3] See also *ibid.*, March, 1954, p. 216.

[4] See Committee Report, *J.A.W.W.A.*, July, 1946, p. 853.

[5] See discussion in *Water Works Eng.*, November, 1952, p. 1060.

that would result from failure to relieve the high pressure caused by heating the water and generating steam. Meters with moving parts are sometimes protected against clogging by some form of screen, usually called a fish screen. All meters should be self-cleansing to prevent the accumulation of grit and other detritus from clogging and wearing the moving parts. Meters should be so constructed that in the event of freezing some inexpensive and easily replaceable part will break and relieve the strain on the other parts. Some meters are made partly of glass or fragile cast iron for this purpose.

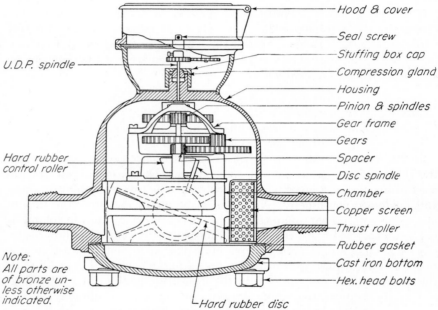

FIG. 18-28. Nutating-disk meter. (*Courtesy of Badger Meter Co.*)

Features to be considered in the selection of a meter include (1) accuracy of measurement and registration for both small and large flows, (2) capacity with minimum head loss, (3) durability, (4) ruggedness, (5) precision of workmanship, (6) ease of repair, (7) availability of spare parts, (8) reputation of manufacturer, (9) freedom from noise, and (10) low cost. Specifications[1] cover various types and classes of cold-water displacement meters for general water-works service and cover materials and workmanship employed in their fabrication. Some features covered by the specifications are as follows:

Head loss: Meters 1 in. and smaller in diameter shall have head loss not exceeding 15 psi, and larger meters not exceeding 20 psi, when rate of flow is that given in Table 18-2.

[1] See *J.A.W.W.A.*, December, 1941; August, 1949, and subsequent issues.

Size: Expressed in terms of nominal size of opening in inlet and outlet spuds or flanges of the meter.

Length: Over all from face to face of spuds or flanges.

Frost protection: Devices, such as cast-iron bottom caps, shall break or yield under normal freezing conditions before meter is damaged.

Accuracy: Meters shall not register less than 98.5 per cent nor more than 101.5 per cent of water passed through the meter.

Pressure: Meters shall operate under pressures of 150 psi or less.

Noise: Limited in some specifications to not more than 10 decibels above room level[1] when operating at full capacity.

TABLE 18-2. Sizes and Capacities of Cold-water Meters—Displacement Type*

Meter size, in.	Safe max. operating capacity, gpm	Max loss of head, psi	Min test flow, gpm	Normal test flow limits, gpm	Speed of piston, revolutions, or nutations, per cu ft
$\frac{5}{8}$	20	15	$\frac{1}{4}$	1– 20	435
$\frac{3}{4}$	30	15	$\frac{1}{2}$	2– 30	250
1	50	15	$\frac{3}{4}$	3– 50	115
$1\frac{1}{2}$	100	20	$1\frac{1}{2}$	5– 100	50
2	160	20	2	8– 160	30
3	300	20	4	16– 300	15
4	500	20	7	28– 500	7
6	1,000	20	12	48–1,000	3

* From Standards American Water Works Association.

Other features sometimes considered include tin coating of cases and measuring chambers; use of acorn nuts on external bolts; pressure test, maybe up to 250 psi; lining of cast-iron bottom caps; drilling of register-box screws for seal-wire holes on two diameters; coloring of register hands; and an inside wiper to clear the inside surface of glass above dial.

Tentative Standard Specifications for Cold Water Meters—Current Type, covering current, velocity, and turbine meters, are published in *Journal of the American Water Works Association*, April, 1946. Such meters are available in sizes from $1\frac{1}{2}$ to 16 in., with capacities of 100 gpm up to 12,400 gpm, and a head loss of not more than 20 psi. They are required to register within 3 per cent above or below accurate readings of the flow through the meter. Venturi meters, not covered by these standards, are in use with throat diameters greater than 48 in.

Tentative Standards Specifications for Cold Water Meters—Compound Type are published in *Journal of the American Water Works Association*, April, 1946. Such meters consist of a combination of a main meter of the current or displacement type and a small displacement meter, in conjunction with an automatic valve mechanism to direct the flow of water through the proper meter. Such meters vary from $1\frac{1}{2}$ to 12 in. in

[1] See Committee Report, *J.A.W.W.A.*, July, 1946, p. 853.

diameter and will carry flows between 2 and 100 gpm for the 1½-in. meter and between 32 and 3,100 gpm for the 12-in. meter, with a head loss not to exceed 20 psi and a precision to register between 97 and 103 per cent, except at the region of "change-over" from one meter to another, when the registration may not be less than 85 per cent of actual flow.

Tentative Standard Specifications for Cold-water Meters, Fire Service Type, are published in *Journal of the American Water Works Association*, February, 1947.

18-21. Size of Water Meters. Sizes of meters and of service pipes are closely related. Information on displacement meters is given in the previous section and in Table 18-2. It is usually better to choose undersize rather than oversize meters because in the latter, although the life may be longer, the accuracy may be poor.

CHAPTER 19

METALLIC CORROSION[1]

Theories of Corrosion

19-1. Importance of Corrosion. Knowledge of the effect of corrosion is important in the selection of materials to be used in water works and in the maintenance of water-works equipment. It has been estimated[2] that the annual per capita cost to water users due to corrosion of cast-iron pipe is about 50 cents, or 10 per cent of the gross revenues of the average utility. Hypotheses that have been advanced to explain corrosion are presented in the following sections.

19-2. Galvanic or Bimetallic Corrosion.[3] A metal when immersed in water or in the solution of an electrolyte, such as corrosive water, tends to go into solution. Cations (ions bearing a positive charge) of the metallic element tend to migrate through the solution and plate out on the surface of an electronegative metal. It is to be noted, however, that the solution must be electrolytically neutral. Hence there must be the migration of anions (ions bearing a negative charge) toward the anode. Camp[4] explains a typical reaction as

$$\text{Metallic element} \underset{\text{reduction}}{\overset{\text{oxidation}}{\rightleftharpoons}} \text{cations} + \text{electrons}$$

$$\text{Fe} \rightleftharpoons \text{Fe}^{++} + 2 \text{ electrons}$$

$$\underset{\text{metal}}{\text{Fe}} + 2\text{OH} \rightarrow \text{Fe(OH)}_2 + 2 \text{ electrons}$$

He lists 267 metallic corrosion reactions, with their electrolytic potentials, and gives examples of quantitative computations of the corrosiveness of water on iron. Where two dissimilar metals are immersed in the same electrolyte, there is an interchange of ions between them or with the electrolytic solution.

---

[1] See also: H. H. Uhlig, "Corrosion Handbook," John Wiley & Sons, Inc., New York, 1948; R. Eliassen and J. C. Lamb, III, *J.A.W.W.A.*, December, 1953, p. 1281.

[2] See H. E. Jordan, *J.A.W.W.A.*, August, 1947, p. 773.

[3] See also C. W. Gleeson, *J.A.W.W.A.*, July, 1941, p. 1249.

[4] T. R. Camp, *J. New Engl. Water Works Assoc.*, Vol. 60, pp. 188, 282, 1946.

The rate of corrosion is determined, in part, by the degree of electrical dissimilarity between the metals in the electromotive series. The relative position of some metals that will enter into bimetallic corrosion is shown in Table 19-1, with the anodic, or most corroded, metal at the top of the list, the flow of current being from the anode to the cathode. The rate of corrosion between any two metals in galvanic corrosion cannot be expressed quantitatively under all conditions. It is dependent more on the amount of current than on the voltage, and on other conditions. For

TABLE 19-1. Metals and Alloys Subject to Corrosion When Placed in Galvanic Contact

Magnesium	Steel or iron	Brass
Magnesium alloys	Cast iron	Copper
Zinc	Nickel	Bronze
Aluminum	Lead-tin	Copper-nickel
Chromium	Lead	Silver
Cadmium	Tin	Mercury
		Gold
		Platinum

The flow of current is from a metal in the list to any other metal below it in the list.

example, higher temperatures speed corrosion reactions because of increased ionization. Gases released from solution, diffusion, turbulence, and lowering of viscosity all tend to enhance the migration of ions. Conditions may become such that the relative anodic and cathodic positions of metals in Table 19-1 are reversed.

Bimetallic galvanic action is not the explanation of all corrosion, nor will one of two dissimilar metals placed in the solution of an electrolyte always corrode. The effects will depend on the concentration of the electrolyte in the solution; on the nature of the metals involved, particularly if they were alloyed; on other factors, such as internal metallic strain, turbulence, temperature, and aeration; and on protective coatings formed by the metals involved. For example, the corrosion of rivetheads is an example of galvanic action caused by an electric current set up between two portions of the same metal of which one part is not under stress and the other is stressed. The graphitic corrosion of cast iron[1] is another example of this phenomenon since it is due to the electrochemical action between the iron acting as an anode and the graphite in the metal acting as a cathode.

19-3. Hydrogenation. Water is an electrolyte, dissociating into H^+ and OH^- ions. The hydrogen ions, acting similarly to metallic anions, will migrate to and plate out on a metallic surface immersed in the water. The surface may become depolarized by the combination of the hydrogen atoms with dissolved oxygen to form water, by their combination with other hydrogen atoms to form hydrogen gas, or by their combination with other substances in solution. In order to maintain electrical neutrality in

[1] See also L. M. Leedom, *J.A.W.W.A.*, December, 1946, p. 1492.

the solution, ions of the metal must be discharged into the solution to neutralize the OH^- ions released by the dissociation of the water. This action causes corrosion of the metal.

The film of hydrogen on the metallic surface forms a protective coating that requires additional voltage in order that metallic ions may be discharged into solution. The additional voltage required is known as "overvoltage." It is a measurable quantity, varying in accordance with the conditions in the solution.

19-4. Electrolysis. If two dissimilar metals are immersed in an electrolytic solution and a direct electric current is passed through the cell thus formed, positively charged ions from the anode will travel to the cathode, release their charge, and plate out on the cathode. The anode is corroded.

19-5. Chemical Reaction. If a metal is immersed in an acid, a chemical reaction occurs, releasing hydrogen gas and forming the salt of the metal.

19-6. Direct Oxidation. Metals in an atmosphere containing oxygen, particularly if the metals are heated, will combine directly with oxygen in the atmosphere. A common example of this is the formation of "mill scale" or magnetite (Fe_3O_4). During this type of corrosion, oxides of iron are formed that tend to spread on the metallic surface. The rust deposit on the metal tends to inhibit further corrosion from this cause.

Oxygen is important in electrolytic corrosion because of its activity in depolarizing the cathode by removing hydrogen as it is formed there. Depolarization by oxygen permits continued corrosion by bimetallic or galvanic action. The same result is effected by agitation with water in contact with the metal since depolarization is enhanced by the removal of hydrogen from the cathode.

19-7. Biologic Action. Bacteria that cause corrosion, particularly the corrosion of ferrous metals, include the sulphate-reducing bacteria, *Vibrio desulfuricans* or *Microspora desulfuricans;* iron-consuming bacteria, such as leptothrix, spirophyllum, crenothrix, and coccobacilli; sulphur bacteria, thiobacilli; and microorganisms that enter into or accelerate electrolytic or ionic reactions. Oscillatoria, a blue-green alga, has been suspected[1] of causing corrosion of iron by depolarizing the metal by removal of the natural protective coating of hydrogen.

The sulphate-reducing[2] bacteria operate in the absence of oxygen (anaerobically) to react with sulphates, and with organic compounds containing sulphur, in the soil to produce hydrogen sulphide. The bacteria do not attack the metal directly. The hydrogen sulphide combines with iron to form compounds of sulphur and iron, or it combines with

[1] See H. C. Myers, *J.A.W.W.A.*, April, 1947, p. 322.
[2] See R. L. Staryek and K. M. Wright, American Gas Association, 1945, abstract in *J.A.W.W.A.*, October, 1946, p. 1210.

water to form sulphurous or sulphuric acid which reacts with the metal, with the release of hydrogen, which is again used in the bacterial metabolism. Iron ions, Fe^+, are precipitated by hydrogen sulphide as ferrous sulphide and as ferrous hydroxide, removing iron molecules from the metal. A result is the lowering of the solution pressure of iron together with removal of cathodic hydrogen which, if not removed, would have retarded corrosion. The prevention of bacterial corrosion by cathodic protection[1] is explained since the depolarization of the cathode is inhibited by the electric current.

The hydrogen-ion concentration of the soil is an important factor in the action since the bacterial destruction of proteins in the soils produces ammonia, a weak base, and the bacterial destruction of carbohydrates produces weak acids. The result of such actions is to render the soil slightly basic, or to increase the pH. For bacterial corrosion of this type to proceed, the pH of the surrounding soil must be between 6.2 and 7.8. Reducing actions take place most effectively under anaerobic conditions. Such conditions are commonly found in swampy or moist organic soils, not necessarily submerged in water.

Thiobacilli cause corrosion by the oxidation of sulphur obtained from the ground or from joint compounds.[2] These organisms produce sulphuric acid which attacks the metal.

Iron-consuming bacteria remove iron that is in solution in the water depending on concentrations of soluble iron or ion compounds of 2 ppm, or greater, to support their activities. The consumed iron is deposited by the bacteria as ferric hydroxide, forming a sheath or tubercule, around a central core, which may contain a small percentage of sulphide of iron. The effect is known as "tuberculation." It has been suggested that the corrosion of steel pipe may result also from the anaerobic reduction of nitrates.[3] Electrolytic and ionic reactions may be biologically accelerated through chemical changes resulting from metabolic reactions during bacteriological growth.

Unfortunately bacterial corrosion is not self-limiting as are some other causes of corrosion, and various means of inhibiting bacterial growth must be employed for prevention. These include treatment of the water to remove bacterial food, chlorination, and chloramination.

19-8. Natural Protective Coatings and Tuberculation. Protective coatings are sometimes produced on corroding metals as a result of the reactions involved. Ferric oxide, or iron rust, is one of the most common forms of such coatings. Its removal apparently accelerates the rate of corrosion of the metal beneath it.

---

[1] See H. H. Logan, *Natl. Bur. Standards (U.S.), Circ.* C450; *Eng. News-Record,* May 2, 1947, p. 109.

[2] See also T. D. Beckwith, *J.A.W.W.A.,* January, 1941, pp. 141, 152.

[3] See also D. H. Caldwell and J. B. Ackerman, *J.A.W.W.A.,* January, 1946, p. 61.

Tuberculation, a common source of difficulty from corrosion, is a combination of corrosion and the formation of protective coating in localized spots. Tubercules are conelike and resemble barnacles. They are usually a result of bacterial action, growing in concentric layers, with a central portion, usually black and soft, which contains sulphide of iron. The outer layers are ferric oxide interspersed with a hard black layer of magnetic oxide. Favorable conditions for the growth of tubercules seem to include an excess of 2 ppm of iron in solution and a fairly high velocity of flow to provide food for bacterial activity.

In the corrosion of ferrous metals by hydrogenation a secondary protective coating of OH^- ions is formed adjacent to the metallic surface as an accompaniment to the formation of H^+ ions. The OH^- ions may combine with substances in solution to form a protective alkaline coating effective in inhibiting further corrosion. If the pH value of the solution is low, the formation of this alkaline coating is inhibited.

Conditions tending to remove protective coatings include high velocity of flow removing the coating by erosion, temperature changes, pH changes, changes in the concentration of dissolved substances, and inability of metallic surface to adsorb a protective coating.

19-9. Cavitation. The effects of cavitation are similar to those of corrosion but are due more to erosion. The sudden and alternate making and breaking of a high vacuum and the creation and condensation of water vapor cause a bombardment of the surrounding surfaces with particles of water and water vapor moving at a high velocity. Erosion, with the appearance of corrosion, is a result.[1]

19-10. Selective Corrosion of Alloys. In the selective corrosion of an alloy one metal dissolves out of the alloy more rapidly than the other. The so-called dezincification of brass is a common manifestation of this phenomenon. It is assumed that the brass dissolves as a whole, but the copper ion is redeposited, leaving the metal low in strength and composed of a spongy mass of copper. The phenomenon is limited to yellow, or high-zinc, brasses in contact with waters, particularly hot waters, carrying free mineral acids or acid-forming salts in the presence of oxygen.

19-11. Grounding of Electric Circuits on Water Pipes. The grounding of electric circuits and equipment on water pipes as a safety measure is permissible under various codes[2] and, when done according to proper standards, has not caused damage to the pipes, to the quality of the water, to property, or to life. Among the restrictions to the practice are that only the secondary distribution circuits of alternating current may be grounded on water pipes. An electrical jumper should be connected around the water meter.

[1] See also C. Oden'hal, *J. Am. Soc. Naval Engrs.*, Vol. 50, No. 2, p. 231, 1938, abstracted in *J.A.W.W.A.*, November, 1940, p. 1964.

[2] See also *J.A.W.W.A.*, April, 1944, p. 383; December, 1945, p. 1298.

Among the objections that have been raised against the practice are that pipes are corroded by electrolysis, electrical shocks have been received by workmen, the water has been given a taste or a color, and fires have been started. The American Research Committee on Grounding[1] has found no proof that any of the above results have been caused by properly installed grounds to water pipes. The practice is prohibited, nevertheless, in certain jurisdictions.[1]

Methods of Retarding Corrosion

19-12. Methods. Metallic corrosion may be retarded by (1) cathodic protection, (2) care in manufacture of the metal through control of its purity and composition, (3) application of coatings or linings, (4) control of the environment of the metal, and (5) treatment of the water. Methods for the treatment of water to retard corrosion are discussed in Chap. 31.

19-13. Cathodic Protection.[2] Galvanic and electrolytic corrosion, hydrogenation, and to some extent bacterial corrosion of metals can be retarded by cathodic protection. Cathodic protection is accomplished by connecting the metal in an electric circuit to the negative pole of a d-c generator,[3] the positive pole being connected to anodes buried in the ground or otherwise grounded. The electric potential of the metal is thus reduced below that of the surroundings, and electric currents will therefore flow from the surroundings to the metal. A diagram of the electrical connections for the cathodic protection of steel pipe is shown in Fig. 19-1. Care must be taken in the cathodic protection of a buried structure, such as a cast-iron pipe line, to prevent damage to a nearby unprotected structure which may be converted into an anode in relation to the decreased potential of the protected pipe.[4]

The object of this method of corrosion prevention is to create an electric current that will prevent the discharge and the migration of metallic ions from the anode to the cathode. The order of magnitude of electric current for each square foot of iron surface[5] ranges from 0.3 to 15 ma.[6] The voltages depend on the resistance of the circuit but should be expected to range between 1.5 and 30 volts.[7] The most desirable current density is the least that will give protection. Direct current should be

[1] See *J.A.W.W.A.*, April, 1944, p. 383; December, 1945, p. 1298.

[2] Cathodic protection has been reported exhaustively in *J.A.W.W.A.* See August, 1948, p. 485; September, 1949, pp. 845, 852; November, 1951, p. 883, with 62 references.

[3] See also H. A. Knudsen, *J.A.W.W.A.*, January, 1938, p. 38.

[4] See also F. E. Dolson, *J.A.W.W.A.*, November, 1947, p. 1074.

[5] See also H. H. Uhlig, *Chem. Eng. News*, December, 10, 1946, p. 3154.

[6] See also W. R. Schneider, *J.A.W.W.A.*, March, 1945, p. 245.

[7] See also G. L. O'Brien, *Water Works & Sewerage*, July, 1942, p. 285.

used. Scott[1] states: "The most preferable material for the electrode is aluminum since its products of solution are non-staining. Platinum, graphite, or the chrome-steel alloys may be used for more permanent electrodes." It has been estimated that cathodic protection of water tanks is less expensive than painting the interior, and the tank does not have to be removed from service.[2]

Corrosion inhibitors, involving the addition of certain chemicals to the water, are associated with cathodic protection[3] in that inhibitors form

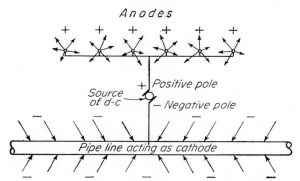

Fig. 19-1. Electric circuit for cathodic protection.

slightly soluble ions that affect the formation of metallic ions, thus inhibiting corrosion. Only manganese salts seem satisfactory, as salts of sodium, chromium, and zinc, whether or not the metal is also under cathodic protection, may result in the intensification of corrosion in localized areas, especially along the water line.

19-14. Care in Manufacture. Since impurities in metal tend to create galvanic couples, resulting in corrosion, the homogeneity of the metal will tend to minimize corrosion. Iron is made more homogeneous in manufacture by the process known as "spellerizing." This consists in kneading the hot iron like dough between rough rolls to produce a more uniform material. The purification of metals to remove cathodic elements of galvanic cells[4] has successfully improved corrosion resistance.

19-15. Alloys and Resistant Materials. Alloys of iron or steel with copper, nickel, or chromium are more resistant to corrosion than iron or steel alone. Special processes for the production of rustless metal are successful, and pipes and fittings of such metal are available.

[1] G. R. Scott, *Proc. 11th Ann. Short Course for Water and Sewage Plant Supts. and Operators*, Louisiana State University, 1948, p. 48.

[2] See also: G. W. Knight, *J. Penna. Water Works Operators' Assoc.*, 1940, p. 152; C. K. Wells, *J.A.W.W.A.*, May, 1952, p. 428.

[3] See also: U. R. Evans, *Ind. Eng. Chem.*, Vol. 37, p. 703, 1945; R. S. Thornhill, *ibid.*, p. 706.

[4] See also Uhlig, *loc. cit.*

Glass-lined, vitreous-lined, rubber-lined, and other lining materials; tarred, extra-heavy, cast-iron pipe; cast iron enameled inside; chemically pure lead; vitrified clay; fiber; asbestos; and other materials are used with satisfaction for conveying highly corrosive materials. High-silica pipe is resistant to acids but is more susceptible to the action of alkalies, particularly soda wastes. Pipes and fittings of high-silica iron and of the same styles and dimensions as standard cast-iron pipes are manufactured. A fiber pipe is manufactured that is resistant to both acids and alkalies but is structurally weak, and its use is confined to drainpipes under chemical-laboratory sinks and similar locations.

19-16. Coatings and Linings. Coatings and linings[1] are used to prevent corrosion, to prevent contamination of the water, and to increase the smoothness of the pipe wall. Coatings and linings used for the protection of iron and steel surfaces include tar or asphaltic materials, enamels, resins, lacquers, zinc, or galvanizing, metallizing,[2] plastics, and paints.[3] Each has shown some success in retarding corrosion. The success of a coating depends as much on the preparation of the surface, whether concrete or metal, as on the material of the coating.[4] Burnett and Masin,[5] as a result of extensive studies, state: "Of the various types of coatings under tests as linings for steel water pipe, phenolic, vinyl, thiokol, vinyl thiokol, and neoprene materials appear to offer the best possibilities."

19-17. Bituminous Coatings and Linings. Coal-tar enamel coatings are used extensively for the protection of steel pipe.[6] The Angus Smith coating, introduced about 1886, is used for cast-iron pipe. This coating consists of a mixture of gas tar, Burgundy pitch, oil, and resin into which the pipe is dipped while hot. About 1931, molten bituminous enamel was introduced. It is applied to the inside of the pipe while hot and the pipe is spinning around its longitudinal axis.[7] The application of enamel coating to the exterior of pipe is done by various devices that pour enamel on the pipe and spread it in overlapping spiral paths. Most coated steel pipe is also wrapped, frequently with asbestos felt saturated with bitumen. It may be finished with a wrapping of heavy paper. Water mains have been lined in place with electrically deposited bitumen.[8]

Asphaltic protective coatings[9] have been tested for the Asphalt Insti-

---

[1] See also H. W. Griswold, *Water Works Eng.*, May, 1949, p. 427.

[2] See also *Water Works Eng.* July, 1952, p. 661.

[3] See also J. R. Baylis, *J.A.W.W.A.*, August, 1953, p. 807.

[4] See also: Paul Weir, *Eng. News-Record*, May 2, 1946; W. H. Cates, *J.A.W.W.A.*, February, 1953, p. 103.

[5] *J.A.W.W.A*, October, 1952, p. 893.

[6] See Specifications, *J.A.W.W.A.*, January, 1940; March, 1950, p. 315; see also G. E. Burnett, *J.A.W.W.A.*, August, 1950, p. 741.

[7] See also: D. Bronson and G. B. McComb, *J.A.W.W.A.*, May, 1943, p. 613; L. E. Goit, *J.A.W.W.A.*, October, 1941, p. 1723.

[8] See also *Eng. News-Record*, Apr. 1, 1948, p. 86.

[9] See also A. H. Benedict, *Eng. News-Record.*, Feb. 26, 1942, p. 49.

tute with the following conclusions: (1) a wide range of performance results from the diversity of materials used, rather than from basic deficiencies in asphalts; (2) asphaltic coatings are less permeable to oxidizing agents than to water; and (3) asphaltic enamels of standard qualities are equal to other bituminous coatings in all respects and are superior to some.

19-18. Resins, Lacquers, and Plastics.[1] Natural resins are obtained from the exudations of various plants. When applied to metals they are sometimes called lacquers. Resins may be prepared synthetically to produce thermosetting and thermoplastic coatings for the protection of metallic surfaces against corrosion. The procedure in their application involves cleaning the metallic surface and the application of the plastic resin coating by brushing, dipping, or spraying. After the evaporation of the solvents used as a vehicle, the coating is baked under controlled conditions. When lacquers and paints are used in connection with cathodic protection, they should be alkali-resistant because of the alkali usually produced at the cathode. Synthetic thermosetting and thermoplastic materials, being developed but not yet in extensive use, have promise of adhering well to metals to resist abrasion and to limit corrosion.[2]

19-19. Paints. Paints for the protection of metals from corrosion should be made of a metallic pigment, usually zinc or lead, mixed with an oil, usually linseed, which will dry to form a thin veneer over the surface of the metal, the pores of the veneer being filled with the metallic pigment.[3] Zinc is a particularly desirable agent because of its electrolytic relation to iron, and its nontoxic properties in potable water.

Varnishes and lacquers form a japanned or enameled surface which may be allowed to dry cold or may be baked on. Such coatings are pleasing in appearance but are sometimes easily broken.

Aluminum and gilt paints, particularly the former, may be successful as protective coatings, but they are relatively expensive. Their appearance is sufficiently attractive to result in their frequent use for the exterior of exposed surfaces, such as towers and elevated tanks. The paint may be sprayed, rather than brushed, on the metal.

19-20. Vitreous Coatings. Vitreous coatings for metal are prepared by running molten silica into cold water. The resulting material is ground in a pugmill with clay and water. When worked to the required consistency, the metal is coated with it by dipping or brushing and, when dried, it is baked onto the metal.

19-21. Zinc Coating and Galvanizing. Galvanizing consists in applying a zinc coating to the metal. This can be done by cleaning (pickling) the metal in acid and then dipping it in molten zinc; or the metal can be electroplated with zinc; or zinc can be applied by the sherardizing process,

---

[1] See also Sec. 19-17.

[2] See also B. Morris and others, *J.A.W.W.A.*, September, 1946, p. 993.

[3] See also G. G. Sward, *J. Penna. Water Works Operators' Assoc.*, Vol. 8, p. 92, 1936.

in which the hot iron is revolved in a drum containing zinc dust.   This process produces the best results, since the threads on threaded pipe are still useful after sherardizing, which is not always the case after galvanizing by other processes.

As a result of tests by the U.S. Bureau of Standards[1] it has been concluded that over a 10-year period the rate of loss of weight of galvanized steel was from one-half to one-fifth of the rate of bare steel.   For long exposure a thick zinc coating is superior to a thin one.   A coating of 2.8 oz per sq ft of surface prevented serious corrosion for 10 years.

19-22. Metallic Plating.   Tin or lead plating or coating is applied in a manner similar to the hot-dip process of galvanizing, except that the iron is passed through the rolls at the same time that it is in the bath of molten tin or lead.   The use of lead may be unsatisfactory in a paint or coating, as sufficient lead may be dissolved, particularly when in contact with corrosive waters, to be injurious to the health of the consumer.

Nickel and copper plating are usually applied electrolytically to the cleaned metal.   Nickel, copper, and tin coatings are sometimes used in the protection of iron; but because of their relatively low electrode pressure, when the coating is once broken, galvanic action is set up between them and the iron, resulting in more rapid corrosion of the iron than if it had not been coated.   Copper-coated steel forms an alloy which is highly resistant to corrosion.

19-23. Metallizing.[2]   Metallizing consists in spraying a coat of molten metal on any surface, metallic or otherwise, that will hold it.   The process successfully protects against corrosion, but since the protective coating is cast only on the surface, it may be broken when the metal is strained in tension.   The process is used also for building up surfaces worn away by friction.   Metallized surfaces are particularly suited to lubricated bearing surfaces as the porous sprayed metal holds the lubricant.

19-24. Linings.   Linings are materials that are caused to adhere to the inside of a pipe to protect it against corrosion, or to make the interior smoother.   The two principal materials used for linings are bituminous enamels and portland cement.   Such linings may provide and maintain a Hazen and Williams coefficient as high as 140 to 145.

19-25. Cement Lining.[3]   Pipes may be lined with cement in the factory, in the field, or in place.[4]   A relatively simple method suitable for use in the field and requiring little equipment consists of standing a piece of pipe

[1] See also Logan and Ewing, *Natl. Bur. Standards (U.S.) Research Paper* 982, 1937.

[2] See also: J. B. Stevens, *J.A.W.W.A.*, January, 1943, p. 53; D. A. Watson, *Water Works Eng.*, January, 1951, p. 49; J. E. Wakefield, *Eng. News-Record*, July 6, 1950, p. 40.

[3] See Specifications, *J.A.W.W.A.*, December, 1939; January, 1940. See also: T. F. Wolfe, *ibid.*, January, 1946, p. 11; R. C. Kennedy, *ibid.*, February, 1953, p. 113.

[4] See also: B. Harkness, *Water Works & Sewerage*, March, 1938, p. 182; G. W. Jones, *Eng. News-Record*, Oct. 17, 1946, p. 104.

on end over a movable mandrel.   A sufficient amount of cement, of the proper consistency, to line the pipe completely to the desired thickness is placed over the mandrel, which is then drawn through the pipe, spreading the mortar along the wall.   In the centrifugal process, which is suitable for pipes up to about 48 in. in diameter, the pipe to be lined is placed in a horizontal position and revolved at a peripheral speed of about 250 fpm about its longitudinal axis.   The cement is spread along the inside of the pipe by means of a long trough which moves in and out of the spinning pipe.   After the required amount of cement is dumped into the pipe, the trough is pressed down to act as a trowel in smoothing and packing the cement, and the peripheral speed of revolution of the pipe is increased up to about 600 fpm.   The thickness of the lining is at least $\frac{1}{8}$ in. for pipes up to 12 in. in diameter and increases to $\frac{1}{4}$ in. for pipes 30 in. and larger.   The centrifugal force, vibration, and rubbing of the trough produce a smooth dense lining which adheres firmly to the inside wall of the pipe and provides a Hazen and Williams coefficient of 140 to 145.[1]

Large-sized pipes are lined with cement by the use of molds; fittings of all sizes are lined by hand; and pipes in place are lined by drawing a mandrel through them, pushing ahead of it sufficient cement mortar to provide the necessary thickness of lining.

The mortar most commonly used consists of one part of portland cement, one part sand, and sufficient water to make a workable paste. Hydraulic cements, which include portland cement, tend to lose lime slowly when exposed to water, the lime being replaced by ferric hydroxide under proper conditions.   This exchange has no detrimental effect on the cement lining and does not affect its ability to protect the pipe from corrosion.

Pipes are lined in place[2] after they have been cleaned and prepared for the process.   The lining may be formed as a soft mortar which is placed by a plunger pulled back and forth in the pipe, or by means of machines which throw the mortar against the sides of the pipe by centrifugal force. Trowels are attached to the machine to smooth the mortar in place. Linings so placed in the field have resisted corrosion and have increased the Hazen and Williams coefficient from about 60 to about 122 to 136.[3] Pipes up to 16 in. in diameter have been lined in place by such machines.

[1] See also: J. E. Gibson, *J.A.W.W.A.*, Vol. 16, p. 427; H. Y. Carson, *ibid.*, Vol. 18, p. 721, 1927.

[2] See also: J. E. Gibson, *J.A.W.W.A.*, May, 1940, p. 819; *Water Works Eng.*, March, 1950, p. 220; April, 1950, p. 300; H. G. Dresser, *ibid.*, April, 1952, p. 343; April 16, 1947, p. 415; *ibid.*, Apr. 2, 1947, p. 353; Mar. 19, 1947, p. 299; Feb. 5, 1947, p. 142.

[3] See also F. H. Rhodes, *J.A.W.W.W.*, January, 1944, p. 64.

STORAGE AND DISTRIBUTING RESERVOIRS

20-1. Purposes of Reservoirs. Reservoirs are used to store water, to equalize flows, to distribute or equalize pressures, and to impound water. A reservoir on the distribution system will equalize rates of flow, will equalize pressures, and will store water for emergencies. Such reservoirs, called distribution reservoirs, are used to adjust a variable rate of demand to a rate of supply that is not equal to the rate of demand. It is possible, by the use of such reservoirs, to reduce the size of pumps necessary to supply the district served by the reservoir, since the peak rates of demand on the pump are diminished by the reservoir. Howson[1] has shown appreciable savings in costs of distribution systems through the installation of elevated storage tanks.

In the design of reservoirs, the Tentative Manual of Safe Practice in Water Distribution[2] should be consulted.

20-2. Classification. Reservoirs on the distribution system may be classified according to their position as surface or elevated, or according to the material of which they are built, such as steel, reinforced concrete, wood, and earth.

Elevated storage is generally more expensive than ground-level storage. McDonald estimated[3] the cost of elevated storage for a 100,000-gal tank to be four times that of a ground-level storage reservoir, and for a 1,000,-000-gal tank the ratio of costs is about 3:1. High-level storage is desirable, however, despite its cost because of the safety factor in the event of temporary shutdown of pumps.

20-3. Capacity.[4] Storage for fire protection should be sufficient so that the required fire demand (Sec. 3-7) may be maintained for a period of 2 hr in small communities up to 10 or 12 hr in the largest communities. When the reserve storage is elevated, the amount of fire reserve in gallons

---

[1] L. R. Howson, *Water Works & Sewerage*, June, 1943, pp. R-79, R-81.

[2] See *J.A.W.W.A.*, June, 1942, p. 917.

[3] N. G. McDonald, *J.AW.W.A.*, July, 1947, p. 637.

[4] See also: R. C. Kennedy, *J.A.W.W.A.*, November, 1940, p. 1819; D. H. Maxwell, *ibid.*, July, 1947; p. 644; L. R. Howson, *Water Works Eng.*, November, 1949, p. 1007; J. E. Kiker, Jr., *Public Works*, May, 1953, p. 74.

may be determined by multiplying the difference between the fire demand F and the reserve fire-pumping capacity P by the duration of the fire T.

Reserve storage(gal) $= [F(\text{gpm}) - P(\text{gpm})]T(\text{min})$ McDonald's[1] empirical formula for reservoir capacity is

$$R = aD + bD + {}^{10}\!/_{24}(D + F - S) \qquad (20\text{-}1)$$

where R = reservoir capacity for balancing the domestic demand, to supply part of the water for fire service, and to provide for the operation of the pumps in the off-peak power-load period, million gal

D = average domestic demand for the maximum month, mgd

F = fire demand, mgd

S = capacity of pumps, mgd

a and b = fractional parts of domestic demand required for balancing and off-peak operation, respectively; a is in the order of $\frac{1}{5}$ and b $\frac{1}{10}$

In some systems, it may be more economical to provide elevated storage for equalizing purposes only, fire reserve being stored in a surface-level reservoir. Under such a system, the water in the reserve storage reservoir must be pumped into the distribution system during the emergency. The reserve storage must always be kept available for immediate use, no part of the capacity provided for it being used for any other purpose.

20-4. Storage to Equalize Flow. Equalizing storage is provided so that a relatively constant rate of supply can provide for a fluctuating rate of demand. The equalizing tank, or reservoir, is connected by a single pipe to the distribution system. When the rate of supply exceeds demand, water flows into the tank. When demand exceeds supply, water flows through the same pipe from the tank. The tank is said to be "floating on the line." The relation between rate of supply, rate of demand, and tank capacity is based on a study of the service required and the costs involved.

The procedure in the determination of the capacity of an equalizing reservoir floating on the line can be shown with the aid of an example. Let the hydrograph of demand of a district be shown by line A in Fig. 20-1, the abscissas of which are time and the ordinates, shown to the left, are rate of flow in thousands of gallons per min. Construct a mass diagram of the rate of demand, as shown by line B. Its abscissas are time and its ordinates, shown on the right, are total flow. Join the ends of line B by a straight line, marked C in the figure. This line represents the mass diagram of pumping into the reservoir, and its slope represents the rate of pumping. Draw two lines parallel to line C and tangent to

[1] McDonald, *loc. cit.*

line B at points 1 and 2, respectively. The vertical distance a, between these two lines, measured on the right-hand scale, is the required capacity of the equalizing reservoir. In the example shown, it is about 1.2 million gal.

Much concerning the operation of the reservoir can be determined from a study of the figure. For example, the reservoir is

1. Full at point 1.
2. Empty at point 2.

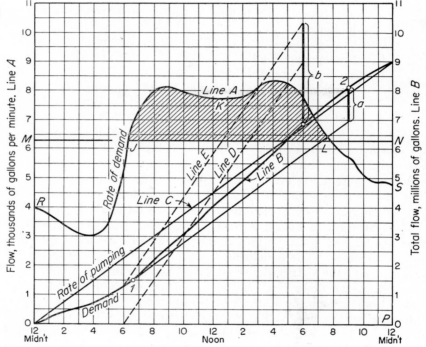

Fig. 20-1. Graphical determination of equalizing reservoir capacity.

3. Filling when slope of line C exceeds slope of line B.
4. Emptying when slope of line B exceeds slope of line C.
5. The rate of flow from or into the reservoir at any time is represented by the difference between the slopes of lines B and C at that time.

If it is desired to install an equalizing reservoir that will permit pumping at a constant rate, during the hours of greatest rate of demand, and so that the total requirements for the day will be pumped during this period, the requisite capacity of the reservoir and the rate of pumping can be determined as follows:

1. Assume the hours of pumping to be from 6 A.M. to 6 P.M.

2. Draw a straight line, such as line D, from 6 A.M. and zero total flow to 6 P.M, with the total flow for the day.

3. The slope of the line just drawn represents the requisite rate of pumping. In this case it is 18 mgd.

4. Draw line E, parallel to line D, and intersecting line B at 6 A.M. The vertical distance between the intersection of line E with the ordinate at 6 P.M., to line B, represents the capacity of the reservoir on the right-hand scale. In this case it is about 3.3 million gal.

Another method of determining the requisite capacity of an equalizing reservoir for the hydrograph of demand shown in Fig. 20-1 is to draw a straight horizontal line representing the average rate of pumping necessary to supply the demand indicated by the hydrograph. This is line MN in Fig. 20-1. Area $OMNP$ is equal to the area under the hydrograph $ORSP$. The shaded area above line MN and below the hydrograph, area JKL, converted to units of volume, represents the required capacity of the equalizing reservoir. In this case, it is 1.2 million gal. The economy of the use of a storage tank is partly indicated by these lines. Without storage, the maximum pumping capacity required must be about 8,300 gpm. A storage tank with a capacity equal to the volume shown in the shaded portion of the curve, marked K in the figure, will require a maximum rate of pumping of only 6,300 gpm.

Storage is required on the distribution system unless the demand curve is followed. To do this, by pumping at various rates, is usually uneconomical. It may be desirable to install storage and pumping capacity to permit pumping at the average rate during the day of maximum demand. allowing one or more pumping units to stand idle on days of lesser demand, or it may be desirable to install only enough storage and pumping capacity to permit pumping at the average rate on the day of average demand, with one or more pumping units standing idle, and to overload all units to meet the peak demand on the maximum day. It is widely conceded that it is economically unjustifiable to provide sufficient pumping and storage capacity to care for the peak demand occurring only once in 3 to 5 years and lasting but a few hours.

20-5. Location. Distributing reservoirs should be located centrally in, or at least as close as possible to, the district that they serve. They should also have sufficient elevation to maintain adequate pressure. The reason for a central location is to reduce friction losses in the distributing pipes by reducing the distance traveled by the water. The advantages afforded by natural elevations should be investigated.

The location of a distributing reservoir has a marked effect on the fluctuations in pressure in portions of a distribution system. This is indicated by the hydraulic grade lines in Fig. 20-2.[1] Care should be

[1] See also *Water Works Eng.*, Oct. 23, p. 1361; Nov. 6, p. 1421; Nov. 20, p. 1473. 1940.

taken to locate the reservoir to obtain the most constant pressure. Two or more reservoirs at different elevations may sometimes be connected to the same distribution system.

20-6. Types. The walls of surface reservoirs are built of earth embankments, lined or unlined, and of masonry or reinforced concrete. The reservoirs may be open or covered. Open earth reservoirs are the least expensive for large capacities, but they have the disadvantage of being subject to leakage. The selection of type, therefore, is usually dependent upon available funds, the value of the water stored, and subsoil conditions.

A surface reservoir, formed by building a dam across a valley, may be classed as a distributing reservoir—if its purpose is primarily to care for fluctuations in pressure and demand rather than to act as a catchment basin in which to store the water precipitated on the drainage area.

20-7. Depth. The depth of a reservoir necessary to give the desired capacity is influenced by the following considerations:

1. Temperature as it may affect the potability of the water, the growth of organisms, or the formation of ice
2. The cost of land area
3. The cost of walls
4. The character of material to be excavated

Shallow water is more subject to undesirable temperature changes than deep water. The effect on shallow water of high summer temperatures may be the imparting of taste or odor to the water, because of the encouragement of objectionable growths. Low winter temperatures may induce a relatively high reduction of capacity because of the formation of ice. On the other hand, rock excavation may be required in order to secure the necessary depth. The cost of embankments and of masonry walls

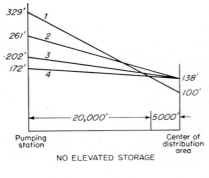

NO ELEVATED STORAGE

1. Maximum day with fire
2. Maximum hourly rate
3. Maximum daily rate
4. Average daily rate

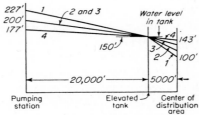

TANK BETWEEN PUMPING STATION AND
DISTRIBUTION AREA

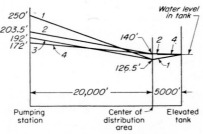

DISTRIBUTION AREA BETWEEN
TANK AND PUMPING STATION

FIG. 20-2. Effect of elevated storage on distribution pressures.

increases rapidly with increasing heights. This disadvantage may be offset by a high cost per square foot of land. For reservoirs having a capacity less than 5 million gal, depths ranging from 12 to 18 ft will ordinarily be economical.

20-8. Foundations. In reservoirs founded on clay or other yielding material, the distribution of pressure over the foundation must be made uniform. This may be done by spreading the wall and column footings,

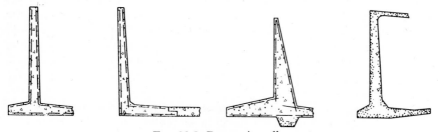

Fig. 20-3. Reservoir walls.

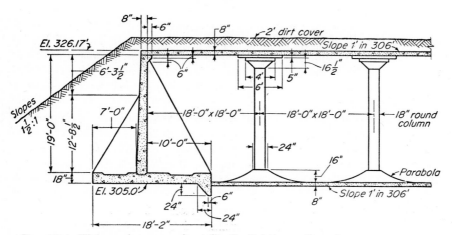

Fig. 20-4. High-service reservoir at St. Paul, Minn. Capacity 18,000,000 gal.

as shown in Figs. 20-3 and 20-4. Rock, well-driven piles, and confined sand make satisfactory foundations requiring no special precautions in design or construction. Chemical soil solidification is reported[1] to have been used successfully in the preparation of foundations.

Earth Reservoirs

20-9. Walls. Except in locations where the topography of the site is particularly advantageous, the walls of earthen reservoirs are formed by

[1] See also C. M. Riedel, *J.A.W.W.A.*, September, 1946, p. 849.

excavating to the required depth below the ground surface and using the excavated material for the building of embankments to the necessary height above the ground surface.   The top width of the embankment should be at least one-fourth of the maximum total height, with a minimum width of 4 ft.   Greater widths are ordinarily used.   The angle of repose of the material (when saturated) will govern the maximum steepness of side slopes.   Slopes steeper than $1\frac{1}{2}$ horizontal to 1 vertical should not ordinarily be used.   The embankments of earthen reservoirs are essentially earth dams, and the same general considerations apply to their design and construction.   Because, however, of the usual proximity of distributing reservoirs to populous districts and on account of the high value of water at that location, special care should be exercised in design and construction, in order to avoid loss of water and to assure the safety of life and property.

An effective joint between the natural ground surface and the embankment may be secured by the removal of all perishable matter, sand, etc., from the original surface and below it to depths to which roots or permeable materials may extend.   If rock is encountered in the foundation, a concrete cutoff wall is necessary.   The wall should extend 12 to 24 in. into the rock and at least 24 in. into the fill.

20-10. Core Walls.   In the absence of suitable materials it becomes necessary to resort to core walls to secure impermeability.   Core walls used for reservoir embankment are essentially the same as those used in earth dams.

20-11. Clay Blankets.   When the substrata under a reservoir are pervious, it may be necessary to line the floor and sides with a layer of impervious material.   A layer of clay, usually called a blanket, 6 in. to 2 ft. thick, sprinkled and rolled, may be used.   In order to avoid the difficulty of rolling on the side slopes, the blanket may be made to connect with the core wall, if one is used.

20-12. Protection of Outlet Pipes.   Cutoff collars or wide flanges of ample dimensions will serve to minimize the seepage along the outside surface of outlet pipes or conduits.   The dimensions and spacing of the collars depend upon the amount of head on the percolating water and upon the material.   The pipe or conduit must be sufficiently strong to carry the weight of the filling upon it with safety.   Danger of the failure of outlet pipes, due to settlement, is minimized by supporting them on undisturbed earth.

20-13. Linings.   Concrete is the principal material used for reservoir linings.   Brick, asphalt, oiled-earth fill lined with concrete,[1] and rubble masonry are also used.   To assure watertightness, bentonite clay has been incorporated with the embankment in new reservoirs and to stop

[1] See also D. A. Blackburn, *J.A.W.W.A.*, May, 1941, p. 876.

leaks in old reservoirs.[1]   The concrete of the floor is laid in blocks about
6 ft square.   The sides may be cast in blocks or in strips about 6 ft wide,
extending the entire height of the side slopes.   The joints between the
blocks or strips may be filled with a bituminous preparation or wooden
strips, in order to increase watertightness.   Tar paper is also used to

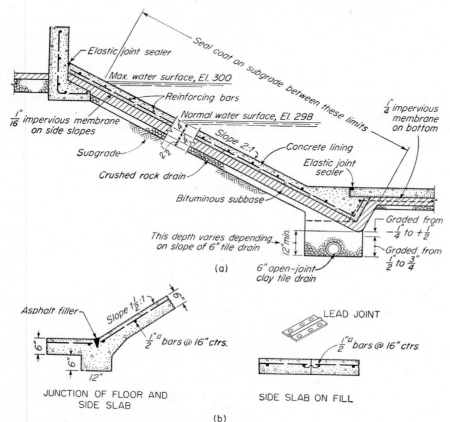

FIG. 20-5. Reservoir-lining details.   [(a) *from J. W. Trahern, J.A.W.W.A., February,
1952, p. 161.*]   (b) Stanford Heights Reservoir, San Francisco, Calif.   (*From
J.A.W.W.A., Vol. 15, p. 119.*)

separate the blocks.   Construction joints are ordinarily used to reduce
cracking due to shrinkage, temperature changes, or unequal settlement.
The thickness of the floor in inches should be about four-tenths of the
depth in feet, with a minimum thickness of 4 in.   A curb should be provided at the base of the slope lining, to protect it from sliding.   Stone
blocks or riprap may be used as lining, to protect embankments against
sloughing or against washing due to wave action.

[1] See also *Water and Sewage*, Vol. 81, p. 14, 1943.

The progress of water that has leaked through a lining may be stopped by the embankment, in which case hydrostatic pressure will be developed. If the reservoir is dewatered more rapidly than this water can escape from the embankment, pressure or uplift is exerted against the reservoir lining. Weep holes are sometimes used to prevent such a condition.   Their use, however, destroys the impermeability of the lining.

Better results are obtained from linings that are reinforced than from plain concrete linings.   The reinforcement prevents cracking due to the weight of the water and effects a better distribution of shrinkage cracks. An area of steel of about one-fourth of 1 per cent of the cross-sectional area of the concrete is usually sufficient.   Either bars or wire mesh may be used for reinforcement.   A watertight lining depending principally on a layer of asbestos-fiber-bound asphalt emulsion[1] was used successfully on the Seneca Reservoir, illustrated in Fig. 20-5.   The underdrainage system is said to be an essential feature of this lining.

Masonry Reservoirs[2]

20-14. Walls.   The masonry walls of reservoirs are usually made of concrete and are of the gravity, cantilever, counterfort, vertical-beam, or cylindrical type.   The overturning force that may be exerted against a reservoir wall is produced by either water or earth pressure.[3]   If no earth fill is placed against the outside, the wall is designed to resist the water pressure when the reservoir is full.   With an earth fill on the outside, the wall is usually designed to resist the earth pressure when the reservoir is empty.   One of the purposes of the fill, if used, may be to effect an economy in design.   In such a case, its function is to counteract the pressure of water by its passive resistance.   The lateral pressure of earth is roughly about one-half the pressure of a column of water of the same height.   The structural members of a wall designed to resist earth pressures are therefore proportionately smaller than those required for water pressure of a corresponding height.   Such an advantage is, however, nullified if the fill is not, or cannot be, properly drained.   When there is a possibility of water collecting at the back of the wall, as a result of leakage or a high ground-water table, the wall must be designed for the water pressure that may be developed on the outside.   When arch or groined-arch roofs are used, it may be required to design the walls to take all or part of the arch thrust.

Gravity walls are proportioned so that they resist by their weight the

---

[1] See also J. W. Trahern, *J.A.W.W.A.*, February, 1952, p. 161.

[2] See also: G. P. Manning, *Water and Water Eng.*, December, 1945, p. 639; H. R. Lupton, *J. Inst. Water Engrs.*, March, 1953, p. 87.

[3] See also I. C. M. Cole, *Water and Water Eng.*, May, 1939, p. 239.

overturning and sliding effects of the pressure against them.   They are no longer used to any great extent in reservoir construction.

Cantilever walls consist of a base and a stem built in the shape of a *T* or an *L*, as shown in Fig. 20-3.   The base is constructed so that its own weight plus that of the stem and a part of the retained fill develops a fixed end for the cantilever, or stem.   The entire structure is proportioned so that the resultant of the vertical and horizontal forces passes within the middle third of the base width.   Sliding is resisted by an adequate width of base or by a cutoff wall under the base.   The thickness of the stem and the base on the side of the fill will be determined by the bending moment at the junction of base and stem, produced by the lateral thrust.[1]   The maximum thickness of the toe of the base is determined by the bending moment produced by the foundation pressures on the toe, between the edge of the base and the front face of the stem.   Reinforcement to resist shearing stresses is provided, if needed.   The thickness of the stem, in inches, required for earth pressures will ordinarily be about equal to the height of the fill, in feet, with a minimum of 8 in.   The cantilever type of wall is usually not economical for retaining an earth fill more than 20 ft in height.   Sections of some cantilever walls are shown in Fig. 20-3.

A counterforted wall is essentially a continuous horizontal or inclined slab, supported by vertical counterforts spaced 7 to 10 ft apart, depending on the height.   The counterforts should have a thickness of about one-twentieth of the height of the wall when earth pressures are resisted.   The thicknesses of the face slab and base slab are designed structurally, with a minimum thickness of 6 in.   The design of counterforted walls is somewhat more complicated than that of cantilever walls, but the counterforted type will show a saving in material for heights of earth of more than 20 ft.   Figure 20-4 shows a detail of a counterforted wall used in a reservoir at St. Paul, Minn.

A detail of an inclined slab-buttressed wall, also at St. Paul, Minn., is shown in Fig. 20-6.   This wall is designed to carry either external or internal water pressure, and no dependence is placed upon the passive resistance of the earth embankment.   The arch thrust of the roof is transmitted to the buttresses through the reinforced beam at the top.   The cutoff wall under the base slab develops additional resistance to sliding.

In beam-type walls, unit lengths of the wall are designed as vertical beams supported by floor and roof.   Keyways at the floor and at the roof provide simple forms for the beam.   This type results in an economical design, when conditions permit its use.

When the reservoir takes a circular or ring shape, advantage may be taken of the cylindrical shape in design.   Stress due to bending is elimi-

---

[1] See also: Dana Young, *Trans. Am. Soc. Civil Engrs.*, Vol. 108, p. 217, 1943; C. M. Stanley, Jr., *ibid.*, Vol. 109, p. 567, 1944.

nated. Stresses carried by the wall are either ring tension or compression, depending on the loading. This type of reservoir will usually require the least thickness of wall, provided the diameter is not excessively large. It is usually the most economical type for small capacities. Its disadvantages lie in the higher cost of form work and less economical use of land. The gunite process requires no outside forms in placing the concrete where reinforcing is used. Figure 20-7 shows the details of a prestressed-concrete tank.[1] The stressing of the reinforcement before filling the reservoir maintains compression in the concrete when the reservoir is full. Cantilever or buttressed walls may have a circular shape in plan

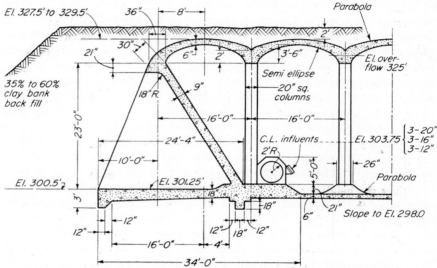

Fig. 20-6. Dale Street Reservoir, St. Paul, Minn. Capacity 30,000,000 gal.

view. Partition walls are provided in reservoirs either to serve as baffles or to permit a part of the reservoir to remain in service while an adjacent part is being cleaned or repaired. It is important that partition walls be designed to resist water pressure from either side in order that either chamber may be emptied.

20-15. Floors. The floors of masonry reservoirs are of three general types: (1) the square block as described under earth reservoirs, (2) reinforced slabs, and (3) groined arches. The first is used when no complications arise from foundation or uplift pressures. Otherwise, reinforced slabs or groined arches are necessary. The slabs or groined arches serve to transmit hydrostatic pressures to the columns. Watertightness is obtained, as in earth reservoirs, by wooden strips, usually of cypress, or by bituminous compounds placed in the joints of the masonry.

[1] See also: I. M. Glace, *Water Works & Sewerage*, March, 1945, p. 83; J. M. Crom, *Proc. Am. Soc. Civil Engrs.*, October, 1950; *Trans. Am. Soc. Civil Engrs.*, 1952, p. 89.

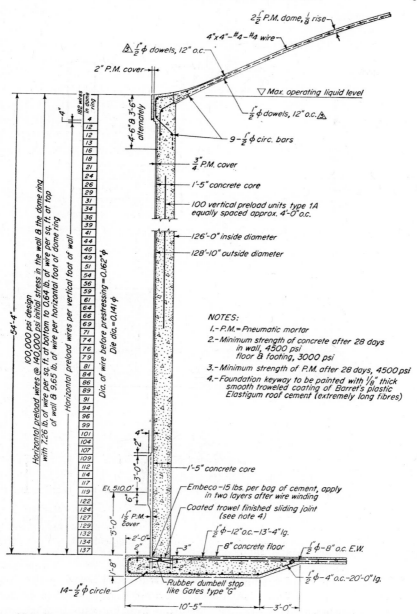

FIG. 20-7. Vertical section through wall of a prestressed reinforced-concrete reservoir. (*Courtesy of Preload Construction Corp.*)

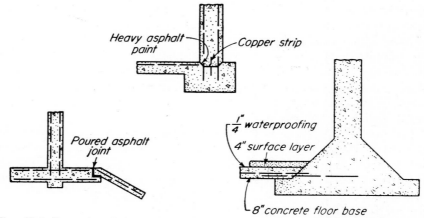

FIG. 20-8. Examples of connections between concrete floors and walls for reservoirs.

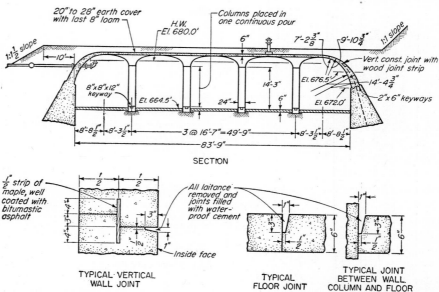

FIG. 20-9. Unreinforced concrete reservoir roof at Springfield, Vt. (*From Eng. News-Record, Sept.* 23, 1943, *p.* 105.)

The connection between the floor and the walls and between the floor and the columns is an important detail. A construction joint is usually necessary to provide against cracks resulting from unequal settlement.[1] Figure 20-8 shows details of floor-and-wall connections.

20-16. Roofs. Reservoir roofs are built of wood and of reinforced concrete. The latter may be of the beam-and-girder, the flat-slab, the

[1] See also L. A. Hosegood, *J.A.W.W.A.*, June, 1954, p. 527.

barrel-arch, or the groined-arch type.[1]   A section through a reservoir at Springfield, Vt., with unreinforced-concrete roof is shown in Fig. 20-9.

Wooden roofs are the least expensive but have the disadvantages of short life and high maintenance cost.   Ordinary rules of timber design are used to determine the size and spacing of columns, girders, and joists. Noncombustible shingles form a good covering material.   The slopes of reservoir roofs are usually too flat for the successful use of ordinary prepared roofing.

Reinforced-concrete roofs are usually designed to support 2 to 3 ft of earth fill.   The purpose of the fill is to protect the water against extremes of heat and cold or to provide for landscaping.   The loading usually used in design is the earth load plus 100 psf.   Figure 20-4 shows an example of a flat-slab roof.   Figure 20-9 shows a detail of a reservoir having a groined-arch roof.

Elevated Reservoirs

20-17. Types.   Elevated reservoirs are used principally as distributing reservoirs where a tank on the ground will not supply needed pressure. They may combine also the services of equalizing and storage reservoirs. The required capacity is determined on the principles outlined in Sec. 20-3.   The effect of elevated storage on distribution pressures is shown graphically in Fig. 20-2.   Among the advantages of the use of elevated storage may be included the reduction of pump capacity and of pumping cost, the reduction of the maximum pressures required at the pump discharge, and the reduction of peak demands on the pumps.   There are two types of elevated reservoirs: standpipes and elevated tanks.   A standpipe usually consists of a cylindrical shell, built of steel or reinforced concrete, having a flat bottom and resting on a foundation on the ground.   An elevated tank is a reservoir supported on a tower.   It is desirable to make the horizontal cross-sectional area of an elevated tank or standpipe relatively large in order to obtain maximum storage volume with minimum pressure variations in the system resulting from the filling and emptying of the tank.   There is an economical useful depth of tank that will give the least total capitalized cost of tank and of pumping.   This depth, for steel tanks, is usually about 20 to 25 ft.

20-18. Standpipes.   The useful storage capacity of a standpipe is the volume of the tank above the elevation required to give the necessary pressure for distribution.   The water in the tank below this elevation serves as additional low-pressure storage available for use with booster pumps, or for fire protection where fire pumping engines are used.   It is often possible to take advantage of a hill or high ground for a standpipe

[1] For method of design of groined arches, see *Trans. Am. Soc., Civil Engrs.*, Vol. 86, p. 180, 1923.

location in order to make the entire capacity of the tank usable. Figure 20-10 shows the details of two steel standpipes.

The design of a standpipe involves the determination of the economical size to perform the required operating function and an analysis of the effect of the loads upon internal stresses, the stability of the structure, and the foundations. The dead load includes the weight of all permanent construction and fittings. The live load includes the weight of the liquid contents and, for regions where snowfall occurs, a snow load of 25 psf of horizontal projection if the roof has a slope of less than 30 deg with the horizontal. A lateral load due to wind is assumed to be 30 psf on a vertical plane surface and 18 psf of projected vertical surface when the

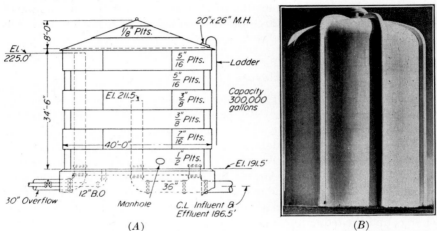

FIG. 20-10. (A) Details of steel standpipe, (B) steel standpipe at Madison, Wis. (*Courtesy of Chicago Bridge and Iron Co.*)

exposure is a cylindrical surface. The point of application of the wind load is considered to be at the center of gravity of the projected area. In locations subject to unusual winds, 40 and 24 psf, respectively, should be used instead of 30 and 18. Wind stresses may be neglected if they are less than 25 per cent of those due to dead and live load.

Foundations for standpipes are usually circular, octagonal, or square in plan and are built of masonry. In order that there shall be no tension on the windward side of the foundation, the latter should be proportioned so that the resultant of the vertical forces (weight of foundation and empty tank) and the horizontal force due to wind will pass through the middle 25 per cent of the diameter of a circular base, through the middle 26.5 per cent of the diameter of the inscribed circle of an octagonal base, and through the middle 33⅓ per cent of the side of a square base. Foundation requirements should be determined from field tests.

Standard references should be consulted for detailed design practice.[1]

[1] See also Standard Specifications for Steel Tanks and Steel Standpipes, *J.A.-W.W.A.*, Vol. 27, p. 1606, 1935, and subsequently.

20-19. Materials for Standpipes. Standpipes are usually built of steel or reinforced concrete. Steel is generally the favored material, as experience indicates that it is difficult to make concrete standpipes watertight under heads greater than 50 ft. Concrete has the advantage over steel of lower maintenance cost, when originally well constructed, and it is adaptable to architectural treatment. The advantages of steel standpipes over concrete are adaptability to high heads, leaks more easily repaired, slightly lower first cost, and greater assurance at the outset of a dependable structure. Steel standpipes are subject to rapid deterioration unless they are painted regularly or otherwise carefully maintained and protected against corrosion. Copper-bearing steel containing not less than 0.2 per cent copper is recommended for the tank and roof material.

20-20. Steel Standpipes. Steel standpipes[1] are commonly erected as cylinders with a vertical axis, the structure resting on a concrete foundation on the ground surface. The structural design, in addition to follow-

TABLE 20-1. Extracts from Tentative Standards Specifications for Elevated Steel Water Tanks, Standpipes, and Reservoirs*

Loads: Dead load is weight of all permanent construction and fittings, with steel at 490 lb per cu ft and concrete at 144 lb per cu ft. *Live load* is the weight of all liquid in the tank. *Snow load* is 25 psf of horizontal projection of surfaces having slope of less than 30 deg with the horizontal. *Wind load* 30 psf on vertical plane surface, 18 psf on projected areas of cylindrical surfaces, and 15 psf on projected areas of conical and double-curved plate surfaces. *Earthquake load* (to be specified by purchaser). *Balcony and ladder,* 1,000 lb at any point in balcony, 500 lb at any point in roof, and 350 lb on each section of ladder.

Unit stresses (in pounds per square inch): Structural steel, tension 15,000; compression, 15,000; shear (webs) 9,750.

Roofs: All tanks storing drinking water should have roofs.

Capacities: For *standpipes and reservoirs* (in thousands of gallons): 50-60-75-100-150-200-250-300-400-500-750-1,000-1,500-2,000-2,500-3,000-4,000. For *elevated tanks:* 5-10-15-20-25-30-40-50-60-75-100-150-200-250-300-400-500-750-1,000-1,500-2,000-2,500.

Shell height: For standpipes and elevated tanks: from 20 to 50 ft by even 2-ft intervals. From 50 to 100 ft by even 5-ft intervals. From 100 to 200 ft by even 10-ft intervals.

Diameters of reservoirs: same as heights for standpipes and elevated tanks.

Accessories: Standpipes, reservoirs, and elevated tanks: overflow, outside tank ladder, roof ladder, roof hatch, vent. *Standpipes and reservoirs:* shell manhole, pipe connection. *Elevated tanks:* tower ladder, roof finial, steel riser pipe, and pipe connection.

* See *J.A.W.W.A.,* December, 1940.

ing good practice, should follow the standard specifications of the American Water Works Association.[1] Some important extracts from these specifications are shown in Table 20-1. The construction of the standpipe is such that the bottom plate, either flat or curved, but usually flat,

[1] See also Standard Specifications, *J.A.W.W.A.,* April, 1949, p. 357; for painting, see August, 1952, p. 747.

rests directly on the concrete foundation and is riveted or welded to the lower ring of the vertical shell, as indicated in Fig. 20-10.

Piping connections to standpipes are shown in Fig. 20-10.   The single inlet-and-outlet pipe is shown terminating at the lower elevation of the useful capacity of the tank.   In no case should this pipe be less than 2 or 3 ft above the top of the drainpipe to avoid draining sludge from the tank into the distributing system.   The drainpipe should terminate at the lowest point in the tank so that the tank can be emptied.   The diameter of the overflow pipe should be computed so that its capacity, utilizing the available head, is equal to the expected maximum rate of pumping into the tank.   The specifications state: "A circular manhole 24 in. in diameter or an elliptical manhole 18 × 24 in. minimum size . . . shall be furnished in the first ring of the tank shell. . . ."

20-21. Cylindrical Concrete Tanks.   The side walls of a cylindrical concrete tank may resist bursting by hoop tension or a combination of

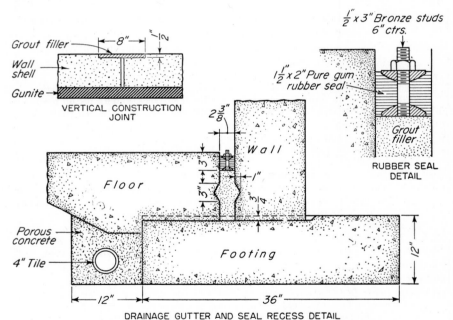

DRAINAGE GUTTER AND SEAL RECESS DETAIL
FIG. 20-11. Flexible joint between floor and wall of a concrete standpipe.

hoop tension and cantilever bending.   The cantilever action is most pronounced immediately above the connection between the vertical walls and the bottom of the tank.   Attempts have been made to minimize the cantilever stresses by the construction of a flexible seal between floor and walls, as shown in Fig. 20-11.   The floor is constructed to be independent of the side wall, which can expand and contract without cracking.   The lower part of the joint is filled with a mixture of sand, cement, and iron rust. The true seal is formed by a pure gum-rubber strip as shown. Prestressed-concrete tanks[1] are built with concrete walls prestressed by tightening steel bands around them to such tension that there is always compression in the tank walls even when filled with water. The steel bands are covered with concrete after stress has been put into them. Advantages claimed for such construction include (1) watertightness, (2) permanence and low upkeep, (3) adaptability to architectural treatment, (4) ease in burying underground, and (5) simple and accurate determination of stresses. Disadvantages include relatively high first cost and great weight if used as an elevated tank.

Meier[2] has pointed out that economical tank heights range between 16 and 45 ft depending on whether minimum concrete or minimum steel is desired and whether conventional or prestressed design is employed. Prestressed design yields savings in concrete up to 36.5 per cent in smallest tanks, and of steel up to 62 per cent in large tanks. Costs per million gallons remain approximately constant up to about 1 million gal capacity. The costs per gallon then rises rapidly for conventional designs between 1 and 3 million gal and increases diminishingly to 6 million gal.

Reinforced-concrete standpipes are designed by two different methods: (1) Steel hoops of sufficient cross-sectional area to resist the tension due to the internal water pressure are embedded in a circular wall built of concrete. (2) A circular concrete wall is built and allowed to set. Steel bands of sufficient cross-sectional area to resist the tension due to the internal water pressure and initial tension are placed around the outside of the concrete and are tightened sufficiently to cause compressive stresses in the concrete. The outside surface of the tank is then sprayed with concrete from an air gun. Experience with tanks designed under the first method has generally shown them to be unsatisfactory. They are difficult to make watertight and are subject to cracking due to temperature changes and to stresses unaccounted for in design. They are also subject to serious damage from frost action. Favorable results have been reported from tanks built by the second method.

The principal advantages of reinforced-concrete tanks are rapid erection and adaptability to inexpensive architectural treatment to improve the appearance. Seepage, efflorescence, and spalling, due to frost action, may nullify the last-named advantage.

20-22. Elevated Tanks. The name "elevated tank" ordinarily refers to the entire structure, consisting of the tank, the tower, and the riser pipe. Elevated tanks are usually cheaper than standpipes, per unit volume of useful capacity, for locations in which pressure requirements

[1] See also: R. C. Kennedy, *J.A.W.W.A.*, January, 1945, p. 76; H. L. Thompson and L. Cross, *ibid.*, June, 1950, p. 544.

[2] E. B. Meier, *J.A.W.W.A.*, May, 1952, p. 442.

necessitate considerable elevation above the surface of the ground. The design of elevated tanks involves the following determinations:

1. The capacity
2. The required elevation
3. The size and shape of the structural members required to resist the stresses
4. Stability of the structure and foundation requirements
5. The type and installation of appurtenances needed for operation

Capacity requirements are discussed in Sec. 20-3.

The elevation of the bottom of the tank depends on the pressure desired at the most remote point in the distribution system served by the tank, as indicated in Fig. 20-2. The designer is referred to standard texts for methods of design of structural members.[1]

The design of the foundation for an elevated tank is important. Unequal settlement causes severe strains on the various members and may cause serious leaks. An exploration of subsurface conditions is made for large structures. The bearing power of the foundation soil should be determined by tests.

Towers supporting elevated tanks are designed to act as a unit with the tank and, therefore, to resist the combined stresses due to weight and bending. Care must be taken to provide for uplift on the windward side, with suitable foundations and proper anchorage. Earthquake stresses are sometimes provided for.[2]

High towers and other structures near airways require special safeguards stipulated in regulations of the Civil Aeronautics Administration.[3] Among these regulations are included notification of contemplated construction, obstruction marking, and hazard lighting.

20-23. Elevated Tanks of Steel.[4] Standard specifications for elevated tanks, standpipes, and reservoirs have been prepared by the American Water Works Association.[5] Recommended practice for the repainting of elevated steel tanks and water-storage tanks, with notes on repairs, have been prepared by the same organization.[6] The thickness of the steel shell of the tank is fixed by the hydrostatic pressure to which the plates are subjected, by the allowable unit stresses, and by the joint efficiencies. The trend in practice since about 1931 has been toward welding.

Typical details of a riveted-steel tower are shown in Figs. 20-12 and 20-13. Tubular legs or columns, as shown in Figs. 20-14 and 20-15, are

---

[1] See also D. A. Leach, *J.A.W.W.A.*, July, 1947, p. 651.

[2] See also A. C. Ruge, *Trans. Am. Soc. Civil Engrs.*, Vol. 103, p. 889, 1938.

[3] See also V. T. Guccione, *Water Works Eng.*, March, 1950, p. 208, and a court ruling on the same subject on p. 246.

[4] See also Leach, *loc. cit.*

[5] See *J.A.W.W.A.*, April, 1949, p. 357; August, 1952, p. 745.

[6] See *ibid.*, October, 1948, p. 1099; November, 1949, p. 1046; August, 1952, p. 746.

used to some extent because of their pleasing appearance and structural advantages.

An ideal bottom shape to give minimum amount of steel is one that puts only tension in the steel. Practical considerations prevent the fabrication of such a shape, and the changes in depth of water in a tank make its design impossible. Flat and conical bottoms accentuate flexural stresses.[1] Hemispherical, ellipsoidal, and radial-cone-shaped

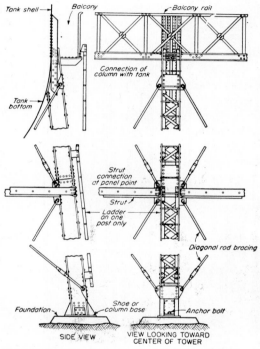

FIG. 20-12. Typical tower details for elevated water tanks. (*Courtesy of Chicago Bridge and Iron Co.*)

FIG. 20-13. Elevated tank at Kings Mountain, N.C. (*Courtesy of Chicago Bridge and Iron Co.*)

bottoms more nearly approach the ideal and are more commonly used. The last two types make it possible to increase the diameter for a given capacity, as compared with a hemispherical-bottom tank, so that the pumping head and pressure variations may be minimized.

Standard tanks are available for a maximum capacity of 1 million gal in the hemispherical-bottom type and 2 million gal in the ellipsoidal-bottom type. The first type is limited to a diameter of about 50 ft and the latter to about 90 ft. Double-ellipsoidal welded tanks with welded

[1] See also C. A. Lee, *Eng. News-Record,* May 4, 1944, p. 100.

tubular columns have been designed with capacities from 50,000 up to 500,000 gal.[1] Maxwell[2] showed that the total cost of elevated steel tanks on 100-ft towers varied, in 1947, approximately as the volume of the tank from $25,000 for a 0.1 million gal tank to $135,000 for a 1 million gal tank.

The hemispherical bottom is widely used for small tanks, but its range in head for a given capacity is greater than for the other types, since its diameter is limited to about 50 ft. Its shape affords low and easily

FIG. 20-14. Ellipsoidal-bottom tank at Sullivan, Ill. (Courtesy of Chicago Bridge and Iron Co.)

FIG. 20-15. Radial-cone-bottom tank at Fort Lauderdale, Fla. (Courtesy of Chicago Bridge and Iron Co.)

calculable stresses. The radial and circumferential stresses are equal to one-half the stresses in a cylinder of like radius, subject to the same hydrostatic pressure.

The riser pipe for an ellipsoidal-bottom tank is used to support part of the weight of the tank and water. The bottom of the tank acts as a diaphragm and eliminates the necessity for an expansion joint between the tank and the riser pipe. Figure 20-14 shows a typical detail of a tank with ellipsoidal bottom.

[1] See also Leach, loc. cit.
[2] See D. H. Maxwell, J.A.W.W.A., July, 1947, p. 644.

Radial-cone and toroidal bottoms make it possible to develop large capacities with low ranges of head. Figure 20-15 shows an attractive type of tank with radial-cone bottom and tubular legs. Steel tanks must be protected against corrosion. Painting, and cathodic protection when properly done,[1] are the most commonly used protective methods.

20-24. Appurtenances for Steel Tanks. The relative simplicity of form of recent tanks, as indicated in Fig. 20-10, has overcome the need for some of the appurtenances on the older type of tanks.

Roofs. The roof of an elevated tank or standpipe may be considered as an appurtenance, since it may act only as a cover. In most cases, the roof provides stiffening for the top of the tank. Roofs are ordinarily used as a protection against temperature changes and contamination caused by birds and flying insects.

Spider Rods. Spider rods are rods radiating from the center of the tank, in a horizontal plane, and are attached to and supported only by the wall of the tank. The rods may be used (1) to hold the tank round during erection; (2) to support scaffolding and permanent interior parts, such as pipes; and (3) to prevent collapse of the shell by wind when the tank is empty. The rods are objectionable in cold climates because they may cause collapse of the tank due to ice forming on them. In cold climates where ice may form in the tank, there should be no obstruction on the inside of the tank to prevent the rise and fall of the ice cap on the water surface.

Ladders. Ladders are supplied for standpipes and elevated tanks to give access from a point 12 ft above the ground-surface foundation to the top of the tank. On tanks without roofs, the ladder should extend to a point 3 ft above the shell. On tanks with roofs, a revolving ladder fastened at the finial in the peak is usually used. The lower end of the ladder is equipped so that a boatswain's chair may be attached to give access to all parts of the shell. Revolving ladders for elevated tanks may extend from the peak to the balcony, in which case the fixed ladder from the balcony to top of the tank is omitted. Figure 20-16 shows the general arrangement of the revolving ladder.

Balcony and Handrail. The width of the balcony should be at least 24 in. for 15-ft-diameter tanks and not less than 30 in. for larger tanks. The floor should have a minimum thickness of $\frac{5}{16}$ in. and be suitably punched for drainage. The handrail is at least 3 ft high and is constructed so as to stiffen the outer chord of the girder. The balcony support forms a part of a circular girder to strengthen the connection between the side walls and bottom.

Riser Pipe. In tanks having hemispherical bottoms, the riser pipe is usually of cast iron and may or may not be provided with a frostproof covering. An expansion joint between tank and riser pipe is required.

[1] See also C. K. Wells, *J.A.W.W.A.*, May, 1952, p. 428.

In ellipsoidal-bottom tanks, the riser pipe is of steel and serves to support part of the weight of tank and its contents. The diameter of the riser pipe is ordinarily 3 to 4 ft for tanks up to 150,000 gal and 5 to 10 ft for larger tanks. The expansion joint and frostproof cover are omitted. A

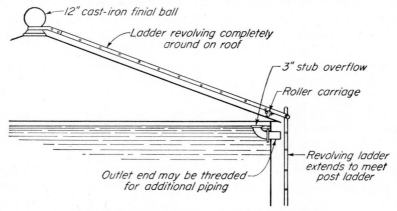

FIG. 20-16. Revolving ladder for an elevated tank.

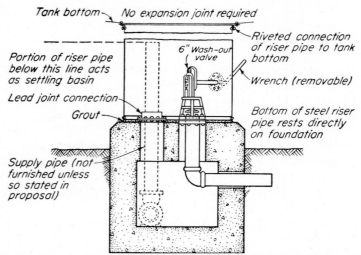

FIG. 20-17. Detail at base of riser pipe of ellipsoidal-bottom elevated tank.

supply pipe, as shown by the dotted lines in Fig. 20-17, admits the water to the riser pipe. A washout valve serves to remove the sediment that collects in the lower portion. Recommended sizes of riser pipes are listed in Table 20-2.[1]

Water-level Indicators. A device to indicate the level of water in an elevated tank or a storage reservoir is essential to its successful operation.

[1] From G. M. Booth, *J.A.W.W.A.*, September, 1944, pp. 957, 963.

TABLE 20-2. Sizes of Riser Pipes and Connecting Pipes for Elevated Tanks*

Capacity of tank, gal	Delivery rate for one-half capacity, gpm	Size of connecting main, in.
100,000	166†	6
200,000	333†	8
500,000	417	8
1,000,000	833	12
2,000,000	1,666	2 at 12 or 1 at 16
5,000,000	4,165	2 at 16 or 1 at 20

* From G. M. Booth, Practical Studies of Distribution Systems, *J.A.W.W.A.*, September, 1944, pp. 957, 963.

† For 5-hr duration.   Others for 10-hr duration.

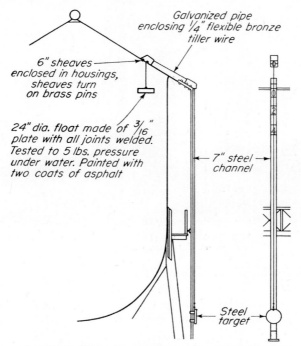

FIG. 20-18. Water-level indicator for elevated tank.

Such devices vary from a simple float and stick subject to direct observation, as shown in Fig. 20-18, to ingenious telephone and radio remote-control devices that transmit information concerning water levels to any desired distance and do it continuously or on demand.[1]

[1] See also: *Eng. and Contr.*, Vol. 44, p. 360, 1915; *Power*, Vol. 38, p. 888, 1913; C. F. Wertz, *Water Works & Sewerage*, May, 1946, p. 182; E. A. Colman and E. L. Hamilton, *Civil Eng.*, June, 1944, p. 257.

Overflow. Overflow of the tank is provided for by connecting a conductor pipe to a pipe through the wall of the tank or to a trough extending around the outside of the tank. One method is shown in Fig. 20-16.

20-25. Paints for Steel Tanks.[1] Paints recommended for steel tanks are self-chalking white paint and aluminum paints. Both are more desirable in appearance and more durable than the old standard, dark green or black graphite paints. The self-chalking paint is pleasing in appearance and on a bright sunny day it keeps the tank contents cooler than any other type of paint will.

Fig. 20-19. Elevated tank at Gate of Heaven Cemetery. Designed by Charles Wellford Leavitt and Son. (*Courtesy of the Chicago Bridge and Iron Co.*)

20-26. Architectural Treatment. The old-fashioned steel tanks are usually unsightly. Because of this fact, their use in some locations is objectionable. Considerable study has been directed toward improving the appearance of steel tanks, and the results have justified the effort, as evidenced by the tanks in Figs. 20-10, 20-13, 20-14, 20-15, and 20-19. With proper attention to details of towers, balconies, and general lines and proportions, steel tanks can be made pleasing to the eye. In places where a steel tank cannot be made to harmonize with the surroundings, they may be covered with masonry or otherwise treated.

[1] See also Leach, *loc. cit.*

CHAPTER 21

DESIGN OF DISTRIBUTION SYSTEMS

21-1. Description of Distribution Systems. A water-works distribution system includes pipes, valves, hydrants, and appurtenances for conveying water; reservoirs for storage, equalizing, and distribution purposes; service pipes to the consumers; meters; and all other parts of the conveying system after the water leaves the main pumping station or the main distribution reservoirs.

The layout of distribution systems may be classified, for convenience, as (1) circle, or belt, systems; (2) gridiron systems; and (3) tree systems. The names are descriptive of the manner in which the distribution pipes are laid out on the plan. Most distribution systems contain features of each type of layout; practically none is an example of one system alone, although the gridiron system is probably the most common, particularly in large cities.

In cities where there are differences in surface elevation of more than about 200 ft, the distribution system may be divided into zones in order to avoid excessive pressures in the lower zones. The different zones are usually supplied by independent pumps or reservoirs, characterized by the terms "high service" and "low service."

Some cities are supplied from two sources, one potable for domestic use and the other less pure for fire protection or industrial purposes. The practice is universally condemned if the two supplies are interconnected or if there is opportunity for use of the impure supply for personal needs or in the preparation of food or beverage. The use of an impure supply should be limited exclusively to fire protection, boiler water, cooling, and similar purposes.

21-2. Design of a Distribution System. The adequacy of a distribution system is determined by the pressures that exist at various points in the system under conditions of operation.[1] On the one hand the pressures must be sufficient to serve the consumers and the fire demand and, on the other hand, the pressures that are unnecessarily high are too costly. Since more than half and usually two-thirds to three-fourths of the cost

[1] See also R. G. Kincaid and R. E. McDonnell, *J.A.W.W.A.*, October, 1946, p. 1151.

of a water works lies in the distribution system it is essential that it be designed economically.

There is no direct method of design that will give the size of pipe on each street. In a new system the pipe sizes must be assumed and the system investigated for the pressure conditions that will result from various requirements of demand. These can be studied by the construction of pressure or piezometric contours, as discussed in Sec. 21-6. The pipe sizes are then changed, if necessary, and the system reinvestigated until satisfactory conditions are indicated. In existing systems, the pipe sizes are known, so that only one investigation for each demand requirement is necessary. But when changes are contemplated, the sizes of new pipes must be treated in the same manner as in the design of a new system.

The factors that cause loss of head or pressure are interdependent and include size of pipe, rate of flow, and friction. Usually, losses due to friction in straight pipe only are considered. If it is desired to include minor losses, it is most convenient to account for their effects by adding a length of straight pipe in which the friction is equivalent to the calculated minor loss.

The friction loss in pipes may increase with time because of corrosion and deposition that occur with use. Since it is usually presumed that a permanent municipal distribution system will be used over a long period of years, it becomes necessary for the engineer to anticipate the future and design the system for the condition that will obtain near the end of the time when the amounts set aside for depreciation will have returned the first cost. For cast-iron pipe a coefficient of $C = 100$ in the Hazen and Williams formula is ordinarily used for original calculation. Table 2-2 gives coefficients for various ages of pipe.

Procedure in design may be as follows:

1. Obtain or prepare a map of the water district showing the character of district and fire risks to be protected. A typical map for a small town is shown in Fig. 21-1.

2. Draw, with a medium pencil, lines down the streets on which it is expected to lay water mains, indicating at the same time the location of feeder mains, crossovers, and other interconnections in the system.

3. Estimate the rates of demand for all purposes, including fire protection, in each pipe and mark these assumed rates on the appropriate pipe.

4. Compute the diameter of each pipe on the basis that $D = 2 \sqrt{Q/\pi V}$ where V is 3 to 5 fps, and indicate this diameter on each pipe.

5. Compute the pressures at various points on the distribution system, drawing piezometric contours if desirable, under assumed critical conditions of "put-ins" and "take-offs." Methods for making these computations are discussed in Secs. 21-4 and 21-5. Revise the pipe sizes on the map as judgment indicates, to give desired head losses and pressures.

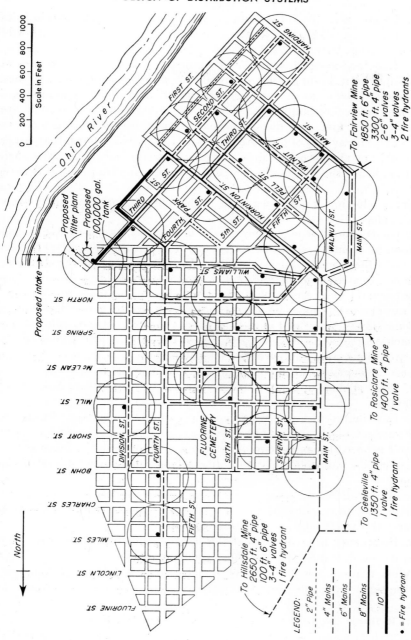

Fig. 21-1. Water-distribution system at Rosiclare, Ill.

6. Locate valves, hydrants, and service pipes according to the principles stated in Secs. 17-21, 21-11, 21-12, and 21-13, using the nomenclature shown in Figs. 22-1 and 22-2.

21-3. Selection of Pipe Sizes. Preliminary estimates for the sizes of pipes in a distribution system are frequently based on experience. When the rate of flow is known the diameter can be determined by assuming a velocity between 3 and 5 fps. The rules for minimum size of pipe are frequently violated to reduce first cost, without proper consideration of over-all economy and of pressure losses.[1] Howson[2] has shown that larger diameters of pipe provide more carrying capacity per dollar expended. He found that the weighted-average size of mains[3] in most cities is close to 7 in.

In the selection of pipe sizes, some of the following principles may serve as a guide:

1. On dead ends, where no fire service is involved, 2- or 3-in. mains may be used for a length of not more than 300 ft, and 4-in. up to 1,300 ft from the last connection to a larger main. Where the pipes are connected at each end to a larger main, and no fire service is involved, 2- or 3-in. pipes may be 600 ft long, and 4-in. pipes 2,000 ft long. No pipes smaller than 6 in. in diameter should be used where fire service is involved, although in some jurisdictions[4] 600 ft of 4-in. pipe is allowed between connections at each end to larger mains. The National Board of Fire Underwriters recommends a minimum size of 8 in. but permits 6-in. pipe in gridirons where the length between connections is not over 600 ft.[5]

2. Pipes should, in general, be interconnected at intervals closer than 1,200 ft.

3. It is better to lay two moderately large mains parallel on streets three or four blocks apart than to lay one large main, even with slightly greater capacity than the two other mains combined, down one street.

4. Arterial mains should be duplicate, but should not be laid in the same street.

5. Where railroads, streams, or other barriers lie between the water source and parts of the city, not less than two, or preferably more, well-separated arterial pipes should cross the barrier.

6. Emergency interconnections that can be made quickly between safe potable supplies should be provided where available.

When a preliminary layout of the distribution system is complete, assumptions are made concerning the rates of flow into and from the

---

[1] See also V. C. Lischer, *J.A.W.W.A.*, August, 1948, p. 849.

[2] L. R. Howson, *Water & Sewage Works*, Vol. 94, p. R-35, 1947.

[3] Weighted average size $= \dfrac{\Sigma(LD)}{\Sigma L}$, where D is diameter of pipe and L its length.

[4] See also Minimum Standards . . . , Michigan, *J.A.W.W.A.*, May, 1952, p. 373.

[5] See also L. R. Howson, *J.A.W.W.A.*, December, 1943, p. 1517; and see also *ibid.*, April, 1945, p. 397.

system at strategic points and the system is analyzed for pressure losses. If these are found to be unsatisfactory, other sizes of pipes are chosen and the system is restudied.

21-4. Analyses of Pressures in Distribution Systems.[1] Methods that have been used in the analyses of distribution systems include[2] (1) the equivalent-pipe method, omitting and combining pipes to form series and parallel compound pipes;[3] (2) graphical methods described by Freeman,[4] by Palsgrove,[5] by Kingsbury,[6] and by Rensselaer Polytechnic Institute;[7] (3) the use of an electric analyzer;[8] and (4) the Hardy Cross[9] method of successive approximations. Methods of analysis of distribution networks are now confined almost exclusively to electrical analyzers and to the Hardy Cross method.

21-5. Hardy Cross Method of Network Analysis.[9] The Hardy Cross method of network analysis makes possible, by mathematical computation alone, the precise determination of the rates of flow through, and the pressure losses in, each pipe in a reticulated water-works distribution system. Although no mechanical or electrical equipment is required, much time may be involved in a solution. The method is basically one of trial and error in which the rate of flow Q through a pipe is assumed and the error in the assumed value is computed from the expression

$$\Delta Q = \frac{\Sigma r Q^n}{\Sigma n r Q^{n-1}} \tag{21-1}$$

where r represents the relative resistance of a pipe, and n and Q are as in the typical flow formula $h = rQ^n$. Since the expression for ΔQ is based on a converging series of increments, repeated applications of the correction to the computed values of Q will produce a result to any desired degree of precision.

The procedure to be followed in the solution of a problem is best explained by the solution of a simple example.

---

[1] See also T. R. Camp, *J. New Engl. Water Works Assoc.*, 1943, p. 334.

[2] See also W. Gavett, *J.A.W.W.A.*, March, 1943, p. 267.

[3] See also W. E. Howland and F. Farr, Jr., *J.A.W.W.A.*, Vol. 33, p. 237, 1941.

[4] J. R. Freeman, *J. New Engl. Water Works Assoc.*, Vol. 7, pp. 49, 152, 1892–1893.

[5] G. K. Palsgrove, *Eng. News-Record*, Vol. 107, p. 422, 1931.

[6] F. H. Kingsbury, *Eng. News*, Vol. 76, p. 1239, 1916.

[7] *Rensselaer Polytech. Inst., Bull.* 37, August, 1932.

[8] See also: T. R. Camp and H. L. Hazen, *J. New Engl. Water Works Assoc.*, December, 1934, p. 383; M. S. McIlroy, *ibid.*, December, 1951, p. 299; *J.A.W.W.A.*, April, 1950, p. 347.

[9] *Univ. Illinois Eng. Expt. Sta. Bull.* 286, 1936; J. J. Doland, *Eng. News-Record*, Vol. 117, p. 475, 1936. See also W. E. Howland and F. Farr, Jr., *ibid.*, February, 27, 1941, p. 50.

Example. Let it be desired to compute the rate of flow in each pipe of the distribution system shown in Fig. 21-2;[1] the pressures at each intersection of two or more pipes; and to draw the 2 psi piezometric contours. The formality of procedure and the tabulation of data and of computations are to follow a standard form for convenience only. A formal procedure is desirable where two or more computers are to check the solution.

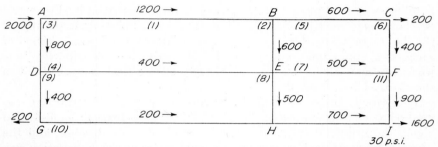

Fig. 21-2. Pipe network for Hardy Cross method of computation of losses of head in the distribution system. (*Layout, but not the rates of flow, originally selected by G. M. Fair, Eng. News-Record, Feb. 27, 1941, p. 50.*)

Solution. 1. Number each circuit from left to right and then downward by lines, using roman numerals. It is necessary to have a system of numbering of circuits in order to identify them.

2. Compute the length of 8-in. pipe with $C = 100$ equivalent to each length of pipe in the distribution system. Record as in work table 21-1. Factors for the

TABLE 21-1. Work Table 1, in Solution by Hardy Cross Method.   Lengths of 8-in. Pipe Equivalent to Pipes in Fig. 21-2

Pipe No.	Diam, in.	C	Length, ft	Equivalent length 8-in. pipe $C = 100$	Pipe No.	Diam, in.	C	Length, ft	Equivalent length 8-in. pipe $C = 100$
1	12	120	2,000	200	7	8	100	500	500
2	6	120	500	1,450	8	6	120	500	1,450
3	8	100	500	500	9	6	120	500	1,450
4	8	100	2,000	2,000	10	6	120	2,000	5,800
5	6	120	500	1,450	11	8	100	500	500
6	6	120	500	1,450	12	6	120	500	1,450

conversion of any size of pipe to an equivalent length of 8-in. pipe are shown in Table 21-2. This table is based on the Hazen and Williams formula and is

[1] This network was used by G. M. Fair in a simplification of the Hardy Cross method, published in *Eng. News-Record*, Mar. 3, 1938, p. 342, and in subsequent discussions; by W. E. Howland and F. Farr, Jr., *ibid.*, Feb. 27, 1941; by J. A. Conklin, *ibid.*, Sept. 11, 1941, p. 96.

TABLE 21-2. Lengths of 8-in. Pipe with $C = 100$ That Are Equivalent to a Unit Length of the Pipe Shown in the Table*

Diam, in.	$C = 50$	$C = 60$	$C = 70$	$C = 80$	$C = 90$	$C = 100$	$C = 110$	$C = 120$	$C = 130$	$C = 140$
2	3,060	2,105	1,650	1,286	1,012	851	712	608	524	456
3	429	294	232	180	141	119	100	84.9	73.3	63.9
4	104	73	56	44	34	29	24.3	20.7	17.8	15.6
5	36	24	19.2	15.0	11.8	9.9	8.3	7.1	6.09	5.3
6	14.6	10.0	7.9	6.1	4.8	4.06	3.4	2.9	2.5	2.2
8	3.49	2.46	1.94	1.51	1.19	1.00	0.84	0.713	0.615	0.537
10	1.22	0.84	0.78	0.51	0.40	0.34	0.285	0.242	0.210	0.180
12	0.50	0.35	0.27	0.21	0.17	0.14	0.117	0.100	0.086	0.075
14	0.234	0.163	0.128	0.10	0.078	0.066	0.055	0.047	0.041	0.035
16	0.122	0.084	0.066	0.051	0.040	0.034	0.029	0.024	0.021	0.018
18	0.068	0.047	0.037	0.029	0.023	0.019	0.016	0.014	0.012	0.010
20	0.0414	0.0285	0.0224	0.0174	0.0137	0.0115	0.0096	0.0082	0.0071	0.00617
24	0.0169	0.0116	0.0091	0.0071	0.0056	0.0047	0.0039	0.0034	0.0029	0.0025
30	0.0058	0.0040	0.0031	0.0024	0.0019	0.0016	0.0013	0.0011	0.00099	0.00086
36	0.00234	0.00163	0.00128	0.0010	0.00078	0.00066	0.00055	0.00047	0.00041	0.00035

* For example, 10 ft of 8-in. pipe with $C = 100$ will give the same head loss as 1 ft of 6-in. pipe with $C = 60$.

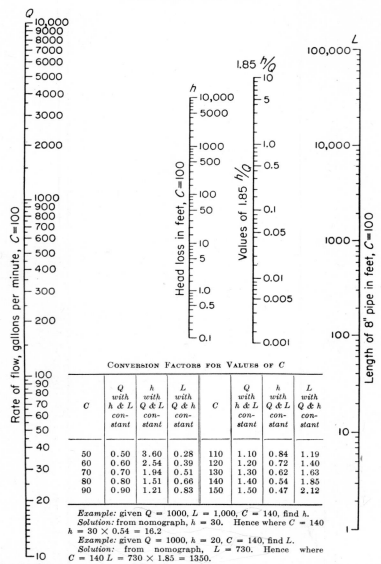

CONVERSION FACTORS FOR VALUES OF C

C	Q with h & L con- stant	h with Q & L con- stant	L with Q & h con- stant	C	Q with h & L con- stant	h with Q & L con- stant	L with Q & h con- stant
50	0.50	3.60	0.28	110	1.10	0.84	1.19
60	0.60	2.54	0.39	120	1.20	0.72	1.40
70	0.70	1.94	0.51	130	1.30	0.62	1.63
80	0.80	1.51	0.66	140	1.40	0.54	1.85
90	0.90	1.21	0.83	150	1.50	0.47	2.12

Example: given $Q = 1000$, $L = 1,000$, $C = 140$, find h.
Solution: from nomograph, $h = 30$. Hence where $C = 140$
$h = 30 \times 0.54 = 16.2$
Example: given $Q = 1000$, $h = 20$, $C = 140$, find L.
Solution: from nomograph, $L = 730$. Hence where
$C = 140$ $L = 730 \times 1.85 = 1350$.

FIG. 21-3. Nomograph for computations of head losses and other conditions of flow in 8-in. pipe, with Hazen and Williams $C = 100$.

TABLE 21-3. Computations of Rates of Flow in Pipes Shown in Figs. 21-2 and 21-4

Line No.	Loop	Pipe	L	Q	h_l	$\frac{nh_l}{Q}$	$\frac{\Sigma nh_l}{Q}$	Σh_l	Δh_l	ΔQ	Q_2	Q_3	h_l	$\frac{nh_l}{Q}$	$\frac{\Sigma nh_l}{Q}$	Σh_l	Δh_l	ΔQ	Q_4	Q_5	h_l	$\frac{nh_l}{Q}$	$\frac{\Sigma nh_l}{Q}$	Σh_l	Δh_l	ΔQ	Q_6
1	1	2	3	4	5	6	7	8	9	10	11		5	6	7	8	9	10	11		5	6	7	8	9	10	11
2	I	1	200	1,200	+8.2	0.013					1,172	1,172	7.8	0.012					1,143	1,143	7.4	0.012					1,150
3		2	1,450	600	+16.2	0.050		24.4	3.8	28	572	606	17.2	0.052		25.0	4.0	29	577	574	15.3	0.049		22.7	0.9	7	581
4		3	500	800	9.8	0.023					828	828	10.4	0.023					857	857	11.0	0.024					850
5		4	2,000	400	10.8	0.050	0.136	20.6			428	397	10.6	0.049	0.136	21.0			426	435	12.6	0.054	0.139	23.6			428
7	II	5	1,450	600	16.6	0.051					566	566	14.9	0.049					569	569	14.5	0.047					576
8		6	1,450	400	7.8	0.036		24.4	5.1	34	366	366	6.7	0.034		21.6	0.4	3	369	369	6.8	0.034		21.3	1.1	7	376
9		2	1,450	572	15.2	0.049					606	577	15.4	0.049					574	581	15.7	0.050					574
10		7	500	500	4.1	0.015	0.151	19.3			534	647	6.6	0.019	0.151	22.0			644	651	6.7	0.019	0.150	22.4			644
12	III	4	2,000	428	12.3	0.053					397	426	12.2	0.053					435	428	12.4	0.054					429
13		8	1,450	500	11.8	0.044		24.1	6.9	31	469	356	6.4	0.028		18.6	2.0	9	365	358	6.4	0.033		18.8	0.3	1	359
14		9	1,450	400	7.8	0.036					431	431	9.0	0.039					422	422	8.7	0.038					421
15		10	5,800	200	9.4	0.087	0.220	17.2			231	231	11.6	0.093	0.213	20.6			222	222	10.4	0.086	0.211	19.1			221
17	IV	7	500	534	4.6	0.016					647	644	6.6	0.019					651	644	6.4	0.018					647
18		11	500	900	12.1	0.025		16.7	15.8	113	1,031	1,013	15.2	0.028		21.8	0.9	7	1,020	1,020	14.8	0.027		21.2	0.4	3	1,023
19		8	1,450	469	10.5	0.041					356	365	6.7	0.034					358	359	6.4	0.033					356
20		12	1,450	700	22.0	0.058	0.140	32.5			587	587	16.0	0.050	0.131	22.7			580	580	15.2	0.048	0.126	21.6			577

computed from the expression

$$\text{Equivalent length of 8-in. pipe} = \left(\frac{8}{D_n}\right)^{4.87} \left(\frac{100}{C_n}\right)^{1.85} \tag{21-2}$$

where D_n = diameter of equivalent pipe, in.

C_n = coefficient of roughness of equivalent pipe

3. Show on Fig. 21-2 the assumed rates and directions of flow in each pipe. Experience and judgment are the best guides to these estimates. The more nearly correct the first estimate the less the work required to attain a desired degree of precision. It is to be noted that at every intersection of pipes the rate of flow entering must equal the rate of flow leaving the intersection.

4. Fill in the figures in work table 21-3, beginning with loop I in Fig. 21-2, working from left to right and downward with the loops. Each loop is assumed to begin at the upper left corner and to terminate at the lower right corner. Flow and head loss in that direction are indicated as positive. If in the opposite direction they are indicated as negative. Values of head loss h_l are computed from the nomograph in Fig. 21-3. It is to be noted that the corrected flow in each circuit is used in the computation of ΔQ in the next circuit.

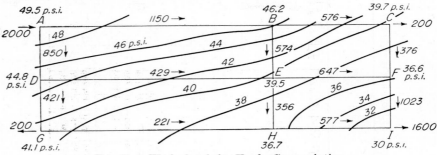

FIG. 21-4. Work sketch for Hardy Cross solution.

TABLE 21-4. Computation of Pressure Losses and of Pressures at Intersections in Fig. 21-4

Pipe No.	Q, gpm	Equivalent length 8-in. pipe, ft	Head loss, ft	Head loss, psi	Pipe No.	Q, gpm	Equivalent length 8-in. pipe, ft	Head loss, ft	Head loss, psi	Intersection	Pressure, psi	Intersection	Pressure, psi
1	1,150	200	7.7	3.3	7	647	500	15.4	6.7	A	49.5	G	41.1
2	574	1,450	15.3	6.0	8	356	1,450	7.0	3.0	B	46.2	H	36.7
3	850	500	10.9	4.7	9	421	1,450	8.6	3.7	C	39.7	I	30.0
4	429	2,000	12.3	5.3	10	221	5,800	10.1	4.4	D	44.8		
5	576	1,450	15.4	6.7	11	1,023	500	15.3	6.6	E	39.5		
6	376	1,450	7.0	3.0	12	577	1,450	15.4	6.7	F	36.6		

5. Repeat the procedure in step 4 until ΔQ is as small as desired. Show the final flows as indicated in Fig. 21-4.

6. Compute the pressure losses between the intersections in feet, using the nomograph in Fig. 21-3, with the equivalent lengths of 8-in. pipe, designating the intersections with letters as indicated in Fig. 21-4, and convert to pounds

per square inch. Computations are shown in Table 21-4. Add the pressure losses along the various routes and show the pressures in pounds per square inch at each intersection, and sketch in the 2 psi contours, as indicated in Fig. 21-4.

21-6. Pressure Contours. Pressure contours may be drawn for all reasonable extremes of put-in and take-off in a distribution system. In general, the contours should be spaced to show a head loss of about 3 to 5 ft per 1,000 ft of 24-in. pipe down to about 25 ft per 1,000 ft of 4-in. pipe. Hydraulic deficiencies in distribution systems[1] become apparent through uneven spacing of pressure contours. Pressure contours for two conditions of put-in and take-off are shown in Fig. 21-5. The contours in Fig. 21-5a indicate that the pipes in the lower right corner are too small for the assumed conditions of flow.

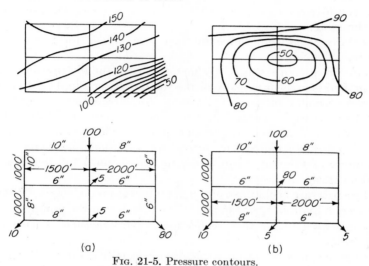

Fig. 21-5. Pressure contours.

21-7. The Electrical Analyzer. An instrument known as an electrical network analyzer makes possible the quick and easy determination of rates of flow and pressure losses in a water-works distribution system without the need for computations after the distribution system has been set up in the analyzer. The equivalent of the flow of water and pressure at any point can be read on the analyzer. The setting up of the equivalent distribution system on the analyzer is not simple, however. "The method provides ready visualization and evaluation of the effects of alternative plans for network construction and operation."[2] The instrument is not widely used in general practice because of its high first cost and the expense of setting up the distribution system. The outstanding

[1] See also Kincaid and McDonnell, *loc. cit.*

[2] M. S. McIlroy in set of notes privately distributed. See also: *J.A.W.W.A.*, April, 1950, p. 347; *J. New Engl. Water Works Assoc.*, December, 1951, p. 299.

advantage of the analyzer becomes apparent after the distribution system is set up and the effect of any combination of put-ins and take-offs can be visualized quickly.

21-8. Service Pressures.   Pressures to be maintained in a distribution system for all services other than fire protection should lie between 30 and 100 psi; 40 to 50 psi in water pipe in the street furnishes satisfactory service.   Pressures below 30 psi are too low to supply water at a satisfactory rate to the upper stories of three- and four-story buildings. Pressures over 100 psi require heavier water pipes and greater care in construction and the maintenance of the distribution system and cause trouble in plumbing.   The public water supply is not always delivered to the top floor of the tallest buildings in a city.   It may be delivered to the fourth and fifth floors.   Above that height, booster pumps must be used in the building.

21-9. Fire Pressure.   Three methods are in use for furnishing fire pressure.   They are:

1. Full fire pressure constantly maintained in the distribution system. This method is used principally in the smaller water-supply systems, and the pressure maintained is often too low for satisfactory fire protection.

2. The pressure is supplied directly from the pumping station, where, on an alarm of fire, it is increased as required.   This method of operation is used in cities of small and moderate size.   As the cities increase in size the number of fire engines in use is increased, until full dependence is placed on them.

3. Fire pressure is obtained through mobile pumping engines that draw water from a hydrant near the fire.   The pressure at the pumping station is not increased under these conditions.   This method is used in the largest cities.

The proper pressure for fire protection is usually expressed as the pressure required at the nozzle of the fire hose.   The National Board of Fire Underwriters recommends 75 psi where more than 10 buildings exceed three stories in height; 60 psi in localities with less risk; and 50 psi in thinly built-up districts.   Where fire pumpers are used, the Board's recommendations permit a minimum pressure of 10 psi at the hydrant, under unusual conditions.   A pressure of 20 psi is considered satisfactory under most conditions where fire pumping engines are used.

21-10. Location of Mains in Streets.   One pipe laid under the parking on one side of a street is commonly all that is provided in a water-distribution system except on streets where the pavement is more than about 40 to 50 ft wide or where some obstruction or other condition prevents pushing service pipes under the street surface without excavating.   On wide and important streets the two-main system may be used involving the placing of a large main on the side of the street where fire hydrants are preferred, and a small pipe on the opposite side of the street where there are to be no fire hydrants. Water mains should, in general, not be laid in alleys or under pavement, where it can be avoided.

21-11. Location of Tees, Specials, and Valves.[1] Valves should be placed on all branches from feeder mains and between feeder pipes and hydrants. Ordinarily not more than three valves are placed at a cross or more than two at a tee. When there is a choice of position the valve should be placed in the smaller of two pipes at the intersection. No length of pipe greater than about 1,200 ft, and preferably not more than 800 ft, should be left without valve control. In high-value districts 500 ft should be the maximum distance between valves. In the construction of a distribution system it is customary to install only the most essential pipes in the expectation that the remaining pipes in the design will be installed as demand increases. Provision for expansion should be made by the installation of the necessary specials at the desired locations. Liberal use of specials that will permit easy connection to the distribution system is highly desirable, since it is not possible to foresee all desirable extensions at the time of design.

21-12. Location of Service Pipes.[2] It is a common rule in water-works practice to allow only one customer on a service pipe. This results in such problems as are illustrated in Fig. 17-30, in which some violations of the rule are shown.

21-13. Location of Fire Hydrants. The spacing of fire hydrants is determined by the area that each hydrant is to serve. The area is partially governed by population, value of district, and methods used for obtaining necessary fire pressure. Table 21-5 shows areas per hydrant approved by the National Board of Fire Underwriters.

TABLE 21-5. Fire Flow and Hydrant Areas*

Population	Required fire flow for average city, gpm	Average area per hydrant, sq ft	
		Engine streams	Direct streams
1,000	1,000	120,000	100,000
4,000	2,000	110,000	85,000
10,000	3,000	100,000	70,000
100,000	9,000	55,000	40,000†
200,000	12,000	40,000	40,000

* National Board of Fire Underwriters.

† 40,000 sq ft is the maximum allowance for direct streams in all cities having a population of 28,000 or more.

The designer should study hydrant spacing also on the basis of economy. Using reasonable assumptions, the annual expense of a hydrant is less

[1] See also H. W. Griswold, *Water Works Eng.*, November, 1951, p. 1066.
[2] See also M. P. Hatcher, *Water & Sewage Works*, Vol. 95, p. R-73, 1948.

than the annual expense of two 50-ft lengths of standard fire hose.   Furthermore, the loss of pressure is usually greater through the hose than through the pipe line serving the hydrant.   There is an advantage also that accrues to the consumer through a reduction in insurance rates resulting from an approved spacing of hydrants.   Hydrants should be placed at street intersections and at such intermediate points as may be required by spacing standards.

Some recommendations concerning hydrant location that may be modified by local conditions include: (1) Place hydrants more than 2 ft and less than 6 ft from the edge of a paved road surface, to avoid interference by traffic[1] and to minimize the length of suction hose to mobile pumpers.   (2) Place hydrants 3 ft or more away from fixed objects, or doorways, and out of traffic lanes.   (3) Set the hydrant so that the lowest

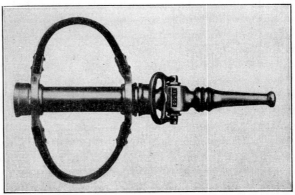

Fig. 21-6. A fire-stream nozzle.   (*Courtesy of American LaFrance Foamite Co.*)

outlet is 18 in. or more above the ground surface, and the highest operating nut is not more than 48 in. above the ground surface.

A convenient procedure in locating fire hydrants is to draw a circle with a radius of about 80 per cent of the assumed length of hose with a hydrant as the center of each circle.   Such an arrangement is shown in Fig. 21-1.   It may be assumed that areas not within a circle are inadequately protected.   High-risk areas should be protected by at least two fire hydrants within reach of every part of the area.

21-14. Fire Streams.   The factors of importance in a fire stream are the number of gallons per minute passing the nozzle, the height of usefulness of the stream, and the distance at which it is useful.   These factors are determined by the shape, size of opening, interior smoothness, and the pressure at the base of the nozzle.   Types of fire nozzles are illustrated in Figs. 2-12 and 21-6.   Distances and heights to which water can be thrown in fire streams are discussed in Sec. 2-24.

[1] See also *Public Works*, January, 1948, p. 36.

The total capacity of fire streams to be provided depends on the size of the city and the character of risk requiring protection. Empirical formulas have been recommended, as stated in Sec. 3-7. These include:

Kuichling: $$Q = 700 \sqrt{P} \qquad (21\text{-}3)$$

and

National Board of Fire Underwriters: $$Q = 1{,}020 \sqrt{P}\left(1 - \frac{\sqrt{P}}{100}\right) \quad (21\text{-}4)$$

where Q = gpm

P = population, thousands

A study of current practice in fire protection will show the use of streams in well-protected cities with a discharge between 175 and 250 gpm, with pressures on the base of the nozzle between 40 and 100 psi. A minimum of 50 psi is permissible.

In general, it can be considered satisfactory in a residential district with no special risks, such as churches and schools, to have available for each building not less than four streams of 175 gpm each, with a pressure at the base of the nozzle of not less than 35 psi. In business, industrial, and other districts, where risks of special value and hazard are to be protected, the capacity, number of streams, and pressures available must be increased. The recommendations of the National Board of Fire Underwriters in this regard are:[1]

In estimating required fire flow, an allowance is made for probable loss from broken connections incident to a large fire. Including this allowance, the total fire flow which should be available is approximately as given by Eq. (21-4); but, in all cases, consideration must be given to the structural conditions as found in the city, and also to the number of companies in the fire department and the amount of outside aid that could be called upon in case of a serious fire. The ratio of the total engine capacity to the fire flow required will be approximately 2:3.

In residential districts, the required fire flow depends upon the character and congestion of the buildings. Sections where buildings are small and of low height and with about one-third of the lots in a block built upon require not less than 500 gpm; with larger or higher buildings, up to 1,000 gpm is required; and where the district is closely built, or buildings approach the dimensions of hotels or high-value residences, 1,500 to 3,000 gpm is required, with up to 6,000 gpm in densely built sections of three-story buildings.

In grading the adequacy of the water supply, two features are considered:

1. The ability to deliver fire flow at any pressure down to 20 psi, except that a minimum of 10 lb is permissible in districts having no deficiency in items . . . and having all hydrants provided with at least one steamer outlet; this is a measure of the ultimate capacity of the system to maintain supply of some sort under conflagration conditions and with the system in full operation.

[1] See Standard Schedule for Grading . . . Fire Defenses, National Board of Fire Underwriters, adopted Dec. 14, 1916, edition of 1942, p. 14.

2. The ability to deliver this fire flow or a part thereof at pressures permitting streams direct from hydrants; these pressures are assumed at 75 lb or more in high-value districts, depending upon the static pressure available, the heights of buildings and the amount of engine capacity in service; 60 lb where not more than ten buildings exceed three stories and in closely built residential districts, and 50 lb in village mercantile districts where buildings do not exceed two stories and in thinly built residential districts. . . .

High-voltage electric transmission lines in a fire area may be a source of danger to firemen because of the possibility that an electric current may follow the fire stream and cause loss of control of the nozzle or direct injury from electric shock. Tests by Sprague and Harding[1] indicate that the relative danger is dependent on the sensitivity of the individual, the voltage of the transmission line, the distance of the nozzle from the line, and the resistivity of the water which may vary from 500 ohms per milliliter for mineralized well water to 6,000 for filtered river water. Allowing a generous factor of safety, minimum distances from nozzle to transmission line for a 3,000-ohm water should be 3 ft for a 440-volt line and 33 ft for a 13,200-volt line. The stream should not be allowed to strike the line if the voltage is higher than 13,200.

21-15. Studies of Existing Systems. Studies[2] to determine the capacity of an existing distribution system are made by direct observation of flows and pressures. Direct observations may reveal closed valves, air pockets, errors in records of pipe connections, and other conditions.

The methods used involve the construction of pressure contours during normal and fire demand. Points on the pressure contours are determined by observations of pressure at selected points on the distribution system. Because of fluctuations in pressure, observations are best made by recording gages. In the study of fire demand groups of four to six hydrants are selected along the larger mains. A central hydrant in each group, preferably taking water directly from the large main, is used to show the static pressure in the group, before and during the test, when water is drawn at measured rates from all other hydrants in the group.

[1] Electrical Conductivity of Fire Streams, *Purdue Univ., Eng. Bull.* 53, 1936.

[2] See also: G. W. Booth, *J.A.W.W.A.*, September, 1944, p. 957; R. G. Kincaid, *Water Works Eng.*, Oct. 18, 1944.

CHAPTER 22

CONSTRUCTION AND MAINTENANCE OF DISTRIBUTION SYSTEMS

22-1. Safe Practice. In the construction and maintenance of a waterworks distribution system the Manual of Safe Practice in Water Distribution[1] will be found to be a valuable guide. It contains standards and specifications applicable in design, construction, and maintenance. A report of a Task Group on Safety Practices[2] contains an exhaustive safety-inspection check list.[3]

22-2. Work Involved in the Laying of Water Mains. The laying of water pipes involves transportation and handling of the pipe and materials, ditching and excavation, backfilling, rights of way, and other problems common to construction work. Excavation can sometimes be avoided by pushing small pipes underground.[4]

When pipes, specials, valves, and other appurtenances to a waterworks distribution system are delivered on the site of the work, they should be inspected for defect, and all rejected parts should be immediately removed from the work. The following extracts are taken from specifications covering the laying, testing, and acceptance of cast-iron water mains.[5]

Pipe Laying. Each pipe shall be laid upon a firm bed and, except on curves, all pipes shall be laid in a straight line. Excavation must be made under the bell of each pipe, so that the entire length of the pipe, except the bell, may be supported on the bottom of the trench. All pipes, specials, valves, and appurtenances shall be cleaned by brushing and by thoroughly scraping out all dirt or other foreign matter before laying.

The ends of pipe shall closely abut upon each other, and the spigot shall be concentrically placed in the hubs or bells, so as to admit a uniform thickness of gasket and lead. The calking shall consist of the specified quantity of well-rammed untarred rope yarn or jute above which shall be poured a sufficient quantity of melted lead to stand flush with the outside of the bell of the pipe

---

[1] Published in *J.A.W.W.A.*, June, 1942, p. 917.

[2] See *ibid.*, June, 1951, p. 423.

[3] See also W. R. La Due, *ibid.*, November, 1953, p. 1211.

[4] See also *Water Works Eng.*, April, 1949, p. 301.

[5] See Specifications C600-49T, *J.A.W.W.A.*; *ibid*, December, 1949, p. 1079.

when the lead is compacted.   The lead shall be compacted with a calking hammer and thoroughly driven around the entire circumference of the pipe.

The contractor shall put caps or plugs on all unconnected ends of pipe and on all unconnected crosses, tees, and branches or wyes.   Pipes laid around curves shall be properly blocked with brick or concrete to take the reaction, and all plugs and blanked openings shall be secured by masses of concrete.

The work of laying the pipes and special castings and of setting of valves, hydrants, and appurtenances shall be of such character as to leave all the pipes and connections watertight.   To assure these conditions, the contractor shall subject the pipe and all appurtenances to a proof of water pressure of not less than 110 psi.

Testing Pipe Joints in Trenches.   The tests shall be made between valves and, as far as practicable, in sections of approximately 1,000 ft in length and within 12 working days of the completion of such sections of mains.   The leakage from the mains and connections for each section tested, while the pressure is at 110 psi, shall not be greater than at the rate of 1,800 gal per 24 hr per mile of pipe, for pipe 14 in. in diameter or less.   To determine the rate of leakage, the contractor shall furnish a suitable pump, pressure gage, and water meter, or other appliance, for measuring the amount of water pumped.   The pressure shall be raised to 110 lb, and it shall be so maintained for a period of not less than 20 min.   If the leakage be at a greater rate than that specified, the contractor shall reexcavate the trench where necessary and shall recalk the joints and replace defective work until the leakage shall be reduced to the allowable amount.

Where it is impracticable to test between valves, or near connections to existing mains, the contractor shall . . . temporarily place caps or plugs on the mains and test the section of the main so closed.

Pipes should usually be laid with the bell end upgrade and in the direction in which work is proceeding, for greater ease in making joints.   They should be laid below the frost line and, at the same time, as shallow as possible, consistent with safety under surface loads.   Depths of 5 to 6 ft are common, except where frost penetration is a factor.[1]   Water and sewer pipes should, in general, not be placed in the same trench, to escape hazards of contamination of the water pipe.   However, where unavoidable, the water pipe should be laid in the same trench higher and to one side of the sewer.[2]

22-3. Raising and Lowering Water Mains.[3]   Maintenance work may involve the changing of the elevation of a water pipe owing to regrading and paving of streets, or for other reasons.   Water pipes have been raised and lowered under pressure without seriously affecting water service, by placing blocks and jacks under the pipes and changing direction little by little.   There is appreciable flexibility in lead joints that permits movement of the pipe.[4]   Even sulphur and cement joints allow a little deflection.   Permissible deflections depend on the type of joint, pipe diameter, and internal pressure.

[1] See also *Water Works Eng.,* July, 1951, p. 679.
[2] See also K. W. Robie, *J. New Engl. Water Works Assoc.,* June, 1948, p. 122.
[3] See also *Am. City,* May, 1953, p. 116.
[4] See also W. B. Bushway, *ibid.,* September, 1944, p. 71.

22-4. Disinfection of Water Pipes.[1] Water pipes must be disinfected before being put into use and, sometimes, during use.[2] Before disinfection, the pipe should be drained, flushed, redrained, and refilled. In refilling care must be taken to avoid entraining or entrapping air in the pipe, primarily to prevent direct contact between the pipe and the disinfectant except when dissolved in the water.

The American Water Works Association recommends: 1. *a.* Keep the interior of the pipe clean. *b.* Swab the pipe interior with an effective bactericide. *c.* Block the open ends of the pipe to prevent trench water from entering. 2. Flush the main with a velocity of at least 2 fps. 3. Chlorinate with chlorine or chlorine water or Perchloron, etc. 4. Apply chlorine or solid disinfectant. 5. Apply disinfectant at one extremity of pipe section with bleed at opposite extremity. The pipe is subjected to any one of the three following treatments, stated in order of preference: (1) A chlorine gas–water mixture is applied at the beginning of the pipe-line extension, or any valved section of it, at such a rate that with a slow flow of water into the pipe the chlorine dose shall not be less than 50 to 100 ppm. The treated water is to remain in the pipe at least 3 hr and preferably longer. At the end of the period the chlorine residual is not to be less than 5 ppm. Following chlorination the pipe is thoroughly flushed, tested, and, if necessary, rechlorinated until a satisfactory bacteriological test is obtained. (2) A solution of calcium hypochlorite or such commercial products as HTH, Perchloron, and Maxochlor or chlorinated lime may be used in the place of chlorine gas. After the pipe has been subjected to a preliminary flushing, a 5 per cent solution of any of the afore-mentioned powders should be injected into the pipe in a manner similar to that required for the addition of the liquid chlorine. (3) Dry calcium hypochlorite or chlorinated lime may be used in such a manner that there shall be 1 lb powder, containing 70 per cent available chlorine, for every 1,680 gal water in the pipe, equivalent to 50 ppm of available chlorine. The dry powder is to be shaken into the suction well of a pump or into a standpipe feeding the pipe line, or it may be shaken into each length of pipe as it is laid. After the materials are introduced, water is admitted very slowly so as to avoid washing the powder to the end of the line. After standing for a few hours the pipe should be flushed until no odor of chlorine can be detected in the water or until a check can be made for residual chlorine.

Jute packing and leathers in pumps, valves, and hydrants are difficult to disinfect and offer a focal point for the growth of bacteria. Although

---

[1] See also: A. N. Heller, *J.A.W.W.A.*, December, 1946, p. 1335; *Water Works Eng.*, Dec. 25, 1946, p. 1513; *Water & Sewage Works*, Vol. 98, p. R-41, 1951; *J.A.W.W.A.*, August, 1953, p. 834.

[2] See AWWA Specifications C601-48, *J.A.W.W.A.*, February, 1948. These require that all new pipe lines shall be chlorinated, and they provide various methods therefor.

pathogenic bacteria will not grow under such conditions the growth and presence of coliform bacteria complicates sanitary analyses and necessitates the destruction of all bacteria. Methods used in the sterilization of jute or hemp, before it is used in a joint, include[1] (1) soaking in chlorine solutions of 50, 100, or 500 ppm, of available chlorine, for 5 min to 2 hr; (2) soaking in a solution of mercuric chloride[2] or Klerol, a mercuric compound using a concentration of 3 mg of mercury per gram of hemp;[3] (3) apply a mild, alkali-activated quaternary ammonium germicide formulation (Polymine D) used at a quaternary salt dilution of 1:500, with a contact period of 7 days;[4] (4) autoclaving with live steam under pressure for 1 to 30 min; (5) boiling for 1 to 30 min; and (6) baking in dry heat. Sotier and Ward[4] state that repeated applications of chlorine, even up to 200 ppm, are usually necessary and "months may elapse before an infected main is sterilized." Autoclaving with live steam under pressure has proved most effective. Klerol (ortho-mercuro-phenol) is reported by Calvert[5] to be a satisfactory disinfecting agent.

22-5. Work Involved in Maintenance. Maintenance of a distribution system involves (1) keeping records; (2) finding, cleaning, and flushing pipes; (3) installing, cleaning, and thawing service pipes; (4) preventing waste; (5) finding and repairing leaks; (6) thawing frozen pipes, hydrants, and meters; and (7) inspecting, caring for, and repairing hydrants, valves,[6] meters, and other appurtenances.

22-6. Records.[7] Knowledge of the location of every part of a waterworks distribution system is essential to proper maintenance.[8] Experience shows that poor records result in "lost" valves, closed or partly closed valves, valves duplicated, mains dead-ended near each other, and other costly and detrimental effects of carelessness and forgetfulness. Good records sometimes discourage, and sometimes help to win, damage suits, aid in establishing water rights, and help to maintain good public relations.

Maps of the distribution system are the most important records to be maintained. Three types of maps are desired: (1) a comprehensive map of the entire system; (2) a larger-scale map showing details; and (3) plats and cards providing information on valves, hydrants, and other appurtenances.

A portion of a comprehensive map is shown in Fig. 22-1, and symbols to

---

[1] See also *Public Works*, June, 1943, p. 18.

[2] See also W. R. La Due, Annual Report, Ohio Conference on Water Purification, 1940, p. 87.

[3] See also C. K. Calvert, *Eng. News-Record*, Vol. 122, p. 788, 1939.

[4] A. L. Sotier and H. W. Ward, *J.A.W.W.A.*, October, 1947, p. 1038.

[5] C. K. Calvert, *ibid.*, January, 1945, p. 46.

[6] See also R. W. Esty, *Water & Sewage Works*, Vol. 94, p. R-84, 1947.

[7] See also F. E. Alderman, *J.A.W.W.A.*, April, 1953, p. 417.

[8] See also Committee Report, *ibid.*, February, 1940, p. 181.

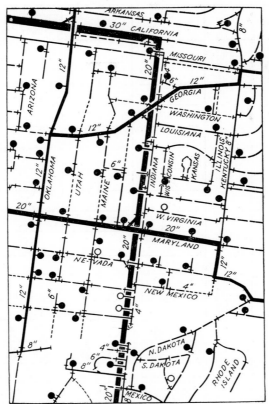

Fig. 22-1. Portion of a comprehensive map of a water-distribution system. (*From Recommended Practice for Distribution System Records, J.A.W.W.A., February, 1940, p. 188.*)

be used are shown in Fig. 22-2. Information to be included on the comprehensive map is listed in Table 22-1. The sectional plats provide a detailed record of distribution-system structures. Information to be shown on such plats is listed in Table 22-2.

A valve record and a hydrant record should be kept because of the importance of quickly obtaining information concerning them. Among

TABLE 22-1. Information Concerning the Comprehensive Map

Material: Original—heavy tracing cloth
         Prints—black line preferred
Scale: Preferred—500 ft per in.
         Maximum—1,000 ft per in.

Items to Be Shown on the Map

1. Street names
2. Sizes of mains
3. Fire hydrants
4. Valves

5. Orientation arrow
6. Scale
7. Date last corrected
8. Complete title

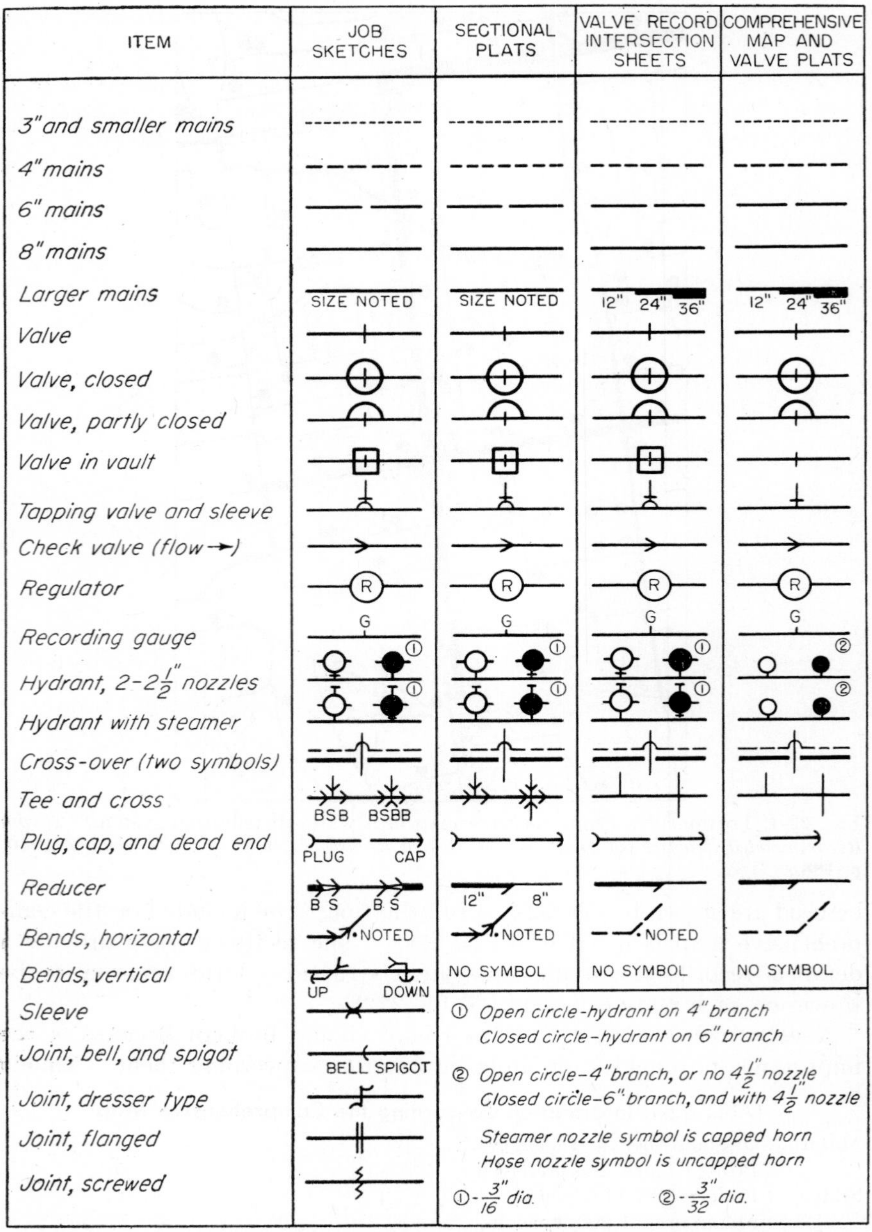

ITEM	JOB SKETCHES	SECTIONAL PLATS	VALVE RECORD INTERSECTION SHEETS	COMPREHENSIVE MAP AND VALVE PLATS
3" and smaller mains				
4" mains				
6" mains				
8" mains				
Larger mains	SIZE NOTED	SIZE NOTED	12" 24" 36"	12" 24" 36"
Valve				
Valve, closed				
Valve, partly closed				
Valve in vault				
Tapping valve and sleeve				
Check valve (flow →)				
Regulator				
Recording gauge	G	G	G	G
Hydrant, 2-2½" nozzles	①	①	①	②
Hydrant with steamer	①	①	①	②
Cross-over (two symbols)				
Tee and cross	BSB BSBB			
Plug, cap, and dead end	PLUG CAP			
Reducer	B S B S	12" 8"		
Bends, horizontal	→•NOTED	→•NOTED	—•NOTED	•NOTED
Bends, vertical	UP DOWN	NO SYMBOL	NO SYMBOL	NO SYMBOL
Sleeve				
Joint, bell, and spigot	BELL SPIGOT			
Joint, dresser type				
Joint, flanged				
Joint, screwed				

① Open circle–hydrant on 4" branch
Closed circle–hydrant on 6" branch

② Open circle–4" branch, or no 4½" nozzle
Closed circle–6" branch, and with 4½" nozzle

Steamer nozzle symbol is capped horn
Hose nozzle symbol is uncapped horn

①-$\frac{3}{16}$ dia.   ②-$\frac{3}{32}$ dia.

FIG. 22-2. Standard symbols for water-distribution systems. (*From Recommended Practice for Distribution System Records, J.A.W.W.A., February, 1940, p. 216.*)

the things to be included on the valve record sheet are the size and make of the valve, direction to open, turns to operate, its number, street or streets on which located, and distance and direction to nearby reference points. Card records may supplement maps and charts, the cards giving information not shown on the map or chart.

TABLE 22-2. Information to Be Shown on Sectional Plat

Material: Original—heavy tracing cloth
            Prints—black line preferred
Size: 20 by 25 in. plus 2- to 3-in. margins
Scale: 50 ft per in. in congested areas
            100 ft per in. in residential areas
            200 ft per in. in rural areas
Index: Coordinates; horizontal spaces lettered, vertical spaces numbered; or horizontal spaces even numbers and vertical spaces odd numbers.

Items to Be Shown on Plats

1. Plat designation or number	13. Block numbers
2. Adjacent plat numbers	14. Lot numbers
3. Street names and widths	15. House numbers
4. Mains and sizes	16. Water account numbers
5. Materials of mains	17. Measurements to service lines
6. Years mains were installed	18. Sizes of taps
7. Work orders of main installations	19. Sizes and materials of service lines
8. Distances from property lines	20. Distances, main to stop box
9. Fire hydrants, numbers and classifications	21. Distances, stop box to property line
10. Valves and numbers	22. Distances to angle points
11. Valve sheet designation shown in margin	23. Distances to fittings
12. Intersection numbers (if valve intersection plats are used)	24. Dead ends and measurements
	25. Date last corrected
	26. Orientation of north arrow
	27. Scale

A well-maintained water works will include the following in a monthly record or report: (1) the length and sizes of pipes laid and retired during the month and the total mileage of each size laid to date; (2) the number of each size of valves; (3) the number, size, and types of fire hydrants; and (4) the number, size, and lengths of services. In keeping records of work done and its cost the "work-order" system should be followed. In this system a card record shows location and nature of work; labor, materials, and equipment used, reclaimed, or retired; and the time involved.

22-7. Cleaning Water Mains.[1] Water mains require cleaning principally to remove soft deposits precipitated from the water, and to remove tuberculation and incrustation from the pipe walls. Other materials

---

[1] See also: J. F. Bailey, *Water and Water Eng.*, August, 1943, p. 317; *Water Works Eng.*, March, 1950, p. 220; April, 1950, p. 300; H. G. Dresser, *ibid.*, April, 1952, p. 343; Apr. 16, 1947, p. 415; Apr. 2, 1947, p. 353; Mar. 19, 1947, p. 299; Feb. 5, 1947, p. 142; AWWA Specifications C601.

are sometimes removed in cleaning, such as lost tools, bolts, and valve parts. The economy of cleaning has been demonstrated frequently through increased pipe capacity.[1] Annual losses of 1 to 1½ per cent of the carrying capacity of pipes are not unusual where pipes are not cleaned. Cleaning may be expected to cost about 5 per cent of the first cost of the pipe, being highest for the smaller pipes. Pipes are cleaned by pushing or pulling a scraping machine through them, such as the machine shown in Fig. 22-3.

A common procedure is to insert the scraping machine into the empty pipe through a Y or T and to push the machine through the pipe by water pressure behind it. A cable may be attached to the scraper to permit its

Fig. 22-3. Hydraulic pipe cleaner. (*Courtesy of Pittsburgh Pipe Cleaner Co.*)

recovery or to indicate its location if it sticks. The water pressure is used to drive the turbine blades if they are included on the scraper. Water passing through, or around, the scraper flushes the scrapings and soft deposits ahead of the scraper. Another method of scraping involves the passage through the pipe of an inflated rubber ball covered by a chain mesh.[2] The deposits may be removed through a hydrant at a lower elevation on the pipe, or through the fitting through which the scraper is removed from the pipe. A successful turbine-scraping machine may restore the pipe capacity, but it may also injure the pipe lining; therefore, once scraping has been started it may have to be repeated more or less frequently. Scrapers travel about 4 mph and require a pressure of about 65 psi when cleaning a 12-in. pipe. Some mechanical scrapers that fit the pipe can be dragged through the pipe to clean it.

[1] See also J. R. Brown, *Water Works & Sewerage*, February, 1944, p. 72.
[2] See also R. L. Derby, *J.A.W.W.A.*, November, 1947, p. 1107.

22-8. Cleaning with Acids and Other Chemicals.

Chemicals may prove effective and economical in the cleaning of pipes but they should be used with full knowledge of the conditions. For example, chlorinated hydrocarbons in domestic water supplies may produce tastes and odors and may be toxic to consumers and to plant life; copper sulphate may be of no value where the alkalinity of the water is high, and chlorine may be ineffective in open waters exposed to sunlight. Acids may be used successfully, particularly in small pipes, for the removal of deposits of calcium carbonate, provided an inhibitor is combined with the acid. An acid inhibitor is a substance that inhibits the release of acid when an acid comes into contact with a metal. The film of hydrogen held by the inhibitor protects the metal against attack by the acid. The inhibitor does not inhibit the action of the acid on the calcium deposit. Inhibitors that have been used successfully include bran, flour, glue, and such other organic substances as aniline, pyridine, and quinoline. Inhibitors containing arsenic should not be used.[1] Before any material is selected as an inhibitor, its effectiveness should be tested for its rate of hydrogen evolution from a standard metallic sample, under the same temperature, acid concentration, and other conditions in which it is to be used in the field. Mick[2] reports that a 0.7 per cent hydrochloric acid solution and 2 per cent aniline oil dosage will cut corrosiveness of acid by 44 per cent, and a 2 per cent aniline oil dosage in a 5 per cent acid solution will cut corrosion by 97 per cent.

22-9. Emptying Water Mains.

Water mains often must be emptied before cleaning. This may be done by opening a blowoff valve or other outlet in the lower end of the pipe and opening a fire hydrant, service connection, or other opening at the upper end to admit air. Under favorable circumstances some of the water may be drained from the main through a fire hydrant, the remainder below the hydrant level draining into the excavation from which it must be pumped. In some cases[3] compressed air, admitted at a high point, has been used to expel the water from the main through a hydrant, thus expediting the emptying of the main and avoiding pumping.

22-10. Flushing Mains and Dead Ends.

Because of the accumulation of rust, organic matter, and other material in the quiet water in dead ends, undesirable odors, tastes, and color, occasionally accompanied by putrefaction, sometimes occur. Routine inspection and thorough flushing may be the remedy. Improper or inadequate flushing can make conditions worse by stirring up sediment without removing it. Flushing is usually accomplished at night by opening a hydrant wide and allowing

---

[1] See also: A. R. Hollett, *J.A.W.W.A.*, May, 1937; V. A. Wordell, *Chem. and Min. Rev.*, Vol. 27, p. 286, 1935.

[2] K. L. Mick, *Water & Sewage Works*, April, 1946, p. R-241.

[3] See also A. C. King, *ibid.*, Vol. 93, p. R-48, 1946.

water to run until clear. In a few cases compressed air has been forced into the main to increase velocity and agitation.[1]

22-11. Air Locks. Loss of capacity of water pipes, either in a long pipe line or in a network, may result from the accumulation of air in a high point in the line or network. Such air locks are difficult to force. They may be relieved by the installation of an air valve or prevented by lowering the pipe where the air lock occurs.

22-12. Cleaning and Repairing Service Pipes. Service pipes clog more easily than mains owing to tuberculation and sediment. Service pipes can be cleaned by dragging or pushing[2] a scraper, or by blowing compressed air, through them, since they are too small to permit the use of a turbine scraper. Tools such as cutting knives, brushes, drags, and scrapers that can be attached to flexible rods and twisted by power are available.[3] Sometimes the pushing of a soluble object, such as toilet paper, through the service pipe is helpful. Trentlage[4] reports releasing a mixture of air and water at a pressure of 1,400 psi into a clogged service pipe with beneficial results in 70 per cent of the attempts, and bursting of pipes in only 10 per cent. Service pipes are sometimes frozen[5] to permit repairs without shutting off pressure in the water main.

22-13. Cleaning and Disinfecting Reservoirs. The cleaning of reservoirs is a routine maintenance duty. The frequency of cleaning and the methods used depend on local conditions and ingenuity. Methods used include draining, hosing, scrubbing, scraping, and refilling. Disinfecting may be accomplished by draining and refilling at the same time that a dose of hypochlorite is applied to give a concentration of free chlorine of about 1 ppm to the water.

22-14. Waste Surveys and Waste Control.[6] A large amount of water passing through a pumping station may be unaccounted for. Cities with all services metered are sometimes unable to account for as much as 20 to 30 per cent of their pumpage. Unaccounted-for water is not necessarily all leakage. Some of it may represent low flows passing through meters too large for the service, and some may represent stolen water. Leakage and waste surveys have commonly reduced both total consumption and unaccounted-for water.[7]

Leaks are undesirable both because they waste water and because they may undermine pavements and other structures. Abandoned service pipes are a prolific cause of leaks.

Waste surveys are conducted by isolating a section of the water-dis-

---

[1] See also R. F. Brown, *ibid.*, Vol. 93, p. R-55, 1946.

[2] See also M. K. Tenny, *Water Works Eng.*, October, 1948, p. 980.

[3] See also L. G. Carlton, *ibid.*, Sept. 11, 1940, p. 1150.

[4] LaV. Trentlage, *Water Works & Sewerage*, June, 1943, p. R-113.

[5] See also *Water Works Eng.*, May 14, 1947, p. 529; Nov. 12, 1947, p. 1365.

[6] See also E. S. Cole, *Water & Sewage Works*, Vol. 96, p. R-45, 1949.

[7] See also J. B. Eddy, *Water Works Eng.*, September, 1952, p. 839.

tribution system by closing the valves controlling the flow of water thereto so that all the water to the isolated district passes through a single pipe. The flow through this pipe is measured, and if it is found to be greater than normal, the "isolated" district is divided into smaller districts and the source of abnormal use is located more closely. Measurements made during the early hours of the morning are more likely to indicate leakage, waste, or abnormal use of water because normal daytime usage is commonly suspended during these hours. The rate of water flow may be measured by inserting a pitometer into the pipe.[1] As this may necessitate uncovering the pipe and boring a hole for the insertion of the pitometer, the following method is sometimes used. All the valves in a section of the water-works distribution system are closed, and water is fed to the district through one or more fire hoses, equipped with meters, which are connected to hydrants on either side of the closed valves.

When excessive consumption is located in a particular district, house-to-house inspection of plumbing may be conducted to locate the waste. Theft of water can sometimes be detected by such surveys.

22-15. Illegal Use of Water. The illegal use of water is usually not a serious economic matter, but it should be guarded against as a matter of principle. Illegal methods include by-passing around the meter, called a "jumper"; inducing low, unrecorded flows through the meter, called "dripping"; in flat-rate services, supplying a neighbor through a hose or turning on water without notifying the water company; drawing water from hydrants without permission, most commonly done by builders; tampering with or reversing the recording mechanism on the meter; wrecking the meter dials; and using hidden connections beyond the meter. Alert and observing meter readers and other water-works employees, encouraged by rewards for the discovery of illicit use of water, are the best cure for such abuses.

22-16. Finding Pipes. Where records are inadequate, underground and subaqueous pipes may become lost. They must usually be located before leaks in them can be discovered. Pipe locators are of two types: one works with the pipe as a part of a closed electric circuit; in the other an aerial picks up the magnetic field induced in the pipe by a radio transmitter or by previous excitation. In the former, after the electric circuit has been completed by electric contacts with two exposed points on the pipe line, the magnitude of sound in earphones will increase as the pipe is approached and will fall silent when the observer is directly over the pipe. In the latter an electric dip needle points to the buried pipe and aids in the determination of its depth.[2]

---

[1] See also E. S. Cole, *J.A.W.W.A.*, February, 1945, p. 181.

[2] See also: B. Miller, *Water Works & Sewerage*, September, 1943, p. 335; C. R. Fisher, *Water & Sewage Works*, Vol. 94, p. R-101, 1947; *Water Works Eng.*, June, 1949, p. 548.

22-17. Finding Leaks.[1] Methods used for the location of leaks in underground pipes and in subaqueous pipes include (1) direct observation, (2) the sounding rod, (3) the hydraulic grade line, (4) water hammer, (5) blowing air into the pipe, (6) putting dye or salt into the water, (7) studying the quality (change of salinity) of the water in a submerged suction pipe,[2] (8) measuring the volume of water required to fill the pipe, and (9) listening either directly for the sound or with the aid of a sonoscope or electronic sound amplifier.[3] Each method is best suited to particular conditions. None is universally applicable or infallible.

Direct observation can scarcely be called a method. It would seem to require no special knowledge to say, "There is a leak," when water is seen gushing up in a city street. However, some skill may be needed to detect a leak where there is a luxurious green spot in a lawn, a soft spot in the ground, a melted patch of snow or ice, or where a spot of frost or dew disappears quickly in the early morning. Any one of these clues may indicate the location of a leak, as may the sudden or otherwise inexplicable increase in the flow in a sewer[4] or the appearance of a "spring" where there should be no spring. Water does not always appear close to the spot from which it left the pipe. After the general location of the leak has been determined, the sounding rod may be required to find it exactly. This instrument is a sharp-pointed metal rod that is thrust into the ground and pulled up for inspection. If moist or muddy, the line of the leak is being followed.

If a pipe leaks so badly that it will empty itself in a short time after it has been shut off, the leak can be found by allowing the pipe to drain. Then the volume of water required to fill the pipe quickly should be measured and this figure divided by the cross-sectional area of the pipe. The quotient will be the distance to the leak.

Leaks in water pipes usually make some sound unless the leak is submerged. Small leaks are likely to make more noise than large ones. The leak may be heard directly; it may be heard by placing the ear on the service pipe in the basement; or a sounding rod may be pushed down until it comes in contact with the pipe and the ear is placed against the rod. Where the unaided ear cannot detect the sound, one of the many simple instruments for magnifying the sound may make the sound audible. These include the aquaphone, the detectaphone, and the sonoscope. The first named is similar to a telephone receiver, without electrical connections. One end of the receiver is placed in contact with the sounding rod or pipe, thus making the sound audible. It is followed until the leak is located. Another device works like a stethoscope.

---

[1] See also *ibid.*, May, 1949, p. 419.
[2] See also G. Hazey, *Water & Sewage Works*, September, 1951, p. 382.
[3] See also Miller, *loc. cit.*
[4] See also D. O. Gross, *Water Works & Sewerage*, June, 1944, p. R-172.

A leak may be detected by following the pipe in the direction of diminishing pressure, *i.e.*, following the hydraulic grade line. If two points can be found on the hydraulic grade line on each side of a leak in a long pipe line and the hydraulic grade lines are passed through these two points on a profile, they will intersect over the location of the leak.

In the application of the phenomenon of water hammer to finding a leak, favorable conditions require a long pipe line without important branches. A valve on the line is opened until the rate of flow becomes constant, and then the valve is *suddenly* closed. The instant of time that the valve is closed and the pressure in the pipe immediately thereafter are recorded. The pressure wave caused by the water hammer will travel along the pipe to the leak, where a part of the pressure wave will be dissipated. The wave of diminished pressure will then travel back to the pressure gage at the valve, and a drop in pressure will be observed. Since the velocity of travel of the pressure wave is as shown by Eq. (10-10) in Sec. 10-7, and the wave has traveled twice the distance between the valve and the leak, the distance to the leak, in feet, is equal to

$$D = \frac{TV}{2} \tag{22-1}$$

in which T is time, in seconds, for the pressure wave to return to the valve and V is the velocity of travel of the pressure wave.

The blowing of air or the placing of coloring matter in a pipe is useful only in submerged pipe. The air bubbles or the coloring matter will appear over the leak. Fluorscein and the slightly cheaper dye uranine, both coal-tar dyes, are the most commonly used dyes. They are detectable in a concentration of less than 1 ppm by the naked eye and up to 1 part in 10 billion with the aid of a fluoroscope. The sample of water observed must be alkaline since acidity bleaches the color which is restored by adding alkalinity. Such dyes cannot be used in potable water since their appearance is undesirable. A slightly increased concentration of salt (NaCl) may be used in the detection of a leak by showing, by chemical analysis, an increased chloride content in the water suspected of escaping from a pipe into which a dose of salt has been placed. The salt concentration is insufficiently increased to be detected by taste.

22-18. Electrical Sound Magnification. The sound emitted by a leak may be picked up by a delicate crystal and magnified up to 10,000 times by vacuum tubes. It is possible to tune the receiver to the pitch of the sound of the leak, excluding interfering sounds. In the M-scope[1] leak locator, a very sensitive instrument, the sound of the leak is followed directly. The effectiveness of the instrument is greatly increased by making direct contact at points along the pipe and following along the

[1] See also C. R. Fisher, *J.A.W.W.A.*, December, 1946, p. 1330.

pipe until the sound can be heard without contact with the pipe. Sound will travel faster and a hundred times as far through pipe as through porous ground.

22-19. Permissible Leakage. Some leakage is to be expected from water pipes laid with the best of care and under favorable conditions. In the Water Works Manual the upper limit for leakage is given by the American Water Works Association as 250 gal per 24 hr per in. diameter of pipe per mile, and in specifications it is stated that "no pipe installation will be accepted until the leakage is less than . . . $ND \sqrt{P} \div 850$, (expressed in gal per hr) in which . . . N is the number of joints in the length to be tested, D is the nominal diameter of the pipe in inches, and P is the average test pressure . . . in psi."

22-20. Pressure Tests.[1] The stoppage of the pipes in a distribution system and increases in the rates of usage, of waste, or of leaks may cause falling off of pressure in some part of the system. The pressure throughout the system should be determined by attaching pressure gages to hydrants and other desirable places. An abnormally low pressure will indicate trouble between the point of low pressure and the nearest point of normal pressure. Further observations of pressure will locate the seat of the difficulty more exactly. The cause of the loss of pressure can then be determined. If a leak or high usage is the cause, there will be a high rate of flow at the point of normal pressure. If the pipe is partly stopped, the rate of flow through it will be low.

The rate of flow through a distribution system is sometimes so low as to render the pressure observations made under conditions of ordinary flow of no value in determining whether or not the pipe is clogged. The stoppage has no effect on ordinary flows, but it may cause serious losses of pressure when fire is being fought. Observations of pressure must therefore be made at hydrants when water is flowing under fire-fighting conditions.

22-21. Freezing of Water in Pipes.[2] The freezing of water in pipes is due to the exposure of the water to a temperature below 32°F. Time, temperature, volume of water, velocity of flow, and environment are factors affecting the rate of freezing. When water is motionless, the rate of freezing can be expressed as

$$t_1 = 2.3 \frac{q}{k} \log \frac{T_2}{T_1} \qquad (22\text{-}2)$$

where t_1 = time, hr, for change in temperature
   T_1 = original difference in temperature between water and air
   T_2 = final difference in temperature between water and air
   q = amount (volume, not rate of flow) of water, kg, in 1 m of pipe

[1] See also W. D. Hudson, *ibid.*, February, 1954, p. 144.
[2] See also T. M. Riddick and others, *ibid.*, November, 1950, p. 1035.

k = loss of heat, kg-cal per hr, for a meter length pipe and for the type of insulation considered for 1°C difference of temperature

Values of k vary from about 0.72 for a poorly insulated pipe to 0.08 for good insulation.[1] Since water in motion is slow to freeze, consumers frequently waste water to prevent freezing; in a few instances water companies have encouraged this practice. It is to be noted that this formula does not give the time required to cause freezing but only the time to change the temperature of the water. Freezing may be assumed to begin when the temperature reaches 32°F, although supercooling of 0.01 to 0.1°F commonly occurs. The first indication of freezing is the formation of frazil ice.[2] The time t_2, in hours, required to freeze water starting at an initial temperature of 0°C is

$$t_2 = \frac{80q}{kT} \qquad (22\text{-}3)$$

where T is the temperature of the outside air expressed in degrees centigrade below zero, and q and k are the same as in Eq. (22-2).

In the design of water pipes to prevent freezing[3] a heat balance should be computed to assure a greater heat input than heat loss. Only a small amount of additional heat is sufficient, even under arctic conditions. The amount of heat to be added can be computed by the method presented by Riddick.[2]

The conditions under which an exposed pipe line will freeze can be judged by a comparison of the expressions

$$H_{\text{input}} = \frac{Q}{D}\left[\frac{1{,}325(T_w - 32)}{l}\right] + 1.7f \qquad (22\text{-}4)$$

$$H_{\text{loss}} = \frac{\Delta t}{(1/h_f) + (L/k) + (L'/k') + [1/(h_r + h_{cv})]} \qquad (22\text{-}5)$$

where Q = rate of flow, mgd

H = Btu per sq ft per hr

D = diameter of pipe, in.

T_w = temperature of water, °F

f = friction loss, ft per 1,000 ft

l = length of pipe line, 1,000 ft

Δt = temperature of air below 32°F, °F

h_r = 0.77 E Btu per sq ft per hr, per degree differential

E = emissivity coefficient from unity for complete absorption to zero for complete reflection

$h_{cv} = h_c \sqrt{W + 0.8/0.8}$

[1] See also S. D. Bleich, *ibid.*, Vol. 18, p. 564, 1927.

[2] T. M. Riddick, *Eng. News-Record*, Nov. 9, 1950, p. 38.

[3] For the prevention of freezing in the Arctic see *Water Works Eng.*, February, 1954, p. 130; *Eng. News-Record*, Feb. 2, 1954, p. 30.

$h_c = 0.55 \, [\Delta t/D]^{0.25}$

W = wind velocity, mph

L = thickness of pipe wall, in.

L' = thickness of insulating material, in.

k = thermal conductivity of pipe wall, Btu per sq ft per hr per °F per in. thickness of pipe wall

k' = thermal conductivity of insulating material, in same units as k

$h_f = 202V^{0.8}/D^{0.2}$ Btu per sq ft per °F transmitted from bulk of water at 32°F

V = velocity of flow of water in pipe, fps.

When water freezes it expands with a force that cannot be resisted by any pipe manufactured. Water expands about one-twelfth of its volume in freezing, *i.e.*, 12 cu ft of water will become 13 cu ft of ice. The pressure and increase of volume usually cause the bursting of the pipe. The freezing of service pipes is more common than the freezing of water mains, because of the smaller volume of water to be cooled in the service pipe, the longer time when there is no movement of water in it, and the greater exposure to which service pipes are often subjected.

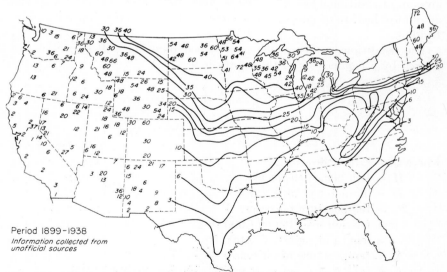

Period 1899–1938
Information collected from unofficial sources

Fig. 22-4. Frost penetration in the United States. (*Courtesy of the U.S. Weather Bureau.*)

Water pipes should be laid below the level of frost penetration. The average depth of frost penetration in the United States is shown in Fig. 22-4.[1] The rate of frost penetration is a function of the duration and the

[1] See also: *Water Works Eng.*, November, 1948, p. 1047; R. F. Legett and C. B. Crawford, *J.A.W.W.A.*, October, 1952, p. 923.

intensity of the air temperature below freezing. Frost will penetrate[1] open gravel soil more quickly but less deeply than tight clay soil. Pavements are generally poor insulators; snow is a good insulator. Insulation consisting of multiple layers of magnesia each 1 in., or less, in thickness, usually covered with one or more layers of waterproof roofing paper or sheet metal, is used in badly exposed locations.

22-22. Thawing Frozen Pipes.[2] The thawing of frozen pipes is accomplished by digging down to the pipe and building a fire in the trench over it, by the use of gasoline torches, by wrapping the pipe in rags and pouring on hot water, by blowing steam on or into the pipe, or by the use of electricity. When electric current is not available, steam under 3 or 4 psi pressure can be blown through a small pipe inserted in the frozen one. All but the use of electricity are generally messy, and the use of open flames within a building is dangerous.

Thawing by electricity[3] is quick, relatively inexpensive, and it can be safe.[4] The factors involved can be formulated as

$$H = I^2Rt \qquad (22\text{-}6)$$

where H = heat, joules
I = current, amp
R = resistance, ohms
t = time current is flowing, sec

The amount that the temperature is raised depends on the current I and the resistance R of the pipe per unit of length. A current of 100 amp will heat 1,000 ft of 1-in. pipe just as rapidly as it will heat 10 ft, but it will take 100 times the voltage to do so. Some data concerning currents, voltages, time, and other conditions in thawing frozen pipes are listed in Table 22-3.

It is to be noted that cast iron heats most readily and copper very slowly. Care must be taken to use the lowest amount of current suitable for the pipe material to avoid melting lead in pipe joints. Sulphur joints do not prevent the electrical heating of pipes, although a higher voltage may be required.

In thawing frozen pipes electrically the procedure is to include the length of frozen pipe in an electrical circuit in which the current and voltage can be controlled. Welding sets are available for this purpose. In thawing a service pipe all possible paths for the current to enter the house must be broken. One line from the transformer or rheostat is con-

---

[1] See also: *Water Works Eng.*, May 27, 1936, p. 739; J. Petrica, *J.A.W.W.A.*, November, 1951, p. 911.

[2] See also: *Water Works Eng.*, December, 1948, p. 1136; *Am. City*, November, 1949, p. 114.

[3] See also F. C. Amsbary, Jr., *Water & Sewage Works*, April, 1946, p. R-40.

[4] See also *Water Works Eng.*, February, 1949, p. 139; January, 1949, p. 51.

nected to the service pipe where it enters the cellar. The other line may be connected to a nearby fire hydrant, to an exposed point on the service pipe beyond the frozen spot, or to a neighboring service pipe likewise disconnected from its house. The cost of electricity used is insignificant, amounting to 1 to 10 cents per service thawed.

TABLE 22-3. Conditions Affecting the Thawing of Frozen Pipes by Electricity

Diam of pipe, in.	Pipe material	Resistance, ohms	Length, ft	Approx* volts	Amp	Time, min	Size of leading wire to use	
							Amp	Size, B. & S.
¾	Wrought iron	82.80	600	60	250	5	200	0
1	Wrought iron	......	600	60	300	10	225	00
1½	Wrought iron	......	600	60	350	10	275	000
2	Wrought iron	......	500	55	400	15	325	0000
3	Wrought iron	......	400	50	450	20		
4	Cast iron	684	400	50	500	60		
6	Cast iron	......	400	50	600	120		
8	Cast iron	......	300	40	600	240		
¾	Copper	9.35	400	40	500	30		
1	Copper	......	400	40	600	60		
1¼	Copper	......	300	35	600	60		
	Steel	63						
	Lead	123						

Relative Resistance of Pipe Metals, Expressed in Ohms per Mil Foot of a Piece of Metal 0.001 In. in Diameter and 1 Ft Long

Metal	Copper	Steel	Wrought iron	Lead	Cast iron
Resistance	9.35	63.0	82.8	123.0	684

* The lowest possible voltage should be used.

22-23. Care of Hydrants.[1]

The principal dangers to fire hydrants are breakage by traffic, injury through ignorance, carelessness, or abuse; and freezing. Traffic injuries may be minimized by setting the hydrant in a safe location; malicious abuse may be prevented by police- and fire-department protection; and the effect of other injuries can be minimized by frequent inspection, test, and quick repairs. Periodic measurements of the rate of discharge from hydrants[2] will serve to indicate changes in conditions.

Frozen hydrants are a serious menace to safety. They can be protected from freezing by covering them with a quickly removable box.

[1] See also E. T. Cranch, *Water & Sewage Works*, Vol. 94, p. R-87, 1947.

[2] See also P. S. Wilson, *ibid.*, Vol. 98, p. R-61, 1951.

This has the advantage also of leaving the top of the hydrant free from snow and ice. The use of antifreeze in the hydrant is undesirable because of the possibility of polluting the water supply. Hydrants may freeze owing to the freezing or clogging of the drainpipe which permits water to stand in the barrel. The fact that a hydrant is frozen can be detected by dropping a small weight, tied to the end of a string, into the barrel through the nozzle. The difference in the sound when the weight hits water, ice, or the valve seat is easily recognized. Frozen hydrants may be thawed[1] by the use of salt (NaCl) or calcium chloride ($CaCl_2$) and by methods applicable to the thawing of frozen pipes. The action of sodium chloride and of calcium chloride is usually slow. Heat from an insulated wire wound around the exposed portion of the hydrant, with adequate current sent through the wire, will be transmitted down through the barrel to thaw the ice. The injection of live steam into the hydrant barrel through a hose is relatively quick, inexpensive, and effective. Jacobson[2] reports the thawing of hydrants in an emergency, in the average time of 3 min, by pouring concentrated sulphuric acid into the hydrant. The heat generated melts the ice before the acid reaches the valve. The acid is expelled from the hydrant when the valve is opened, and the acid is so dilute as to be harmless if properly handled. The first flush of water from the hydrant may be carried through a hose to the fire pumper where it is adequately diluted to prevent injury to personnel and equipment.

[1] See also *Water Works Eng.*, October, 1949, p. 927; November, 1949, p. 1011.
[2] E. E. Jacobson, *Water & Sewage Works*, April, 1946, p. R-42.

Purification of H₂O
① *Filtration*
② *Chlorination*

RELATION OF THE QUALITY OF WATER TO HEALTH AND TO INDUSTRY

23-1. Water and the Public Health. Experience has shown that an improvement in the quality of the public water supply is followed by an improvement in the public health.[1] Pollution of the public water supply and outbreaks of disease have been traced to various causes, among them being the contamination of surface watersheds by human activities, the leakage of polluted water into wells or other sources of underground water, the breakage of aqueducts or of submerged distribution pipes permitting the leakage into them of polluted water, the inundation of parts of a water works by floods of contaminated water, the relaxation of vigilance in the purification or sterilization of a public water supply, the dropping of carrion into reservoirs by birds, and the creation of breeding places for mosquitoes and other flying insects.

23-2. Diseases Borne by Water. The variety of forms of living matter borne by water seems unlimited, but the varieties of pathogenic germs that can be carried by water are relatively few. This is because of the unnatural environment offered to the pathogenic germs in natural waters. The natural environment of pathogenic germs is the human body and the bodies of some other warm-blooded animals.

Among the best-known specific diseases whose germs can be borne by water are typhoid fever, dysentery, and cholera. Typhoid fever has become a significant index of sanitation in a community since the almost complete disappearance of cholera and of dysentery in the United States.[2]

Water has been suspected of carrying infectious hepatitis,[3] tularemia,[4]

---

[1] See also W. T. Sedgwick and J. S. McNutt, *J. Infectious Diseases*, Vol. 7, p. 489, 1910.

[2] See also: A. E. Gorman and A. Wolman, *J.A.W.W.A.*, February, 1939, p. 225; *J. Am. Med. Assoc.*, Vol. 131, p. 817, 1946; M. N. Baker, *Eng. News-Record*, Sept. 5, 1946, p. 100.

[3] See also: J. R. Neefe and J. Stokes, Jr., *J. Am. Med. Assoc.*, Vol. 131, p. 817, 1946; R. E. Trussell, *Am. J. Hyg.*, Vol. 45, p. 33, 1947; J. D. Farquhar and others, *J. Am. Med. Assoc.*, July 19, 1952, p. 991; J. R. Neefe and others, *Am. J. Public Health*, April, 1947, p. 365.

[4] See also M. I. Tsareva, *Public Health Eng. Abs.*, May, 1948, p. 23.

and there is evidence that poliomyelitis may be water-borne.[1]   Maxcy[2] has stated that there is reason to believe that poliomyelitis is not water-borne.   Lensen[3] has stated that the virus of poliomyelitis can be inactivated in water by proper chlorination.   It is known that "swimmer's itch" and other skin infections designated as *Schistosome dermatitis* affect bathers.   The causative agent is said to be the cercaria, the free-swimming larval stage of certain parasitic worms of the family Schistosomatidae.   An epidemic of amoebic dysentery that occurred in Chicago[4] in 1933 attracted nationwide attention because of the spectacular nature of the outbreak and the wide distribution of the resulting cases over the country.   The epidemic resulted from the pollution of ice water by sewage that escaped from a leaky and surcharged soil pipe passing over a water cooler in a prominent hotel in Chicago.

Gastroenteritis[5] is a nonspecific enteric disturbance which may be either water-borne or food-borne.   It is caused by bacteria of the Salmonella group such as *S. typhosa*, causing paratyphoid fever, by other organisms, or it may be caused by inorganic irritants.

The transportation, by water, of pathogenic bacteria causing specific diseases will occur only under exceptional circumstances.   Pathogenic bacteria, viruses, and other disease-causing organisms that can be water-borne are discussed in Secs. 25-2 and 25-3.   Fatal poisonings of animals and humans by toxic algae have been recognized.[6]

23-3. Other Diseases Due to Water.   Diseases other than those of organic origin that may be related to the quality of the water include goiter; lead poisoning; other metallic poisonings; fluorosis, or mottled enamel of the teeth; dental caries; and nonspecific intestinal derangements.

The absence of iodine from water is assumed to be a contributing cause of goiter.   "One of the most extraordinary facts of recent medicine and surgery is that goiter may be a factor in the occurrence of malignance or cancer."[7]   The amount of iodine that may be required to maintain health is so small as to be undetectable in routine sanitary or mineral water analysis.   It has been suggested that the addition of 0.1 lb of sodium iodide per million gallons of water will prevent goiter, and this has been attempted in a few places.[8]   Greater reliance is now placed by the public in the mixture of sodium iodide with common table salt.

---

[1] See also R. R. Scobey, *Arch. Pediat.*, Vol. 63, p. 567, 1946.

[2] K. F. Maxcy, *J.A.W.W.A.*, August, 1949, p. 696.

[3] S. G. Lensen and others, *ibid.*, September, 1946, p. 1069.

[4] See *Natl. Insts. Health Bull.* 166, 1936.

[5] See also A. I. Ross and G. H. Gillespie, *Public Health Eng. Abs.*, October, 1952, p. 30.

[6] See also: D. G. Steyn, *ibid.*, July, 1948, p. 24; Handbook of Selected Biological References, p. 9, *Public Health Bibliography Series* 8, U.S. Public Health Service, 1953.

[7] From W. Weston, *Am. J. Public Health*, Vol. 21, p. 715, 1931.

[8] See also "Water Works Practice," American Water Works Association, 1925, p. 275.

Methemoglobinemia is a disease of infants, sometimes fatal, resulting from the ingestion of nitrates found in some waters.[1] Water used in preparing the infant's feeding formula should contain no more than 10 or possibly 20 ppm of nitrate nitrogen.

Lead is sufficiently soluble in water to be a menace to health. The dangers of lead poisoning are increased because of the tendency of the human body to store rather than to eliminate lead when the lead ingested exceeds 0.3 to 0.6 mg per day per capita.[2] Small quantities of lead, if taken regularly, may be stored in the system until a sufficient quantity has been accumulated to produce the symptoms of lead poisoning. Evidence has been produced[3] to cast some doubt on the inability of the body to eliminate lead, but its subtle dangers are, nevertheless, quite real. Since 0.5 ppm in water is considered dangerous to health, the use of lead in contact with potable water is considered, by some authorities, to be dangerous. Neither lead nor zinc paints should be used on surfaces in contact with potable water. Asphaltum, silicate, or enamel paints are to be preferred.

Other metals whose presence in too large a concentration may derange bodily metabolism sufficiently to cause disease include copper, zinc, and iron. In general, however, physiological effects of the small quantities of these metals found in natural waters or dissolved from conduits or containers may be beneficial rather than injurious to health.

Intestinal derangements may result from the presence in water of an excess of magnesium sulphate, or other alkaline substances, or of undesirable organic matter or even from the lack of certain substances to which the body has become accustomed.[4]

Outbreaks of gastroenteritis have occurred which, from certain aspects, appeared to be water-borne but where bacterial pollution of the water supply was not indicated by the conventional methods of water examination. Authoritative opinion indicates that there is no definite information at present that this physiological derangement is water-borne.[5] It has been concluded also that where the degree of hardness of water is such as to make it fit for domestic use no physiological derangement will result from drinking the water.[3]

23-4. Fluorosis, Fluorides, and Fluoridation. A minimum amount of fluorides is desirable in a potable water to aid in the prevention of dental

[1] See also: G. Walton, *Am. J. Public Health*, August, 1951, p. 986; R. L. Faucett and H. C. Miller, *J. Pediat.*, November, 1946, p. 593; M. Ferrant, *ibid.*, p. 585.
[2] See also R. A. Kehoe, Abstract, *J.A.W.W.A.*, January, 1948, p. 101.
[3] See also S. S. Negus, *Water Works Eng.*, Mar. 2, 1938, p. 266.
[4] See also S. S. Negus, *J.A.W.W.A.*, February, 1938, p. 242.
[5] See also Symposium, *ibid.*, August, 1937, p. 1137.

caries,[1] and the maximum amount is limited by the need for the prevention of fluorosis, a defect of the enamel of the teeth. Evidence points to the defect being caused by the action of fluorine or fluorides on the teeth during eruption in childhood. Normally formed teeth are not known to become mottled after eruption.[2] Fluorosis may be avoided by the use of natural waters low in fluoride and, in a few localities, by the removal of excess fluorides from the water.

The addition of fluorides to water, known as fluoridation, is widely practiced.[3] Justification for the addition of fluorides to water has invoked wide discussion and has resulted in approval by many scientific organizations.[4] Some cities[5] are adding fluorides to maintain an optimum level of 1.0 ppm of equivalent fluorine in the public water supply. It has been satisfactorily demonstrated that at such a concentration no tastes will be created.[6] Some information on chemicals and equipment used in fluoridation is given in Table 23-1. In addition to the chemicals shown in the table "Flural," a proprietary substance,[7] was introduced in 1951. It has the combined properties of fluoridating and flocculating the water. The application and handling of fluorides, principally sodium fluoride,[8] requires special feeding machines and care because of dust hazards to the operator. Dry-feed machines are used in most water works, the machine resembling those described in Sec. 27-29.

23-5. Protection of Sources.[9] Wells and other works for the collection of ground water, and reservoirs, intakes, and similar structures for the collection of surface water require protection against contamination. Pollution may travel underground for great distances,[10] particularly through underground watercourses such as exist in limestone regions. In the construction of shallow wells in rural districts it is generally considered satisfactory to locate the well more than 100 ft from the nearest known source of pollution and to protect the top of the well, by means of a watertight curbing and cover, from contamination by surface drainage. In the construction of deep wells for municipal water supplies the log of

[1] See also G. J. Cox, *J.A.W.W.A.*, November, 1939, p. 1926.

[2] See also: Smith, Lamk, and Smith, *Univ. Ariz. College Agr., Tech. Bull.* 32, June 10, 1931; J. H. Rider, *J.A.W.W.A.*, November, 1935, p. 1516.

[3] See also: *Water Works Eng.*, September, 1952, p. 84; Census of Plants Using Fluoridation, *J.A.W.W.A.*, June, 1952, p. 553; August, 1953, p. 893; H. C. Medbery, *ibid.*, July, 1953, p. 745; Committee Report, *ibid.*, September, 1954, p. 920.

[4] See also *J.A.W.W.A.*, July, 1949; September, 1951, p. 672; January, 1952, p. 1; April, 1953, pp. 376, 387.

[5] See also L. F. Menczer, *Am. J. Public Health*, November, 1952, p. 1414.

[6] See also *Water Works Eng.*, February, 1953, p. 126.

[7] See also W. E. White, *J.A.W.W.A.*, January, 1952, p. 71.

[8] See also *Water Works Eng.*, April, 1952, p. 331.

[9] See also *New York State Dept. Health, Bull.* 21, 1942.

[10] See also R. G. Butler and others, *J.A.W.W.A.*, February, 1954, p. 97.

TABLE 23-1. Chemicals Used in the Fluoridation of Public Water Supplies*

Chemical	Solubility at 77°F, grains per 100 ml	Lb required for 10^5 gal to feed 1.0 ppm	Min gal solution required for feeding 1.0 ppm to 10^5 gal at 77°F	Purchase package	Form of chemical	Types of feeders‖	Supplemental items for consideration
A	4.0	2.0	5.8	100-lb bags 375-lb bags 125 and 375-lb drums	Powder	† ‡	a–h b–h
B	4.0	1.9	5.6	100-lb bags 125 and 375-lb drums	Powder	† ‡	a–h b–h
C	0.76§	1.4	21.9	110-lb bags 125-lb drums 425-lb bbl	Powder	‡ ‡	c, d h
D	3.5	3.5	0.335	50-gal wood bbl 100-lb rubber drum	Dilute solution	† †	d–f h–j

* From Illinois State Department of Public Health.
† Positive-displacement solution feeder.
‡ Dry feeders with solution mixing device.
§ Per cent solubility from 0.43 to 0.73, from 32 to 77°F.
‖ Machines are available for feeding hydrofluosilicic acid in solution.
A = sodium fluoride (NaF) 42.5 per cent available ion. See AWWA Specifications 5W1.90T or B701-50T, *J.A.W.W.A.*, September, 1950, p. 897.
B = sodium fluoride (NaF) 44.4 per cent available ion.
C = sodium silicofluoride (sodium fluosilicate), Na_2SiF_6; 60 per cent available ion.
D = hydrofluosilicic acid, 30 per cent H_2SiF_6; and 23 per cent available ion.
a Ceramic crocks or other corrosion-resistant containers.
b Conditioning make-up water to minimize clogging by sludge.
c Respirator (dust mask).
d Rubber gloves.
e Residual.
f Weighing scales.
g Polyphosphate feed to stabilize solution and minimize incrustation.
h Automatic stop-start controls.
i Acidproof aprons.
j Industrial goggles for protection against acid.

the well should be kept to record the location of strata supplying undesirable water. This is later cased off before the completion of the well. Additional precautions must be taken to prevent the pollution of the well from surface contamination. This is done by waterproofing the top of the well so that water cannot enter it and by providing drainage channels away from the top to prevent its becoming submerged.

The protection of the quality of a surface-water supply can be divided into two parts, that furnished by the policing and care of the watershed[1] and that furnished by the treatment of the water. The latter is by far the more effective and, in most instances, the more dependable. Some authorities permit almost unrestricted use of reservoirs for recreational purposes,[2] limiting protection to the prevention of gross pollution by sewage or industrial wastes and the purification of water before distribution. Others depend on isolation of the reservoir and watershed, allowing none but accredited employees of the water works to trespass on either. All grades of restriction of use are to be found between extremes, each giving apparent satisfaction locally.

Extreme vigilance should be devoted to the detection of the outbreak of water-borne disease on or in the neighborhood of a watershed, and steps should be taken immediately to isolate the sources of infection. Where the watershed is large or is beyond the control of the water-works authorities, reliance cannot be placed on the continuous purity of the supply. Only purification will protect.

23-6. Protection against Oil and Birds. The location of overland oil-transmission lines[3] on watersheds is a threat to the purity of public water supplies, demanding adequate legal control. Birds may be controlled by shooting, by various methods of frightening them away such, for example, as the use of stuffed owls in infested localities, and sometimes by crisscrossing wires 10 to 20 ft above the water surface.

23-7. Afforestation of Watersheds.[4] Watersheds are afforested to discourage trespassing, as a protection against erosion, to provide revenue,[5] and for other purposes. The effects of forests on a watershed[6] may include (1) losses of runoff through interception and transpiration, (2) increase of total runoff through reduction of evaporation as compared with that from bare ground, (3) reduction of peak and increase of minimum runoff rates, and (4) possibly an improvement in quality of runoff

[1] See also Symposium, *J.A.W.W.A.*, May, 1954, p. 403.

[2] See also L. S. Finch, *J.A.W.W.A.*, October, 1946, p. 1138.

[3] See also: D. N. Fischel, *ibid.*, November, 1946, p. 1285; *Water Works Eng.*, March, 1952, p. 223; *Am. City*, September, 1952, p. 128.

[4] See also: J. M. Heilman, *J.A.W.W.A.*, January, 1947, p. 871; N. C. Brown, *Water Works Eng.*, Feb. 6, 1946, p. 122.

[5] See also R. C. Hawley, *J.A.W.W.A.*, October, 1946, p. 1105.

[6] See also E. N. Munns, *ibid.*, October, 1946, p. 1111.

water as compared with that of runoff from open fields of either cultivated or fallow ground. There is a difference of opinion concerning the effect of forests on watersheds as indicated by the preceding statements.[1]

23-8. Deterioration of Quality. After treatment the quality of water may change as a result of various causes. In a distribution system the quality of water may be affected by (1) corrosion of the pipes; (2) flushing, which dislodges foreign matter; (3) ingress of dirt and living organisms through leaks; (4) cross connections with polluted water; (5) aftergrowths of organisms, including bacteria, algae, schizomycetes, worms, and insects; and (6) solution of metals with which the water comes in contact. The deterioration of quality after purification may be subtle, discouraging, and more difficult to correct than the undesirable characteristics of the original raw water.[2]

23-9. Effect of Storage. Storage of water may either benefit or injure its quality. It is usually beneficial, however, as settleable matter will be removed by sedimentation, pathogenic bacteria and many others will die as a result of the unfavorable environment, decomposing organic matter will be oxidized, and color will be bleached out in open reservoirs. The storage of water may be detrimental to its quality because of the growth of microorganisms in it. This is particularly true in the storage of treated waters or in the storage of ground waters in open reservoirs, as a favorable environment with sufficient food is provided without the existence of predatory organisms to combat the increase of an undesirable species. The covering of the reservoir, used for the storage of treated water, will not assure the absence of difficulties, because the presence of desirable foods and the absence of light will encourage the growth of fungi, such as crenothrix. If a reservoir is to be covered, care should be taken to exclude insects, particularly flying insects, which lay eggs in the water, resulting in the production of undesirable larvae therein.

The character of the catchment area materially affects the quality of impounded water because of the food supply and the type of organisms contributed to the reservoir. Swamps, rivers, or lakes may contribute sudden increases in organisms that are flushed into the reservoir by rains or freshets. Seasonal increases in organisms to which the environment or the body of water is favorable may result in the appearance of organisms in large numbers in the reservoir into which these bodies of water are drained.

The shape, depth, and area of a reservoir affect organic growths in stored water. A large surface area with a shallow depth is conducive to organic growth, since many troublesome organisms grow in the light near

---

[1] See also: C. L. McGuiness, *U.S. Geol. Survey, Circ.* 114, June, 1951, p. 47; W. R. La Due, *Water & Sewage Works*, Vol. 94, p. R-13, 1947; *Am. City*, January, 1952, p. 86.

[2] See also N. J. Howard, *J.A.W.W.A.*, Vol. 28, 1044, 1936.

the surface. Irregularly shaped shore lines increase the surface area for equal capacity. They encourage the growth of organisms along the shore, called littoral organisms; and they furnish coves, inlets, and protected harbors for growing organisms. A reservoir with a rough bottom is open to a similar objection in that the depressions furnish centers for organic growth.

The storage of water will sometimes affect its temperature undesirably, particularly that of ground water, which may be brought to the surface cool and palatable, only to be changed to a tepid, distasteful liquid after storage under a hot sun, in shallow reaches, over submerged vegetation.

23-10. Cross Connections.[1] To drink the mixture from a recently used water closet, to bathe in the waste liquids discharged from a urinal, to plunge into the diluted contents of a bedpan, to purge a wound with the drainage from an operating table, is worse than disgusting. Such conditions may result from the existence of a cross connection.

A cross connection is any physical connection, either direct or indirect, that will permit or may possibly permit the flow of nonpotable water into a conduit or receptacle containing potable water. A direct connection consists of a continuous conduit leading nonpotable water into the potable water supply. An indirect connection consists of a gap or space across which nonpotable water may fall or be sucked, blown, or otherwise made to enter the potable supply.

Cross connections may occur in the distribution system controlled by the water works or in the house plumbing controlled by the consumer. Their effect, however controlled, is to deliver polluted or contaminated water to the consumer resulting in death, disease, or property damage.

The existence of permanent or temporary, active or potential cross connections is more extensive than is generally appreciated. Thousands of cases of water-borne disease resulting from unsuspected cross connections are recorded in the literature. The water works may be financially liable and the management may be criminally liable for injuries resulting from the existence of cross connections.

Some common types of cross connections exist where hydrant drains discharge into sewers, water pipes are laid in the same trench with sewer pipes or pass through sewer manholes, outlets to fixtures containing polluted water are above the inlets, etc. Dangerous temporary cross connections occur where a hose attached to a water pipe is allowed to hang in a container of polluted water or which may contain polluted water. A serious hazard from cross connections occurs along the water front where ships take water from the public water supply. If the fire pump on the ship, drawing polluted water from the harbor, is started before the shore connection to the public water supply is broken, polluted water is

[1] See also: R. F. Goudey, *J.A.W.W.A.*, March, 1941, pp. 391, 495; *Water Works Eng.*, March, 1951, p. 238; F. O. A. Almquist, *ibid.*, October, 1952, p. 968.

pumped into the public water supply.   Ships are known to have polluted themselves, other ships, and shore installations in this manner.

Eternal vigilance is the price of cross-connection prevention.   Potential hazards must be eliminated.   Single check valves are unsatisfactory safeguards.   Under certain conditions double check valves with facilities for drainage between them are permissible.   Other protective devices in practice include (1) air-relief valves and vacuum breakers designed to admit air and break any vacuum in the water lines; (2) flush valves and integral vacuum breakers that keep the valves closed when a vacuum is applied; (3) other ingenious types of valves designed to close on actual or impending backflow, none of which is generally accepted by health authorities; (4) swing connections that permit a private water supply to be connected either to the public water supply or to a polluted source of water but not to both simultaneously; (5) nipples, permitting the temporary connection of fire pumps drawing water from a polluted source; (6) the use of open tanks at heights greater than 34 ft.; and (7) the provision of a vertical air gap greater than about 1 in. between the inlet and the outlet level of a fixture.

Crossovers and interconnections should not be confused with cross connections.   A crossover or interconnection is a connection between two potable public water supplies, or between districts in the same supply.

Cross connections are made for various reasons, among which may be included the following: to permit the supplementing of an uncertain or inadequate private water supply by means of the public water supply; to furnish water from or to the public water supply for fire protection; to permit the filling, flushing, or cooling of fixtures or other equipment; and for other reasons.   The making of cross connections is difficult to prevent; their existence is hard to detect; and their correction may be inconvenient and expensive.   They are best cured by breaking the connection or by abating the conditions that permit the potential danger.   Check valves and gate valves are not considered satisfactory safeguards.

23-11. Governmental Control over Water Quality.   Many Federal agencies are concerned with the quality of different types of public water supplies.   These agencies, together with some information concerning their activities, are listed in Table 23-2.

The standards of quality for public water supplies served to the public by interstate carriers, adopted by the U.S Public Health Service, which has jurisdiction over them, have had a highly beneficial effect on the quality of most municipal water supplies.   Although the Service has no legal jurisdiction over the quality of a local public water supply, the moral effect of the possible condemnation of the supply for use in interstate traffic is ordinarily sufficient to cause the water-works authority to maintain a high standard of quality.

In most states and territories, control over the quality of the public water supplies of the region is vested by law in the state or territorial department of health. Under such laws the quality of the water, the method of operation of the water works, and projects for the alteration or extension of works providing water for public use are subject to review by the health authority. In most large cities the responsibility is left with the local health authority or the water works.

TABLE 23-2. Federal Agencies Concerned Now or Formerly with Urban and Rural Water Supplies

Agency	Urban	Rural	Agency	Urban	Rural
Bureau of Agricultural Engineering[a]	.....	DS	International Joint Commission[c]	SR	
Forest Service[a]	.....	DSC	Public Health Service[d]	SR	
Soil Conservation Service[a]	.....	DSC	Corps of Engineers[e]	S	
Division of Grazing[b]	.....	DSC	Emergency Conservation Work[f]	C	C
General Land Office[b]	DSR	DSR	National Resources Committee	S	S
National Park Service[b]	DSC	....	Panama Canal[f]	DSC	
Office of Indian Affairs	.....	DSC	PWA[f]	C	C
U.S. Geological Survey	DS	DS	RFC[f]	C	
Boundary Commission, U.S., Mex[c]	SCR	....	WPA[f]	C	C
			B. and D.S.A.[g]		

C means supervises construction.
D means collects data.
R means regulates non-Federal activity.
S means carries on studies and research.
[a] Department of Agriculture
[b] Department of Interior.

[c] State Department.
[d] Federal Security Agency.
[e] U.S. Army.
[f] Independent agencies.
[g] Business and Defense Services, Department of Commerce. See *J.A.W.W.A.*, January, 1954, p. 41.

23-12. Standards of Quality. The setting of a standard of quality to which all acceptable water supplies must conform has frequently been attempted and has, as frequently, been shown to be unsuitable for all conditions. It is considered to be impossible to set standards that will not exclude some potable waters or that may not include some unsatisfactory waters. Nevertheless there has been a continued demand for acceptable standards of general application. The widespread voluntary adoption of the standards of the U.S. Public Health Service for the Quality of Water on Interstate Carriers is an indication of the general desire for some form of acceptable yardstick of water quality. Some data on the quality of raw water suitable for purification for a public water supply and for swimming, promulgated by the California State Water Pollution Control Board,[1] are shown in Table 23-3.

[1] See "Water Quality Criteria," published at Sacramento, Calif., 1952.

TABLE 23-3. Fresh-water Quality Requirements*

Characteristic, ppm unless otherwise stated†	Domestic water supply	Bathing or swimming	Characteristic, ppm unless otherwise stated	Domestic water supply	Bathing or swimming
Bacteria per ml:			Total solids:		
Opt. max.	1.0	None	Opt. max.	500	
Max.	50	1.0	Max.	1,500	
BOD:			Chlorides:		
Opt. max.	None	5	Opt. max.	250	
Max.	0.5	10	Max.	750	
D.O.:			Fluorides:		
Opt. min.	5	5	Opt. max.	0.5–1.0	
Min.	2	2	Max.	1.5	
Oil:			Toxic metals:		
Opt. max.	None	None	Opt. max.	None	0.1
Max.	2	2	Max.	0.5	5
pH (not ppm):			Phenol:‡		
Opt.	6.8–7.2	6.8–7.2	Opt. max.	1	5
Critical.	6.6–8.0	6.5–8.6	Max.	5	50
Turbidity:			Boron:		
Opt. max.	5	5	Opt. max.		
Max.	20	20	Max.		
Color:			Sodium, %:		
Opt. max.	10	10	Opt. max.		
Max.	30	30	Max.		
Suspended solids:			Hardness:		
Opt. max.	10	50	Opt. max.	100	
Max.	100	100	Max.	250	
Floating solids:			Temp, °F, max.	60	65
Opt. max.	None	None	Odor,§ max.	‖	‖
Max.	....	Gross	Taste§ max.	‖	‖

* From "Water Quality Criteria," State Water Pollution Control Board, Sacramento, Calif., 1952.

† Opt. signifies optimum. Opt. max signifies highest desirable maximum. Max signifies top limit permissible. Min signifies minimum.

‡ Parts per billion.

§ Signifies disagreeable.

‖ Noticeable.

Standards of water quality can be divided into three types:[1] (1) for water of exceptionally great natural purity,[2] (2) for pure waters from a restricted area,[3] (3) for limits of matters permitted in waters.[4]

[1] See J. J. Hinman, *J.A.W.W.A.*, Vol. 7, p. 281, 1915.

[2] See *Public Health*, Michigan, Vol. 7, p. 9, January–March, 1912.

[3] See R. Haynes, *J. Anal. & Applied Chem.*, Vol. 5, p. 289, 1891.

[4] See Drinking Water Standards, *J.A.W.W.A.*, March, 1946, p. 361; *ibid.*, January, 1949, p. 3.

The following are extracts from the Drinking Water Standards for Interstate Carriers adopted by the U.S. Public Health Service:[1]

1. Definitions of Terms.   A standard portion of water for bacteriological test is designated to be either 10 ml or 100 ml.   The standard samples in the bacteriological test may consist of five portions of either of the above sizes.   If a sample collected for bacteriological examination is from a disinfected supply, the sample must be freed of any disinfecting agent within 20 min from the time of collection.

2. As to Source and Protection.   The water supply shall be (a) obtained from a source free from pollution, or (b) obtained from a source adequately purified by natural agencies, or (c) adequately protected by artificial treatment.

The water system in all its parts shall be free from all known sanitary defects, and health hazards shall be systematically removed at a rate satisfactory to the reporting agency and to the certifying authority.

3. As to Bacteriological Quality.   The minimum number of samples to be collected from the distribution system and examined . . . is based upon the relationship of population served.   Of all the standard 10-ml portions examined per month not more than 10 per cent shall show the presence of organisms of the coliform group.   Of all the 100-ml portions examined per month not more than 60 per cent shall show the presence of organisms of the coliform group.

The procedure given, using a standard sample composed of five standard portions, provides for an estimation of the most probable number of coliform bacteria present in the sample as set forth in the following tabulation:

Number of portions		MPN* of coliform bacteria per 100 ml	
−	+	When five 10-ml portions are examined	When five 100-ml portions are examined
5	0	Less than 2.2	Less than 0.22
4	1	2.2	0.22
3	2	5.1	0.51
2	3	9.2	0.92
1	4	16.0	1.60
0	5	More than 16.0	More than 1.60

* M.P.N. means most probable number.

Physical characteristics.   The turbidity shall not exceed 10 ppm (silica scale), nor shall the color exceed 20 (cobalt scale).   The water shall have no objectionable taste or odor.

Chemical Characteristics.   The presence of lead in excess of 0.1 ppm, of fluoride in excess of 1.5 ppm, of arsenic in excess of 0.05 ppm, of selenium in excess of 0.05 ppm, of hexavalent chromium in excess of 0.05 ppm, shall constitute ground for rejection of the supply.

Salts of barium, hexavalent chromium, heavy metal glucosides, or other substances with deleterious physiological effects shall not be added to the system for water-treatment purposes.

[1] See J.A.W.W.A., March, 1946, p. 361.

The following chemical substances which may be present in natural or treated waters should preferably not occur in excess of the following concentrations when more suitable supplies are available in the judgment of the certifying authority: Cu should not exceed 3.0 ppm; Fe and Mn, 0.3 ppm; Mg, 125 ppm, Zn, 15 ppm; chloride, 250 ppm; sulphate, 250 ppm.

Phenolic compounds should not exceed 0.001 ppm in terms of phenol.

Total solids should not exceed 500 ppm for a water of good chemical quality. However, if such a water is not available a total solids content of 1,000 ppm may be permitted.

23-13. Scoring Water Supplies.
The scoring of the sanitary quality of water supplies has been attempted by sanitarians, the scoring being based on the sanitary survey and a sanitary analysis of the water. The numerical weights given to the various conditions in scoring indicate their relative values in the opinions of the respective sanitary authorities. Such scores may be a guide to judgment in the selection of a proposed source for a water supply.[1]   No scoring system is widely used.

23-14. Quality Requirements for Industrial Water Supplies.[2]
The quality of potable water is not satisfactory for all industrial purposes. Qualities required by some industries are listed in Tables 23-4[3] and 23-5.[4]

TABLE 23-4. Quality of Water Required for Some Industrial Processes*
(Ppm, except for pH)

	Brewing	Textiles	Kraft paper, bleached†	Ice	Ice	Textiles
Color.........	0–10	5–70	25	5	Oxygen consumed, 3	COD, 8
Turbidity......	0–10	0.3–25	40	1–5	Silica, 10	Heavy metals, 0
Taste and odor.	None to low	....	...	None to low	Fluoride, 1	
Dissolved solids.	500–1,000	....	300	170–1,300	MgSO₄, 130–300	Ca, 10
pH............	6.5–7.0				MgCl, 171–300	Mg, 5
Alkalinity......	75–80‡					SO₄, 100
	80–150§	....	75‖	30–50		Chloride, 100
Fe............	0.1–1.0	0.1–1.0	0.2	0.03–0.2	MgCO₃, 50	Bicarbonate, 200
Mn............	....	0.5–1.0	0.1	0.2	CaSO₄ 300	
Fe-Mn........	....	0.2–1.0	...	0.2	CaCl₂, 300	
Hardness......	....	0–50	100	70–72	Na₂SO₄, 300	
					NaCl, 300	

* From "Water Quality Criteria," State Water Pollution Control Board, Sacramento, Calif., 1952.
† Additional limitations are: silica, 50 ppm; sulphate, 220 ppm; free CO_2, 10 ppm.
‡ Light beer.
§ Dark beer.
‖ Methyl orange alkalinity.

[1] See also Committee Report, *Proc. Texas Water Works Short School*, March, 1950, p. 36.

[2] See also S. T. Powell, *J.A.W.W.A.*, January, 1948, p. 8; and an exhaustive résumé in "Water Quality Criteria," State Water Pollution Control Board, Sacramento, Calif., 1952.

[3] See also: "Water in Industry," National Association of Manufacturers, New York, December, 1950; E. Nordell, "Water Treatment for Industrial Purposes," Reinhold Publishing Corporation, New York, 1951; G. M. Fair and J. C. Geyer, "Water Supply and Waste Water Disposal," John Wiley and Sons, Inc., New York, 1954.

[4] See a more comprehensive table in "Water Quality and Treatment," p. 66, American Water Works Association, 1950.

TABLE 23-5. Quality of Water Required for Boiler Feed*

(Expressed in ppm, except for pH)

Characteristic	Pressure, psi 0–150	Pressure, psi 150–250	Pressure, psi 250–400	Pressure, psi Over 400
Color	80	40	5	2
Oxygen consumed	20	10	5	1
Dissolved oxygen	1.4	0.14	0	0
Hydrogen sulphide†	5	3	0	0
Total hardness, CaCO₃	80	40	10	2
Sulphate-to-carbonate ratio	1:1	2:1	3:1	3:1
Aluminum oxide	5	0.5	0.05	0.01
Silica	40	20	5	1
Bicarbonate	20	20	5	0
Carbonate	200	100	40	20
Hydroxide	50	40	30	15
Total solids‡	3,000–500	2,500–500	1,500–100	50
pH min	8.0	8.4	9.0	9.6

* From "Water Quality Criteria," State Water Pollution Control Board, Sacramento, Calif., 1952.

† Except when odor of live steam is offensive.

‡ Depends on design of boiler.

23-15. Purposes and Methods of Water Treatment. Public water supplies are treated primarily to protect the public health. They are treated also (1) for aesthetic reasons, e.g., in the removal of taste, odor, color, and turbidity; (2) for economic reasons, e.g., in softening to minimize laundry costs; (3) for industrial purposes, e.g., in the preparation of boiler feed water,[1] and (4) occasionally for other reasons such as swimming pools, to reduce corrosiveness, or to combat goiter or fluorosis.

Common methods of treating water include (1) sedimentation, either plain or with coagulation, (2) filtration through sand, and (3) miscellaneous methods. These include disinfection; aeration; softening; removal of iron, manganese, and other minerals; the prevention of tastes and odors; and the correction of corrosiveness. It is to be noted that mechanical, chemical, and biological methods and equipment are involved in water treatment and it is to be emphasized that the principal purpose is the protection of the health of the public. Conventional water-treatment works involve separate structures and equipment for each step in the process, but circular steel tanks incorporating chemical mixing, coagulation, settling, and filtration in one unit are in use.[2]

[1] See also R. C. Ulmer, *Industry and Power*, June, 1950, p. 97.

[2] See also *Eng. News-Record*, Jan. 1, 1953.

CHAPTER 24

MEASURES OF THE QUALITY OF WATER SUPPLIES

24-1. Considerations of Quality.[1] Water to be used for a public water supply must be potable, *i.e.*, drinkable. It should not be chemically pure because water devoid of dissolved and suspended matter is both unpalatable and unhygienic. It is generally believed that the presence of certain minerals in water is essential to health,[2] and for this

TABLE 24-1. Desirable and Undesirable Mineral Matter in Water

(The amounts are stated in parts per million of the ion indicated. They are to be taken as suggestive only)

Use	Desirable or permissible					Undesirable or objectionable					
Domestic, drinking, and cooking	Ca 30	Mg 10	Li 5	HCO₃ 150	I 0.01	CO₃ 20	SO₄ 100	Cl 200	Fe 0.5	F 2.0	
Washing	Na 10	HCO₃ 60				Ca 10	Mg 5	Cl 500	SO₄ 500	Fe 0.1	
Laundry	None					All					
Irrigation	Ca 40	Mg 20	K			Na 10	Cl 100	SO₄ 200	CO₃ 10	B 0.2	
Textile manufacturing	None or very little					Ca 10	Mg 5	SO₄ 100	Cl 100	HCO₃ 200	Fe 0.1
Sugar manufacturing	None					Ca 20	Mg 10	SO₄ 20	Cl 20	HCO₃ 100	Fe 0.1
Pottery manufacturing	Na 50	HCO₃ 200				SO₄ 20	Cl 20				
Steam boiler	None					Ca 5	Mg 5	SO₄ 100	HCO₃ 100	Cl 100	

reason certain waters are considered to be more healthful than others. Water that is ideal as a beverage may not be suitable for all other purposes, *e.g.*, it must be soft for washing and bathing, it should be free from dissolved gases if used for the manufacture of ice, and it must be free

[1] For a discussion of the physical properties of water see W. H. Rodebush, *Illinois State Water Survey, Bull.* 41, p. 163, 1952.

[2] See also J. B. Peters, "Body Water," published by Charles C Thomas, Publisher, Springfield, Ill., 1935.

from color in the manufacture of certain kinds of paper.   Some desirable and some undesirable constituents of water for various purposes are listed in Table 24-1.

Chemically pure water is not found in nature because of the almost universal solvent power of water.   Natural waters, which may contain both desirable and undesirable constituents, may be polluted by drainage from either rural or urban regions.   Polluted water is defined as an otherwise inoffensive water fouled by sewage or other liquids or suspensions rendering it offensive to sight and smell and unsatisfactory for potable, culinary, or industrial purposes.   Contaminated water is a specific type of pollution involving the introduction into otherwise potable water of toxic materials, bacteria, or other deleterious substances which make the water unfit for use.   Infected water is water contaminated with pathogenic organisms.[1]

The quality of a proposed source of a public water supply should be judged on the basis of a sanitary survey of the source, a complete analysis, and a study of the economic and aesthetic considerations involved.   Permissible concentrations of undesirable characteristics in raw waters are limited only by the ability and cost of methods for their removal by treatment processes.   For example, the increasing use of synthetic detergents in the early 1950's made their removal an important problem.[2]

24-2. Sanitary Survey.   A sanitary survey of a source of water supply is a study of the environmental conditions that may affect its potability. The sanitary survey, aided by analyses, together with knowledge of the significance of the factors involved, furnishes sufficient data on which to base the acceptance or rejection of the water as a source for a public supply.   Recommendations governing the scope of a sanitary survey have been made by the U.S. Public Health Service.[3]   An inspection may be worth more than an analysis and may save both the delay and expense incident thereto.   A first step in a sanitary survey is the determination of the natural source of the water.

24-3. Natural Waters.   Natural waters may be classified as meteorological, surface, or ground waters.   Certain characteristics are typical. For example, meteorological waters are high in dissolved oxygen; surface waters are high in suspended matter and may be turbid or colored; and ground waters may be hard, high in dissolved carbon dioxide, and relatively high in dissolved minerals.

Meteorological waters are precipitated from the atmosphere as rain, hail, snow, dew, etc.   They are used as a public water supply mainly on

---

[1] Definitions are based on "Water Quality and Treatment," p. 29, American Water Works Association.

[2] See also: A. R. Todd, *Water & Sewage Works*, February, 1954, p. 80; G. Ainsworth, *Water and Water Eng.*, February, 1954, p. 80.

[3] See *Public Health Repts.*, Apr. 10, 1925, p. 693.

oceanic islands, where other sources are not available. Meteorological waters are usually potable without treatment provided the catchment area and subsequent storage facilities are properly protected.

Surface waters provide the most common source of large municipal supplies but, because of almost universal pollution of the ground surface, the sanitary quality of natural surface waters is universally considered to be unsafe for use as a public water supply without treatment. Good surface waters should be saturated with dissolved oxygen and should have a chloride content no higher than normal for the region. The temperature of surface waters fluctuates with the season, sometimes being undesirably high. Dissolved minerals characteristic of the region are likely to be present. Total solids may be high. Vegetation may become so dense as to increase the organic content and affect the odor, color, and tastes of the water.

Ground waters are natural waters that are found below the surface of the ground. Temperatures are usually constant, with an average of 2 to 3°F higher than the average yearly air temperature of the region. The temperature increases about 1°F for each additional 50 to 100 ft of depth. In percolating through the ground carbonic acid and organic acids are absorbed. The acidity of the water increases the solubility of other matters, particularly mineral matter, with a result that the amount of dissolved matters in ground water is usually high. The oxygen dissolved in water before it percolates through the ground is usually exhausted by the oxidation of organic matter, with a result that ground waters are usually deficient in dissolved oxygen. Thus, certain substances may be held in higher concentration in ground waters than in surface waters. It is the solution of mineral substances that causes hardness, alkalinity, and salinity in ground waters. The colloidal suspension of silica, alumina, and iron oxide is enhanced by alkalinity.

Relatively high alkalinity and low hardness, together with the presence of silica, alumina, and possibly of iron and manganese, are characteristics of waters that have been in contact with granites, basalts, and gneisses, *i.e.*, primary rocks. Water in contact with dolomites, limestones, sandstones, and shales, *i.e.*, the so-called secondary rocks, becomes impregnated with bicarbonates of calcium and of magnesium, and with chlorides.

Generally speaking, the sanitary quality of ground waters is satisfactory for use as a beverage without treatment, but the amount of dissolved minerals and other characteristics may require treatment of the water for domestic and other purposes.

24-4. Water Analyses. Water analyses supplement the information from a sanitary survey in the determination of the quality of water. The form of analysis most commonly used in the study of a public water supply is the *sanitary analysis*. This includes a physical, a chemical, a bacteriological, and occasionally a microscopical analysis. Standard methods for the making of sanitary water analyses have been published by the American Public Health Association.[1] Theroux and others[2] have prepared a laboratory manual to simplify some of the tests. Test procedures in the study of aquatic history have been compiled by Ellis.[3] The constituents and characteristics determined in a sanitary analysis are not always, in themselves, undesirable, but they may point to conditions or qualities that are undesirable. Mineral analyses are made primarily to determine the suitability of water for industrial and other purposes.

24-5. Sampling. Because of the probable daily and seasonal changes in the quality of a natural water, it is desirable that samples for analysis should be collected frequently and over a long period of time. In the laboratory control of a purification process, samples should be taken with sufficient frequency to permit the necessary changes in the method of operation. The proper collection of a sample of water for analysis is of great importance because of the danger of contamination at the time of sampling or the collection of a nonrepresentative sample. The condemnation of a valuable source of water supply might result from a dirty finger in the mouth of a sampling bottle or the collection of a concentration of scum from the surface or sediment from the bottom.

24-6. Physical Analyses. The characteristics of water that are reported in a standard physical analysis include temperature, color, turbidity, odor, and taste. In addition the specific conductance may be determined.

24-7. Temperature. The most desirable range of temperatures for a public water supply is between 40 and 50°F. Natural waters are seldom found below 40°F. As the temperature rises above 50°F the water becomes less palatable and less suited to certain uses, such as air conditioning. Temperatures above 80°F are undesirable, and above 90 to 95°F the water is unfit for a public supply. Records of the temperature of the raw water are desirable in the operation of a treatment plant because the character of the load changes with temperature, and more or less coagulant may be required. Temperature observations at the source in a deep lake or river may guide the operator in securing water from the most desirable depth or location.

24-8. Color. Color in water has little sanitary significance, except possibly to indicate the source of the water. Color is undesirable

[1] "Standard Methods for the Examination of Water and Sewage," 9th ed., American Public Health Association, 1946.

[2] F. R. Theroux and others, "Laboratory Manual for Chemical and Bacterial Analysis of Water and Sewage," 3d ed., McGraw-Hill Book Company, Inc., New York, 1943.

[3] M. M. Ellis and others, Determination of Water Quality, *U.S. Fish & Wildlife Service, Research Rept. 9,* 1948.

aesthetically; it may stain materials, or affect some industrial process, and it may complicate coagulation in treatment. Standards of the U.S. Public Health Service limit the intensity of color in an acceptable water to 20 and preferably to less than 10 ppm.

Color in water is usually due to organic matter in colloidal suspension, but it may be due to mineral or organic matter in solution, as a colloid, or in suspension. The coloring materials may be procured by surface waters when flowing through swamps, or by ground waters through the solution of minerals. Since color can be removed through adsorption by colloids, and since turbidity is caused principally by colloidal matter, turbid waters are less likely to be as highly colored as clear waters subjected to similar conditions. Swampy waters may appear black because of ink formed by a combination of organic acids with tannates and gallates. A yellow tinge may indicate an iron-bearing water colored when the iron was thrown out of solution either by oxidation or through the release of carbon dioxide.

24-9. Turbidity. Turbidity is a measure of the resistance of water to the passage of light through it. Turbidity is caused by suspended and colloidal matter in the water. The color and turbidity of a water may reveal, to an experienced eye, the source of the water. For example, if a river intake is near the confluence of two streams, the turbidity or color of water from the intake would reveal which of the streams is contributing most of the flow into the intake.

Sediment producing visible turbidity is ordinarily composed of fine particles of sand and clay and, as such, it is not particularly detrimental to the potability of the water or to most industrial uses. A turbidity indicating surface runoff would suggest possible pollution and might cause condemnation of the water as a source of a public supply without adequate treatment.

Turbidity greater than about 0.5 ppm may be noticeable to the consumer when the water is held in a white enamel container. Turbidities of natural surface waters may vary from one to thousands of parts per million. The U.S. Public Health Service limits permissible turbidity to 10 ppm, with the suggestion that it not exceed 5. Turbidities of less than 0.1 ppm can be obtained by treatment.

Variations in the turbidity of the raw water at a treatment works may occur suddenly, resulting in undesirable effects on the process. An "electric eye" has been devised that will warn an operator of changes in the turbidity that will require a change in plant operation.[1]

24-10. Odors and Tastes.[2] Odors and tastes in water may result from any one or a combination of such conditions as the presence of

[1] See also: *Water and Water Eng.*, July 20, 1933, p. 457; D. D. Gross, *Eng. News-Record*, May 21, 1931, p. 865.

[2] See also A. M. Buswell, *Ind. Chem. Sales*, 1947.

microorganisms, either dead or alive; dissolved gases such as hydrogen sulphide, methane, carbon dioxide, or oxygen combined with organic matter; mineral substances such as sodium chloride, iron compounds, and carbonates and sulphates of other elements; and phenols[1] and other tarry or oily matter, especially after chlorination. Some tastes, such as those imparted by dissolved oxygen or carbon dioxide, are desirable.

An increasing cause of disagreeable tastes in water is pollution by acid mine wastes and by industrial wastes, of which coal and wood distillation form a large part. These tastes are characteristically medicinal or phenolic, are detectable in extremely dilute concentrations of the order of one part per billion, are intensified by chlorination, and are difficult to remove.

Tastes may originate also in the treatment process as a result of chlorination or through the solution of or reaction with substances in the water-distribution pipes such as asphaltic or bituminous coatings on pipes or on reservoirs.

The odor of water changes with temperature, sometimes not being noticeable when the water is cold. It is usually sufficient in a routine analysis to determine only the odor when cold, but a thorough analysis should include a statement of the odors, both hot and cold, since the biological history of the water may be revealed by its odor. Equipment is in use[2] which makes possible the rapid determination of odor quality and intensity at any time and as frequently as desired.

24-11. Specific Conductance. The specific conductance of water[3] is the reciprocal of the resistance in ohms of a column of the water 1 cm long and having a cross section of 1 sq cm, at a specified temperature, usually 25°C. It is commonly reported in mhos. The specific conductance is used as a measure of the quality of the water, particularly in chemical and minerological industries, in the study of polluted waters, and in some treatment processes, and in the study of industrial wastes. "In general, excepting in plains and desert regions, the specific conductance of inland fresh waters supporting a good fish fauna lies between 150 and 500 $\times$ 10^{-6} mho at 25°C."[4] Dorsey[5] states that the "specific conductance of pure water at 25°C is in the neighborhood of 5.5 $\times$ 10^{-8} mho; for purest rainwater at 17.6°C, 128 $\times$ 10^{-6}; and for sea water at 25°C, about 500 $\times$ 10^{-4}."

24-12. Sanitary Chemical Analysis. In a sanitary chemical analysis of water only those tests are made that will reveal the sanitary quality of

[1] See also Panel Discussion, *J.A.W.W.A.*, May, 1953, p. 491.

[2] See also H. H. Gerstein, *Pure Water*, May, 1951, p. 90; *J.A.W.W.A.*, May, 1951, p. 373.

[3] See also L. V. Wilcox, *ibid.*, August, 1950, p. 775.

[4] See also Ellis and others, *loc. cit.*

[5] N. E. Dorsey, "Properties of Ordinary Water Substance," Reinhold Publishing Corporation, New York, 1940.

the water.   A quantitative analysis of the constituents of the water is not made.   A guide to the interpretation of a sanitary chemical analysis is shown in Table 24-2.   Some nonstandard indexes to the classification of ground waters are shown in Table 24-3.

TABLE 24-2. Guide to the Interpretation and Use of Sanitary Chemical Analyses of Water

(Based on average conditions in Pennsylvania.   Results expressed, where possible, in parts per million)

Indicator	Good	Fair	Suspicious	Average sewage (comparative)
Color................	0	0 −5	5 and up	High
Odor................	None	Negligible	Noticeable	Strong
Turbidity............	0 −0.2	0.2 −1.0	1.0 and up	50 and up
Alkalinity...........	5 −100	5 −125	[1]	50 −150
Hardness............	5 −50	50 −100	[2]	
Carbon dioxide........	1 −5	5 −10	10 and up	
pH..................	6.0 −7.2	6.0 −7.5	[3]	5.0 −8.0
Total solids..........	10 −50	10 −100	100 up	200 −1500
Dissolved..........	100%−96%[4]	96% −90%	90% and under	75%−25%
Suspended.........	0 −4%	4 −10%	10% and up	25 −75%
Volatile...........	0 −10%	10 −20%	20% and up	25 −75%
Fixed.............	100%−90%	90 −80%	80% and under	25 −75%
Chlorides............	1 −2	2 −5	5 and up	20 −150
Oxygen consumed.....	0 −0.1	0.1 −1.5	1.5 and up	25 −125
Nitrogen:				
Ammonia...........	0.002−0.02	0.02 −0.05	0.05 and up	5 −50
Albuminoid........	0.010−0.05	0.05−0.1	0.100 and up	7 −35
Nitrites...........	0.000−0.001	0.001−0.003	0.003 and up	0 −0.2
Nitrates...........	0.000−0.10	0.10 −0.50	0.50 and up	0 −10.
Iron................	0.0 −0.1	0.1 −0.3	0.3 and up	
Manganese..........	0.0 −0.1	0.1 −0.2	0.2 and up	
Dissolved oxygen......	100%	90 −100%	90% and under	0

[1] Below 5 or above 125.   [2] Below 5 or above 100.   [3] Below 6 or above 7.5.   [4] Per cent of total solids.

24-13. Acidity, Alkalinity, and Salinity.   Acidity is generally considered to be undesirable in the source of a public water supply because natural waters are normally alkaline.   Low acidity is not, however, detrimental to potability.   No standard limitations of acidity or alkalinity are placed on potable water.   Both characteristics are expressed in terms of equivalent weight of calcium carbonate, which is not a measure of their reacting abilities.   This is measured by the concentration of hydrogen or hydroxyl ions present, usually expressed as pH.

Alkalinity represents the content of carbonates, bicarbonates, hydroxides, and, occasionally, silicates and phosphates present in water. Alkalinity is commonly found in natural waters in the form of carbonate of soda and as bicarbonate of calcium and of magnesium. Caustic alkalinity, caused by hydroxides, is an undesirable characteristic. It is seldom found in natural waters.

Salinity represents the presence of neutral salts such as the chlorides and sulphates of calcium, magnesium, sodium, and potassium.

TABLE 24-3. Classification of Ground Waters*

	Class AA Excellent (1, 2, 3)	Class A Good (1, 2, 3)	Class B Limited (2, 3), poor (1) even if treated	Class C Unsatisfactory (1, 2, 3)
Coliform organisms per 100 ml, MPN...	<100 (1)†	<1,000 (1)	<10,000 (1, 2)	<10,000 (1, 2)
Sodium ratio........	<35 (1, 2)	35–50 (2)	50–80 (1, 2, 3)	<80 (2, 3)
	Ppm			
Color..............	<10 (1)	<20 (1)		
Turbidity..........	<5 (1)	<10 (1)		
Toxic minerals......	<0.05 (1)	<0.05 (1)	<0.05 (1, 2)	1.0 (2)
Heavy metals.......	<5.0 (1)	<5.0 (1)	<10.0 (1, 2)	10.0 (2)
Iron...............	<0.1 (1)	<0.25 (3)		
Phenolic compounds..	None (1)	<5.0 (1)	<25	>25
Magnesium.........	<15 (1)	<125 (1)	>125 (1, 3)	
Fluorides..........	0.5–1.0 (1)	0.5–1.0 (1)	>1.0 (1)	
Total solids........	<300 (2)	<500 (1)	500–1,500 (1, 2)	>3,000 (2, 3)
Chlorides..........	<100 (2)	<250 (1)	500–800 (2)	>800 (2, 3)
Sulphates..........	<100 (2)	<250 (1)	500–800 (2)	>800 (2, 3)
Sodium bicarbonate..	0 (1)	0–50 (2)	50–100 (2)	>100 (2, 3)
Boron.............	<0.5 (2)	0.5–1.0 (2)	1.0–5.0 (2)	>5.0 (2)

* From R. F. Goudey, *J.A.W.W.A.*, October, 1947, p. 1010.

† Limited by (1) domestic, (2) irrigational, or (3) industrial requirements.

24-14. Aluminum. Compounds of aluminum found in natural waters and in domestic water supplies resulting from the use of aluminum cooking utensils have no pathological significance. Water supplies properly treated with aluminum compounds, such as aluminum sulphate, contain less aluminum than the untreated water because of the insolubility of the aluminum compounds formed and their removal by sedimentation and filtration.

24-15. Arsenic. Despite the general use of arsenical compounds in the spraying of crops, arsenic is rarely found in natural waters. There is, however, a recorded instance of a fatality resulting from arsenic in a water supply.[1] The U.S. Public Health Service standards limit the presence of arsenic to 0.05 ppm, and the British limit is set at 0.2 ppm.

[1] See: L. Wyllie, *Can. Public Health J.*, Vol. 28, p. 128, 1937; R. Coughlan, *Life*, Nov. 1, 1954, p. 126.

24-16. Boron. Less than 30 ppm is tolerable in potable water. Some boron is desirable for the support of plant life. Few, if any, public water supplies in the United States are known to contain more than about 1.5 ppm.

24-17. Calcium, Magnesium, and Sodium Salts. Although the presence of these substances in most waters has no sanitary significance, they may be so detrimental to domestic and industrial uses as to render the water unfit as a public supply.

Compounds of calcium, which are the most commonly found dissolved mineral substances in natural waters, are supplied from three principal sources: limestone, gypsum, and calcium chloride. Limestone is soluble in water to the extent of 13 ppm. If carbon dioxide is present the solubility of the calcium carbonate may increase to 1,000 ppm. Gypsum ($CaSO_4$) is soluble to the extent of 2,000 ppm and calcium chloride($CaCl$) is so highly soluble as to render water unfit as a beverage long before saturation is reached. Magnesium salts have a pronounced laxative effect on persons unaccustomed to them. Standards of the U.S. Public Health Service limit magnesium to 125 ppm. Magnesium compounds are found in concentrations up to 5 to 20 per cent of the amount of calcium. Sodium is found most commonly in deep ground waters, or at higher underground elevations near the seacoast. It is usually in the form of sodium chloride.

24-18. Carbon Dioxide. Carbon dioxide in water may be a result of the decomposition of organic matter or of the metabolism of some organisms. In this action dissolved oxygen is converted to carbon dioxide. Hence, in general, as carbon dioxide increases, dissolved oxygen decreases. A high carbon dioxide content may, therefore, indicate biological activities; and high dissolved oxygen may indicate a high degree of purity of the water. This is not always true, however, since a few organisms secrete oxygen; or ground water high in carbon dioxide may enter the lake or river from submerged springs, thus increasing the carbon dioxide content of the water without affecting its sanitary quality.

Free carbon dioxide may be found dissolved in ground waters up to 50 ppm, although the concentration is normally much less than this. Its normal concentration in surface water is in the neighborhood of 0.5 to 2.0 ppm.

Carbon dioxide is desirable in water at a concentration known as the carbonate balance, discussed in Sec. 31-23. At this concentration it should impart a desirable taste and it should affect the solubility of carbonates so that a light film may be laid down on metallic surfaces to protect them from corrosion.

24-19. Chlorides. The presence of chlorides in a concentration higher than is found in natural waters in a region is an indication of pollution. Generally an excess of chlorides is a danger sign. Since soluble chlorides are generally unaffected by biological processes they can be reduced mainly by dilution. Although U.S. Public Health Service standards limit chlorides to 250 ppm, higher concentrations have no pathological effects and concentrations up to 700 ppm impart no taste that can generally be detected.

24-20. Chlorine. Dissolved free chlorine is not found in natural waters. Its presence in treated water results from disinfection with chlorine and the leaving of a residual for the sake of safety against the existence of pathogenic bacteria. The customary residual is in the neighborhood of 0.1 to 0.2 ppm. Residuals up to 2 ppm are successfully carried but may result in widespread complaints of unpleasant tastes. Chlorine must not be confused with chlorides, for they are not the same.

24-21. Chromium. The presence of chromium indicates pollution by industrial wastes since compounds of this metal are not found in natural waters. Public Health standards permit a maximum of 0.05 ppm of chromium in an approved water supply.

24-22. Colloids. Colloids may affect the quality of raw water, action in coagulation, and the process of filtration.

Finely divided matter may exist as a true solution, as a colloidal suspension, or as a true suspension. The particles in a solution grade in size to become particles in a "colloidal solution," or sol, and thence to sizes in a suspension. The smaller particles in a sol, which can pass from one point to another between the larger particles, are called the continuous, or closed, phase or, frequently, the dispersion medium, and the larger particles constitute the disperse phase. For example, smoke represents a colloidal state, or sol, in which the atmosphere is the dispersion medium and the fine particles of carbon in the smoke are the disperse phase. Activated carbon may be considered as an example of a sol in which the dispersion medium is the gas and the disperse phase is the carbon.

Colloidal particles are assumed to have dimensions that do not exceed 1μ, or micron, and that may approach the size of a molecule, *i.e.*, 0.1 to 0.5 millimicron. The existence of such particles can be detected by the Tyndall phenomenon and the Brownian movement. The presence of colloidal particles can be detected by the Tyndall cone and by the fact that they affect very slightly, if at all, the boiling and freezing points of the dispersion medium. Colloids diffuse slowly, do not pass through parchment paper, and do not settle.

A better understanding of the reason for the special reactions of colloids may be gained through a conception of the specific surface of a colloid, *i.e.*, the ratio of its surface to its volume. If a cubic centimeter could be divided into the smallest colloidal particles, each a cube with an edge of 0.1 millimicron, the total surface area would be 600,000,000 sq cm, or 15 acres, per cubic centimeter of material. With such an enormous surface in contact with the continuous phase it is to be expected that characteristic reactions will take place in sols (suspensoids).

A suspensoid, or sol, in which water is the dispersion medium and particles of clay, silica, or precipitated chemicals are the disperse phase is the most common form of colloid encountered in water purification. Suspensoids may be precipitated by the addition of an electrolyte, by changing the concentration of the disperse phase, or by means of electricity. The electrical charges on the colloids are apparently neutralized by those of the electrolyte, permitting the colloidal particles to come together. The colloidal particles in a suspensoid are sometimes protected against the action of precipitating agents by the presence of an external agent. Such particles are called protected colloids. For example, gelatin added to a silica sol will make the precipitation of the sol more difficult than if the gelatin were not present.

An emulsoid differs somewhat from a suspensoid in that the disperse phase combines, to some extent, with the continuous phase, rendering the breaking of the emulsion and the precipitation of the disperse phase difficult. Soap, gelatin, some oils, and many sludges found in water and sewage treatment mix with water to form emulsoids. Emulsoids of amphoteric substances, such as gelatin and other proteins, may be precipitated by the adjustment of the pH or the addition of certain soluble salts. Emulsoids may be broken by agitation, by altering the viscosity, or by changing the surface tension of the emulsifying or stabilizing agent. A change of temperature may change the viscosity, or various chemicals or electricity may be used to change the viscosity or the surface tension or both.

24-23. Copper. Copper is not present in significant quantities in natural water. Its use as copper sulphate in the control of microscopic organisms and its presence in food tend to pollute water supplies. The presence of copper is therefore an indication of pollution. However, ingestion of more than 100 mg per day is necessary to cause physiological reactions, and Public Health Service standards permit a maximum concentration of 3.0 ppm of copper. Such a limit[1] places no inhibition on normal doses of copper sulphate used in the control of microscopic organisms. Extremely small quantities of copper are sometimes considered to be hygienically desirable.[2]

24-24. Fluorine. Fluorides are found in natural waters and are desirable at a minimum limit of about 0.6 to 1.5 ppm to prevent dental caries, and at a maximum of about 3.0 ppm to prevent mottling of the enamel of the teeth of infants. The maximum limit permitted under the Public

[1] See also F. B. Mallory, *J. New Engl. Water Works Assoc.*, Vol. 41, p. 27, 1927.

[2] See *J.A.W.W.A.*, January, 1943, p. 98; February, 1943, p. 135; March, 1946, p. 362. See also: W. G. Schneider, *J. New Engl. Water Works Assoc.*, Vol. 44, p. 435, 1930; R. M. Palmer, *Proc. Am. Soc. Sanitary Engrs.*, 1930–1931, p. 364.

Health Service standards is 1.5 ppm. Dangerously toxic concentrations would probably not be encountered below about 115 ppm. The fluoridation of water is discussed in Sec. 23-4.

24-25. Dissolved Gases. The solubility of gases in natural waters is a function of the temperature of the water and the pressure and concentration of the gas in the atmosphere. The laws of the solubility of gases in water control the concentration of such gases as oxygen, nitrogen, and carbon dioxide found in acceptable water.

24-26. Hardness. Hardness in water is that characteristic which prevents the lathering of soap. It is caused principally by the solution in the water of carbonates and sulphates of calcium and magnesium, although the chlorides and nitrates of these two elements and sometimes of iron and of aluminum are effective to a lesser degree in causing hardness. Total hardness is expressed in various ways, the standard American practice being in parts per million by weight in terms of calcium carbonate. The hardness of water is satisfactorily determined by the versenate method introduced by Schwarzenbach.[1] The method is faster and less complicated than that included in the ninth edition of Standard Methods.

The U.S. Geological Survey has classified waters of various degrees of hardness, as shown in Table 24-4. The total hardness of natural waters

TABLE 24-4. Hardness of Water

Class	1	2	3	4
Hardness, ppm..........	0–55	56–100	101–200	201–500
Degree of hardness.......	Soft	Slightly hard	Moderately hard	Very hard

used as sources of public water supplies ranges from slightly below 10 ppm to about 1,800 ppm. Such amounts of hardness have no sanitary significance, but above 100 to 200 ppm the usefulness of the water for domestic and industrial purposes is limited.

The effects of hardness in water include the inhibition of lathering with soap, the formation of an insoluble precipitate or curd with soap, the formation of scale in water-heating vessels and cooking utensils, and other difficulties. The removal of hardness, known as water softening, is discussed in Chap. 29.

24-27. Hydrogen Sulphide. Hydrogen sulphide is objectionable in a public water supply above a concentration of about 1.0 ppm, because of the typical "rotten-egg" odor, although its healthful qualities at higher concentrations are prized at some health spas. Other objections include the tarnishing of metals in contact with it and its corrosive qualities.

[1] See H. Diehl and others, *J.A.W.W.A.*, January, 1950, p. 40; J. D. Betz and C. A. Knoll, *ibid.*, p. 49.

Since hydrogen sulphide is found in natural waters its presence does not necessarily indicate pollution.

24-28. Iodine. Iodides are rarely found in natural waters in quantities sufficient to render the water unfit for public use.[1] A concentration up to 1.0 ppm is considered desirable to prevent goiter. At one time the application of iodides to the public water supply was advocated[2] but dependence may now be placed on the use of iodized table salt.

24-29. Iron. Iron is objectionable in a public water supply because it causes stains on plumbing fixtures and on clothing and textiles in the laundry, it may cause tastes and odors, and it offers difficulties in manufacturing processes. Sulphate of iron causes acidity and corrodes ferrous metal and brass. Bronze and lead-lined pipes are required to carry waters heavy in iron sulphate. The presence of iron in water normally has no sanitary significance.

Organisms whose life processes depend on compounds of iron may cause taste and odor and may create what is known as "red water." Such organisms are sometimes known as "iron bacteria." Compounds of iron found in ground waters are usually in the form of ferrous carbonate ($Fe(HCO_3)_2$), which is soluble only in the absence of oxygen. In the presence of oxygen it is quickly oxidized to ferric hydroxide ($Fe(OH)_3$), which is insoluble. The presence of iron is common in ground water because of the wide distribution of hematite in nature and its solubility in water containing carbonic acid. The sulphates of iron frequently result from contact of the water with coal and with iron ores. The quantity of iron in ground water may increase after development of a well owing to the accumulation of organic matter which, on decomposition, will produce acid that dissolves an increasing amount of iron from the soil.

Most ground waters, even in iron-bearing regions, contain less than 5 ppm of iron, some falling into the range between 5 and 15 ppm, with a maximum of 40 to 50 ppm for acid mine waters. The U.S. Public Health Service standards for potable water limit the total amount of iron and manganese, taken together, to a maximum of 0.3 ppm.

24-30. Lead. The presence of lead is undesirable in water because of its tendency to accumulate in the body, resulting in plumbism. Standards for potable water limit its concentration to 0.1 ppm. Its presence in natural waters is unusual, but it may be found in water supplies that have come in contact with lead containers such as lead pipes, lead-lined tanks, and lead paints.

24-31. Manganese. Manganese behaves so much like iron in reactions in natural waters that it is sometimes difficult to distinguish between them. Manganese is not so widely distributed as iron in nature so that

[1] See also L. B. Loeb, *ibid.*, April, 1934, p. 461.

[2] See "Water Works Practice," American Water Works Association, p. 275, 1925.

it is less frequently encountered. The total content of iron and manganese in potable water is limited to 0.3 ppm.

24-32. Methane. Methane is a colorless and odorless gas, soluble in water. It is sometimes found in ground water in sufficient concentration to be released, on reaching atmospheric pressure, to mix with air and create an explosive mixture[1] containing 5 to 15 per cent of methane. Where the presence of methane is below a concentration of 1.4 ppm, at a temperature of 57°F, sufficient methane cannot escape from the water to form a 5 per cent mixture with the surrounding air. Since the gas is lighter than air[2] it can be excluded from a building by closing the top of the well casing and leading a vent pipe from the inside of the casing to the outer air. The vent pipe should be at least 2 in. in diameter and it should be protected against clogging by frost, birds, and other causes.

24-33. Nitrogen, Nitrates, and Nitrites. Nitrogen is an inert gas making up about 80 per cent of the atmosphere. It has no sanitary significance in water. Compounds of nitrogen are reported in a sanitary water analysis as total organic nitrogen, albuminoid ammonia, free ammonia, nitrites, and nitrates. The presence of nitrogenous compounds indicates only the presence of organic matter in the water. The nature of the compound indicates the relative remoteness of the contact of the water with the organic matter. Either free or albuminoid ammonia in water is generally considered evidence of recent pollution unless present in low concentration, as indicated in Table 24-2. The presence of nitrogenous compounds in a sanitary analysis requires explanation; it signifies nothing otherwise. Nitrogenous compounds in water that has been treated serve as food for aftergrowths in distribution pipes and reservoirs and are considered to be undesirable.

The presence of nitrites and nitrates indicates an organic contact sufficiently remote to permit of some oxidizing action on organic matter. Nitrate in water is commonly reported in terms of the nitrogen equivalent, but in mineral analyses results are reported in terms of the acid radical (NO_3) and, as such, in ground waters it may have sanitary significance as a cause of methemoglobinemia, discussed in Sec. 23-3.

The total nitrogen in natural waters is seldom sufficient to require its removal by purification processes. The total nitrogen in polluted waters may, however, be high, as indicated in Table 24-2.

24-34. Oxygen.[3] The word *oxygen* is used in reporting chemical analyses as dissolved oxygen, and also in the terms biochemical oxygen

---

[1] See also: A. M. Buswell and C. C. Larson, *J.A.W.W.A.*, December, 1937, p. 1978; L. W. Fisher and W. H. Sawyer, Jr., *Science*, Jan. 5, 1951, p. 7; *Water Works Eng.*, September, 1952, p. 850.

[2] The weight is 0.544 that of air.

[3] See also L. M. Zoos and others, *Trans. Am. Soc. Mech. Engrs.*, January, 1954, p. 69.

demand, oxygen consumed–permanganate, and oxygen consumed–dichromate. The tests are unrelated and their results signify different things. Only the dissolved oxygen test indicates oxygen content of the water. Surface waters of a satisfactory quality should be saturated with dissolved oxygen. The concentration of dissolved oxygen in water exposed to air at various temperatures is shown in Table 24-5. Under-

TABLE 24-5. Solubility of Oxygen in Water

(Under an atmospheric pressure of 760 mm mercury, the atmosphere containing 20.9% oxygen)

Temperature, °C...	0	1	2	3	4	5
Oxygen, ppm......	14.66	14.23	13.84	13.48	13.13	12.80
Temperature, °C...	6	7	8	9	10	11
Oxygen, ppm......	12.48	12.17	11.87	11.59	11.33	11.08
Temperature, °C...	12	13	14	15	16	17
Oxygen, ppm......	10.83	10.60	10.37	10.15	9.95	9.74
Temperature, °C...	18	19	20	21	22	23
Oxygen, ppm......	9.54	9.35	9.17	8.99	8.83	8.68
Temperature, °C...	24	25	26	27	28	30
Oxygen, ppm......	8.53	8.38	8.22	8.07	7.92	7.63

saturation or supersaturation in surface waters indicates pollution. Underground waters deficient in dissolved oxygen may be satisfactory as a public water supply because of the exhaustion of the dissolved oxygen by reactions with dissolved minerals. Oxygen is a highly active gas and its presence in water may contribute to its corrosiveness.

Oxygen consumed–permanganate is a measure of organic matter, particularly carbonaceous matter, that is chemically consumed in the test on digesting the sample of water with potassium permanganate in a bath of boiling water. In general, a water of good quality should be low in oxygen consumed, as indicated in Table 24-2. Oxygen consumed–dichromate, sometimes known as chemical oxygen demand, is not a "standard" test. It is performed by digesting the water with oxidizing agents other than potassium permanganate, particularly with potassium dichromate. It too indicates the presence of undesirable organic matter.

Biochemical oxygen demand, usually abbreviated to BOD, is a measure of the amount of oxygen demanded by living organisms in the water to oxidize organic matter present as food for the organisms. BOD is a characteristic, not a constituent, of the water. Unpolluted water should have less than 5 ppm of BOD. Higher amounts are danger signals demanding investigation of the cause before the water is pronounced potable. The test is seldom used in the determination of the quality of a water supply because inorganic pollution may be present when the BOD is low.

24-35. Phenol. Phenols in water supplies result from pollution by industrial wastes. They are undesirable in concentrations above 0.001 ppm because of the taste produced in combination with chlorine. At such low concentrations phenols have no hygienic significance.

24-36. Phosphate. Phosphates are not significant in natural waters, but the use of polyphosphates in the prevention of corrosion may result in their presence in a public water supply. Generally speaking, the concentration resulting from such treatment has no hygienic or aesthetic significance but, unfortunately, like compounds of nitrogen, phosphates may serve as food for aftergrowths in distribution systems.

24-37. Radium and Radioactivity in Water.[1] The need for knowledge concerning radioactivity in water, its measurement,[2] its physiological effects,[3] and methods for its reduction[4] is increasing in importance because of the increase in the use of radioactive isotopes in medicine and in industry.

The radium (Ra^{226}) content of natural surface and ground waters is reported by Love[5] as varying between 0.36 and 3.90×10^{-12} gram per liter. The American Water Works Association[6] points out that the upper tolerance limit for radium is not a factor in the quality of public water supplies and that at the highest concentration of radium in waters in the United States it would be necessary for an individual to drink 2,180 gal per day to obtain a minimum dose as prescribed in medical practice.[7]

The radioactivity of most natural waters is far below the maximum permissible concentration set by Morton[8] as follows:

Levels of Radioactivity Permissible in Water Supplies.[8] Maximum permissible concentration for continuous exposure beta, gamma, or alpha emitter: 10^{-7} μc (microcurie) per milliliter of water.

Emergency level permissible for temporary use immediately following an atomic explosion: Beta-gamma activity: for 10-day use, safe concentration 3.5×10^{-3} μc per ml; acceptable risk, 9×10^{-2} μc per ml. For 30-day use safe concentration is 1.1×10^{-3} μc per ml; acceptable risk is 3×10^{-2}.

Alpha activity: for 10-day use, safe 2×10^{-4} μc per ml; acceptable risk, 5×10^{-3} μc per ml. For 30-day use, 6.7×10^{-5} μc per ml; and acceptable risk, 1.7×10^{-3} μc per ml.

[1] See also J. B. Hursh, Abstract, *J.A.W.W.A.*, February, 1954, p. 70, P. & R.

[2] See also W. J. Lacy and B. Kahn, *ibid.*, January, 1954, p. 55.

[3] See also J. B. Hursh, *ibid.*, January, 1954, p. 43.

[4] See also S. Goodgal and others, *ibid.*, January, 1954, p. 66.

[5] S. K. Love, *Ind. & Eng. Chem.*, July, 1951, p. 1541.

[6] "Water Quality and Treatment," p. 62, 1925.

[7] See also: Loeb, *loc. cit.*; J. B. Hursh, *J.A.W.W.A.*, January, 1954, p. 43.

[8] R. C. Morton, *Civil Eng.*, September, 1952, p. 141. For British emergency tolerance levels see W. R. Loosemore, *Nucleonics*, October, 1953, p. 36.

The fact that natural waters may be expected to be low in radioactivity is indicated by the radioactivity of the Clinch River which receives the drainage from the Atomic Energy Plant at Oak Ridge, Tenn. This activity is in the order of 10^{-9} μc per l.[1]   On the other hand, some radio-active spring waters contain as much as 2×10^{-4} μc per l.   In general, the problem of radioactivity in natural waters is not acute and the probability of the contamination of reservoirs or water supplies by atomic bombs or atomic wastes seems remote.[2]

A method and instruments for monitoring water to determine the changes in its radioactivity are described by Loosemore.[3]

24-38. Selenium.   Selenium, like arsenic, is found in water supplies principally as a result of the spraying of fruits and vegetables.   It is usually present in insignificant concentrations, but waters with more than about 0.05 ppm of selenium should not be used for a public water supply.

24-39. Silica.   Silica is present in many natural waters in concentrations between 2 and 60 ppm, and to a maximum of over 110 ppm.   It has no sanitary significance at these concentrations but it is objectionable because of the scale formed in steam boilers.

24-40. Sulphate.   Sulphates are of hygienic significance because of their laxative effects.   The concentration is limited therefore to a maximum of 250 ppm.   However, tolerance can be acquired to higher concentrations which are in use in some communities, the higher concentration being disturbing only to persons not accustomed to them.

24-41. Tin.   Compounds of tin, in the concentrations normally encountered in natural waters, are of no sanitary significance, cause no pathological conditions, are harmless aesthetically, and are of no special consideration in most industrial processes.

24-42. Zinc.   Extremely small concentrations of zinc are sometimes thought to be hygienically desirable, but concentrations greater than 15 ppm are undesirable.[4]

24-43. Hydrogen-ion Concentration.   The hydrogen-ion concentration in water in connection with its mineral content may be of physiological importance because the metabolism of an individual accustomed to a water of a particular pH and mineral content may be disturbed, with consequent digestive disorders, when changing to a water with a different combination of pH and mineral content, despite the fact that both waters are potable and salubrious to those habitually consuming them.   This fact serves to explain, in part, digestive disorders experienced by travelers sometimes attributed to change of drinking water.

---

[1] See O. R. Placak and R. J. Morton, *J.A.W.W.A.*, February, 1950, p. 135.

[2] See also W. A. Rodger, *ibid.*, June, 1950, p. 533.

[3] *Loc. cit.*

[4] See also J. G. Cox, *J.A.W.W.A.*, November, 1939, p. 1926.

24-44. Hydrogen-ion Concentration and the pH Scale.[1]

Knowledge of the significance of the hydrogen-ion concentration is used in water-works practice principally in the chemical control of treatment processes. Hydrogen-ion concentration and the pH scale are directly associated, as follows:

It is known from the law of mass action that in the solution of an electrolyte the following relation exists:

$$\frac{\text{Concentration of cations} \times \text{concentration of anions}}{\text{Concentration of undissociated molecules}} = \text{a constant}$$

This constant is called the dissociation constant of the electrolytic solution. It has been determined from the electrical conductivity of pure water and from the law of mass action that

$$\frac{\text{Concentration of H ions} \times \text{concentration of OH ions}}{\text{Concentration of undissociated HOH molecules}} = 10^{-14}$$

But since the concentration of H^+ ions must equal the concentration of OH^- ions, for electrical neutrality, and the concentration of undissociated molecules in pure water is practically 100 per cent or unity, the relationship between H^+ and OH^- ions can be written as

$$\text{Concentration of } H^+ = \frac{10^{-14}}{\text{concentration } OH^-}$$

From this relationship the concentration of OH^-, or other negative ions, can be expressed in terms of the equivalent hydrogen-ion concentration. For example, if it is known that in a molal solution of a strong base the concentration of OH^- ions is 0.004, then

$$H^+ = \frac{10^{-14}}{4 \times 10^{-3}} = \frac{10^{-11}}{4}$$

and

$$pH = \log 4 \times 10^{11} = 11.6$$

In pure water the concentration of H^+ ions equals the concentration of OH^- ions for electric neutrality. Therefore, the hydrogen ion concentration of pure water is $\sqrt{10^{-14}} = 10^{-7}$, and the pH of pure water is 7.0. All acid substances will have a higher concentration of hydrogen ions, giving a pH below 7.0; and all alkaline substances will have a higher concentration of OH^-, or other negative ions, equivalent to a lower concentration of hydrogen ions, resulting in a pH greater than 7.0.

---

[1] Difficulties with computations involving the pH scale have led H. H. Thornberry (*Trans. Illinois State Acad. Sci.*, Vol. 44, p. 35, 1951) to propose the enH decimal scale which overcomes some of the objections to the pH scale and permits the solution of problems by simple arithmetic. The enH scale has not been widely used, however.

24-45. Examples of pH Computations. Keys to the solution of problems involving pH computations are the definition of pH and the statement of the law of mass action to the effect that

$$\frac{\text{Concentration of anions} \times \text{concentration of cations}}{\text{Concentration of undissociated molecules}} = \text{a constant}$$

Example. Let it be desired to determine the average pH of two electrolytic solutions, one with a pH of 6.0 and the other with a pH of 8.0.

Solution. The H^+ concentration of the first solution is 0.000001, and of the second it is 0.00000001. The average H^+ concentration is the mean of these two figures, or 0.000000505. The pH is the log of the reciprocal of this figure, or 6.3. It is to be noted and emphasized that the average pH is *not* $(6 + 8)/2 = 7.0$.

Problem. Determine the pH and the dissociation constant of a 0.1 molal solution of acetic acid which is 98.7 per cent undissociated.

Solution. Acetic acid is $H^+C_2H_3O_2{}^-$; hence

$$\frac{H^+(0.1)(0.013) \times (0.1)(0.013)\text{acetic}^-}{(0.1) \times (0.987)} = k$$

$$pH = \log \frac{1}{(0.1)(0.013)} = \log 0.0013 = 2.9$$

$$\frac{(0.1)(0.013) \times (0.1)(0.013)}{(0.0987)} = k = 0.0000171$$

Problem. Determine the pH of a molal solution of ammonium hydroxide, a weak base that is practically undissociated, and has a dissociation constant of 0.000018.

Solution

$$\frac{NH_4{}^+ \times OH^-}{(1)NH_4OH} = 0.000018$$

hence, concentration of OH^- ions $= \sqrt{0.000018} = 0.0042$. Then,

$$\text{Concentration } H^+ = \frac{10^{-14}}{0.0042} = \frac{10^{-11}}{4.2}$$

and
$$pH = \log 4.2 \times 10^{+11} = 11.6$$

24-46. Relation of pH to Acidity and Alkalinity. There is no correlation between the expression for the pH of an electrolyte and the expression of its acidity or its alkalinity. The fact that these are not the same is indicated by the acidities of 0.1 normal solutions of hydrochloric, sulphuric, and acetic acids. By definition the acidities are the same, whereas the pH's are respectively 1.08, 1.2, and 2.89. The acidity of a solution is expressed as the number of parts per million, by weight, of equivalent $CaCO_3$. Alkalinity is reported in a similar manner. The terms alkalinity and acidity are significant, therefore, in indicating the weight of chemical radicals in solution, these substances having some bearing on industrial, commercial, and potable properties of water. Neither indicates the chemical activities of the electrolytes. On the other hand, pH, or hydrogen-ion concentration, of a solution is a direct measure of its chemical activity and may also have some bearing on its sanitary and industrial qualities.

24-47. Practical Applications of pH. The pH of natural waters is largely dependent on the CO_2 equilibrium and lies between 7.0 and 8.0 to 8.5. In general, lower pH indicates too great an acidity for use as a beverage. The pH of distilled water may be 6.5 or lower, because of the solution in it of carbon dioxide. The significance of pH is therefore of doubtful value in a sanitary water analysis.

The reduction of the amount of alum required for coagulation has proved a valuable return from application of knowledge of pH in water treatment. Some additional advantages of such knowledge, enumerated by Eddy,[1] are (1) the prevention of the passage of alum through filters and the prevention of its afterprecipitation in distribution systems; (2) prevention of corrosive action; (3) control of small plant and animal life through ability to control the optimum living conditions, a factor of doubtful value; (4) possible reduction in size of coagulating basins due to better flocculation; and (5) possible increase in the efficiency of bacterial removal.

The control of pH is of such importance in water treatment and in industrial processes that automatic devices for its control are in wide use in the field.[2] These devices control the dosage of chemicals automatically to maintain any predetermined value of pH.

24-48. Mineral Analysis. Mineral analyses are made to determine the industrial and commercial qualities and possibilities of water. They are not considered of value in interpreting the sanitary quality of water.

In the performance of a mineral analysis it is customary to make only the determinations shown in the first column of Table 24-6. The substances that these ions are supposed to form are assumed by combining them in accordance with some rule of hypothetical combinations.[3] "Standard Methods[4]" specifies that hypothetical combinations may be reported by combining the milliequivalents of basic and acid radicals according to the following scheme of uniformity:

1. Silica, as found, except in alkaline waters containing silicates.

2. Iron and aluminum oxides, as found, except in special cases of acidity.

---

[1] H. P. Eddy, *J. New Engl. Water Works Assoc.*, Vol. 35, p. 385, 1921.

[2] See also: R. T. Sheen, *Ind. Eng. Chem.*, November, 1947, p. 1443; *Water Works Eng.*, January, 1952, p. 47; February, 1952, p. 127.

[3] See also W. F. Langelier and H. F. Ludwig, *J.A.W.W.A.*, Vol. 93, p. R-148, 1946.

[4] "Standard Methods for the Examination of Water and Sewage," 8th ed., p. 54, 1936; 9th ed., p. 7, 1946.

3. Combinations of the positive radicals should be made with the negative radicals in the following order:

Positive radicals, cations	Negative radicals, anions
Calcium	Carbonate
Magnesium	Hydroxide
Sodium	Sulphate
Potassium	Chloride
	Nitrate

Hypothetical combinations for a typical ground water are shown in col 4 of Table 24-6.

TABLE 24-6. Mineral Analysis of a Sample of Ground Water Showing Hypothetical Combinations

Determination made	Ppm	Hypothetical combination	Ppm
Iron, Fe................	2.1	Silica......................	80
Manganese, Mn.........	....	Iron oxide, Fe_2O_3..............	3.9
Silica, SiO_2..............	80	Aluminum oxide, Al_2O_3........	27.0
Alumina, Al_2O_3..........	27	Calcium carbonate, $CaCO_3$......	72.0
Calcium, Ca.............	1,220	Calcium hydroxide, $Ca(OH)_2$....	
Magnesium, Mg.........	530	Calcium sulphate, $CaSO_4$.......	45.8
Ammonia, NH_4..........	13.8	Calcium nitrite, $CaNO_2$........	2.4
Sodium, Na.............	5,207.2	Calcium nitrate, $CaNO_3$........	1.3
Potassium, K...........	627.3	Calcium chloride, $CaCl_2$.......	3,260
Sulphate, SO_4..........	32.3	Magnesium chloride, $MgCl_2$.....	2,080
Nitrate, NO_3...........	0.8	Sodium chloride, NaCl.........	13,480
Nitrite, NO_2...........	1.3	Potassium chloride, KCl........	1,198
Chloride, Cl............	12,250	Ammonium chloride, NH_4Cl.....	41.1
Alkalinity, M.O.........	72		
Nonvolatile............	28.2		
Residue................	32,100		

24-49. Industrial-water Analysis.[1] Methods for reporting the analyses of waters for industrial uses differ from procedures used in reporting either sanitary analyses or mineral analyses. Among the major differences noted in the tentative standard methods of the American Society for Testing Materials[2] may be included constituents reported and units used. Constituents reported include, for example, total CO_2, metallic oxides, silica, the important metallic cations such as Ca^{++}, Mg^{++}, Na^+, K^+, Fe^{++}, Fe^{3+}, Al^{3+}, Mn^{++}, and nonmetallic anions such as CO_3^{--}, HCO_3^-, OH^-, PO_4^{3-}, HPO_4^{--}, H_2PO^-, SO_4^{--}, HSO_4^-, Cl^-. Units used in reporting concentrations are entitled *equivalents per million*, or epm.

[1] See also Standard Methods for Reporting Results of Analysis of Industrial Water, ASTM, D1125-50T.

[2] American Society for Testing Materials Standards Supplement, Part III, p. 541, 1940.

An equivalent per million is a gram-equivalent weight per million grams of the solution. It can be converted to parts per million by multiplying it by the equivalent weight of the ion. For example, 2.2 epm of HCO_3^-, whose equivalent weight is 61, equals 134 ppm. The use of equivalents per million is advantageous in stoichiometrical computations. Where extremely pure water is desired its quality may be determined by the standard electrical conductivity tests, the quality being expressed in micromhos[1] per centimeter at 25°C. The electrical conductivity of water is discussed also in Sec. 24-11.

[1] See also Standard Definitions of Terms Relative to Industrial Water, ASTM 1129-51.

CHAPTER 25

LIVING ORGANISMS IN WATER

25-1. Life in Water.[1] Living organisms can be divided into three classes according to their size, as macroscopic, microscopic, and bacteria. Macroscopic organisms are so large that the species can be distinguished by the unaided eye; a fish or a snail would be an example. Microscopic organisms are so small that the aid of a microscope is necessary to distinguish the species, *e.g.*, Daphnia or Asterionella, as shown in Fig. 25-1.

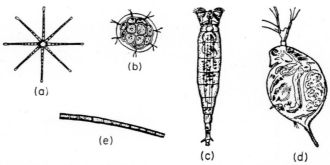

(a)

(b)

(e)

(c)   (d)

Fig. 25-1. Microscopic organisms. (a) *Asterionella gracillima* (colorless) × 188; (b) Pandorina (green) × 385; (c) *Rotifer citrimus* × 170; (d) Daphnia × 35; (e) Crenothrix × 500.

Bacteria are so small that even the aid of a microscope is insufficient to permit the complete identification of species. This must be done with the aid of stains, reaction to nutrient media, or other environmental conditions. The kinds and numbers of microorganisms growing in surface waters vary with the season, with the food supply, and with other factors. In the plant kingdom, schizomycetes and other fungi show the greatest independence to seasonal changes, to temperature, and to depth of growth in water. They may be found at all seasons at various depths but, being sensitive to light, are more frequently found in covered reservoirs, pipes, and near the bottom of lakes and reservoirs.

[1] See also P. L. Gainey and T. H. Lord, "Microbiology of Water and Sewage," Prentice-Hall, Inc., New York, 1952.

Natural waters, particularly surface waters, may abound in various kinds of organic life, some of which are detrimental to the use of the water for a public supply.

25-2. Bacteria in Water. Bacteria vary greatly in size. The largest known bacterium is *B. butschlii*, which is about 60μ in length and 5μ in diameter. One μ, called a micron, is approximately $1/25{,}000$ in. *Dialister pneumonsintes* is one of the smallest organisms that has been described. It is 0.15μ in diameter and 0.3μ in length. The various kinds of bacteria are almost numberless, the vast majority being either beneficial or harmless to man. Those bacteria which cause disease in man are known as pathogenic.

Bacteria that may be considered normal to natural waters, some of which may not be removed from the water in the process of purification, and which may cause difficulties in some industrial processes but will not cause disease in man, include the genus *Pseudomonas* and various species of the genera *Serratia, Flavobacterium,* and *Chromobacterium.* Non-pathogenic bacteria that may be carried into water from the ground include such genera of the genus *Bacillus* as *B. subtilis* and *B. cereus* var. *mycoides, B. marcerans,* and *B. polymyrax.* These bacteria, including *Sphaerotilus dichotomus,* have no sanitary significance but some may interfere with standard tests for coliforms. The iron and sulphur bacteria, mentioned in Sec. 25-7, have no sanitary significance but are the cause of difficulties in water-distribution systems, particularly the deterioration of water quality after purification.

Practically all pathogenic bacteria that can be borne by water are indigenous to the intestinal tract of warm-blooded animals, particularly man; unfortunately their isolation from natural water is difficult by laboratory means. Normally, water-borne pathogenic bacteria will not multiply in the unfavorable environment of natural water or laboratory culture media. There is, however, a harmless bacterium, known as *Escherichia coli,* normally present in the intestinal tract of warm-blooded animals, which is relatively easily isolated and identified. The presence of this organism in a sample of water is taken to indicate the presence of fecal matter in the water and is a warning that pathogenic bacteria indigenous to the intestinal environment may also be present; hence the importance of the *E. coli* test. It is the only specific form of bacterium for which a search is made in studying the sanitary quality of a water supply, and upon its presence or absence alone is often based the opinion of the safety of the water for drinking purposes.

25-3. Bacteriological Analysis. A rapid and widely applicable presumptive test that will produce reasonably uniform results with most waters is a great need in water-works practice. Changing techniques in bacteriological analyses are presaging changes in standard methods in order to meet this need. The validity of classifying bacteria as of fecal and nonfecal origin within the coliform group is questionable and some sanitarians believe the coliform group too inclusive because an excessive incidence of these organisms may be found in waters of good quality. Among recent techniques and devices[1] in bacteriological analyses may be included: (1) the use of the selective action of antibiotics in separating bacterial species; (2) the use of sulfonamides in the reduction of false positive reactions; (3) variations in nutritive requirements among organisms or groups of organisms as a basis for their separation; (4) the utilization of biochemical tests for the detection of coliform organisms; (5) the use of the electron microscope in the identification of organisms, none too promising;[2] and (6) the use of the membrane filter discussed in the next section. Despite the advances in bacteriological techniques, interpretations of bacterial analyses continue to be based on three more or less standard tests: the 20°C count on gelatin, the 37°C count on agar, and the coliform count, or the *E. coli* index. The limitations made by the U.S. Public Health Service on the number of bacteria permissible in potable water are stated in Sec. 23-12.

25-4. Molecular Membrane Filters. An approved bacteriological technique involving the use of a unique membranous filtering material known as MF Millipore Filter was suggested by the U.S. Public Health Service in 1951[3] for use in making bacterial counts, coliform estimations, and the isolation of some pathogens of the Salmonella group. The technique makes possible tentative counts in 10 hr, coliforms in 15 hr, and *S. typhosa* in 30 hr.

25-5. The E. Coli Index. The *E. coli* index[4] for a single sample is the reciprocal of the smallest quantity of the sample, expressed in cubic centimeters, which would give a positive *E. coli* test. For example, if three dilutions of a sample, 1:1, 1:10, and 1:100, are analyzed and a positive result is found in both the higher dilutions, the smallest quantity of the sample that will give a positive result is one one-hundredth of a cubic centimeter. By definition, the *E. coli* index is therefore 100. When an apparently anomalous but nevertheless rationally probable case occurs wherein a negative result is obtained in a dilution between two positive results, the positive observation at the higher dilution is interchanged in the record with its next lowest negative result and the index is based on the changed data. The index is more accurate when computed from a series of tests. Under such conditions, the procedure in computing it is as follows:

[1] See also H. G. Neumann, *J.A.W.W.A.*, January, 1950, p. 57.

[2] See also J. R. Baylis, *ibid.*, January, 1950, p. 66.

[3] See also: H. F. Clark and others, *ibid.*, November, 1952, p. 1052; *Public Health Repts.*, Vol. 66, p. 951, 1951; J. H. Bush, *Water & Sewage Works*, April, 1953, p. 151; A. Goetz and N. Tsuneishi, *J.A.W.W.A.*, December, 1951, p. 943.

[4] See "Standard Methods for the Examination of Water and Sewage," American Public Health Association, 9th ed., p. 205, 1946.

1. Record the ratio of positive to total tests, arranged in the order of magnitude of the quantities examined.

2. Record the differences between successive ratios.

3. Find the product of each difference and the reciprocal of the larger quantity in col. (1) in the table.

4. The *E. coli* index is the sum of these products.

Example: Daily *E. coli* determinations were made for a month at a particular filter plant, with the following results:

(1) Quantities tested, cc	(2) Number tests	(3) Number positive	(4) Ratio (3):(2)	(5) Differences between lines in col. (4)	(6) Product
1.0	30	20	0.67		
0.1	30	5	0.167	0.503	0.503
0.01	30	4	0.133	0.034	0.34
0.001	20	1	0.05	0.083	8.3
E. coli index...					9.13

The reciprocal method of determining the *E. coli* index is not altogether satisfactory because of anomalies that may arise in its use. In the reciprocal method, observations in col. (3) must fall on the probability curve to give consistent values in col. (6). For example, if in line 4, col. (3), the figure were 2, the value in col. (6) would be 3.3. Obviously, for a greater number of positive tests, we should have a higher index. The error results from assuming a value of 2, which falls off the probability curve in col. (3). The "most probable number" method has been standardized.[1]

25-6. The Most Probable Number (MPN) of E. Coli.

The MPN of *E. coli* is defined as "that bacterial density, which if it had been actually present in the sample under examination, would more frequently than any other have given the observed analytical results."[2] Procedure in the determination of the concentration of *E. coli* in a sample of water involves the examination of a number of portions of different size. In observing such samples by standard methods,[3] it is assumed that this variation will follow the "probability curve"[4] and that the MPN can be determined

[1] See "Standard Methods of Water Analysis," 8th ed., pp. 218, 223, American Public Health Association, 1936; R. Pomeroy, *J.A.W.W.A.*, March, 1940, p. 478.

[2] See F. R. Theroux and others, "Analysis of Water and Sewage," 3d ed., p. 257, McGraw-Hill Book Company, Inc., New York, 1943.

[3] See "Standard Methods of Water Analysis," 8th ed., American Public Health Association, 1936; Theroux and others, *loc cit.*

[4] See also: J. K. Hoskins, *9th Ann. Rept. State Sanitary Eng.*, p. 61, 1928; R. A. Noble and M. L. Sutherland, *Pure Water*, September, 1952, p. 155.

from the expression

$$y = \frac{1}{a}[(1 - e^{-N_1\lambda})^p(e^{-N_1\lambda})^q][(1 - e^{-N_2\lambda})^r(e^{-N_2\lambda})^s][(1 - e^{-N_3\lambda})^t(e^{-N_3\lambda})^u][\cdots]$$

where N_1, N_2, N_3 = sizes, cc, of portions examined

$\quad\quad\quad\quad$ p, r, t = numbers of portions of respective sizes giving positive tests for *E. coli*

$\quad\quad\quad\quad$ q, s, u = numbers of portions of corresponding sizes giving negative tests for *E. coli*

$\quad\quad\quad\quad$ λ = concentration of *E. coli* per cc

$\quad\quad\quad\quad$ y = probability of occurrence of the particular results if the concentration from which the result was drawn was λ

$\quad\quad\quad\quad$ e = base of Napierian logarithms (2.72)

$\quad\quad\quad\quad$ a = a constant for any particular set of observations the determination of the value of which may, therefore, be omitted in routine computations of λ

For example, in a series of observations the results of the *E. coli* determinations gave

10 cc	10 cc	10 cc	10 cc	10 cc	1 cc	0.1 cc
+	+	+	−	−	+	−

In this case, then,

$$N_1 = 10, \quad N_2 = 1, \quad N_3 = 0.1, \quad p = 3, \quad r = 1,$$
$$t = 0, \quad q = 2, \quad s = 0, \quad u = 1$$

Substituting and transposing,

$$ay = (1 - e^{-10\lambda})^3(1 - e^{-\lambda})(e^{-10\lambda})^2(e^{-0.1\lambda})$$

25-7. Iron and Sulphur Bacteria. Many different microorganisms grow in water and add to the difficulties of its purification. Among these undesirable organisms may be included[1] (1) iron bacteria, (2) sulphur bacteria, (3) sulphate-reducing bacteria, and (4) nonspecific bacteria causing iron transformations. Difficulties caused by these organisms include fouling of the water supply and corrosion or clogging of the distributing pipes.[1]

Iron bacteria are bacteria capable of using dissolved compounds containing iron. They include *Crenothrix, Leptothrix, Spirophyllum, Gallionella,* and others.[2] Concentrations of iron as low as 0.1 ppm will support the life of such organisms in water. The organisms secrete iron and deposit ferric hydroxide. Iron bacteria oxidize ferrous iron to ferric iron and precipitate ferric hydrate. Some sulphur bacteria increase acidity,

---

[1] See also R. S. Starkey, *J.A.W.W.A.*, October, 1945, p. 963.

[2] See also *Water Works Eng.*, Oct. 2, 1946, p. 1179; Oct. 16, 1946, p. 1236.

and this tends to dissolve iron; under specific conditions insoluble iron sulphate may be produced. Sulphate-reducing bacteria may cause the precipitation of iron by the production of sulphide from the reduction of sulphate. These bacteria also effect the aerobic corrosion of iron. Other bacteria cause changes in the iron content of water by altering the environmental conditions, such as (1) changes in reaction, (2) changes in degree of oxidation or reduction, (3) production and decomposition of compounds of iron, and (4) changes in the carbon dioxide content of the water. No single set of methods can be used to determine the nature of these organisms or to identify them in the laboratory. Their control is sometimes effected by the use of chlorine, copper sulphate, and the removal of their food supply, such as dissolved iron, nitrogen, or sulphur.

25-8. Microscopic Organisms. Microscopic organisms are found principally in surface waters, although a few fungi and other organisms are occasionally found in ground waters or in waters stored in the absence of light. The principal objection to the presence of microscopic organisms in a public water supply is the tastes and odors they produce. Plankton toxic to man are known but rarely occur in the sources of public water supplies.[1] Poisonous plankton are mentioned also in Sec. 23-2.

Some plants and animals found in natural waters, in water-purification works, and in distribution systems, are listed in Table 25-1. The electron microscope has been found to be of value in the study of microscopic organisms in water.[2]

Algae follow regular seasonal variations. The food supply of the diatom is presumed to consist of carbon, nitrates, ammonia, silica, and mineral matter. These constituents are found in the lower strata of lakes, under conditions unfavorable to the growth of diatoms. The growth of diatoms at the surface is increased following the spring and fall turnovers which bring food to the surface where oxygen and a moderate intensity of light are available. Diatoms grow most abundantly near the surface, although they will be found at all depths above the thermocline. There are, therefore, two seasonal increases in the growth of diatomaceae, the spring and the fall. Diatoms are found at temperatures between 35 and 75°F, the optimum temperatures being between 40 and 60°. Chlorophyceae are most abundant in midsummer at 60 to 80°, and cyanophyceae in the early fall at 70 to 80°. Chlorophyceae and cyanophyceae are more buoyant than diatoms and may contain oil globules or gas bubbles to aid their buoyancy. They are, therefore, found more frequently near the surface and may even form a scum thereon. No fixed rule can be stated as to their general location, as variations in both seasonal and depth distribution are to be found.

[1] See also: T. A. Olson, *Water & Sewage Works*, February, 1952, p. 75; *Water Works Eng.*, November, 1952, p. 1054.

[2] See also W. W. DeBerard and J. R. Baylis, *Eng. News-Record*, Apr. 29, 1948, p. 93.

TABLE 25-1. Partial List of Microorganisms That Are Troublesome in Water Supplies, Together with a Statement of the Amount of Chemical Required for Their Extermination[a]

Organism	Odor	CuSO₄,[b] ppm	Cl₂,[c] ppm	Organism	Odor	CuSO₄,[b] ppm	Cl₂,[c] ppm
Diatoms:				**Cyanophyceae (Continued):**			
Asterionella[d]	AGF	0.12–0.20	0.5–1.0	Cylindospermum	G	0.12	
Cyclotella[d,e]	fA		1.0	Gloeocapsa (red)		0.24	
Diatoma[e]	fA			Microcystis		0.2	
Fragalaria[e]		0.25		Oscillaria[e]		0.2–0.5	
Melosira[d,e,f]		0.20–0.33		Rivularia	MG		
Meridion	A			**Schizomycetes:**			
Navicula[e]		0.07		Beggiatoa[e]	vO, D	5	
Nitzchia[f]		0.5		Cladothrix		0.2	
Synedra[d,e]	EA	0.36–0.5	1.0	Crenothrix[e]	vO, D[g]	0.33–0.5	0.5–1.0
Stephanodiscus		0.33		Leptothrix			
Tabellaria	AGF	0.12–0.5	0.5–1	Sphaerotilus natans	vO, D	0.4	
Chlorophyceae:				Spirophyllum			0.25
Cladaphora		0.5		Thiothrix[d,e]	vO, D		0.5–1
Closterium		0.17		**Fungus:**			
Coelastrum[e]		0.05–0.33	1.0	Achlya			0.6
Conferva[e]		0.25		Leptomitus		0.4	
Desmidium		2.0		Saprolegnia		0.18	
Dictyosphaerium	GNF		0.5–1	**Miscellaneous:**			
Draparnaldia		0.33		Chara[e]		0.1–0.5	
Eudorina	fF	2–10		Chironomus (bloodworm)			15–50
Entomorpha		0.5		Nais			1.0
Gloeocystis	O	0.5		Nitella flexilis[h]		0.1–0.18	
Hydrodictyon	vO	0.1		Patomogeton[e]		0.3–0.8	
Microspora		0.4		**Protozoa:**			
Palmella		2.0		Busaria	im, sm, F	0.33	0.3–1
Pandorina	fF	2–10		Ceratium	VF	0.24–0.33	0.3–1
Protococcus			1.0	Chlamydomonas		0.36–1.0	
Raphidium		1.0		Cryptomonas	cv	0.5	
Scenedusmus		1.0		Dinobryon[d]	AVF	0.18	0.5
Spirogyra[e]		0.12	0.7–1.5	E. histolytica		25–100	0.5
Staurastium	G	1.5		Euglena		0.5	
Tetrastrum			1	Glenodinium	F	0.5	
Ulothrix		0.2		Mallomonas	AVF	0.5	
Volvox[d]	F	0.25	0.3–1	Peridinium	F'	0.5–2	
Zygnema				Synura[d]	CM'FB	0.12–0.25	0.3–1
Cyanophyceae:				Uroglena[d]	FO'C'	0.05–0.2	0.3–1
Anabena[d]	MGV	0.12–0.48	0.5–1	Rotifer, Stentor			0.24
Aphanizomenon[d]	MGV	0.12–0.5	0.5–1	**Crustacea:**			
Clathrocystis	SGV	0.12–0.25	0.5–1	Cyclops[d,e,f]			1–3
Coleosphaerium[d]	SG	0.2–0.33	0.5–1	Daphnia		2.0	1–3

A = aromatic. B = bitter. C = cucumber. C' = cod-liver oil. cv = candied violets. D = decayed. E = earthy. F = fishy. F' = fishy, like clamshells. G = grassy. im = Irish moss. M = moldy. M' = muskmelon. N = nasturtium. O = offensive. O' = oily. S = sweet. sm = salt marsh. V = vile. f = faint. v = very.

[a] From W. C. Purdy Methods for the Biological Examination of Water, *Proc. 9th Ann. Water Works School, Univ. Kansas,* 1931, and from other sources.

[b] Residual, in most cases.

[c] Applied.

[d] These organisms have been affected by chlorine, producing a characteristic odor. In many cases they have been controlled by doses of chlorine ranging from 0.3 to 3.0 ppm, depending largely on the amount of organisms present.

[e] These organisms have caused troubles other than odor.

[f] These may be controlled by excess lime; 5 ppm in the case of diatoms.

[g] Medicinal with chlorine.

[h] Objectionable.

Protozoa, as a group, do not show any marked seasonal maxima, because of the different characteristics of the organisms in the group. They are most commonly found near the surface; some form a scum; and other genera, avoiding bright sunlight, are most abundant at depths of 2 to 3 ft. Different genera are to be found at all depths. The growth of protozoa is dependent more on the food supply than on the season, whereas plant growths show more distinctive seasonal variations. Rotifera are found at all seasons but are most abundant in the summer. Crustacea show variations in different bodies of water but have no marked maxima.

25-9. Macroscopic Organisms.[1] Macroscopic flora more commonly than fauna cause trouble in water. The most troublesome plants include cattails, hyacinth, eelgrass, and seaweeds. Occasionally bloodworms and other larval forms of flying insects appear and *Anguillula*, a small round worm common in rivers and ponds, is said[2] to infest public water supplies but to cause no pathological symptoms among the population. An interesting account of an infestation of a water conduit by fresh-water mussels (*Dreissensia polymorpha*) is given in *Journal of the Institution of Water Engineers* (Vol. 6, p. 370, 1952).

Although the presence of such macroscopic organisms as these is undesirable, it is usually tolerated because of the difficulty of removing them. Tastes, odors, and color caused by them may be removed in the process of purification.

The cultivation of a balanced fish life in reservoirs is considered to be desirable in the control of undesirable small macroscopic and some microscopic organisms. Knowledge of the cultivation of fish is desirable for such control.[3]

25-10. Limnology. Limnology is the science that deals with fresh waters other than running streams. The quality of water from such sources is affected by physical features, aquatic life, climate, location, and other factors. The physical features include the depth of the water, the shape of the bottom, and the character of the banks and the shore line. The aquatic life includes microorganisms and, to a slight degree, bacteria. Climate is an important factor affecting the quality of the water supply through temperature, wind, precipitation, evaporation, and light. The location of the body of water affects its quality through the proximity of habitations and the use of the water for recreational and other purposes.

25-11. Rheology. Rheology is the science that deals with the properties and characteristics of streams. Physical, chemical, and biological factors affect the quality of the water in natural streams somewhat as they do in relatively quiescent bodies of water. In a flowing stream,

[1] See also Secs. 23-2 and 30-27.
[2] See J. M. Caird, *Water & Sewage Works*, June, 1951, p. 266.
[3] See also J. M. Caird, *Water Works Eng.*, Vol. 98, p. 240, 1940.

however, the changes in environmental conditions and in the quality of water are so sudden as materially to affect the nature of the plankton. Such changes, resulting in the self-purification of a polluted stream, are effected principally by sedimentation, dilution, aeration, light, and biological activities.   The degree of self-purification of a polluted running stream before it reaches the water-works intake should be known to the engineer before recommending the stream as a source of water supply.

CHAPTER 26

PLAIN SEDIMENTATION

26-1. Process. The process of treating water by plain sedimentation requires the retention of the water in a basin so that the suspended particles may settle as a result of the action of gravity and other forces. Plain sedimentation is suitable as a purification process only for relatively pure waters containing undesirable amounts of suspended solids. There is no upper limit to the amount of settleable solids that may be present in water to be treated by plain sedimentation, as experience has shown that water containing a high concentration of suspended matter is more easily clarified by sedimentation than a water containing a low concentration of suspended matter, particularly if the particles are finely divided without being colloidal. Plain sedimentation may be useful as a process preliminary to further treatment in order to lighten the load on subsequent processes. Better operation of subsequent purification processes is secured through the less variable quality of the water delivered to them; there is a lowered cost in the cleaning of the chemical coagulating basins; no chemical is lost with the sludge discharged from the plain settling basin; and fewer chemicals are used in subsequent treatment. All surface waters are not sufficiently turbid to justify presedimentation.

Sedimentation basins are now operated almost exclusively on the continuous-flow principle, in which water flows through the basin continuously in a horizontal direction, entering and leaving at the same rate. The fill-and-draw method of operation is obsolete and vertical flow is practiced almost exclusively with coagulation, as explained in Sec. 27-38. Sludge may be removed from a basin by emptying the basin and flushing or scraping the sludge from it, or it may be removed intermittently or continuously by mechanical devices without interrupting the operation of the basin. The extra cost of the mechanisms in mechanically cleaned basins can be saved through the reduction of the size of the basins required to give the same or better results.

Some results of plain sedimentation are shown in Table 26-1. It is evident from these results that treatment by plain sedimentation alone cannot serve to produce a water safe as a public supply.

26-2. Sedimentation-basin Design. Among the forces and conditions affecting the sedimentation of matter suspended in water are

The force of gravity

The size and specific gravity of the settling particles

Coagulation or coalescence of the settling particles

The depth and shape of the basin

The viscosity (temperature) of the water

The presence of convection and other currents

The method of operation of the basin

Electrical phenomena

Biological activities

TABLE 26-1. Reduction of Turbidity and Bacteria in Various Stages of Water Treatment

	Toledo,[a] Ohio, August, 1923– July, 1924	Youngs- town,[a] Ohio, Oc- tober, 1923– September, 1924	Niagara Falls,[a] N.Y., Oc- tober, 1923– September, 1924	Cincin- nati,[a] Ohio	Louis- ville,[a] Ky.
Turbidity:					
Raw water.................	185	56	21		
Per cent removed by plain sedimentation[b].............	....	82.7			
Per cent removed by coagula- tion.....................	87.0	92.5	42.2		
Bacteria, 48 hr at 20°:					
Raw water, 1,000 per cc.....	14.1	8.69	9.96		
Per cent removed by:					
Plain sedimentation.......					
Coagulation.............	80.0	0.32[c]	50.1		
Filtration...............	94.2	0.022[c]	85.6		
Chlorination.............	96.9	0.053[c]	99.86		
B. coli index:					
Raw water.................	1,650	5,450	8,290	0.685	30.9
Per cent removed by:					
Plain sedimentation.......	....	....	....	47.2	92.9
Coagulation.............	81.9	0.005[c]	64.9	87.6	94.8
Filtration...............	98.8	0.007[c]	0.98[c]	98.5	0.097[c]
Chlorination.............	0.27[c]	0.001[c]	0.015[c]	0.355[c]	0.0193[c]

[a] Studies of the Effect of Water Purification Processes, *Public Health Service, Bull.* 172, 1927.

[b] Percentage removal shown is the percentage of the amount in the raw water.

[c] 100 minus the percentage removal.

Other forces and conditions probably exist but are neither definitely nor easily recognizable. The difficulties of making allowances for all these forces and conditions are apparent, with the result that the design of plain sedimentation basins is usually based on experience with other waters of a similar character or upon tests made upon the particular water to be treated. A committee of the American Society of Civil Engineers states:[1]

   . . . despite the various influencing factors . . . best results will be obtained with a straight flow through the basin, where the [coagulated] water is introduced at one end through a diffuser wall, passed through enough training walls along its line of travel to "iron out" discrepancies in velocity of flow, and taken out at the other end over a submerged weir or enough large openings so as not to influence the uniform velocity through the basin. If a uniform velocity can be maintained throughout the length of basin, conditions for subsidence become ideal, and the ideal is approached in long, narrow basins such as tunnels, large pipe lines, and canals.

Important conditions to be considered in the design of a rectangular sedimentation basin, either with or without interruption of operation for the removal of sludge, include (1) the period of detention, (2) the number and capacity of basins, (3) the velocity of flow, (4) the depth of the basin, (5) the relation of the length to the width of the basin, (6) the inlet and outlet devices, (7) the cover or roof, (8) the provisions for cleaning, and (9) the sludge-storage capacity. Many of these conditions depend on others, on the quality of the water to be treated, and on the desired results.

Materials used in the construction of settling basins, filters, and other containers are the same as those used for reservoirs, as described in Chap. 20.

26-3. Theory and Practice.[2] It takes time for a settling particle to reach the bottom of the sedimentation basin. This time is provided by retarding the velocity of flow, in a horizontal-flow basin, and making the length of flow, or the period of detention and the depth, such that the settling particle will reach the bottom before reaching the outlet from the basin. It would seem, therefore, that the shorter the period of detention, the shorter the required length of the basin and the less the required depth. The absurd conclusion is reached that a basin without length or depth is the most desirable. Hence, experience with existing basins is the best basis for design.

Attempts have been made to formulate mathematical expressions applicable to the determination of the dimensions of sedimentation basins. Notable among these attempts are those of Hazen,[3] Slade,[4] Camp,[5] and

   [1] Water Treatment Plant Design, *Am. Soc. Civil Engrs. Manual of Practice* 19, 1941, p. 43.
   [2] See also G. M. Fair and J. C. Geyer, "Water Supply and Waste Water Disposal," p. 584*ff.*, John Wiley and Sons, Inc., New York, 1954.
   [3] Allen Hazen, *Trans. Am. Soc. Civil Engrs.*, Vol. 73, p. 43, 1904.
   [4] J. J. Slade, Jr., *ibid.*, Vol. 102, p. 289, 1937.
   [5] T. R. Camp, *Sewage Works J.*, September, 1936, p. 742.

Carpenter and Speiden.[1]   In view of the number of conditions and constants involved it becomes the custom to base the design of sedimentation basins on experience with successful basins.

The theoretical velocity of vertical settling of a particle might be computed from Stokes' law which is in the form

$$V = \frac{gd^2(D_1 - D_2)}{18\nu} \tag{26-1}$$

where g = acceleration due to gravity

D_1 = density of settling particle

D_2 = density of water

d = diameter of settling particle

ν = coefficient of viscosity of water.   At 25°C it equals 8.94 millipoise = 0.001 cgs unit

All units are in the cgs system

The actual rate of settling of fine particles in sedimentation basins is affected by so many conditions that Stokes' law is not applicable to field conditions.

Conditions of importance frequently neglected in theoretical studies of sedimentation basins are velocity energy and density currents.   Entering velocities are difficult to dissipate, particularly in large basins, and may even build up to create tornadolike "storms" among settling particles. Density currents may create "splash" near inlets that will prevent sedimentation in the region, and inadequate outlet devices may concentrate or create currents that will draw settling particles or previously settled sludge, from or near the bottom of the basin, at the same time that particles suspended nearer the water surface are undisturbed.

26-4. Depth.   Depths of horizontal-flow sedimentation basins of all types range normally between 10 and 18 ft, with 10 to 15 ft being most common.   These depths include allowance for sludge storage, if provided. Greater depths, up to 20 to 25 ft, are found in vertical-flow basins.

26-5. Period of Detention.   The term *period of detention*, as used in practice, is equal to the volume of the basin divided by the volumetric rate of flow through the basin.   It is equal to the time required to fill the basin at the given rate of flow.   This period is greater than the *flowing-through period* which is the average time required for a small amount of liquid to pass through the basin at the given rate of flow.

The flowing-through period has been determined by (1) observing the time for a dye to pass through the basin; (2) the use of chemicals, such as calcium or sodium chloride placed in the water; and (3) observations of the behavior of slurries of suspended matter placed in the water.   In the use of dyes and chemicals it has been customary to base the time on the center of gravity of the area under the curve of time vs. concentration at

[1] L. V. Carpenter and H. W. Speiden, *ibid.*, March, 1935, p. 200.

the effluent. The observation of the behavior of slurries by a beam of light directed into the basin at night has been found effective.

The efficiency of displacement is the ratio of the flowing-through period to the period of detention, multiplied by 100. Efficiencies of basins now in use vary roughly between 5 and 50, with some as high as 90.[1] Periods of detention found in existing basins vary from a portion of an hour to many days but, since the greater removal occurs during the first few hours, basins are usually designed for a period to be counted in hours rather than in days. If the basin is to be well designed, a test should be made to determine the proper period of detention. A long period, equivalent to a large-capacity basin, is insufficient alone to assure effective performance. Effectiveness and economy may be better attained in a well-designed small basin than in a large basin with a long period of detention. Many detention periods in practice range up to 6 to 8 ft, with shorter periods where coagulation is used. The shortest detention periods used, between 1.5 and 3 hr, are to be found in mechanically cleaned basins.

26-6. Capacity and Number of Basins. The net capacity of all sedimentation basins in a plant should be the product of the detention period and the nominal rate of flow on which the plant is designed. In large plants an excess capacity may be provided to allow for unexpected situations, but in small plants allowance of extra capacity is not always necessary, as shutdowns of the basins can be timed for conditions when the quality of the raw water is such as to permit a shorter period of sedimentation.

It is desirable to design a plant to permit the use of different periods of detention in operation to conform to variations in the quality of the raw water. This can be done by providing a number of units whose combined capacities are equal to the total required for the capacity of the plant. Where two or more basins are provided, it may be desirable to make them of different capacities so that a greater variety of periods of detention may be used. Flexibility in operation can be obtained by connecting the basins in such a manner that any basin can be operated alone or in any combination with the other basins, in parallel or in series. The number of units to be built is limited by the cost and the desired permissible fluctuations in detention periods. Under conditions in which treatment cannot be interrupted there should not be less than two units, preferably three, to permit the shutdown of one basin.

26-7. Circular Settling Basins. Circular plain-sedimentation basins are less commonly used than rectangular basins in water treatment because of economical considerations. However, in small plants, where continuous removal of settled sludge by revolving scrapers is desired, and where steel can be used economically, circular tanks may be used, as their

[1] See also J. F. Walker, *J.A.W.W.A.*, September, 1946, p. 1078.

hydraulic characteristics, when properly designed, may be highly satis-factory.[1]   In general, circular horizontal-flow tanks are designed to admit the influent at the center of the tank and to withdraw the effluent in a peripheral trough at the outer edge of the tank, or at some predetermined distance between the center and the outer edge.   This trough is called a *launder*.   Upward-flow vertical basins are used, as explained in Sec. 27-39.

Some considerations essential to successful design include (1) the creation of a uniform velocity in the vertical riser in the center of the tank; (2) a satisfactory diffuser to distribute the water evenly without undue loss of head; (3) the absence of turbulence within the tank; (4) the provision of a zone of velocity less than 10 fpm, and preferably below 1 fpm, at the bottom of the tank adjacent to the sludge blanket; and (5) protection from wind disturbance.

26-8. Velocity of Flow.   The nominal velocity of flow in a plain-sedimentation basin is equal to the volumetric rate of flow divided by the vertical cross-sectional area of the basin.   In general, the slower the velocity the more efficient the removal of settling solids, other things being equal.   No sedimentation basin should provide a velocity greater than 1 fpm, and many basins are in existence with velocities of 0.1 to 0.01 fpm.

26-9. Surface Area.   Practice has shown that the ratio of surface area to volume of tank is a factor to be considered.   It is recommended that the load per square foot of surface area of a settling basin shall be between 300 and 4,000 gal per day for granular solids, 800 to 2,000 gal per day for amorphous slow-settling solids, and 1,000 to 1,200 gal per day for floccu-lent material.   Too great a surface area in relation to tank volume is conducive to the creation of currents by the wind.

26-10. Relation of Length to Width.   A long narrow basin is preferable, from the viewpoint of settling efficiency, to one so wide that cross currents will develop.   If the unit costs of the various parts of the basin are known the dimensions to give the least cost can be determined by the calculus. Such dimensions will possibly not give the most effective sedimentation, however.   The designer should therefore select those dimensions that will give satisfactory settling efficiency and follow the economical dimen-sions as closely as possible.   The ideal length is one that will give the proper flowing-through period, with a channel width not to exceed 40 ft and not less than one-fourth of the length.   Where conditions of economy require a large over-all width of basin, a larger ratio of length to width of flowing-through channel can be obtained by the use of round-the-end baffles, as indicated in Fig. 26-1.   In order to minimize eddy currents the distance between the end of the baffle and the wall of the basin should equal or exceed the width of the flowing-through channel.

[1] See also G. E. Hubbell, *ibid.*, Vol. 30, p. 335, 1938.

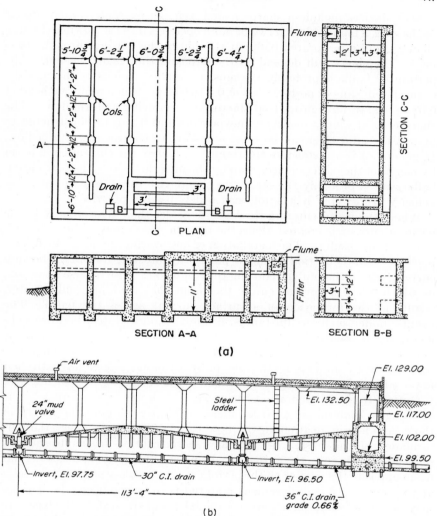

FIG. 26-1. Settling and coagulating basins. (a) Water-works settling basin at Ironwood, Mich. (*From Eng. News, Vol. 70, p. 1193.*) (b) Typical covered coagulation basin for hand cleaning.

26-11. Inlet and Outlet Devices and Baffles.

The importance of inlet and outlet devices and of baffles in the successful operation of a sedimentation basin cannot be overemphasized. Through the correct use of such devices a small basin may perform more effectively than a large basin. The inlet and outlet devices in rectangular basins with horizontal flow should be arranged to distribute and collect incoming and outgoing water as uniformly as possible across the vertical cross section of the flowing-through channel.

Such devices include a sharp-crested weir, an overflow trough similar to the weir, a manifold with two or more openings into the flowing-through channel, and a perforated baffle at the end of the flowing-through channel.[1] The choice will depend on the cost and the results desired. The perforated baffle is probably the most effective. Velocities through the diffuser-wall slots or perforations of 0.4 to 0.8 fps, which require a head of 0.01 to 0.02 ft, have proved satisfactory in producing uniform flow. The sharp-crested weir is relatively inexpensive and it can be constructed to permit the adjustment of its crest elevation to control the rate of flow. In general, it is less effective to attempt to control the currents in a basin by means of the outlet devices than by the inlet devices. The perforated-baffle wall is probably the most effective device for stilling of entrance-velocity energy[2] but it has not been widely used in practice.

Where the water entering the basin is colder than that already in the basin, a current is created along the bottom which may reduce the efficiency of the results. The installation of low overflow baffles, which form pockets for the collection of sludge, partially protecting it from the bottom current, may be helpful in reducing the condition. The reverse situation, in which a warm current enters the basin that contains colder water, results in the formation of a surface current across the basin. The results, under such circumstances, are not so undesirable, because sedimentation is occurring in the equivalent of a very shallow basin and the bottom sludge is undisturbed. Surface currents can be broken up to some extent by submerging the inlet or by use of hanging baffles with their lower edges submerged 12 to 18 in. below the surface.

Outlets from sedimentation basins may be designed as overflow weirs or troughs, sometimes called launders. The location and the length of these launders in relation to the flow through the basin affect the performance of the basin. In primary sedimentation basins to remove settleable solids only, the outlet may be placed at the end of a rectangular basin opposite the inlet or on the periphery of a circular tank with the inlet at the center. Where flocculent material is to be removed, the launder may be placed somewhere between the inlet and the wall of the basin, to avoid the effect of "density currents" that tend to carry settled solids to the extreme end of sedimentation basins.

To minimize surges in a sedimentation basin the rate of flow per foot of the outlet weir should not exceed 200,000 gal per day and should preferably be less than one-fourth of this. In some cases it may be desirable to make an appreciable portion, if not the full length of the weir, vertically adjustable in order to place better control of the basin in the hands of the operator.

Baffles are sometimes used in sedimentation basins in the expectation

[1] See also A. B. Morrell, *J.A.W.W.A.*, 1932, p. 1442.
[2] See also J. D. Walker, *ibid.*, September, 1946, p. 1078.

that velocity distribution will be improved and dead spaces avoided. Improvement may be expected[1] only where the design is based on knowledge derived from test and experience. Guesswork may make conditions worse. In double-flow tanks the direction of flow is horizontal either with an influent at each end and an effluent in the middle or an effluent at each end and the influent in the middle. Economical and successful double-flow tanks are in operation and in some cases the effectiveness of existing sedimentation tanks might be improved by conversion to double flow.

26-12. Control of Water Level. The elevation of the surface of water in a basin in usually fixed by the elevation of the outlet weir and the depth of water permitted over it. To prevent overflow some control device must be placed on the inlet such as those shown in Fig. 18-18.

26-13. Covers. It is best, where possible, to leave plain-sedimentation basins uncovered, as the conditions of operation can be better observed. The principal purposes of covers may be to avoid difficulties from wind and ice, to prevent contamination of the water, to avoid the growth of organisms, and to improve the appearance of the plant. Where covers are used, care must be taken to provide access to the basin, to permit the ingress and egress of air to compensate for fluctuations of the volume of water in the basin, to avoid fungus growths, and to avoid egg laying by flying insects.

26-14. Sludge Storage. The allowance made for the storage of sludge depends on the period between cleanings and the amount of material removed from the water. Only test and experience can dictate the proper allowance. Since the proper depth of a sedimentation basin is indeterminate, designers decide on a convenient depth and assume that a portion of the capacity of the basin will be required for sludge storage.

The quantity of sludge to be handled may be roughly approximated from the expression

$$Q = \frac{SP}{240P_1} \qquad (26\text{-}2)$$

where Q = tons of wet sludge to be handled per million gallons of water treated

S = suspended matter in raw water, ppm

P = percentage of suspended solids removed by plain sedimentation

P_1 = percentage of solids in the sludge

Where continuous mechanical removal of the sludge is provided no sludge-storage space is required.

26-15. Draining and Cleaning. The cleaning of the basin may be provided for by making the bottom a series of steep-sided hoppers or by

---

[1] See also: E. S. Hopkins, *Eng. News-Record*, Apr. 3, 1947, p. 80; Walker, *loc. cit.*

sloping the bottom slightly to a gutter or to an outlet through the wall. Under such conditions the bottom of the basin should slope not less than 2:100. The outlet should be controlled by a sluice gate or valve, as shown in Fig. 26-2; or the outlets may be placed in the bottom of the basin and protected by mud valves. Control is provided by a single valve placed beyond the walls of the settling basin. It is undesirable to place an underdrain beneath the floor or walls of a settling basin when there is to be water under pressure in the drain because of the difficulty of cleaning the drain or making repairs. Leaks in such a drain may undermine the floor or the wall of the basin.

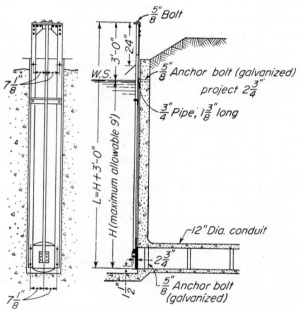

Fig. 26-2. Sluice-gate assembly for heads of 6 to 9 ft.

If a drainage valve is opened when the basin contains a quantity of water, the force of the current will remove some of the settled solids. The remainder must be removed by hand or by machine or by hydraulic flushing. It is desirable to provide water pipes for this purpose which will furnish a quantity of water under pressure to a flushing hose and nozzle. Basins have been cleaned by floating dredges without interrupting service or increasing turbidity.[1]

26-16. Continuous Sludge Removal. In some sedimentation plants constructed for chemical coagulation or for softening plants, provision has been made for the continuous removal of sludge, obviating the need for allowing sludge-storage space in the design of the basin. Continuous

[1] See *Eng. News-Record*, Sept. 5, 1946, p. 102.

cleaning is accomplished by a series of scrapers or squeegees, which are dragged along or around on the bottom of the settling basin, sweeping the deposited material to one end, or to the center, of the basin. The linear velocity of the squeegees does not exceed about 15 fpm. The slow movement does not create undesirable currents and requires but little power for operation. In one instance 2.8 hp was required to drive a 200-ft-diameter cleaner.

In some installations, experience has indicated that it is more economical to install sedimentation basins with continuous removal of sludge because of the saving in sludge-storage capacity, the increased efficiency of the results obtained, and the avoidance of sludge decomposition. The continuous return, to the inlet of the sedimentation basin, of a portion of the deposited sludge has been found, under proper conditions, to increase the efficiency of the process.

CHAPTER 27

SEDIMENTATION WITH COAGULATION

27-1. The Application of Chemicals as Coagulants. It has been found that by the addition of certain chemicals to water an insoluble, gelatinous, flocculent precipitate will be formed which, in its formation and descent through the water, will adsorb and entrain suspended and colloidal matter, will hasten its sedimentation, and will remove particles more completely and rapidly than by plain sedimentation. The addition of a coagulant may serve also to aid in the removal of color, odor, and taste from water. The chemicals ordinarily used as coagulants, when properly applied, are harmless to the consumer of the water.

In practice the method consists of mixing the coagulating chemicals with the water in sufficient strength to produce the required precipitate and then allowing the water to stand quietly in, or to flow slowly either horizontally or vertically upward through, a sedimentation basin in which the coagulant settles to the bottom.

The period of detention to be used can be determined best by test made under operating conditions. The quality of the water, the kind of coagulant, and the physical conditions in the coagulating basin all affect the necessary period of detention. The desirable period of detention at any plant will vary with the quality of the water, the temperature, and other local conditions. Normal variations at different plants are found between 1 and 12 hr. Wider variations have been recorded. It is desirable, therefore, to design coagulating basins so that the period of detention may be varied.

Sedimentation with coagulation is not commonly used as a complete method of treatment, but it is used rather as a preliminary step in the preparation of water for filtration. Some results of coagulation are shown in Table 26-1.

27-2. Control of Coagulation. The proper operation of the coagulating basin can be determined only through experience in the laboratory and the field with the water to be treated. The chemical control of coagulation is made difficult owing to the extremely dilute solutions in which reactions must take place. Among the characteristics of the water and the conditions of operation that affect the control of coagulation are color, turbidity, temperature, alkalinity, pH, hardness, and free carbon dioxide. It is desirable that experience with these factors be plotted against the coagulant dose and treatment results, so that repetition of the conditions of treatment may permit the finding of equal or better results in operation.

Temperature is an important factor in the control of coagulation. In general, floc forms more quickly at moderate temperatures and larger amounts of coagulant are required in summer than in winter. This apparent anomaly may possibly be explained by the fact that coagulation is a manifestation of electrochemical phenomena and that the seasonal adjustments of pH are more effective than those of temperature in affecting it. At temperatures below 40°F difficulty may be encountered in securing good floc formation.[1]

Since floc formation is closely related to hydrogen-ion concentration and to anion and cation relationships,[2] the control of pH is an important factor in the control of coagulation. The point of optimum coagulation may be as low as pH 3.8 for highly colored soft swamp waters, or it may be greater than 8.0 with other waters. The optimum pH for the coagulation of most waters is slightly below 7.0. The optimum for various coagulants will usually be found to lie within the pH ranges shown in Table 27-1. The control of pH by the addition of sulphuric acid has been successful in the few plants that have used it, the addition of alkali being equally successful and more extensively practiced. The use of a recording potentiometer may be necessary in turbid waters that show rapid changes in pH because colorimetric determinations are too slow.

In addition to the control of coagulation through observations of the various factors mentioned, it is desirable that periodic observations be made in the laboratory. These should determine (1) the first appearance of floc, (2) the appearance of the floc after 5 min and after 30 min, and (3) the appearance of the supernatant liquor and the settleability of the floc at the end of the time corresponding to the detention period in the settling basin. The condition of the floc may be observed at important points in its development with the aid of a submerged light shining through the water against a black cross painted on a white background, or similar device. A floc slightly larger than a pinhead is the most desirable size. Larger particles settle slowly, owing to the large surface in contact with the water, and they are fragile, tending to break into particles so small as to possess some colloidal characteristics.

It has been found advantageous in some plants to apply the coagulant at two or more points in the treatment process. This is known as double, or fractional, coagulation. It has not been extensively practiced.

---

[1] The theory of floc formation is presented by T. R. Camp, *Proc. Am. Soc. Civil Engrs.*, September, 1953, p. 283-1.

[2] See also W. F. Langelier and H. F. Ludwig, *J.A.W.W.A.*, February, 1949, p. 163.

The recirculation of precipitated material into the water entering the coagulation basin has proved advantageous in some plants in which the material serves as a catalyst or synergist and supplies nuclei for floc formation and precipitation. The procedure is particularly effective in upward-flow basins in which the water passes through a "blanket" of precipitated material.

27-3. Coagulants.[1] A few of the many substances used in the coagulation of water are listed in Table 27-1. Among the more commonly used coagulants are aluminum sulphate, ferrous sulphate together with calcium hydroxide, and sodium aluminate. Other chemicals sometimes used include:

Activated alum, a proprietary, acid-treated, insoluble silicate containing 18.74 per cent Al_2O_3, and less water of crystallization than filter alum. It forms a tough floc and aids in the coagulation of waters low in turbidity.

Ammonia alum $[(Al_2(SO_4)_3(NH_4)_2 \cdot 24H_2O)]$ is used in "alum pots" as a coagulant in pressure filters since its solubility is about one-twentieth of filter alum. It contains 3 to 7 per cent of ammonia by weight.

Black alum is filter alum containing 2 to 5 per cent of activated carbon. It is used in combined coagulation and taste and odor removal.

Chlorinated copperas is a mixture of ferric chloride and ferric sulphate. It may be more effective in coagulation than copperas. It is especially useful in coagulation in conjunction with prechlorination. Among the advantages claimed for its use are a tough floc, good settling with little carry-over to the filters, wide range for optimum pH between 6 to 8 or 9, a compact floc of hydrated ferric oxide which does not dissolve in water at values of pH above 3.5, and is particularly effective in color removal compared with ferric and ferrous hydroxides with colloids having an isoelectric point below 7.0.[2] It has not been used widely in practice.

Clay, bentonite, fuller's earth, and other adsorptive clays assist in coagulation of relatively clear waters, particularly when combined with other coagulants, such as alum. Their adsorptive properties are sometimes effective in taste and odor removal.

Sodium aluminate ($NaAlO_2$) may be used at a concentration of about 0.2 grain per gal, with alum in coagulation of cold water. It is used also in the lime-soda water-softening process to coagulate calcium carbonate and magnesium hydroxide.

Sulphuric acid has many uses, such as pH adjustment, regeneration of base-exchange materials, and in coagulation.

Other chemicals that have been used include calcium chloride, barium hydroxide, and sodium sulphate.

[1] See also C. R. Cox, Water Supply Control, *New York State Dept. Health, Bull.* **22**, p. 48, 1943.

[2] See also L. L. Hedgepeth, *Ind. Eng. Chem.*, September, 1931, p. 534.

TABLE 27-1. Some Chemicals Used in Water Treatment[a]

Substance (1)	Weight, lb per cu ft (2)	Troublesome characteristics (3)	Approximate storage space, cu ft per ton, and how shipped (4)	Storage-container materials (5)	Solution strength, % and properties (6)	Materials suitable for handling (7)	pH range for best coagulation (8)	Normal dose, grains per gal (9)
Aluminum sulphate $(Al_2(SO_4)_3.18H_2O)$, alum	39	Dusty	33. In 200-lb bags, 400-lb bbl, and in bulk	Concrete, steel, or wood	0.25–5.0,[b] acid and corrosive	Lead, rubber, acid-resistant bronze, cast iron	5.5 – 8.0[d]	0.3–0.5
Ferrous sulphate $(FeSO_4.7H_2O)$, copperas	46	Cakes at temp above 20° in moist air, stains	31. In 200-lb bags, 400-lb bbl, and in bulk. 100% $FeSO_4.7H_2O$	Concrete, steel, or wood	0.25–6.0,[b] acid and corrosive	Rubber, lead, Dur-iron, and 18-8 stainless steel	8.5–11.0	0.3–3.0
Calcium oxide[c] (CaO), quicklime	65	Dusty, slakes on standing in air	32. Wood barrels, metal drums, bulk	Concrete, steel, or wood	Up to 25,[b] alkaline and incrustant	Rubber, iron, cement		
Calcium hydroxide $(Ca(OH)_2)$, hydrated lime	50	Dusty	48. In bags or bulk	Concrete, steel, or wood	Up to 20,[b] alkaline and incrustant	Rubber, iron, cement		
Sodium aluminate $(Na_2Al_2O_4)$	58	Hygroscopic	20 sq ft per ton in drums[e]	Store in shipping containers	0.25–6.0,[b] alkaline	Rubber, iron	....	0.2–2.0
Sodium carbonate (Na_2CO_3), soda ash.....	..	Dusty	33. Same as alum	Same as alum	Up to 6.0,[b] alkaline	Rubber, iron		
Ferric chloride[i] $(FeCl_3)$.....	63	Acid, corrosive staining liquid	61. See notes[f] and[i]	Rubber-lined concrete, steel, or wood	3–4, acid and corrosive	Acidproof materials	5.0–11.0[g]	0.5–3.0
Ferric sulphate $(Fe_2(SO_4)_3$,[h] Ferrisul	70	Stains	28. Same as alum	Same as alum	1–6.5, acid and corrosive	Rubber-lined, Dur-iron, and 18-8 stainless steel	5.0–11.0[g]	0.5–3.0
Sodium silicate $(Na_2SiO_3.Na_2O + SiO_2)$	..	Alkaline and sticky	50 sq ft per ton in drums	Store in shipping containers	Up to 6	Rubber and iron		

[a] See also *Water & Sewage Works*, May, 1949, p. 184.
[b] Can be fed dry also.
[c] CaO expands on prolonged storage and may burst its containers.
[d] Used also in softening plants at pH above 10.0.
[e] Solid phase in steel drums; 100-lb bags. Liquid phase 32% $Na_2Al_2O_4$ + 10% NaOH in steel drums.
[f] Crystals, 60% in 55-gal, hardwood barrels; anhydrous, 100-lb steel drums; liquid, 42%, 12-gal carboys, rubber-lined tank cars.
[g] J. E. Kerslake and others, *J.A.W.W.A.* October, 1946, p. 1161, give range from 4.0 to 11.0.
[h] In anhydrous form, 90% $Fe(SO_4)$; in crystalline form, 60% $(FeSO_4)$.
[i] Shipped in 39 to 45 per cent solutions in glass carboys, rubber-lined drums, and tank cars.

It has been found that the addition of silica[1] in the form of a colloidal hydrous silicon dioxide, possessing strong negative charge, materially shortens the time required to produce coagulation with aluminum or ferrous sulphate.[2] It was found to be of little value when used with ferric salts. A more effective form of silica, known as activated silica,[2] is a result of reaction between sodium silicate and sulphuric acid. The silica is an aid to coagulation but it is not a coagulant.[3] Where water softening is combined with coagulation the use of activated silica will greatly expedite coagulation with alum. The amount of silica (SiO_2) added should be approximately 40 per cent of the aluminum sulphate used. The use of silica is not universally approved as small amounts of silica in water may damage boilers.[4]

The approximate chemical compositions and costs of some coagulants are shown in Table 27-2.

TABLE 27-2. Approximate Composition and Cost of Coagulating Chemicals

Chemical constituent	Coagulating chemical						
	Potash alum	Sulphate of aluminum	Sulphate of iron	Ammonia alum	Chemical	Relative cost per lb	Lb per cu ft*
(1)	(2)	(3)	(4)	(5)	(6)	(7)	(8)
Matter insoluble in water..........	.....	0.30	0.50	....	Alum	$1.10	60.0
Alumina (Al_2O_3).................	10.77	17.00	.....	11.0	Ferrous sulphate	0.70	66.0
Iron (Fe_2O_3 and FeO)............	.....	0.25	57.50	....	Lime†	0.35	36.0†
Potash (K_2O).....................	9.93	.....	.....	....	Soda ash	1.00	42.0
Sulphur trioxide (SO_3)...........	33.76	38.70	28.80	26.0	Sodium aluminate	2.70	
Ammonium sulphate (($NH_4)_2SO_4$)*.	.....	.....	.....	14.0	Ferric chloride	2.05	
Aluminum sulphate ($Al_2(SO_4)_3$)....	.....	.....	.....	37.0	Bleaching clay	0.75	
Water........................	45.54	43.75	13.20	0.5	Activated carbon	.....	13.5
					Activated alum	.....	58.0

* See Specifications, *J.A.W.W.A.*, November, 1950, p. 1087.
† $Ca(OH)_2$.

27-4. Aluminum Sulphate. Aluminum sulphate $[(Al_2(SO_4)_3 \cdot 18H_2O)]$, commonly called alum, is probably the most widely used chemical for the coagulation of water because of its excellent floc formation, its relative economy, its stability, and its ease in handling.[5] It has been manufactured in some plants from bauxite.[6] Calcium sulphate is formed when alum reacts with the natural alkalinity of water, as shown in reactions in

[1] See also: H. R. Hay, *J.A.W.W.A.*, June, 1944, p. 626; *Water & Sewage Works*, December, 1946, p. 479.

[2] See also H. J. Wheaton and J. G. Walker, *Chem. Inds.*, 1950, pp. 710, 802.

[3] See also H. R. Hay, *Water & Sewage Works*, May, 1953, p. R-107.

[4] See also R. V. Andrews, *J.A.W.W.A.*, January, 1954, p. 82.

[5] See also J. E. Kerslake and others, *ibid.*, October, 1946, p. 1161.

[6] See Specifications for Bauxite, *ibid.*, July, 1950, p. 707.

Sec. 27-5, thus increasing the sulphate hardness to a slight extent. The increase of free carbon dioxide may be objectionable because of its corrosive nature unless removed by subsequent decarbonation. The presence of appreciable amounts of sodium and potassium compounds may cause the alum floc to appear in fine particles which are almost colloidal and are ineffective in coagulation, will not settle, will pass through a sand filter. The difficulty can sometimes be remedied by increasing the dose of alum.

Commercial alum is a dirty gray or yellowish crystalline solid, available in lump, rice, granular, or powdered form, containing about 17 per cent $Al_2(SO_4)_3$. It is an acid salt, corrosive to most metals and to some concretes. Its solubility is 86.9 parts in 100 parts of water at 0°C. Alkalinity is required when it is applied to water.

27-5. Coagulation with Alum. In order that aluminum sulphate may react to form a precipitate, it is necessary that the water into which the alum is placed shall contain some alkalinity, usually in the form of calcium carbonate. The hypothetical reactions that occur are

1. Alum and natural alkalinity

$$Al_2(SO_4)_3 \cdot 18H_2O + 3CaCO_3 \cdot H_2CO_3 = Al_2(OH)_6 + 3CaSO_4 + 6CO_2 + 18H_2O \quad (27\text{-}1)$$

2. Alum and soda ash[1]

$$Al_2(SO_4)_3 \cdot 18H_2O + 3Na_2CO_3 + 3H_2O = Al_2(OH)_6 + 3Na_2SO_4 + 3CO_2 + 18H_2O \quad (27\text{-}2)$$

3. Alum and lime

$$Al_2(SO_4)_3 \cdot 18H_2O + 3Ca(OH)_2 = Al_2(OH)_6 + 3CaSO_4 + 18H_2O \quad (27\text{-}3)$$

That which actually happens is much more complicated than the foregoing reactions would indicate. The amount of alum necessary to give perfect coagulation cannot be foretold by chemical analysis or other hypothesis. Theoretically 1 grain per gal commercial alum ($Al_2(SO_4)_3 \cdot 18H_2O$) requires 7.7 ppm of alkalinity as $CaCO_3$; practically the amount required may vary between 4 ppm for highly colored waters up to 6 to 7 ppm. More than the theoretical amount is used because part of the aluminum ions appear to combine directly with impurities in the water.

27-6. Practical Considerations in the Use of Alum. The absence of sufficient natural alkalinity to complete reaction (27-1) is unusual. In general, 8 to 10 ppm of alkalinity as calcium carbonate will react with 1 grain per gal of alum, forming aluminum hydroxide, although it is well known that none of these reactions goes to completion, for most of them are reversible, each depending for its equilibrium upon all the others. Where there is less than 20 ppm of natural alkalinity as $CaCO_3$ in the water, about 0.35 grain of lime or 0.5 grain of soda ash should be added

[1] See Specifications for Soda Ash, *J.A.W.W.A.*, February, 1952, p. 165.

per grain of alum.   The reactions are shown in Eqs. (27-2) and (27-3). Where sodium carbonate or lime is added to increase the alkalinity of the water, the chemical should be thoroughly mixed with the raw water for a short time before alum is added.   If it is added too long before the coagulant, some softening action may occur, necessitating the application of more chemicals.   Doses used in practice vary between 0.3 and 2.0 grains per gal, depending on many factors the understanding of which requires a broad knowledge of the reactions involved.

27-7. Difficulties with Alum.   Difficulties with alum mentioned in Secs. 27-4 to 27-6 include a slight increase in sulphate hardness, an increase in carbon dioxide, and the formation of a colloidal precipitate in the presence of sodium or potassium.   This last difficulty may be avoided by the use, in cold waters, of about 0.2 grain sodium aluminate per gallon.   If it becomes necessary to add alkalinity to improve coagulation, there is danger of fixation of color of the water if the added alkali is too strong.[1]   The reaction is seldom fully completed, and high concentrations of colloidal matter sometimes hinder the reaction, with a result that residual alum remains in the water that goes to the filters.   It is difficult to adjust the coagulation through pH control, because the optimum range of pH values is small and the application of alum depresses the pH.   Where the optimum pH is low, 4.4 to 5.0 as in some soft colored waters, it may be economical to depress the pH by the use of sulphuric acid, resulting in a smaller amount of alum being required.   If secondary or double coagulation follows, sodium aluminate may be added, and also lime, to increase the pH to about 6.5 to improve the formation of aluminum hydroxide floc when alum is added.

27-8. Residual Aluminum Compounds.   Water coagulated with alum contains aluminum compounds in solution.   The exact nature of these compounds is so complex that it is the practice to report them as aluminum or aluminum oxide (Al_2O_3) by determining the concentration of aluminum ion (Al^{3+}) and converting to equivalent alumina by multiplying by 3.77.   Residual alum cannot be reported in this manner, as it is incorrect to assume that the residual aluminum compound is aluminum sulphate.   Since aluminum hydroxide is soluble in water to the extent of 0.3 to 0.5 ppm, some residual alumina is to be expected, but the amount should not exceed about 0.3 ppm.   Colorimetric tests, using either the dye alizarin red or logwood, are satisfactory for routine operation control.[2]

27-9. Coagulation with Iron Salts.   Iron salts are said to produce a faster forming, denser, quicker settling, and less easily broken up floc than alum, particularly at low temperatures.   The effectiveness of iron salts at wide pH values makes them useful in the removal of manganese at values of pH above 9.0 and in the avoidance of floc solution when lime

[1] See also *Water and Water Eng.*, Mar. 31, 1934, p. 177.
[2] See also C. R. Cox, *Water Works Eng.*, Feb. 17, 1937, p. 217.

is added for carbonate balance, and in the coagulation of colored waters at pH values below 5.0.

27-10. Coagulation with Ferrous Sulphate.[1] Ferrous sulphate has an advantage over alum in that it may be less expensive and the floc is heavier and sinks more rapidly. An outstanding disadvantage is the need for using lime with it. More complete chemical control is required, and there are greater dangers from afterprecipitation in the distribution system due to the reaction between surplus lime and bicarbonate alkalinity. Ferrous sulphate is unsuitable for the treatment of soft colored waters because they are best coagulated at a pH below 7.0.[2] The color appears to become set by the addition of alkali to colored waters; hence the use of ferrous sulphate is limited to those waters in which alkalinity will not interfere with color removal. It is best suited to use in turbid waters of high natural alkalinity. There is usually insufficient alkalinity in natural waters to react with ferrous sulphate, so that lime must usually be added to produce a floc and in order to avoid soluble compounds of iron remaining in the treated water.

27-11. Reactions with Ferrous Sulphate. The chemical reactions that occur when ferrous sulphate and lime are used in coagulation depend, in part, on the order in which the chemicals are added to the water.

When iron is added first, the reactions are

$$FeSO_4 \cdot 7H_2O + CaCO_3 \cdot H_2CO_3 = FeCO_3 \cdot H_2CO_3 + CaSO_4 + 7H_2O \quad (27\text{-}4)$$
$$FeCO_3 \cdot H_2CO_3 + 2Ca(OH)_2 = Fe(OH)_2 + 2CaCO_3 + 2H_2O \quad (27\text{-}5)$$
$$4Fe(OH)_2 + 2H_2O + O_2 = 4Fe(OH)_3 \quad (27\text{-}6)$$

When lime is added first the reactions are

$$FeSO_4 + Ca(OH)_2 = Fe(OH)_2 + CaSO_4 \quad (27\text{-}7)$$
$$4Fe(OH)_2 + 2H_2O + O_2 = 4Fe(OH)_3 \quad (27\text{-}8)$$

The ferrous hydroxide $Fe(OH)_2$ forms a desirable, heavy, gelatinous precipitate. It is, however, oxidized according to Eq. (27-6) to ferric hydroxide $Fe(OH)_3$ likewise a satisfactory gelatinous precipitate.

27-12. Amount of Iron and Lime Required. As with other coagulants, the amount of ferrous sulphate required is most commonly determined by experience with the water being treated. The amount of lime required is affected by the amount of ferrous sulphate added and the amount of carbon dioxide present, which must be neutralized. A slight excess of lime, 1 to 5 ppm, should be added, if sufficient alkalinity is present, to enhance the precipitation of ferric hydroxide through the formation of calcium carbonate crystals about the ferric hydroxide. Too great an excess of lime should be avoided in order to prevent afterprecipitation

---

[1] See Standard Specifications, *J.A.W.W.A.*, October, 1950, p. 975.

[2] See also E. Bartow and others, *Proc. Am. Soc. Civil Engrs.*, December, 1933, p. 1529.

effects. The amount of ferrous sulphate to be added is dependent, mainly, on the turbidity, the natural alkalinity, and the free carbon dioxide in the raw water.

27-13. Sodium Aluminate. Sodium aluminate ($NaAlO_2$) is an alkaline compound, a typical analysis of the best grade being Al_2O_3, 55 per cent; combined Na_2O_3, 34 per cent; Na_2CO_3, 4.5 per cent; $Na(OH)$ (excess), 6.3 per cent. The use of sodium aluminate is advantageous under certain conditions because there is no need for any additional alkali. There is an immediate precipitation of all the aluminum hydroxide because of the rapidity of the reaction and the presence of alkali. It does not increase the noncarbonate hardness and can be mixed with lime and soda ash solution, thus making it unnecessary to provide additional equipment for its application. Among other advantages claimed for it may be included the elimination of corrosive qualities of the water, a wide range of pH, quick flocculation, and no need for the addition of alkali. Its cost has been an important factor in preventing its wider adoption in practice.[1]

27-14. Ferric Coagulation. Ferric chloride ($FeCl_3$), ferric sulphate ($Fe_2(SO_4)_3$), and a mixture of the two, known as chlorinated copperas, are coagulants whose greatest field of usefulness is being found, probably, in sewage treatment.[2] Among the advantages claimed for ferric coagulants may be included:[3] (1) Coagulation is effective over a wider range of pH than with alum. (2) The time required for floc formation, conditioning, and settling is, in many cases, considerably shorter than that required for alum. (3) Filter runs have been increased in several tests. (4) Manganese is successfully removed at pH values above 9.0. (5) Very little iron is carried through with the effluent. (6) Hydrogen sulphide is removed, and tastes and odors are reduced. (7) There is a decreased tendency toward the formation of mud balls compared with aluminum floc. (8) Under some conditions the ferric coagulants are more economical than aluminum hydroxide.[4]

27-15. Ferric Chloride.[2] When ferric chloride is added to water the following reaction occurs:

$$FeCl_3 + 3H_2O = Fe(OH)_3 + 3H^+ + 3Cl^- \qquad (27\text{-}9)$$

The ferric hydroxide is precipitated, forming a desirable coagulant which is heavier than aluminum hydroxide and requires a shorter detention period and less careful adjustment of pH. Acidities that are encountered with some soft highly colored waters make their coagulation with alum impossible, but they may be coagulated successfully with ferric compounds. Ferric chloride has been used with success also in waters con-

[1] See *Water and Water Eng.*, Mar. 31, 1934, p. 177.

[2] See also C. G. Hyde, *J.A.W.W.A.*, May, 1935, p. 631.

[3] See also A. P. Black, *ibid.*, 1934, p. 1713.

[4] See also *Water Works & Sewerage*, September, 1932, p. 301.

taining hydrogen sulphide because, in contrast to alum, ferric chloride is an oxidizing agent, whereas alum is a reducing agent. In treating sulphide waters, the ferric salt is reduced to the ferrous state, after which it behaves like ferrous sulphate in the lime and iron process. The successful use of pulverized limestone in connection with ferric chloride has been reported.[1]

Solutions of ferric chloride have a highly astringent action on wood, making it necessary to tighten wooden storage tanks frequently. The material is also corrosive to metals requiring storage and transportation in nonmetallic materials, such as ceramics, or certain of the newer ferrous metal alloys.[2] Materials recommended include rubber, glass, ceramics, and stainless steel.

Ferric chloride cannot be applied through dry-feed machines because of the hygroscopic characteristics of the compound. It must therefore be applied in aqueous solution in a strength between 2 per cent in small plants to 20 per cent or more in large well-equipped plants. The strength chosen depends on the rate of use and the precision with which dosing is to be controlled.

27-16. Chlorinated Copperas. Chlorinated copperas is a mixture of ferric chloride and ferric sulphate prepared by adding chlorine to a solution of ferrous sulphate in the ratio of 1 part chlorine to 7.8 parts copperas. The salt is highly corrosive and should be handled in the manner recommended for ferric chloride. It is claimed that the effectiveness of copperas is increased as a coagulant and the necessity for high alkalinity is eliminated. The coagulant may be prepared in the plant by dosing a solution of the copperas with chlorine. Among the advantages claimed for the use of chlorinated copperas as a coagulant are:[3] (1) It produces a desirable floc formation with tough particles of floc. (2) Floc formation usually settles well, with only a small residual going to the filters. (3) The coagulating effect has a wide range of optimum pH from 8 or 9 to 6. (4) A compact floc of hydrated ferric oxide, which does not dissolve in alkaline waters, is formed at all pH values above 3.5. (5) The coagulant is particularly effective in color removal compared with the relative ineffectiveness of ferric and ferrous hydroxides on colloids having an isoelectric point below 7.0.[4]

27-17. Handling Iron Coagulants. Both ferrous and ferric coagulants are difficult to handle, being corrosive, staining, and deliquescent. Sludge from settling basins and wash water will stain streams a typical brown iron color. Ferric chloride should be handled as indicated in Sec. 27-15.

[1] See also C. H. Spaulding, *J.A.W.W.A.*, November, 1951, p. 793.
[2] See also J. M. Potter, *Water Works & Sewerage*, January, 1935, p. **12**.
[3] See also L. C. Billions, *ibid.*, 1934, p. 73.
[4] See also Hedgepeth, *loc. cit.*

Ferric sulphate is not deliquescent and is less corrosive than ferric chloride and can therefore be stored and handled with greater ease. It does not dissolve readily, necessitating special equipment to apply it successfully. The water ratio of approximately 2 parts water to 1 part ferric sulphate should be carefully controlled because on going into solution considerable heat is generated, which assists solution when the volume of water is not too great. Storage solutions should not be made in strengths less than about 1 per cent to prevent rapid hydrolysis of the coagulant. Hydrolysis is practically instantaneous and will occur at pH of 5.0 to 6.0.

27-18. Coagulation with Clay. Coagulation with clay has been experimented with in a few water-purification plants, but it is rarely used in practice. The function of the clay is probably to provide colloidal nuclei for the adsorption of finely divided and colloidal matter in the water. Only special forms of clay are suitable for the purpose, and the cost of the process depends on the availability of suitable materials. Clay has been applied at various rates, reports varying between 0.1 and more than 7.0 grains per gal.[1]

Bentonite, which swells greatly on wetting, has the property of exchanging the alkali and the alkaline-earth ions[2] and it is possible that the difference in colloidal properties of various clays may be due to variations in composition resulting from such base exchange. It has been found by test that the coagulating effects of bentonite are not materially affected by the pH of the water and that with equivalent dosages bentonite flocs are uniformly more voluminous and more rapid in settling than alum flocs.

27-19. Electrolytic Coagulation.[3] Coagulation has been effected by passing water through a series of aluminum sheets spaced about $\frac{1}{8}$ in. apart. Opposite electrical charges on alternate plates discharge trivalent ions into the water, using a low-voltage high-amperage current. Advantages claimed for the process include fast floc formation, independence from pH, better clarification, and tough floc. Costs are variable within a wide range but are seldom prohibitive.

Experience with the process is not wide but tests made on the Potomac River[4] indicate a consumption of electric power of approximately 1,080 kwhr per million gal, making a total cost of $18 to $30, exclusive of a small overhead charge, of which $15.84 is for power and the balance for aluminum sheets at $480 per ton.

27-20. Lime. Lime is used in water treatment less for coagulation than for other reasons such as to increase pH and add alkalinity in coagulation,

---

[1] See also: Carl Leipold, *Water Works & Sewerage*, August, 1933, p. 304; R. I. Dodd, *J. Penna. Water Works Operators' Assoc.*, 1932, p. 65.

[2] See also H. L. Olin and H. W. Peterson, *J.A.W.W.A.*, April, 1937, p. 513.

[3] See also F. E. Stuart Jr., *Public Works*, April, 1947, p. 27.

[4] See also C. F. Bonilla, *Water and Sewage*, March, 1947, p. 21.

to reduce carbonate hardness in water softening, to reduce dissolved carbon dioxide, as a disinfectant, and to increase the length of filter runs in the presence of algae.[1]   Physical and chemical characteristics of lime are listed in Table 27-1.

Unslaked lime or calcium oxide (CaO) is a dry, white, amorphous powder, with a specific gravity of about 3.15 and a dangerous affinity for water which it can remove from the air or combine with in the liquid state with generation of heat.   The action is called *slaking* and it results in the formation of the relatively inert $Ca(OH)_2$, or slaked lime, with a specific gravity of about 2.08.   This material is likewise an amorphous white powder, relatively insoluble in water.

27-21. Costs and Weights of Chemicals.   In general, the relative costs of the different coagulants are as listed below, the least costly being stated first: (1) lime and iron, (2) alum alone, (3) alum and lime, (4) alum and soda ash, (5) sodium aluminate.   The approximate relative costs, per 100 lb, of the various chemicals are shown in Table 27-2.

27-22. Handling and Storing Chemicals.   Dry chemicals are delivered to water-purification plants in paper or burlap bags, in wooden barrels which are usually paper lined, and in bulk, sometimes in paper-lined box cars.   The chemicals should be stored in a dry place at a moderate and fairly uniform temperature.   These conditions are necessary to prevent deliquescence and caking.   Temperatures above 70°F are undesirable. It is frequently desirable to store chemicals on the floor or floors above the chemical preparation room so that gravity may be used in the preparation of the solutions or changing of the feeding devices.   Chemicals in bags are usually piled on the floor, two bags high.   Those in bulk should be stored in bins so designed and located that they can be withdrawn from the bottom of the bins and delivered where desired.   The bins should be relatively deep, exposing but a small amount of chemical to the atmosphere.   The bottom slope should not be less than 45 deg from the vertical.   Corrosive, volatile, or deliquescent chemicals, including such chemicals as ferric chloride, both liquid and solid, sodium aluminate, sodium hydroxide,[2] ammonium chloride, and liquid and gaseous materials, must ordinarily be stored in shipping containers.   Some materials suitable for handling chemicals are shown in Table 27-3.

Equipment provided for the handling of chemicals should include hand trucks, elevators, overhead tracks, cranes, mechanical conveyors, and pneumatic conveyors.   The last named are particularly useful in handling dry dusty chemicals such as hydrated lime.

27-23. Preparation of Solutions.   In the preparation of chemical solutions a satisfactory method, with chemicals that are easily dissolved, such as alum, ferrous sulphate, or soda ash, is to place the chemical in a metal

[1] See also J. R. Baylis, *Pure Water*, August, 1949, p. 113.
[2] See Specifications, *J.A.W.W.A.*, December, 1951, p. 1021.

TABLE 27-3. Materials Suitable for Handling Chemicals*

Material	Alum	Iron sulphate	Activated silica	Alkalies	Chlorine water	Fluorides
Steel or cast iron.................			S	S		
Brass and bronze..................	S		S			
Type 316, stainless steel...........	S	S	S	S		
Type FA20, stainless steel.........	S	S	S	S		
Lead............................	S	S	S			
Rubber.........................	S	S	S	S	S	S
Polythene......................	S	S	S	S		S
Uscolite........................	S	S	S	S	S	S
Polyvinyl chloride...............	S	S	S	S	S	S
Vinylidene chloride..............	S	S	S	S	S	S
Phenolic resins..................	S	S	S		S	S
Furan resins....................	S	S	S	S	S	S
Glass and glass-lined..............	S	S			S	
Porcelain and stoneware...........	S	S			S	
Wood..........................	S	S	S			

S means material is satisfactory for this chemical.

* From L. R. Honnaker and M. L. Monack, *J.A.W.W.A.*, May, 1953, p. 469.

basket, perforated-concrete box, or perforated wooden box and to spray warm water over the chemical. The water, containing the chemical in solution, is retained in solution tanks. The storage tanks may be large enough to hold sufficient solution for one operation shift, or large enough to dissolve the contents of one shipping container. The first size may be conducive to operation responsibility and efficiency, the latter to convenience and safety in operation. Another satisfactory method is to use the solution pot, a container into which the chemicals are placed and through which the water flows, as indicated in Fig. 27-1. Enough chemical is placed in the pot to maintain a saturated solution in the effluent pipe. The rate of flow of solution is proportional to the rate of flow through the main water pipe.

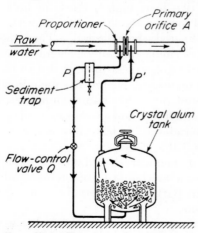

Fig. 27-1. Pot-type chemical feed. (*Courtesy of the Permutit Co.*)

Recommended strengths of solutions are given in Table 27-1. Solutions for direct application to the water to be treated should be more dilute than storage or "stock" solutions, in order to increase the precision of control of dose. However, too high a dilution is undesirable because of the possibility of premature chemical reactions and because of the bulk of solution to be handled.

27-24. Storing Chemical Solutions. Containers for the storage of chemical solutions are made of wood, steel, concrete, glass, rubber, brass, copper, lead, and metallic alloys. Materials to be used for storing various chemicals are listed in Tables 27-1 and 27-3. Wood and steel are not widely used because of their short life in the presence of most chemicals used in water treatment. They may be protected by acid-resistant paint, bituminous compounds, or lead lining, or the steel may be enameled.

Weak acid solutions may be stored in concrete, enameled iron, or lead-lined containers. Alkaline solutions may be stored in iron tanks. Lime should be slaked only in an iron tank as the heat generated will injure most other materials. Hypochlorite of lime should be stored in rubber-lined or vitreous tanks.

27-25. Stirring. The stirring of most solutions is essential to prevent settling and stratification. It can be accomplished by slowly moving paddles in the tank. There should be at least two paddles in the tank, revolving in opposite directions, to avoid the creation of a vortex. Air agitation may be used for chemicals that will not be affected thereby. Ferrous sulphate must be protected against oxidation even when paddles are used.

27-26. Chemical Feed. Economy and success in the use of chemicals require that the chemicals be accurately fed at a rate proportional to the rate of flow of water being treated. Chemical-feed devices in common use will meet these requirements whether dry-feed or solution-feed.

27-27. Solution-feed Devices. A simple form of fixed-rate, solution-feed device may consist of an orifice in the bottom of

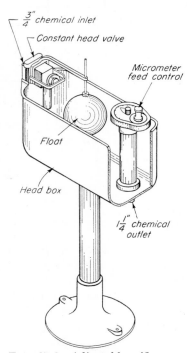

Fig. 27-2. Adjustable-orifice solution-feed tank. (*Courtesy of Infilco.*)

a small tank containing the solution, somewhat as shown in Fig. 27-2. Either, or both, the size of the orifice and the head on it are adjustable by the operator to give any rate of flow desired within the limits of the capacity of the device. A proportional-flow, chemical-solution feeder is shown diagrammatically in Fig. 27-3. The rate of flow of solution into the water can be read by means of the calibrated indicator.   The rate of flow is indicated by the position of the rotor which is held in suspension in the gradually tapered glass tube by means of the stream of water rising through the tube to enter the chemical-feed tank.   This water, being lighter than the chemical solution, displaces an equal volume of the solution without mixing with it.

Feed of a chemical solution as a fixed proportion of the rate of flow of water through the plant can be controlled by (1) a reciprocating, solution-feed pump synchronized with the main pumps; (2) devices depending on the principle of the venturi tube; (3) the head loss across an orifice; (4) a movable inlet pipe in a solution-feed tank into which the solution flows

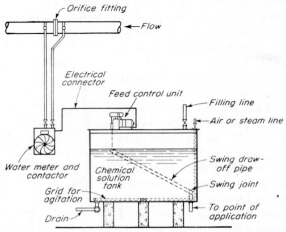

Fig. 27-3. Electrically controlled constant-feed or proportional-flow feed tank. (*Courtesy of the Permutit Co.*)

through an orifice at the surface, as shown in Fig. 27-3 (a flexible cable attached to the pipe is wound on a drum which is revolved at a rate proportional to the flow of water.   As the cable unwinds the orifice in the outlet pipe is lowered); (5) continuous pH analyzers that control solution flow electrically; (6) an electrically controlled swing drawoff pipe; and (7) other ingenious devices.

27-28. Pipes for Chemical Solutions.[1]   Solution-feed devices should be arranged, where possible, so that the solution falls into the raw water by gravity, thus avoiding the need for pipes or pumping.   Materials used for pipes are the same as those used for storage tanks and are listed in Table 27-1.   Lead, bronze, and brass are suitable for conveying alkalies, although brass is not commonly used.   Rubber, in the form of chemical hose, seems to stand up well under any solution, and where flexible hose is used stoppages may sometimes be cleared by bending and pressing the hose.

[1] See also L. R. Honnaker and M. L. Monack, *J.A.W.W.A.*, May, 1953, p. 469.

Pipe lines should be laid on a continuous slope, as steep as possible, leading without bends, to cleanouts. Air traps in the lines must be avoided. Where bends are necessary cleanouts should be provided so that a rod can be inserted in the pipe to or beyond the next cleanout. Straight runs may have cleanouts at about 20-ft intervals. Provision should be made for drainage at cleanouts. A wye, tee, or cross makes a satisfactory cleanout. Provision should also be made for flushing the pipe with water under pressure; duplicate pipes are sometimes desirable to permit cleaning of one while the other is in service.

27-29. Dry-feed Apparatus. Dry-feed devices are desirable because of simplicity, relatively small space required, neatness, and freedom from corrosion. All chemicals cannot be handled in dry-feed apparatus because of caking, clogging, and deliquescence. The desirable characteristics of a chemical that is to be fed dry are uniformity of size of grain, constancy in composition, permanency under prevailing conditions of temperature and pressure, and freedom from being hygroscopic or efflorescent. Aluminum sulphate is fairly fine and uniform and gives little trouble. The dry feeding of alum is especially advantageous, as it avoids the corrosiveness of alum solutions on the pipes that convey it. Hydrated lime is more troublesome than alum because of its tendency to bridge orifices and to take up moisture. Iron sulphate is sometimes quite troublesome, as the number of molecules of water of crystallization depends on the temperature, with the result that, in changing temperature, stored iron sulphate may become a solid mass in the bin.

Dry feeders fall into three classes: (1) those feeding less than 100 lb per hr; such machines consist of a chemical hopper, feeding mechanism, drive, and a dissolving chamber; (2) a feeder in which chemicals are stored in bins or in extension hoppers above the feeder which has the same essential parts as the first type; and (3) a high-rate feeder, all on one floor, usually provided with a bucket elevator and feeder combination. Volumetric control is more common than gravimetric control. In practically all machines arching of the chemical in the hoppers is prevented by vibratory or internal mechanical agitation. Common forms of chemical-feed machines are shown in Fig. 27-4.

Dry-feed machines are preferably driven by constant-speed electric motors. Although the amount of power required is small, water motors are undesirable because of fluctuations of water pressure. The rate of feeding can be adjusted by controlling the space between the hopper and the tray and by controlling the intensity of vibrations of the tray. Without auxiliary gravimetric control, volumetric feeders need close attention to assure accurate feeding. Dry-feed machines are available that are dependable and accurate. They may be designed to feed at a constant rate or proportioned to the rate of flow through the plant, and they may be equipped with rate-of-feed gages and be suspended on recording scales so that a check of their performance can be maintained.

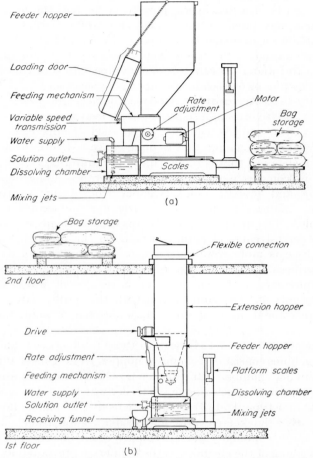

FIG. 27-4. Dry-chemical feeders. (*From Paul A. Coffman, Water & Sewage Works, September,* 1953, *p.* 338.)

27-30. Some Conditions Affecting Coagulation. Among the principal factors affecting coagulation are the following:

1. Quantity and kind of coagulant.

2. Characteristics of the water, including suspended matter, temperature, and pH.

3. Time, violence, and method of mixing.

Temperature has more influence on the rate of formation of floc than it has on the amount of coagulant required. However, where rate of flocculation is too slow for proper plant operation, it may be necessary to increase the chemical dose. Optimum pH ranges for some coagulants are shown in Table 27-1.

27-31. Mixing, Flocculation, and Coagulation. The conditioning of water preparatory to filtration may be divided into three stages: (1) mixing of applied chemical, (2) flocculation, and (3) coagulation and sedimentation. The first period involves violent agitation of the water to distribute the chemical through it and to secure complete reaction. The second period involves slow and gentle stirring with sufficient time to build up floc, and the third period involves partial removal of the floc by sedimentation allowing sufficient floc to pass to the filters to form an artificial schmutzdecke[1] on the surface of the sand.

Among the factors to be considered in the design and control of mixing and flocculating devices are the time of detention and the velocity of the currents. In general, the time of mixing should be as short as possible, consistent with satisfactory results. The aim is to secure, as nearly and as quickly as possible, a thorough diffusion of the chemical throughout the incoming water. The duration of the period of flocculation depends on the condition of the raw water, the kind and amount of chemical used, the type of flocculator, and the desired results. It can be determined best by laboratory control, and experience with the water in hand.[2]

In general, periods of flocculation used in practice are in the order of 30 to 60 min when preparing water for coagulation, and slightly longer for lime softening. It is to be appreciated that, in general, a good flocculation is to be expected in a shorter time with highly turbid waters than is required for an equal amount of coagulation when the turbidity is low. Horizontal velocities of flow as high as 0.5 to 1.0 fps are recommended[3] in baffled mixing basins and in flocculators without mechanical agitation. Care should be taken to keep the floc in suspension with just enough agitation to prevent breaking it up. This type of motion seems of greater importance than the velocity of flow. A circulatory, twisting, sweeping confusion of the floc, resembling snow swirls, has been found best.[4] It is undesirable to form either a large, feathery, and fragil floc, or a tough, tenacious floc that lacks adsorptive capacity.

27-32. Mixing Devices. Mixing devices include (1) pumps, (2) baffled basins, (3) spiral-flow basins, (4) basins with mechanically driven paddles, (5) air agitation, and (6) the hydraulic jump. Mechanical stirring devices are usually found most satisfactory. Circular tanks equipped with revolving paddles are sometimes used. A hopper bottom is provided for the removal of sludge which should not be allowed to

[1] See Sec. 28-1.

[2] See also E. L. Bean, *Water Works Eng.*, January, 1953, p. 33.

[3] See also Water Treatment Plant Design, *Am. Soc. Civil Engrs., Manual of Engineering Practice* 19, p. 19, 1941.

[4] See also M. C. Smith, *Water Works & Sewerage*, April, 1932, p. 103.

accumulate. The speed of the paddles and the length of mixing period should be adjustable to permit flexibility in operation. Mixing periods found in practice vary between the brief time of passing through a pump to a period of detention from 5 to 30 min in a mechanical mixing tank. There is an optimum period which must be determined by test. One type of flash mixer is shown in Fig. 27-5.

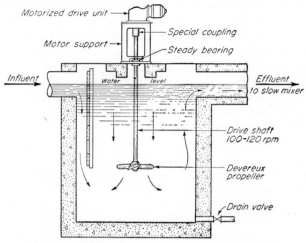

FIG. 27-5. Flash mixer. *(Courtesy of Link-Belt Co.)*

27-33. Baffled Basins. Basins through which water flows horizontally, back and forth, past around-the-end baffles placed 2 to 3 ft apart, or in which it flows up and down, past under-and-over baffles about 2 to 3 ft apart, are known as baffled basins.[1] They may serve as combined mixing and coagulation basins, depending on the turbulence of flow. Their use is becoming less general because of the advantages of mechanical mixing and mechanical flocculating basins.

Disadvantages of baffled basins, when compared with mechanical devices, include (1) less flexibility of control; (2) greater loss of head, which may amount to 1 to 2 ft in baffled basins and to practically nothing in the mechanical flocculator; and (3) greater expense of construction due to baffle walls. Loss of head in around-the-end baffled basins, for 180 deg turn of direction of flow, can be expressed as $3.22V^2/2g$, where V is the mean velocity of flow.[2]

27-34. Spiral-flow or Tangential-flow Basins. In circular basins the mixing or flocculating effect may be obtained by admitting the water tangentially at the periphery and withdrawing it at the center. The average induced rotating velocity in such tanks, with diameter not greater than about 40 ft, lies between 0.5 and 0.75 fps, with an energy

[1] See also *Public Works*, January, 1948, p. 44.
[2] See also Water Treatment Plant Design, *loc. cit.*

requirement equivalent to about 1 ft of head loss. The depth is usually equal to or greater than the diameter. Disadvantages of such tanks include (1) short circuiting, (2) flow variations affect the intensity of agitation velocity, (3) high velocities at the periphery and low velocities at the center, and (4) velocities are not easily adjusted to meet plant conditions.

27-35. Mechanical Flocculators. Mechanical flocculators are displacing other forms of flocculators because they provide numerous gentle contacts between the flocculating particles that are essential to successful floc formation. Such contacts occur in a manner not provided by other methods of flocculation. Among the advantages of mechanical flocculators may be included (1) reduction of 10 to 40 per cent of the amount of chemical required by a baffled basin, (2) better floc formation with resulting diminution in required coagulating basin capacity, (3) less filter washing, (4) cost of installation lower than baffled basins, (5) flexibility of

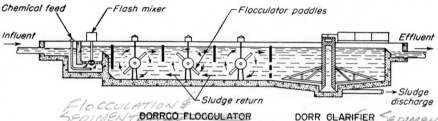

FIG. 27-6. Horizontal-flow mixing, flocculating, and coagulating unit. (*Courtesy of the Dorr Co.*)

operation through control of speed of paddles, (6) good control of currents, (7) relatively low head loss or power requirements, (8) ease of installation in existing plants, and (9) marked improvement in treatment with activated carbon. Among the disadvantages may be included (1) low velocity near paddle shaft, (2) dead spaces in corners, (3) need of equipment maintenance, and (4) bad short circuiting.

Mechanical flocculators may be either circular tanks with paddles revolving on a vertical shaft, or rectangular tanks with paddles revolving on a horizontal shaft. A combination chemical feed, flash mix, flocculator, and clarifier involving horizontal flow is shown in Fig. 27-6. The walking-beam flocculator, a proprietary device, alternately raises and lowers inverted V-shaped troughs called "dashers" which are equipped with adjustable slots to allow varying degrees of agitation. Circular basins are used with paddles revolving about a vertical shaft with the direction of revolution of adjacent paddles opposed or with some fixed and some moving paddles, to prevent the production of a vortex. Such flocculators are more commonly used in the laboratory and in small plants.

A common type of mechanical flocculator consists of a horizontal, continuous-flow, rectangular basin into which the water enters at the bottom, either at the side or at the middle of one end, and from which it leaves at the opposite side or middle of the other end, inducing spiral flow. In passing through the basin the water encounters one or more slowly revolving paddles with the paddle shaft parallel to the direction of flow.

In the design of flocculator paddles for a horizontal-flow, rectangular basin, the length of the horizontal shaft is placed at right angles to the direction of the flow of water, and the paddles are spaced so that the shortest distance between tips is not greater than 2 to 3 ft. Clearance between bottom and side walls may be 6 in., although 12 in. is sometimes allowed. The paddles revolve so that the top moves toward the outlet of the basin with their tips just below or protruding an inch or so above the water surface. The total area of each paddle, depending on the type of paddle and other conditions, may be between 10 and 25 per cent of the vertical cross-sectional area of the basin. The velocity of the paddle should be as fast as possible without breaking up the floc. Peripheral speeds vary between 1 and 2 fps, with the higher speeds preferred. Some designs have been arranged with adjustable speeds to permit tapered flocculation in which the speed near the inlet is greatest. In a few plants stator paddles have been provided to interrupt the excessive roll otherwise created.[1] Velocities of flow recommended in practice lie between 0.5 and 0.7 fps in the direction of flow, with a period of detention between 10 and 60 min.[2] In paddle- or air-agitated flocculators this speed is maintained in the turbulence created by agitation. Power requirements for paddles lie between 3 and 6 kwhr per million gal water treated for a 60-min period of flocculation.

27-36. Flocculation with Diffused Air. Floc conditioning may be accomplished by blowing air from a grid of perforated pipes or other diffuser placed on the bottom of the basin, through which water is flowing.[3] Depths of 7 to 12 ft are satisfactory, with a maximum practical depth of about 15 ft. Porous tubes, porous plates, or perforated pipes may be used for air distribution. Where perforated pipes are used laterals may be spaced 3 to 5 ft apart, with $\frac{1}{16}$-in.-diameter perforations on 3- to 6-in. centers. The distribution pipes, or porous distributors, should be placed in valleys with concrete ridges between them. About 0.5 cu ft air per min per sq ft tank area may be required.

Advantages of air agitation include (1) flexibility of control, (2) low first cost and ease of installation, and (3) aeration combined with mixing. Among the disadvantages are (1) unevenness of agitation between bottom and top of basin, and (2) clogging of air pipes and diffusers.

[1] See also Smith, *loc. cit.*

[2] See Water Treatment Plant Design, *Am. Soc. Civil Engrs., Manual of Practice* 19, 1941.

[3] See also G. E. Willcomb, *J.A.W.W.A.*, 1932, p. 1416.

27-37. Measurement of Floc.[1] Three recognized methods have been proposed for the rapid routine examination of floc: (1) the dissolved-color method of Nasmith,[2] Baylis's floc detector,[3] and the cover-glass method of Willcomb.[4] To aid in the control of flocculation Willcomb has proposed a floc index number as shown in Table 27-4.

TABLE 27-4. Willcomb's Floc Index*

Index number	Corresponding description of floc
0	Colloidal floc. Absolutely no signs of agglomeration
2	Faint. Floc in minute particles not discernible by the ordinary observer
4	Distinct. Floc well formed but uniformly distributed
6	Decided. Floc large in size and about to precipitate
8	Excellent. Deposition of floc well established but not complete
10	Complete. Floc practically all deposited. Supernatant liquid practically clear

* See *J.A.W.W.A.*, Vol. 24, p. 1416, 1916.

In order to resist passage through pores of a filter, floc must be both large and strong. Factors affecting strength may be formulated into a floc index as he^3/d, in which h is the head necessary to force the floc through a bed of sand of uniform size e and depth d. Where the uniformity coefficient is low, e may be the effective size. Where e is expressed in millimeters and other dimensions are in feet, floc indexes of 1 or less are weak and 5 is attainable and desirable.

27-38. Coagulation Basins. The coagulation basin is designed to receive the water from the flocculation basin and to retain it a sufficient time to permit the sedimentation of the proper amount of floc, permitting some to pass on to the filter. The horizontal velocity of flow in the coagulation basin should be as slow as possible, not to exceed 3 fpm, and preferably less than 1 fpm. The basin should be designed to avoid turbulence and to provide a uniform horizontal velocity throughout. Periods of detention vary between wide limits in practice, but commonly periods lie between 2 and 6 hr, the shorter time being more frequently used. The principles of design are the same as for plain-sedimentation basins.

Coagulation basins may be equipped with continuous scrapers for the removal of settled floc, operating similarly to those described in Sec. 26-16. Such basins, sometimes known as clarifiers, have been found efficient, economical, and effective due, in part, to the continuous removal of sludge, the possibilities of sludge recirculation, and the prevention of putrefaction of the sludge.

[1] See also H. E. Hudson, Jr., *ibid.*, Vol. 40, p. 868, 1948.
[2] G. G. Nasmith, *ibid.*, Vol. 22, p. 396, 1930.
[3] J. R. Baylis, *ibid.*, Vol. 11, p. 824, 1924.
[4] See also Willcomb, *loc. cit.*

27-39. Coagulation with a Sludge Blanket.[1]

The sludge blanket clarifier, known also as the suspended-solids contact unit,[2] usually consists of a vertical-flow circular tank in which the coagulated water enters a downcomer in the center of the tank, the downward deceleration in the flaring tube permitting better floc formation. At the bottom of the downcomer the direction of flow of the water is reversed upward, rising around the outside of the downcomer with a decelerating velocity such that at some controlled elevation the velocity is no longer sufficient to lift the settling particles. A layer of suspended flocculent particles is

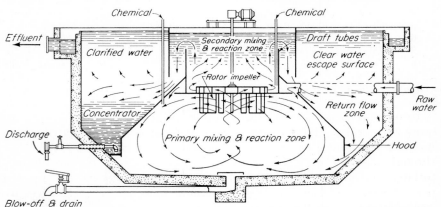

FIG. 27-7. An Accelerator, combining chemical mixing, reaction, floc concentration, and clarification. (*Courtesy of Infilco.*)

formed, known as a *sludge blanket*, which acts as a screen or filter to hold suspended matter. The line of demarcation of the sludge blanket is usually sharply defined, the water above it being clarified and comparatively free from settleable matter. The location and character of the sludge blanket are controllable by the operator, between limits. The increasing weight of the sludge collected in the blanket causes large particles to settle into the conical bottom of the tank from which it can be removed hydraulically, either continuously or periodically, without interrupting the operation of the basin. Clear water is removed at the surface. Upward velocities of about 0.25 to 0.3 fpm have been used. One of the several proprietary devices available is illustrated in Fig. 27-7.

[1] See also F. D. Prager, *Water & Sewage Works*, April, 1950, p. 143.
[2] See also *J.A.W.W.A.*, April, 1951, p. 263.

CHAPTER 28

SLOW SAND AND RAPID SAND FILTRATION

28-1. Theory of Filtration. The common method for the filtration of a public water supply is to pass it through a layer of sand. It has been found by experience that, by passing water through sand, suspended and colloidal matter is partially removed, the chemical characteristics of the water are changed, and the number of bacteria is materially reduced. These phenomena are explained on the basis of four actions: mechanical straining, sedimentation or adsorption, biological metabolism, and electrolytic changes.

Mechanical straining removes the particles of suspended matter that are too large to pass through the interstices between the sand grains. It cannot remove colloidal matter or bacteria too small to be strained out.

Sedimentation and adsorption account for the removal of colloids, small particles of suspended matter, and bacteria. The interstices between the sand grains act as minute sedimentation basins in which the suspended particles settle upon the sides of the sand grains. These particles adhere to the grains because of the physical attraction between the two particles of matter and because of the presence of a gelatinous coating formed on the sand grains by previously deposited bacteria and colloidal matter.

Biological metabolism is the growth and life processes of living cells. This, together with electrolytic actions, causes chemical changes that occur in a water filter. Matter is used in the metabolism of all organisms. The chemical combinations of this matter are altered by the growth of the organism. Since there are living organisms on sand filters, it follows that the chemical make-up of the matter put upon the filter will be altered by the growth of the organisms on the bed.

In explaining the chemical changes that occur during filtration it may be assumed that electrical charges on the sand grains and on the ionized matter in the water react to alter the chemical constituents in the water. Ultimately the electrical charge on the filter is exhausted and the filter must be cleaned to renew these charges.

The action in a filter occurs principally at the surface of the sand in the layer of matter deposited thereon. Other actions take place in the gelatinous coating on the sand grains within the body of the filter. The surface layer contains a zoogloeal jelly in which the biological activities are at their highest. This layer is called the *schmutzdecke* (dirty skin). The successful operation of slow sand filters in particular is dependent on it. During filtration the pressure required to force the water through the schmutzdecke and the gelatinous coating within the body of the filter increases sufficiently to necessitate the cleaning of the filter.

28-2. Filtrability of Water. The ability of a water to be filtered, or its *filtrability*, has been expressed quantitatively as the volume of water obtained per unit head loss when passed at a standard rate through a unit area of a standard filter.[1] This is known sometimes as the *filtrability index*. Knowledge of the value of the index is useful in treating a raw water before filtration since the higher the index the greater the volume of water that will be filtered between cleanings of the filter. Observations of the filtrability index are useful also in the control of the various filtration devices in a treatment plant.

Slow Sand Filtration

28-3. A Slow Sand Filter. A slow sand filter consists of a watertight basin containing a layer of sand 3 to 5 ft thick, supported on a layer of gravel 6 to 12 in. thick, somewhat as shown in Fig. 28-1. The gravel is

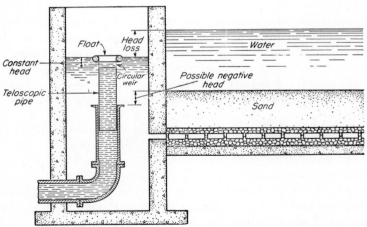

FIG. 28-1. Diagram to show possibility of development of negative head in a slow sand filter.

underlain by a system of open-joint underdrains, placed 10 to 20 ft apart on centers, which lead the water to a single point of outlet where a device is located to control the rate of flow through the filter.

[1] See also: P. L. Boucher, *J. Inst. Civil Engrs.*, February, 1947, p. 417; H. E. Babbitt and E. R. Baumann, *Univ. Illinois Eng. Expt. Sta. Bull.* 425, 1954.

The size of sand is specified in terms of its effective size and its uniformity coefficient.   In general the former is about 0.35 mm and the latter about 1.75.

In operation the filter is filled with water to a depth of 3 to 5 ft above the surface of the sand, as indicated in Fig. 28-1.   The water is passed through the sand layer at a rate of about 2.5 to 7.5 million gal per acre per day (mgad), averaging about 3.0 mgad in most plants.[1]   This rate is continued until the difference between the water level on the filter and in the outlet chamber is slightly less than the depth of water above the sand. This difference between water levels is known as the *loss of head*.   When it has reached its permissible limit the filter is thrown out of service, about an inch of sand is scraped from the top of the bed[2] and may or may not be replaced with clean sand before the filter is put back into service.[3] The loss of head before cleaning is seldom allowed to exceed the depth of water over the surface of the sand, and after cleaning it may be about 6 in.   A normal period of operation between cleanings should be 2 to 3 months, or longer.

28-4. A Slow-sand-filter Plant.   The parts of a slow-sand-filter plant, as indicated by the flowing-through diagram in Fig. 28-2, may include all

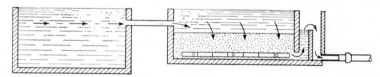

FIG. 28-2. Diagram showing path of water flowing through a slow-sand-filter plant.

or none of the following, except the filter, which is essential:

1. Intake or coarse screen and low-lift pumps
2. Water-conditioning devices such as fine screens, microstrainers, roughing filters, and plain-sedimentation basins (chemical coagulants may not be used)
3. The slow sand filter
4. The clear-water-storage or equalizing basin

The principal appurtenances of a slow-sand-filter plant through which water does not flow include the control building in which the offices and operator's quarters are located and which may house the low-lift pumps, and the sand-storage and sand-washing equipment.

Roughing filters of the rapid-sand-filter type may be used in preparing the water for slow sand filtration.   Such filters may have coarser sand and will operate at higher rates than the standard rapid sand filter.   No chemical coagulant will be used.   The use of roughing filters permits a

[1] See also P. Karalekas, *Am. City*, September, 1952, p. 99.
[2] See also E. L. Mosley, *Public Works*, February, 1953, p. 116.
[3] See also A. J. Minkus, *J. New Engl. Water Works Assoc.*, September, 1948, p. 242.

higher rate of filtration on the slow sand filter and may permit longer filter runs between cleanings. The clear-water-storage basin acts as an equalizing reservoir to permit a constant rate of filtration on the slow sand filter together with provision for a fluctuating rate of demand.

It is to be emphasized that no chemical coagulant is used preceding slow sand filtration. The artificial schmutzdecke provided by the floc carried over onto the filter is undesirable as it will shorten the filter runs uneconomically.

28-5. Water Surface and Rate Control. The elevation of the water surface on a slow sand filter may be held constant by means of a float-controlled valve; through the control of the low-lift pumps; or through other means. The rate of flow is controlled by a rate controller on the effluent pipe. The details of an " open-type " rate controller are shown at the left in Fig. 28-1 and in Fig. 28-21. The vertical length of telescopic pipe shown in Fig. 28-1 is supported by an annular ring which floats on the water surface at a fixed distance above the submerged open end of the pipe. The flow of water falling into the outlet pipe is constant since it falls under a fixed head over a circular weir of fixed length. As the head loss through the sand increases, to maintain the same rate of filtration, the water surface in the rate controller drops, the tube in the controller telescoping into the effluent pipe.

The rate of flow through the filter near the outlet is greater than the rate remote from the outlet. This is due to the greater length of flow through the underdrainage system and the fact that the head loss from all points on the filter to the rate controller is the same. Underdrainage systems are usually designed so that such differences in rate of filtration over the filter are insignificant.

28-6. Sand Washing. When a filter is to be washed it is thrown out of service, drained, and a layer of sand about 1 in. thick is removed from the surface and conveyed, hydraulically or otherwise, to a central point where the sand is washed by scrubbing it with clean water, and stored for return to the filter. Devices are available which make possible the washing of the sand in place without draining the filter. These include the Blaisdell washing machine,[1] the Swade Selecteur,[2] and the Swade method.[3]

28-7. Results of Slow Sand Filtration. The principal purpose of a slow sand filter is to remove bacteria from water. Slow sand filters are highly efficient in this accomplishment, being reliable, when not over-loaded, for the removal of 98 to 99 per cent of the bacteria in the raw water. They will also remove suspended and settleable matter not removed in the sedimentation basin, and they will have some beneficial effect on odors and tastes, particularly when due to algae or suspended

---

[1] *Eng. Contr.*, Aug. 26, 1914, p. 210.

[2] M. N. Baker, *Eng. News-Record*, Sept. 19, 1946, p. 100.

[3] *Water and Water Eng.*, July, 1949, p. 351.

matter. It is possible that they may, under favorable circumstances, have some slight effect in the reduction of color. They are not highly efficient in the removal of colloidal matter.

Although the removal of 98 to 99 per cent of the bacterial content of a raw water is desirable, it may be insufficient to prevent the passage of pathogenic bacteria so as to assure complete safety against water-borne disease. Absolute safety can be secured by filtration followed by sterilization.

Rapid Sand Filtration

28-8. A Rapid Sand Filter of the Gravity Type. A rapid sand filter of the open gravity type consists of an open watertight basin containing a layer of sand 30 to 36 in. thick, supported on a layer of gravel 6 to 12 in.

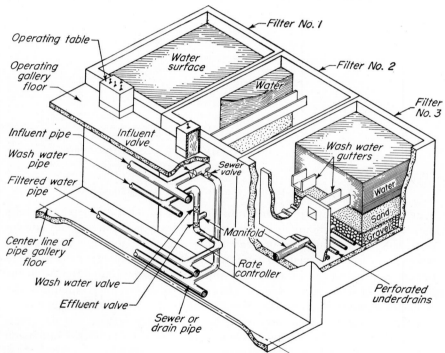

FIG. 28-3. Schematic cutaway drawing of a rapid sand filter.

thick, somewhat as shown in Fig. 28-3. Such filters are commonly constructed of concrete, although steel has been used for small units. The gravel is underlain by an underdrainage system which leads to a single point of outlet where the rate controller is located.

Water to be filtered enters the filter through the opening in the front wall leading into the wash-water gutters. The water fills the filter until the surface stands at a fixed elevation about 3 to 5 ft above the gutters during normal filtration. When it is time to wash the filter it is taken out of service and the water surface is drawn down nearly to the sand surface. Wash water is then admitted beneath the sand and, rising rapidly, lifts the sand so that the volume of the expanded sand is about 150 per cent of its volume during normal filtration. The rising wash water, carrying with it dirt removed from the sand, flows into the wash-water gutter under conditions of open-channel flow, and leaves the filter through the sewer valve which has been opened at the end of the wash-water gutters.

28-9. A Gravity-type Rapid-sand-filter Plant. A flowing-through diagram of a gravity-type rapid-sand-filter plant is shown in Fig. 28-4.

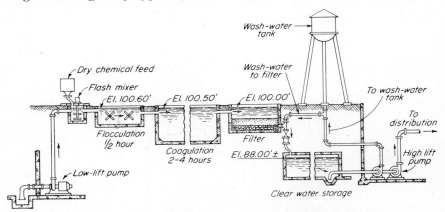

FIG. 28-4. Flow-through chart of a rapid-sand-filter plant.

A general plan of a plant is shown in Fig. 28-5. Other essential parts of a plant include the chemical handling and storage equipment; the laboratory; the control building or head house and the operating gallery; the wash-water and the wash-air equipment; the pipe gallery; the pump and blower equipment; and the various appurtenances in connection with the operation of this equipment. The chemical equipment includes the room for receiving and storing the chemicals, the solution-storage tanks, and the mixing and feed devices.

It is to be noted that chemical coagulation is essential to the operation of a complete rapid-sand-filter plant.

28-10. Comparison of Slow Sand and Rapid Sand Filtration. The outstanding features of operation that distinguish the slow sand from the rapid sand filter are the rate of filtration, the method of cleaning, and the absence of preliminary chemical treatment of the water in slow sand filtration. In comparing the two types of filters it is found that the slow sand filter is less likely to go wrong under inexperienced operation; it does not require such skilled attendance; the amount of head consumed is less;

it is preferred by some because of the greater reliability of the removal of bacteria; the operating costs may be less per unit volume of water treated; and it is best adapted to waters low in color, turbidity, and bacterial count.   Among the features of rapid sand filters that make them more desirable than slow sand filters may be included lower first cost; smaller area of land required; the effluent is clearer, has less color, and is sparkling; a smaller amount of sand is required for construction; the method

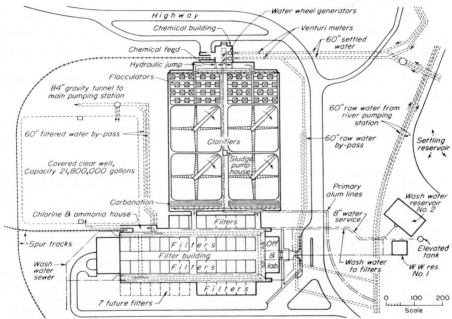

Fig. 28-5. Plan of a large water-purification plant.   (*Taken by permission from "The Sanitary Industry," by Johns Manville, Industrial Products Division.*)

of cleaning leaves the filter out of service for a few minutes only; treatment can be more quickly adjusted to variations in raw-water quality; and, finally, the capitalized cost of the plant is less.

Slow sand filters were the first type developed for water purification, dating back to 1829.   The first rapid sand filter was constructed at Somerville, N.J., in 1884.   Since then the construction of rapid sand filters has almost supplanted slow-sand-filter construction in the United States, and the ratio of rapid sand to slow sand filters in other countries has steadily increased.   A slow-sand-filtration plant was constructed at Leicester, Mass., in 1946.[1]   The Metropolitan Water Board in England continues to construct slow sand filters.[2]

[1] See *Water Works Eng.*, Sept. 4, 1946, p. 1056.
[2] See "Manual of British Water Supply Practice," 1950, p. 349.

28-11. Design of a Rapid Sand Filter. After the basic decisions concerning capacity, location, etc., have been made an early step in design is the sketching of a general plan. If the capacity of the plant is not large an all-steel or "package" plant, which includes chemical mixing, coagulation, and filtration, all in one prefabricated unit, may be used.[1] Although the sketch of the general plan may be among the first drawings made, the final general plan may be the last drawing completed because of changes made in the component parts during the design. A general plan is shown in Fig. 28-5. Topographic contours and special features of a site should be shown so that sketches of the parts of the plant, or pieces of paper representing those parts to scale, can be moved about on the plan until a suitable arrangement is found.

Features to be considered in the layout of a rapid-sand-filter plant include:

1. Economy in construction and in operation
2. Future extensions
3. Soil conditions, foundations, and structural problems
4. Interior and exterior appearance
5. Flexibility in operation
6. Compactness and convenience to minimize materials required, minimize head losses, and simplify operation
7. Utilization of topography to minimize excavation and backfilling, and to make use of gravity in operation

A summary of design and operating data of 56 rapid-sand-filter plants in the United States and Canada is presented by Hardin.[2]

28-12. Plans and Specifications. Plans and specifications may be either[3] (1) briefly descriptive, indicating the type of plant required, its capacity, location, etc.; or (2) detailed and complete, covering in minute detail the quality and quantity of materials to be included, the quality of workmanship required, and the exact type and character of every item. The latter type of plan and specifications is in more general use. It is the type prepared by a competent engineer in the best interests of his client to secure a satisfactory plant at the least possible cost.

28-13. Capacity of Plant. The capacity of a rapid-sand-filter plant depends on the average rate of demand, the fluctuations in the rate of demand, and the clear-water storage provided. It may be as great as the maximum peak demand load, where no clear-water storage is provided, or as small as the average rate of demand, where the clear-water storage is sufficient to care for all fluctuations in demand. The economical filter capacities and the amount of clear-water storage to be provided lie between these two extremes. The economical capacities can be deter-

---

[1] See also *Eng. News-Record*, Jan. 1, 1953, p. 33.

[2] E. A. Hardin, *J.A.W.W.A.*, December, 1942, p. 1847.

[3] See also W. E. Stanley, *ibid.*, 1933, p. 105.

mined only by a study of the costs of various complete designs using different capacities.

The ratio of plant capacity to average pumpage will differ greatly among cities.[1] The ratio appears to be generally more than 2, and it has been found to be as high as 3.2. Large cities will, as a rule, have a smaller ratio than smaller cities. In very small plants it may be economical, because of operating conditions, to operate the plant but a few hours a day, thus necessitating considerable overcapacity of filter plant and reserve storage capacity. Consideration must be given also to

FIG. 28-6. Blomquist Filtration Plant, Cedar Rapids, Iowa. (*Courtesy of Leo Louis, Superintendent.*)

safety in the event of partial shutdown, fire reserve, and other local conditions that may affect the plant operation.

28-14. Filter Buildings. The filter building should be of pleasing design and should be surrounded by attractive grounds. The exterior of the building at Cedar Rapids, Iowa, is shown in Fig. 28-6. Such structures are required to increase the confidence of the public in the quality of the water delivered by the filter plant and in the ability of the waterworks officials. The public, not acquainted with the technicalities of water treatment, is likely to judge the quality of the water as much from the appearance of the plant, both inside and out, as from the appearance and taste of the water. It will be difficult to convince the public that excellent water can be delivered from filters in wooden tubs located in an unsightly shed.

[1] See A. B. Morrill, *ibid.*, Vol. 16, p. 582, 1926.

Facilities to be considered in the design of the interior of the filter house should include:

Laboratory

Office

Chemical-mixing and feed-device room

Convenience of access and of routing

Toolroom

Heating, lighting, and ventilation

Chemical storage room

Operating gallery

Machine shop

Pump and blower room and room for special equipment

Janitor's room

Filters

The interior of the filter house at Des Moines, Iowa, is shown in Fig. 28-7. This plant has been arranged for the convenience of the operator;

Fig. 28-7. Filter operating floor at Des Moines, Iowa. (*Courtesy of Dale L. Maffitt and V. R. Kreier.*)

each room needing outside light is well illuminated; the chemical storage room is large, well ventilated, and dry; the chemicals can be brought into the building with ease; and the interior of the building is pleasing to the eye. White is desirable for interior decoration, as it impresses the visitor favorably and improves the morale of the operating personnel.

The T-shaped plan for a filter building is satisfactory where local conditions will permit. The front portion of two to three stories contains the laboratory, offices, chemical-storage and preparation rooms, and the pump room, if one is required. The shaft of the T is one or two stories and contains the pipe gallery, the operating floor, and the filters. This portion of the building does not always extend to full height over the entire length of the filter. The outside walls of the second story of the building may be supported about one-third to one-half way from the operating gallery to the back of the filter at such a distance that the operator, standing on the floor of the operating gallery, can see the edge of the wall to the water surface at the back of the filter. This is illustrated in Fig. 28-8, which shows a cross section of the plant at Meriden, Conn. Expense is saved by including only a portion of the filter within the building. The portion of the filters outside the building is covered with a flat concrete slab, which serves to protect the filters from pollution and also as a place to store sand temporarily removed from the filter. Outside walls are sometimes omitted in tropical climates.

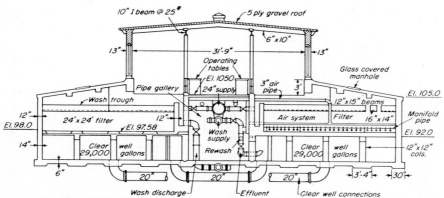

FIG. 28-8. Section through rapid-sand-filter plant at Meriden, Conn. (*From Water Works, January*, 1927, *p.* 508.)

Excellent interior lighting is important for the sake of appearance and to promote cleanliness. It is essential over the filter to permit proper operation. In some plants, skylights over the filter units have improved daytime illumination. Condensation on the interior walls of the filter building may be minimized by avoiding air movements over the surface of the filters and by the installation of insulation at the roof. The cost of the insulation may be more than repaid by the saving of fuel. Unit heaters in filter plants are conducive to condensation of water and should be avoided.

"Sweating" caused by condensation of moisture on cold pipes is detrimental to good operation and injurious to equipment. It is particularly troublesome in pipe galleries. It can be prevented by conditioning the air to remove the moisture, or by insulating the troublesome pipes. A ground-cork insulation painted with aluminum paint is effective and is attractive in appearance.[1]

[1] See also "Water Supply and Treatment," p. 56, National Lime Association, Washington, D.C., 1951.

Filter buildings require more heat than is needed by most buildings because of the high heat losses within the building, through the outside walls and roof, and absorbed by the water being treated.   It is essential that the temperature be kept above freezing, particularly around small pipes controlling the hydraulic valves and other equipment.   Comfortable temperatures must, of course, be maintained in the laboratory, office, and operator's rooms.

Chemical handling, storage, and feed devices, the laboratory, and other features in connection with the chemical control of the plant should be placed in close proximity to each other within the filter building, both

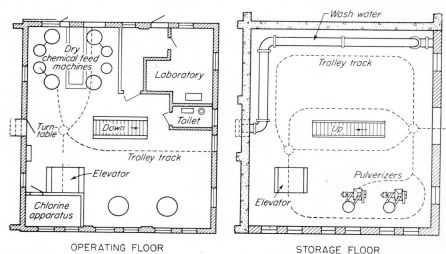

OPERATING FLOOR   STORAGE FLOOR

FIG. 28-9. Floor plan of chemical house at Defiance, Ohio.   (*From J.A.W.W.A., Vol. 7, p. 445.*)

for the convenience of the operator and to assure uninterrupted operation at lower costs.   The floor plan of a chemical house at Defiance, Ohio, which embodies these features, is illustrated in Fig. 28-9.

It is desirable to include a "sight" well by which visitors may observe the clarity of the purified water by seeing an illuminated scale submerged, vertically, in a well lined with glazed white tile.   If feasible, the raw water and the clear water may be passed through contiguous wells to emphasize before-and-after effects.

28-15. Laboratory.   A laboratory is essential to proper operation of a water-treatment plant.   If there are other municipal services requiring laboratory control the combination of all such services in one laboratory may be desirable in a small city, but usually not so in a larger community.[1] Conditions to be considered in laboratory design include (1) location for greatest convenience; (2) size to provide for personnel, equipment, and

[1] See *Water Works Eng.*, April, 1950, p. 305.

service; (3) utilities, such as cold and hot water, compressed air, vacuum, illuminating gas, electricity; and (4) other special utilities. In general, it is desirable to locate the laboratory near to or connected to the chief operator's office and at the same time provide a view from the laboratory of the operating floor in the filter house.

Windows facing, unobstructed, toward a north light are desirable. They should equal in area approximately 25 per cent of the floor space, with their tops close to a 12-ft ceiling. Direct sunlight is undesirable in the room. Artificial lighting should provide not less than 40 ft-candles on working surfaces, with a white (uncolored) light. Heating and ventilation should provide normal-comfort temperatures with about six changes of air per hour. Special ventilation hoods should be provided for the removal of chemical fumes. The floor space in the smallest laboratory should not be less than about 300 sq ft, with 1,000 sq ft for a moderate-sized laboratory, and larger accommodations where chemical, bacteriological, biological, and other work is to be done.

The equipment and instrumentation of a laboratory depend on the nature and extent of the work. Discussions of this subject and lists and descriptions are to be found in various periodicals.[1]

28-16. The Filter. A perspective drawing of a rapid sand filter is shown in Fig. 28-3. Among the important parts of the unit which are determined in design are:

1. Capacity of filter unit
2. Length and width of filter unit
3. Arrangement and dimensions of wash-water gutters
4. Filtering material
5. Underdrainage system
6. Depth of filter box

28-17. Rate of Filtration. The standard rate of filtration through a rapid sand filter, which has been adopted as a result of experience, is 2 gal per sq ft of filter surface per minute. This is equal to a rate of 125 mgad, an older form of expressing the rate. Practice is tending toward higher rates in conjunction with greater care in water conditioning before filtration and the use of coarser sand.[2] The highest rates used are reported from Chicago[3] where rates up to 5 gal per sq ft per min have been used. The adoption of such rates has been made possible by the type of preliminary treatment and the filtering sand used. Such rates should not be used without demonstration that the hydraulics of the plant and pretreatment of the water are adequate.[4]

---

[1] See *J.A.W.W.A.*, September, 1951, p. 725; February, 1953, p. 129; *Water Works Eng.*, May 1, 1946, p. 482; Aug. 21, 1946, p. 968; *Am. City*, December, 1951, p. 135.

[2] See J. R. Baylis, *J.A.W.W.A.*, July, 1950, p. 687; *Pure Water*, May, 1950, p. 90.

[3] See *Eng. News-Record*, July 10, 1947.

[4] See C. R. Cox, *Water & Sewage Works*, October, 1953, p. 400.

28-18. Capacity of Filter Unit.[1] Rapid sand filters of the open gravity type can be built of any convenient nominal capacity, but it has been general practice to construct them in some even multiple or fraction of 1 mgd in order that appurtenances may be found available in standard sizes. Units up to 5 mgd are among the largest that have been constructed. It is usually desirable to have two or more units, in order that when one is out of service the others may carry on without dangerous overload. The smaller the number of units the fewer the appurtenances but the larger the wash-water equipment that will be required.

28-19. Length and Width of Filter Unit. It is customary to make the length of rectangular filter boxes greater than the width because of economy in the utilization of space and in the layout of the piping. Economy and convenience are the only two criteria that fix the relation between these two dimensions; these criteria, in turn, depending on local conditions and the layout of the plant. As a guide to general practice it will be found on investigation of existing plants that where filters are located on both sides of a pipe gallery the ratio of length to width of a filter box lies between 1.11 and 1.66, averaging about 1.25 to 1.33.

28-20. Wash-water Gutters. Materials used for wash-water gutters include concrete, wrought iron or steel, cast iron, aluminum, monel metal, and rarely wood.

Various arrangements of wash-water gutters are shown in Fig. 28-10. It is a general rule of good practice that the horizontal travel of dirty

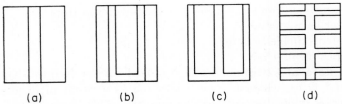

(a)   (b)   (c)   (d)

Fig. 28-10. Diagrams showing arrangements of wash-water gutters in rapid sand filters.

water over the surface of the filter shall be less than 3 ft before reaching the gutter. For this reason the distance from edge to edge of gutters should not exceed 6 ft and preferably should be less than 4½ ft.

In Fig. 28-10a the arrangement is suitable for only the smallest filters, which are not over 6 ft in width. Figure 28-10b shows an arrangement suitable for somewhat larger filters. Figure 28-10c is a modification of this layout in which some of the wash-water gutters are placed against the side walls of the filter. This is not considered good practice because of the loss of the use of one side of the wash-water gutter which is placed against the filter wall. The arrangement in Fig. 28-10d is suitable for

[1] See also H. A. Thomas, Jr., *Eng. News-Record*, Dec. 25, 1947, p. 52.

and is used in the large filters.   It consists of a central gutter extending through the length and the entire depth of the filter, separating it into two almost independent parts.   Each of the lateral gutters empties into this deep central gutter.   No water is taken over the edge of the central gutter.

The upper edge of the wash-water gutter should be placed sufficiently near to the surface of the sand so that a large quantity of dirty water is not left in the filter after the completion of washing.   At the same time the edge of the wash-water gutter should be placed sufficiently far above the surface of the sand so that sand will not be washed into the gutter. The edge of the trough should be slightly above the highest elevation of the sand as expanded in washing.   Where this height cannot be determined by test, a convenient rule is to place the edge of the gutter as far above the surface of the undisturbed sand surface as the wash water rises in 1 min.   Air and water should not be applied simultaneously with such gutter heights.   The gutter should be large enough to carry all the water

Fig. 28-11. Wash-water gutters.

delivered to it with at least 3 in. between the surface of the water flowing in the gutter and the upper edge of the gutter.   Otherwise the gutter becomes submerged, reducing the efficacy of the wash.   The gutter may be made with the same cross section throughout its length, or it may be constructed with a varying cross section, increasing in size toward the outlet end.   The bottom of the gutter should clear the top of the sand by 2 in. or more.   It is not always economical to construct gutters with uniform cross section, because saving may be possible when the bottom of the gutter is sloped so that the front portion is deeper than the rear. Sections of wash-water gutters are shown in Figs. 28-3 and 28-11.

In the determination of the dimensions of wash-water gutters, various methods are in use.   A satisfactory method is illustrated in Fig. 28-12. Another method is presented by Stein.[1]

28-21. Quality of Filtering Materials.   Sand is used extensively as a filtering material because of its availability, its relatively low cost, and the satisfactory experience with it.   Other materials that have been used include crushed anthracite,[2] glass, and proprietary products.   Standard

[1] M. F. Stein, *J.A.W.W.A.*, Vol. 13, p. 411, 1925.
[2] See also J. A. Oldenburg, *Public Works*, May, 1950, p. 50.

specifications for filtering materials have been published by the American
Water Works Association.[1]

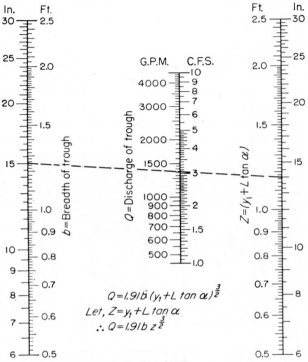

Fig. 28-12. Nomograph for the design of wash-water gutters. (*From Eng. News-
Record, Vol.* 90, 1923, *p.* 882.)   To use this diagram for the design of a wash-water
gutter, the required capacity and the width of the gutter must be known.   If the
gutter is not rectangular in cross section, a gutter of equal rectangular area must be
computed, and this later changed to the desired shape.   With the discharge from the
gutter Q and the breadth of the gutter b known, determine z from the diagram.   The
depth of water at the upper end y_1 is next determined from the expression $y_1 = z - LS$,
in which L is the length of the gutter, and S is the slope of the bottom of the gutter.
The depth of water at the lower end of the gutter y_2 is equal to $\frac{2}{3}(y_1 + LS)$.

Some substitutes are reported in tests and experience to have produced
satisfactory results.[2]   Among the advantages claimed for anthracite over
sand are[3] longer filter runs, less wash water used, and cleaner filter beds.[4]

[1] See *J.A.W.W.A.*, March, 1949, p. 289, with bibliography.

[2] See also J. R. Baylis, *Water Works & Sewerage*, October, 1934, p. 352.

[3] See also: E. L. Streatfield, *Water and Water Eng.*, December, 1946, p. 662; Turner
and Scott, *Water Works & Sewerage*, April, 1933, p. 135; September, 1933, p. 330;
C. P. Hoover, *ibid.*, November, 1933, p. 394; O. J. Ripple, *ibid.*, Vol. 83, p. 255, 1936;
H. G. Turner, *J.A.W.W.A.*, April, 1944, p. 431; R. Mounsey, *Am. City*, May, 1953,
p. 83.

[4] See also H. G. Turner, *Water & Sewage Works*, Vol. 96, p. R-57, 1949.

The advantages claimed for coal over sand may be due to its lighter specific gravity and greater porosity.

28-22. Size and Depth of Filtering Material   Filtering sand should, in general, be of such a size as to hold a large quantity of floc without permitting its passage through the filter and without increasing the difficulties of washing; it should permit long filter runs; and when washed it should cleanse itself so as to be free from adhering particles without requiring a velocity of wash water so high as to carry away particles of sand. Some of these requirements are mutually inconsistent. For example, fine sand will prevent the passage of floc and will deliver a good quality of effluent but will reduce the length of the filter run and may make washing difficult, whereas coarse sand will do the reverse. A sand layer made up of small-sized grains will expand further when being washed than one consisting of large-sized grains subjected to the same rate of washing. As the grains become more widely separated, their tendency to strike each other is lessened, and the difficulty of cleansing is increased. On the other hand, the larger the sand grains the greater the force with which they will strike together and the easier it will be to keep the bed clean. With coarser sand, filters can be run longer between washings, they can be washed cleaner, and the number and size of mud balls will be reduced, and it will not be necessary to remove and clean the sand so often. Practice is tending toward the use of coarse sand to permit high rates of filtration. However, if sand becomes too coarse the efficiency of bacterial removal diminishes. Filter beds of coarse sand should be deeper than those of fine sand, and the rate of rise of wash water should be greater for equal effects in filter washing.

The effective size (Hazen's) of sand ordinarily used is between 0.4 and 0.55 mm, with a uniformity coefficient not greater than 1.75[1] or less than about 1.35. Variations found in practice lie between 0.3 and 0.6 mm. Successful use of greatly increased rates of filtration at Chicago,[2] discussed in Sec. 28-17, is attributed, in part, to the filter sand used. It has been shown that the expression of sand size in terms of Hazen's effective size is not suited to the rate of filtration in use there. The term *per cent size* is used, that being the size of particle that has the stated per cent, by weight, of materials finer in size. Chicago's filter-sand specifications and typical size distribution of samples of sand are illustrated in Fig. 28-13.

Uniformity of size of grain is desirable because of the tendency of sand grains to group in strata of similar size. A stratum of fine material beneath a stratum of coarse material may cause clogging within the filter, and a stratum of coarse material beneath a stratum of fine material may result in a reduction of pressure within the filter sufficient to release

[1] See Committee Report, Filter Sand for Water Purification Practice, *Proc. Am. Soc. Civil Engrs.*, Vol. 62, p. 1543, 1936; *J.A.W.W.A.*, August, 1953, p. 872.
[2] See *Eng. News-Record*, July 10, 1947, p. 110.

dissolved gases, causing either "air binding" or a "blow" that will break through the filter surface.

The depth of filtering material should be the thinnest possible commensurate with safe bacteriological removal. Thicknesses of strata used in practice lie between 24 and 30 in., the latter being common.

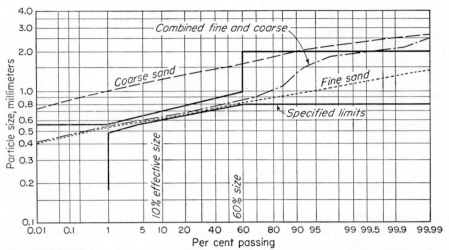

Fig. 28-13. Graph showing Chicago's filter-sand specifications and a typical size distribution of samples of sand obtained.

28-23. Filter Gravel. Gravel is placed between the sand and the underdrainage system (1) to prevent sand from entering the underdrains and (2) to aid in uniform distribution of wash water. The gravel should accomplish both purposes without being displaced by the rising wash water. Sizes of gravel in use vary from 1½ in. at the bottom to ⅛ in. at the top of the gravel layer,[1] with depths of gravel between 9 and 18 in. The faster the rate of application of wash water, the larger the gravel size required and the deeper the bed. In some plants metal screens have been fastened between the gravel and the sand to prevent movement of the gravel. They have caused difficulties when improperly installed.

28-24. Underdrainage Systems.[2] An underdrainage system is required in a filter for two purposes, to remove water that has filtered through the sand, and to distribute wash water uniformly beneath the sand. Types of underdrainage systems in use include (1) manifold and pipe laterals, with the pipes either perforated or equipped with strainer heads, the perforated-pipe laterals being more commonly used (in some layouts a precast concrete block, known as a Wagner block, is used

[1] See also S. T. Barker and H. F. Ferguson, *J.A.W.W.A.*, Vol. 13, pp. 150, 154, 1925.
[2] See also R. Hazen, *ibid.*, March, 1951, p. 208; M. L. Stuppy and others, *ibid.*, June, 1954, p. 548.

between perforated-pipe laterals); (2) vitrified-tile block, known as Leopold block, with orifices and water passages, as indicated in Fig. 28-14; (3) false bottoms, precast or otherwise, such as the Wheeler bottom, shown in Fig. 28-15; (4) porous-plate bottoms, as shown in Fig. 28-16; (5) concrete ridge-and-valley bottoms, as shown in Fig. 28-17; (6) the Permutit precast sectional concrete bottom with expansible strainers; and (7) nozzle-type bottoms, as described by Hulsbergen.[1] These are suitable mainly for combined air and water washing. The

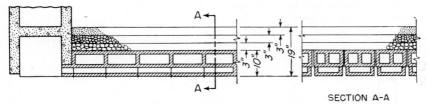

SECTION A-A

FIG. 28-14. A Leopold-block underdrain, with glazed-tile blocks furnishing passages for the water, instead of using lateral pipes. (*From Richard Hazen, J.A.W.W.A., March, 1951, p. 208.*)

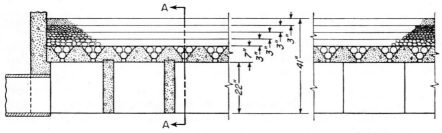

SECTION A-A

FIG. 28-15. The Wheeler filter bottom, consisting of solid, inverted, truncated pyramids with water connections at the apex of each pyramid, and the pockets filled with cement or glazed earthenware spheres. (*From Richard Hazen, J.A.W.W.A., March, 1951, p. 208.*)

Jewell subsurface underdrain[2] is placed immediately below the sand surface as a supplement to the underdrainage system. Many underdrainage systems, such as Leopold blocks, Wagner blocks, and the Wheeler bottom, are proprietary developments. The perforated-pipe underdrains are subject to individual design.

28-25. Perforated-pipe Underdrains.[3] A perforated-pipe underdrain, such as is illustrated in Fig. 28-18, consists of a central manifold to which a series of branch pipes is attached. Cast iron is most commonly used for manifold and laterals. Holes are bored in the lower portion of

[1] C. W. Hulsbergen, *Water & Sewage Works*, December, 1952, p. 481.

[2] See *Water Works Eng.*, Feb. 2, 1938, p. 159.

[3] See also D. A. Schmitt and P. O. Macqueen, *J.A.W.W.A.*, June, 1942, p. 857.

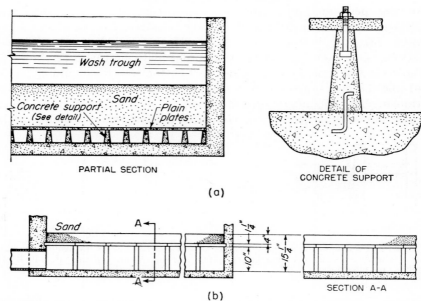

PARTIAL SECTION

DETAIL OF
CONCRETE SUPPORT

(a)

SECTION A-A

(b)

Fig. 28-16. Porous-plate filter bottoms. (a) Detail of concrete support. (*Courtesy of the Carborundum Co.*) (*b from Richard Hazen, J.A.W.W.A., March, 1951, p. 208.*)

the branch pipes, somewhat as indicated in Fig. 28-18. The holes are located so that the wash water is directed downward at an angle between 30 and 60 deg with the vertical. Erosion or corrosion of the metal around these holes may be minimized by lining the holes with a brass or bronze bushing. It has been customary to place the branch pipes on 6- to 12-in. centers, the larger distance being preferred, with $\frac{1}{4}$- to $\frac{1}{2}$-in.-diameter holes placed on 3- to 8-in. centers along the pipe. The smaller the spacing the smaller the individual holes. In some successful designs there are two or more manifolds interconnected by branch pipes.

As a guide to satisfactory design the following principles, attributed to Jenks and Ellms,[1] may be used:

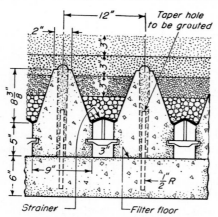

SECTION THROUGH FILTER UNDERDRAIN

Fig. 28-17. Section through a concrete ridge-and-valley underdrain.

[1] See H. N. Jenks, *ibid.*, Vol. 28, p. 1541, 1936; J. W. Ellms, *ibid.*, Vol. 18, p. 664, 1927.

1. The ratio of length of lateral to its diameter should not exceed 60.

2. The diameter of perforations in the laterals should be between ¼ and ½ in.

3. The spacing of the perforations along the lateral may vary from 3 in. for a diameter of perforations of ¼ in. to 8 in. for a diameter of perforations of ½ in.

4. The ratio of the total area of the perforations in the underdrainage system to the total cross-sectional area of the laterals should not exceed

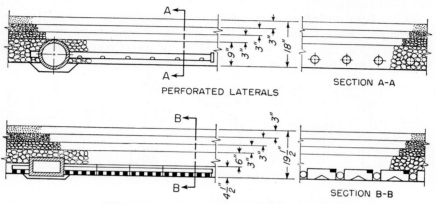

PERFORATED LATERALS

SECTION A-A

PERFORATED LATERALS WITH WAGNER BLOCKS

SECTION B-B

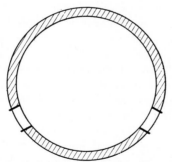

Fig. 28-18. Perforated pipe underdrains. *(From Richard Hazen, J.A.W.W.A., March, 1951, p. 208.)*

0.5 for a diameter of perforation of ½ in., and should decrease to 0.25 for a diameter of perforation of ¼ in.

5. The ratio of the total area of the perforations in the underdrainage system to the entire filter area may be as low as 0.002.

6. The spacing of the laterals may be as great as 12 in. for satisfactory diffusion but is limited by the total head available.

7. The rate of washing may be varied from 6 to 36 in. per min provided the foregoing factors are used in design.

8. The sum of the cross-sectional areas of the laterals should be at least twice the sum of the cross-sectional areas of the perforations in the laterals.

9. The area of the manifold feeding the laterals should be 1.75 to 2.00 times the sum of the cross-sectional areas of the laterals which are fed in the washing process.

The principles on which the number and size of openings in perforated-pipe underdrains are determined are equally applicable to other systems of underdrainage.

28-26. Pipe-and-strainer Underdrains. These are similar to the perforated-pipe underdrains except that perforated strainer heads, such as those shown in Fig. 28-19, may be used. The use of such underdrains is now confined principally to small filter units.

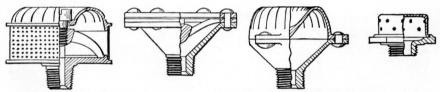

Fig. 28-19. Strainer heads. (*Courtesy of American Water Softener Co.*)

28-27. Porous-plate Underdrains.[1] The use of porous-plate underdrains, such as the Aloxite plates shown in Fig. 28-16, is increasing in practice. Among the advantages claimed for such underdrains may be included (1) freedom from gravel and from graded sand, the entire filtering medium being homogeneous; (2) an even rate of filtration and of wash-water distribution over the whole area of the bed; and (3) resistance to corrosion. The problem of holding the plates in place has been solved but such plates cannot be used successfully in waters that lay down a carbonate film because the cleaning of the plates is difficult.

28-28. Air Distribution. In filters using air in washing the underdrains must be adapted to its use, or a special air-distribution system must be provided. The pipes and manifold of this system are placed immediately above the pipes of the water underdrainage system in such a manner as to interfere as little as possible with the water strainers. The design of a separate air-distribution system follows principles similar to those in the design of a pipe-and-strainer system for water. The holes in the air strainers are made about the same size and total area as the holes for the water system. The size of the air pipes is based on a velocity of flow of compressed air of about 2,000 fpm.

[1] See also: T. R. Camp, *J. New Engl. Water Works Assoc.*, March, 1935, p. 10; *Water Works & Sewerage*, March, 1937, p. 84; H. T. Hotchkiss, *Water & Sewage Works*, Vol. 93, p. R-139; F. C. Roe, *ibid.*, June, 1949, p. 225; W. H. Berkeley, *J.A.W.W.A.*, June, 1952, p. 491.

Air and water can be sent through the same pipes by using a long stem on the strainer head, the open-ended stem protruding about one-half of the diameter into the air pipe.   A small hole in the stem, close to the top of the air pipe, permits the passage of air into the strainer, water passing into it through the open end of the strainer stem.   Air and water should not be used simultaneously in washing when the surface of the water is above the edge of the wash-water gutter to avoid blowing sand into the gutters.

28-29. Depth of Filter Box.   Considerations of economy demand that the filter box be made as shallow as possible.   The depth may be determined by the required distance between the bottom of the box and the necessary freeboard above the edge of the wash-water gutter, or the maximum head to be permitted in the operation of the filter.

The *minimum* depth of the filter box will be the sum of the following:

1. Height required by the strainer system and the covering of gravel. This is seldom less than 8 in.

2. Thickness of the sand bed.   This is commonly made about 30 in.

3. Distance between the top of the sand and the edge of the wash-water gutter.   This is equal to the distance that the wash water will rise in the filter in 1 min, if air wash is not used.

4. Desirable freeboard above the wash-water gutter.   The minimum should be about 6 in.   A greater depth is preferable to provide a factor of safety against overflowing the filter box, for flexibility, and to provide adequate positive head between filter washings.

Filter boxes are seldom constructed with a depth less than 6 to 8 ft, and are usually deeper.

In fixing the requisite depth of the filter box the greatest permissible head loss in operating the filter is frequently of more importance than the factors listed.   Where the pressure in the filter is not permitted to fall below atmospheric, the depth of the filter box must be equal to the maximum loss of head in the filter plus sufficient freeboard to prevent loss of water over the top of the filter.   Where the pressure in the filter underdrains may be below atmospheric, the depth of the filter box may be equal to the maximum permissible head loss in the filter plus the necessary freeboard and less the allowable negative head at the bottom of the filter.   The greater the negative head the less the required depth of the filter box, but the greater the possible difficulties in operation.[1]

28-30. Negative Head.   The negative head at any point in a filter is equal to the intensity of vacuum at that point and is usually a maximum at the point where the water enters the underdrainage system.   It is represented by N in Fig. 28-20.

An undesirable feature of the existence of negative head in the operation of a filter is the occasional release of dissolved gases from the water

[1] See also A. B. Morrill, *J.A.W.W.A.*, April, 1934, p. 445.

into the sand layer, due to the decrease of pressure.   These gases may either accumulate in the sand, causing what is known as *air binding*,[1] or they may break through the filter, leaving an opening through which water may pass with imperfect treatment.   A result of air binding is the failure of the water to pass through the filter where the bubble of gas has accumulated.   This may result in loss of capacity of the filter or an over-loading of other portions of the filter.   The use of negative head has the advantages, in design, of permitting shallower filter boxes and, in operation, of permitting longer filter runs, provided no other difficulties arise.

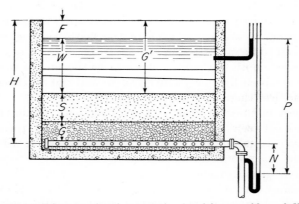

Fig. 28-20. Diagram showing negative head in a rapid sand filter.

28-31. The Loss of Head in Filter Operation.   The frictional resistance to the passage of water through the filtering medium and the underdrains of a rapid sand filter causes a loss of head in the operation of the filter. This loss of head is equal to the vertical distance between the surface of the water on the filter and the elevation of the hydraulic grade line at the filter outlet.   This elevation can be determined by placing a piezometer in the effluent pipe and observing the elevation of the water in the piezometer tube.

The loss of head in a rapid sand filter immediately after washing should not be more than 4 to 6 in.   The finer the sand or the greater the rate of filtration, the greater the initial head loss.   As the filter grows dirty during a run, the head loss builds up until the maximum permissible loss of 10 to 15 ft is reached.   The maximum loss of head usually allowed is 8 to 10 ft.   Greater loss is undesirable because of the tendency of the water pressure to pack the sand so tightly as to cause difficulties in washing or possibly to cause the water to break through the sand without filtration.

28-32. Control of Water Level on Filter.   The elevation of the surface of the water on a rapid sand filter is frequently fixed by the elevation of

[1] See also J. R. Baylis, *Water Works & Sewerage*, November, 1930, p. 379.

the outlet weir from the coagulating basin. The water surface in the filter cannot fall below this elevation, because, if it tends to do so, water is fed more rapidly from the coagulating basin to maintain the constant level. The loss of head in the conduits between the coagulating basin and the filter, being negligible, makes it possible to design the plant with the water surface on the filter and on the coagulating basin at the same elevation. Where water is pumped onto the surface of the filter, or another method for feeding the filter is used, the water level on the filter may be maintained by a float-controlled inlet valve which opens as the water level tends to sink and closes as it tends to rise.

An overflow leading from the filter box to the waste-water pipe is desirable unless provision is made to prevent overflow during washing. The capacity of the overflow conduit should be greater than that of the wash-water equipment.

28-33. Rate Control. A constant rate of filtration is desirable on a rapid sand filter, because either a sudden increase in rate may cause water to break through the filtering material without proper treatment, or the sudden increase in negative pressure required to pull water through the filter may release dissolved gases. A sudden reduction in the rate of filtration may likewise release a bubble of gas that has been entrained in the sand, causing it to make a hole through the filter bed. A constant rate of filtration may be secured by hand or by automatic control.

28-34. Manual Rate Control. There are two successful methods for manual rate control. In the first one, the water is applied to the filter at a constant rate. The constant rate of applied water is secured through the control of the influent valve. At the start of a filter run, the effluent valve is opened slightly, so that the loss of head through it and through the sand may be such as to maintain just sufficient depth of water on the sand to prevent the surface of the sand from disturbance by the entering water. As the sand becomes clogged, and the loss of head through the filter increases, the depth of water on the sand will increase. After it has increased to any desired limit, the effluent valve should be opened in order to decrease the loss of head through it. When the effluent valve is finally opened wide and the surface of the water approaches the top of the filter box, it is necessary to wash the filter for another run. It is to be noted that in this method of manual control the elevation of the surface of water in the filter is constantly changing.

In another method of manual control, a constant depth of water can be maintained on the filter. The effluent will pass through the venturi meter or other calibrated tube or orifice. The rate of discharge can be maintained approximately constant by opening the discharge valve to compensate for the loss of head through the filter. Such a method is not used frequently and is suitable mainly in small temporary installations.

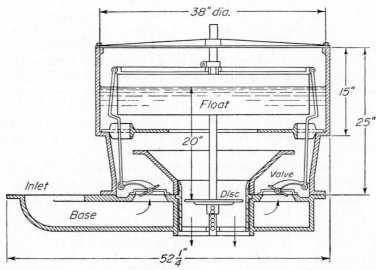

FIG. 28-21. Open or float-type rate controller. *(From C. G. Richardson, Water & Sewage Works, April, 1953, p. 123.)*

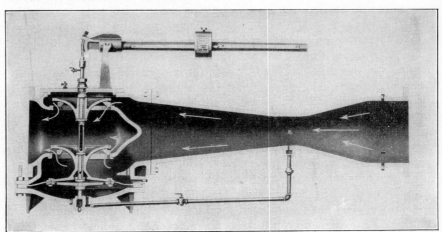

FIG. 28-22. Simplex rate controller; a closed-type controller. *(Courtesy of Simplex Valve and Meter Co.)*

28-35. Automatic Rate Control.[1]   There are two types of automatic rate controller, one open and the other submerged.   The operation of an open-type controller is explained in Sec. 28-5.   Open-type controllers, such as are shown in Figs. 28-1 and 28-21, are seldom used on rapid sand filters.

Many types of submerged rate controller are in use, but practically all of them depend on the principle of the venturi tube for their action.

[1] See also C. G. Richardson, *Water & Sewage Works*, April, 1953, p. 133.

Rate controllers are manufactured devices whose dimensions and capacities have not been widely standardized. A Simplex rate controller is shown in Fig. 28-22. It operates as follows: The direction of flow of water through the apparatus is shown in the figure. If the rate of flow increases through the venturi tube, the pressure in the control chamber where the balanced valve is located and the pressure at the throat will both increase, but the increase in the control chamber will be larger. The increased pressure on top of the flexible disk shown in the figure will force the balanced valve down, thus cutting down the rate of flow. The position of the valve controls the rate of flow through the device, and this position is regulated by means of the movable weight on the lever, as shown.

Other types of submerged rate controller are in use. In one the differential pressures in the venturi meter are conveyed to an "actuator" which in turn controls the flow in two high-pressure water pipes which actuate the hydraulic cylinder on the filter discharge pipe so that the discharge-valve opening will maintain a constant rate of flow. In another type a butterfly valve is placed in the effluent pipe.[1] A counterweighted arm on the valve spindle is connected to a float on the surface of the water on the filter. If for any reason this surface tends to rise the valve is opened to compensate for the head loss on the filter. The effluent rate is thus automatically kept equal to the influent rate.

When the clear-water basin of a filtration plant becomes filled, it is desirable to cut down the rate of filtration. This may be done automatically by a master controller which affects the controller on each filter.

The accuracy of operation of a rate controller can be tested by filling the filter box with water, closing all but the effluent valve, and observing the rate at which the water level drops on the filter. The discrepancy between the setting of the rate controller and the rate of the dropping of the water in the filter box will indicate the error of the controller.

28-36. Pipe Gallery. The pipe gallery is the corridor beneath the operating floor and between the two rows of filters facing each other, in which the pipes, valves, rate controllers, and some other equipment necessary to the functioning of the filters are usually placed. Where only one row of filters exists the pipe gallery is the corridor in front of the row of filters. A cross section of a typical pipe gallery is shown in Fig. 28-8. Each main pipe has a branch to each filter, and each branch has a gate valve which is controlled from the operating floor, usually from the operating table. Other pipes and conduits, such as heating pipes and electric conduits, may be placed in the pipe gallery for convenience. The pipes necessary for filter operation normally found in a pipe gallery, and the velocity of flow normally provided in design in each pipe, are listed

[1] See T. J. Riddick, *J.A.W.W.A.*, August, 1952, pp. 733, 742.

in Table 28-1. The velocities are approximately economical in each case, except as noted for the influent pipe.

TABLE 28-1. Velocities of Flow in Pipes in a Pipe Gallery

Pipe	Velocity, fps, for cast-iron pipe*
Influent	1–2†
Effluent	4‡
Wash water	10
Wash air	40
Waste water or sewer	5–10‡
Filtered-water waste	5–10‡

* Somewhat lower velocities are allowed in concrete conduits.

† Slower than strictly economical, to avoid breaking floc.

‡ All available head between filter and clear-water storage basin, or other outlet, should be utilized.

The size of the main conduits in the gallery should be changed along the gallery as the branch pipes remove or add water to them, except in the case of the wash-water or wash-air pipe. Where only one filter is to be washed at a time, the flow in the branch wash-water or wash-air pipe is the same as the flow in the main pipe, and hence the branch and the main pipes are of the same size.

Some point of the branch air pipe should be placed at an elevation higher than the highest possible elevation of the surface of the water in the filter. This precaution is taken in order to avoid the possibility of siphoning the contents of the filter box into the air piping.

The location of the pipes and the conduits in the pipe gallery should be such as to secure the greatest convenience in working on and inspecting the conduits. Good light, good ventilation, good drainage, and a wide, unobstructed passageway for the entire length of the gallery are conducive to proper care of the equipment placed in it. Dampness in the pipe gallery is difficult to control. It may be diminished by insulating the cold-water pipes, and it can be prevented by dehumidification of the air in the gallery.[1]

28-37. Materials, Joints, and Supports for Pipes. Cast iron and concrete are the principal materials used for conduits in a pipe gallery. Steel pipe is sometimes used for conveying wash air. Threaded joints are seldom used on pipes more than 8 in. in diameter. Flange joints make a neat appearance, are easy to connect when the pipe is in proper position, and are extensively used. An undesirable feature of the use of flanged joints is the difficulty of taking up small discrepancies in the position of the pipe, as the flange joint is inflexible. Such pipes may be passed through a concrete wall by means of a packed sleeve, somewhat as indicated in Fig. 28-23. The bell-and-spigot joint is probably the least expensive to make, and slight errors in the location of the pipe can be

[1] See also F. G. Gordon, *Pure Water*, July, 1951, p. 132.

taken up by the play allowed in the bell. The joint occupies considerable space, however, and space is required in which to calk it. Specials with bell-and-spigot ends take more space than is required by any other form of cast-iron special. When bell-and-spigot joints are used, care must be taken to prevent the blowing open of the joints due to unbalanced pressure on dead ends. To avoid this possibility, some form of end restraint is necessary on a bell-and-spigot pipe line with lead joints. Where the end of the pipes cannot be anchored or braced against a permanent structure, it may be necessary to tie the pipe together with cables.

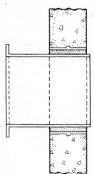

The connections, specials, and lengths of pipe used in fitting up the pipe gallery should be made according to standards available in manufacturers' stocks in order to secure the greatest economy. The cost to manufacture fittings not in stock is so much greater than for standard fittings that the use of nonstandard fittings in small plants is almost prohibitive.

The pipes of the pipe gallery should be well supported because of their weight and the shocks that come on them in operation. In general, each piece of pipe should be so supported that the weight does not come on a joint where the axis of the pipe is in any position other than vertical. This is particularly true of bell-and-spigot joints.

Fig. 28-23. Cast-iron pipe with packed opening passing through a concrete wall.

28-38. Valves in Pipe Galleries.[1] Control valves, usually gate valves, are subject to frequent use, requiring design features including (1) rugged construction; (2) hydraulic, electric, or manual control; (3) rising stem, outside screw-and-yoke pattern; (4) water-supply pipes to hydraulic valves tapped into the cylinder wall, not the cylinder head, to permit ease of removal of the head; (5) heavy, bronze tail rod on the hydraulic piston, passing through a stuffing box in the cylinder head, with a bronze eyelet on the protruding end of the rod to permit manual operation of the valve in the event of loss of hydraulic power; and (6) fully bronze mounting in the valve. Valves should be placed, in general, with the stem vertical and opening upward, with a stop that can be placed to hold a hydraulic valve in position. If a large gate valve is placed with the disk in a horizontal position, either flat or on edge, a heavy bronze track should be provided on which the disk rides until just before contacting the valve seat.

28-39. Washing Filters.[2] A filter should be washed when the loss of head through it has reached the maximum permissible. The washing of

---

[1] See also Water Treatment Plant Design, *Am. Soc. Civil Engrs., Manual of Engineering Practice* 19, p. 78, 1940.

[2] See also J. R. Baylis, *J.A.W.W.A.*, February, 1954, p. 176.

a rapid sand filter is accomplished by reversing the flow of water through it. In some plants the sand is agitated with air or by mechanical rakes while it is suspended in the rising stream of wash water. The use of mechanical rakes is now obsolete, and the use of air is not extensive.

The quality of the wash water should be as good as that of the effluent from the filters where filtration is for hygienic purposes. The dirty water from the filters is usually run to waste, but in some plants this water is of sufficient value to justify its reclamation and purification. This may be accomplished by sedimentation, after which the effluent from the wash-water salvage basin is passed through the filters.

The steps in the washing of a rapid sand filter, in which water alone is used for washing, are as follows:

1. Close the influent valve and allow the water in the filter to drain down somewhat. Some operators allow the water to drain down to the edge of the wash-water gutter; others, to near the top of the sand; and others, to a midway point.

2. Close the effluent valve.

3. Open the waste-water valve to the sewer.

4. Open the wash-water valve gradually, to prevent dislodgment of the gravel by entrapped air, and allow the wash water to flow through the filter and out through the wash-water gutters until it is certain that the filter is properly cleaned.

5. Close the wash-water valve.

6. Close the waste-water valve to the sewer after the water in the filter has drained down to the edge of the wash-water gutter.

7. Open the influent valve slightly.

8. Open the rewash valve, and allow some of the water to drain to the sewer. (This step is frequently omitted.)

9. Close the rewash valve.

10. Open the effluent and the influent valves. The filter is now back in service.

The wash water, as a rule, should be turned on gently at first to avoid concentrating it at a few spots in the underdrainage system, resulting in mixing the gravel with the sand. At some plants, wash-water rate controllers are used which operate either automatically or manually.[1]

When air agitation is used it is undesirable to apply both air and water simultaneously because of the danger of disturbing the gravel or of losing the sand into the wash-water gutter. Jet action of wash water against the gravel or against the sand above the gravel is undesirable to avoid dangers of disturbing the gravel or causing mounds and craters in the filter bed. The wash-air valve is sometimes opened before the wash-water valve in order to break up the sand surface, making the passage of the wash water through the sand easier at the start.

[1] See also C. I. Dodd, *ibid.*, March, 1937, p. 322.

28-40. Surface Wash. Surface wash, in rapid-sand-filter practice, refers to a method of applying wash water or mechanical agitation, or both, at or near the surface of the sand in the filter. Many different schemes are in use for which satisfaction is claimed.[1] In some plants a wash-water distribution system has been suspended about 4 in. above the undisturbed sand surface with holes facing down to supply water jets under high pressure. During washing both surface and subsurface wash may be used simultaneously, the swirling motion of the wash water serving to scrub the sand grains effectively against one another. In some plants the surface may be broken up with a high-pressure stream from a fire hose; in others a surface washing device may be improvised by attaching a length of perforated pipe to a fire hose, the device being moved about on the sand surface during washing.

The Palmer filter-bed agitator is a widely used proprietary device. It consists of a revolving arm composed of a perforated pipe driven by approximately horizontal jet reaction, suspended slightly above the undisturbed surface of the sand. The agitator is used in conjunction with subsurface wash.

28-41. Sand Expansion. When a filter is being washed the sand should be expanded to about 140 to 150 per cent of its undisturbed volume. The location of the surface of the sand during washing can be determined with the aid of a properly protected electric light on the end of a rod held in the hands of the operator,[2] by means of an inverted hollow counterweighted cone[3] connected to an indicator on the operating table or other convenient location, and by other means. The purpose of expanding the sand is to rub the sand grains together. Too much expansion will disperse the grains so that they will not contact each others, and too little will result in too little rubbing together. Since the amount that the sand is expanded is a function of the viscosity of the wash water, its rate of rise, and of other conditions; and since the viscosity varies with the temperature, and the temperature with the season, it follows that the rate of washing should not be the same throughout the year. Conditions during washing should be observed carefully by the operator and experience must be the principal guide to the best rate and amount of washing. Adjustable rate-of-flow controllers are sometimes installed on wash-water pipes, connected to a visible indicating gage, to enable the operator to know at what rate the filter is being washed.

28-42. Wash-water Pressure. The pressure at which the wash water should be applied is about 15 ft of head of water as measured in the underdrains. In the determination of the discharge pressure from the

---

[1] See also J. R. Baylis, *J. New Engl. Water Works Assoc.*, Vol. 51, pp. 1, 26, 1937.

[2] See also: G. F. Gilkinson, *Proc. 9th Ann. Water Works School Univ. Kansas*, 1931, p. 106; E. S. Hopkins, *Eng. News-Record*, May 23, 1929, p. 844.

[3] See also *Water Works Eng.*, Jan. 5, 1938, p. 33.

wash-water pump or tank, the loss of head in the underdrainage system and in the pipes leading to it should be computed. These losses have been reported[1] as between 10 and 63 ft, dependent on the rate of washing and on other conditions.

Wash-water pressure can be obtained in any one of three ways: (1) by means of an elevated storage tank into which water is pumped continuously at such a rate as to fill the tank between washings, (2) by means of a wash-water pump that operates only when a filter is being washed, or (3) by taking water from the water-works distribution system in the streets through a pressure-reducing valve. Both the first and the second methods are frequently used. The disadvantages of the third method are so great as to preclude its use in well-designed plants. The advantages of the first method are that only a relatively small pump is needed and that it can be operated continuously at the highest efficiency. A disadvantage is that a large, and usually unsightly, wash-water storage tank is needed. The advantage of the second method is that the tank is not required. The wash-water pump is large and expensive, however, and because of its intermittent use cannot be operated to the best economy.

28-43. Capacity of Wash-water Equipment. Normally the rate at which wash water is applied, where no other agitation is provided, is 2 cu ft water per min per sq ft filter surface, equivalent to a rise in the filter box of 24 in. per min. The tendency in design is toward higher rates of washing, primarily because of the larger sizes of sand being used, which require a faster application of water for equal expansion. The capacity of the wash-water storage tank should be sufficient to give a normal wash to two filters for a period of 5 to 6 min at the maximum rate without requiring the refilling of the tank.[2]

28-44. Disposal of Used Wash Water.[3] The polluted condition of the used wash water from a filter creates a problem in its disposal. Methods of disposal include (1) discharge into the public sewer; (2) treatment in a wash-water salvage plant, returning the salvaged water to the filter plant and disposing of the sludge as discussed in Sec. 29-10; or (3) by sedimentation, either with or without coagulation, disposal of the supernatant into a nearby body of water, and treatment of the sludge as discussed in Sec. 29-10.

28-45. Wash-air Equipment. Wash air is usually applied by means of a blower or compressor, but it may be supplied through a wash-air storage tank in which air is accumulated between washings. Wash air should be applied at a rate of about 2 to 5 cu ft free air per min per sq ft filter surface for a period of about 5 min. The air pressure is slightly greater than the

---

[1] See G. G. Dixon, *Water Works & Sewerage*, April, 1933, p. 104.

[2] See Water Treatment Plant Design, *loc. cit.*

[3] See also H. R. Hale, *J.A.W.W.A.*, December, 1947, p. 1219.

depth of water above the air-distribution system plus the friction in the air pipes, which is usually quite small. The wash-air storage tank should hold at least double the amount of air necessary to wash one filter. The compressor supplying the wash-air storage tank should have sufficient capacity to refill the tank between washings.

All wash-water and wash-air pumping equipment should be installed in duplicate as a factor of safety in the event of sudden breakdown and in order that repairs may be made on one pump or blower while the load is being carried by the other machine.

28-46. Amount of Washing. Only experience will tell when the filter has been washed sufficiently. The appearance of the rising water in the filter and the ability of the operator to see through the water to the sand layer are usually guides on which the judgment is based. When the wash water is flowing through the filter, the sand should appear to rise evenly in all parts of the filter, and care must be taken not to wash so vigorously as to carry the sand into the wash-water trough. The wash is usually stopped when the water is sufficiently clear for the sand to be visible. On completion of the wash, the sand should settle back into place so as to present a smooth level surface. The duration of a wash is usually in the neighborhood of 3 to 6 min. It is desirable to use as little water for washing as possible, because of the cost of the water. In a properly operated plant the quantity of wash water used should not exceed about 2 per cent of the total amount of water filtered. Lower amounts have been attained, and higher amounts are sometimes encountered.

Some conclusions based on experience in the washing of filters are[1] (1) the use of air in washing may do more harm than good, because of air bubbles entrained in the sand and gravel, and the blowing of gravel into the sand; (2) rise of wash water under standard rates of backwash is insufficient to remove heavier clay particles and encourages their accumulation in the filter bed; (3) insufficiently washed sand grains may adhere to one another under pressure of normal flow, causing undulations and cracks in the filter surface; (4) the refilling of filters after draining, by running backwash water through the underdrains, endangers security of the gravel layer which may be mixed with the sand.

28-47. Operating Tables and Equipment. An operating table holds the equipment for the control of the filter. One is illustrated in Fig. 28-24. Valves controlled from the operating table include

Influent	Waste water or sewer	Wash air
Effluent	Wash water	Rewash

Other equipment placed on the operating table includes

Loss-of-head gage	Sampling device	Rate-of-flow gage

[1] See also T. D. Key, *Water and Water Eng.*, January, 1949, p. 25.

Valves may be operated either manually, electrically, or hydraulically. A hydraulically operated valve is illustrated in Fig. 18-3. Where the valves are operated manually they are controlled by handwheels placed on stands and not on the operating table. Where the valves are controlled hydraulically or electrically, the control handles or buttons are grouped on the operating table in such a manner that the operator can observe what is happening in the filter. Since the sequence of steps in washing is fixed, automatic interlocking equipment has been found advantageous in some plants.

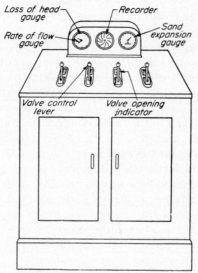

In conveying pressure from the pipes in the gallery to the gages on the table, or in protecting cables attached to hydraulic valves, copper tubing is desirable because of the corrosion of steel piping.

28-48. Loss-of-head Gages. The simplest form of loss-of-head gage is illustrated in Fig. 28-20. This type of gage is not suited for general use, because the levels of the surfaces of the water in the two piezometers are usually too far apart when it is time to wash the filter to be seen from one position. In order to overcome this difficulty, it is necessary to transmit information of these two water levels to the same place so that they can be compared. Since only the difference in elevation of these two water surfaces is important, this is the information that is usually conveyed to the operator by the loss-of-head gage on the operating table.

FIG. 28-24. Operating table for a rapid-sand-filter plant. (*Taken by permission from "The Sanitary Industry," by Johns Manville, Industrial Products Division.*)

28-49. Sampling Devices. As the water leaving a filter is under atmospheric pressure, it will not rise to the height of the operating table to permit sampling at a convenient point. A common method of raising the water to the table for sampling is by means of a small hand pump placed on the operating table. In taking a sample, considerable water should be pumped to waste, through the drain provided on the operating table, in order to assure the collection of a representative sample.

28-50. Clear-water Basin. The clear-water basin acts as an equalizing reservoir which permits the filter to act at a constant rate. The reservoir capacity is based on the principles outlined for an equalizing reservoir in Sec. 20-4. The prediction of the fluctuations of demand to be met after the completion of the filter plant does not always justify so detailed a study as is required in the determination of the capacity of an equalizing reservoir. It is commoner practice to allow a certain number of hours of storage, usually in the neighborhood of 8 to 12 hr. Supplementary storage on the distribution system is frequently desirable.

The clear-water basin should be carefully protected against contamination. A lightproof and insectproof roof should be provided to prevent the growth of algae in the basin and to prevent access to the basin by insects which cause trouble by laying eggs in the water. Such a roof will serve also as a protection from birds and other surface sources of contamination. Manholes in the basin roof should be made watertight, but ventilation is necessary in order to avoid abnormal air pressures when the reservoir is being filled or emptied. No sewers should be permitted within the neighborhood of the clear-water basin, and the basin should be secure against leakage from either within or without.

28-51. Operation of a Rapid-sand-filter Plant. The operation of a rapid sand filter for a public water supply is a responsible task upon which the health and lives of a community depend. It may include such duties as (1) observation of the characteristics of the raw water to determine procedure in subsequent treatment; (2) chlorination of the raw water; (3) control of coagulation through pH adjustment, and the selection of coagulants and the adjustment of dosages and mixing, flocculating, and coagulating equipment; (4) application of activated carbon; (5) filter washing; (6) postchlorination; (7) taste and odor control; and (8) duties connected with the maintenance and operation of plant, equipment, and buildings and grounds.

Routine observations that should be recorded in the control of the operation of a filtration plant should include (1) the quantity of water treated daily; (2) length of run of each filter between washings; (3) percentage of wash water used for each filter; (4) quantity of chemicals used and rates of application for all purposes; (5) alkalinity, turbidity, color, temperature, and possibly the solids in the raw, settled, filtered, and chlorinated water; and (7) presumptive tests for coliforms in the raw, settled, filtered, and chlorinated water.[1]

Conditions that must be guarded against in the operation of a filtration plant include (1) formation of mud balls, (2) cracking or shrinking of the filter bed, (3) overloading, (4) shortening of filter runs, (5) air binding, (6) loss of sand, (7) growth of sand particles, and (8) displacement of the gravel.[2]

28-52. Floc Penetration. The filter may be penetrated deeply by floc. The depth of penetration is dependent on such conditions as rate of filtration, head loss through the filter, and density of suspended matter in the water, porosity of the filtering material, temperature, and floc indexes

---

[1] See also C. P. Hoover, *J.A.W.W.A.*, 1933, p. 1279.

[2] See also H. E. Hudson, Jr., *J. New Engl. Water Works Assoc.*, March, 1937, p. 1.

described in Sec. 27-37. In general, under satisfactory conditions of operation, floc should penetrate not more than 2 to 6 in., after which the head loss through the filter should increase rapidly, necessitating washing of the filter.

28-53. Mud Balls. Mud balls consist of grains of sand, and of material carried over from the coagulating basin, stuck together in clumps varying from the size of a pea to 1 to 2 in. or more in diameter. Because of their lighter specific gravity, balls are found most densely collected at or near the top of the filter; but when of a specific gravity equal to or heavier than that of the sand[1] they may be distributed throughout the sand and, in some cases, attached firmly to the gravel. Mud balls accumulate over spots where the rising swirls and velocities of the wash water are least violent, thus inducing unevenness in the rise of wash water and aggravating the inequality of the filter wash.[2]

Large caked lumps of sand are more commonly found attached to the gravel or to the side walls of the filter. It is believed that the cause of mud-ball formation is insufficient washing of the sand which permits gelatinous material to adhere to the surface of the sand grains. The effect is noticed particularly in fine sands, less than 0.4 mm in diameter, and is aggravated by the presence of microorganisms, manganese, and other substances in the water. Although a 50 per cent expansion of the sand is effective in minimizing the production of mud balls, it is not a certain preventive. Control of the quality of the water applied to the filter has been found an effective preventive of mud-ball formation in some plants.[3]

Methods of removing mud balls and hard spots in the filter after they have formed include (1) dipping them off the surface with strainers while wash water is running through the filter at a slow rate; (2) breaking them up with rakes and sharp hoes and subsequently washing off the particles; (3) washing the sand in place to break up the mud balls either with a high-velocity jet issuing from a nozzle with which the sand may be prodded and stirred, or by means of a high-velocity surface wash; (4) washing the filter or allowing it to stand full for some time, up to 48 hr, with a solution of some chemical, as described in Sec. 28-55; (5) digging out the hard spots with shovels; or (6) removing, cleaning, and replacing the sand.

Baylis[4] describes how to determine the size and volume of mud balls and states that where the volume of the balls in the top 6 in. of the filter is less than 0.1 per cent of the volume of the sand in the same space, the condition of the filter may be considered excellent, but where it is 5 per

---

[1] See also J. R. Baylis, *ibid.*, March, 1937, p. 1.

[2] See also E. S. Hopkins, *J. Penna. Water Works Operators' Assoc.*, 1932, p. 74.

[3] See also J. R. Baylis, *Water Works & Sewerage*, January, 1935, p. 20.

[4] J. R. Baylis, *J.A.W.W.A.*, July, 1937, pp. 1010, 1022.

cent or over, the filter is in a very bad condition. Among the principal objections to the presence of mud balls in a filter is the danger from cracking and clogging of the filter bed.

28-54. Cracking and Clogging of Filter Bed. Cracks in the filter bed and the pulling away of the sand from the side walls are caused by the compression of the soft gelatinous coating on the sand grains which allows the grains to push together as the head loss is increased during the operation of the filter. The condition is remedied by much the same methods as the formation of mud balls is overcome. The effect of such shrinkage of the filter bed is to permit dirty matter to penetrate deeply into the bed, even into the gravel, and to impair both the washing of the filter and the efficiency of filtration.

Baylis[1] has shown hypothetically, as indicated in Fig. 28-25, how cracks form in filters and dirt and coagulant penetrate the bed.

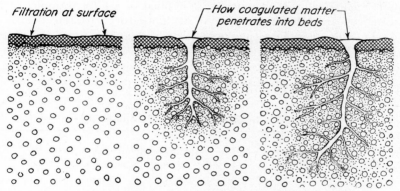

FIG. 28-25. Diagram showing cracking and penetration of a rapid sand filter. (*Courtesy of John R. Baylis.*)

28-55. Cleaning Rapid Sand Filters. It may be necessary, at times, to clean the filter sand or the gravel to overcome difficulties from mud balls, cracking, and other causes. Usually cleaning serves only as a temporary expedient. The cause of clogging should be corrected. Various chemical treatments have been used, such as caustic soda, sulphuric acid, hydrochloric acid, soda ash, sulphur dioxide, and chlorine.[2] Chlorine may be used where the material to be removed is of biologic origin; copper sulphate may be effective against algae; caustic soda for alum deposits and organic material; hydrochloric acid or carbonic acid against calcium carbonate; and sulphur dioxide for dissolving iron, manganese, or alum. H.T.H., Perchloron, or Clorox may be used in

[1] J. R. Baylis, *Pure Water*, December, 1952.

[2] See also: J. C. Geyer, *J.A.W.W.A.*, May, 1937, p. 668; *Water Works Eng.*, Feb. 2, 1938, p. 149; J. R. Baylis, *J. New Engl. Water Works Assoc.*, Vol. 51, p. 1, 1937; C. R. Cox, Water Supply Control, *New York State Dept. Health*, *Bull.* 22, pp. 77ff., 1943.

small filters.   Liquid chlorine may be used more economically on large filters.   Chlorine may be applied as a solution at a concentration of about 50 ppm of available chlorine.   The solution should stand in contact with the sand for 4 to 24 hr or longer.   Caustic soda can be applied as a solution or, preferably, by spreading 1.0 to 3.0 lb of the flaked material per square foot of the filter surface.   The soda is dissolved by allowing the wash water to rise 4 to 5 in. above the sand.

Sulphur dioxide has been used, as a patented process,[1] to clean filter sand coated with iron or manganese.   A 1 to 2 per cent aqueous solution of sulphur dioxide is pumped into the filter and circulated through the underdrains and the filter for about 24 hr.   The method is not recommended where the sand grains are coated with calcium carbonate because of the possibility of cementing the grains together with calcium sulphate or sulphite which might be formed.[2]

Before acids or other chemicals are applied to a filter, samples of the sand to be cleaned should be tested in the laboratory with the chemical to be used.   Some concentrations and periods of application of chemicals that have been used with varying degrees of success are indicated in Table 28-2.   After chemicals have been used, the filter should be thoroughly washed to remove the loosened substances and to remove the chemicals.

TABLE 28-2. Chemicals Used for Cleaning Filters

Chemical	Amount of chemical used or strength of solution	Period of contact, hr
Caustic soda and soda ash.........	NaOH 1.8 psf	48†
	Na$_2$CO$_3$ 5.2 psf	
Caustic soda....................	0.8–1.2 psf	22–72
Soda ash......................	0.2 lb per gal	24–36
Sulphuric acid.................	0.092 psf	4
Chlorine......................	10–12 lb per million gal and 50 ppm	48
Sulphur dioxide*...............	2 per cent	16

* *Water Works Eng.*, Feb. 2, 1938, p. 149.
† Tank heated with steam.

The handling of chemicals used in the cleaning of rapid sand filters is hazardous.   A special committee of the American Water Works Association has reported on precautions and methods in the handling of such chemicals.[3]

[1] U.S. Patent 2,069,621.

[2] See also: C. F. Angle, *Water & Sewage Works*, March, 1947, p. 1947; J. P. Harris, *Public Health Eng. Abs.*, June, 1948, p. 31.

[3] See Third Report of Committee on Chemical Hazards in Water Works Plants, *J.A.W.W.A.*, March, 1939, p. 489.

Mechanical methods of cleaning filters in place include raking, scraping the surface, use of a high-pressure water jet, ejecting the sand, and the use of steam. In some cases the sand may be removed either by hand tools or by a hydraulic ejector and cleaned outside the filter. All these methods have been found helpful in overcoming unexpected difficulties, but they should not be depended on as routine procedure. The cause of the difficulty should be discovered and remedied.

28-56. Maintaining Filter Runs. The length of the filter run is affected by the character of the influent water, the rate of filtration, the loss of head permitted between washings, and the thoroughness of each wash. The character of the water that is applied to the filter is under the control of the operator insofar as he is able to affect it in the coagulating basin through the application of chemicals, more satisfactory conditioning, or a change in the period of subsidence. Only experience with the particular water being treated can serve as a guide in any particular plant but, in general, an increase in turbidity or in certain microorganisms will shorten filter runs.[1] Experience reported by Baylis[2] shows the length of filter run at a 2 gpm per sq ft rate to be about 2.3 times the length at a 5 gpm per sq ft rate, *i.e.*, about 8 per cent more water passes through a filter between washings at the higher rate of filtration.

The runs may be lengthened by a more thorough pretreatment of the water or by diminishing the rate of filtration. Where too high a loss of head is permitted between washings, the length of run may be diminished by air binding resulting from the accumulation of gases thrown out of solution as a result of the reduced pressure in the filter. A remedy is the reduction of the loss of head between washings. In some plants the length of run may be increased by "bumping" the filter occasionally between washings. A filter is bumped by preparing it, in the ordinary manner, for washing and turning on the wash water for a moment to break up the schmutzdecke.

28-57. Loss of Sand. Sand is carried out of the filter by wash water usually as a result of the increase in the size of the sand grains by material that adheres to them, reducing the specific gravity of the clump and exposing more surface to the rising wash water. The loss of sand is particularly noticeable as the temperature of the wash water decreases because of the increased lifting power of the water with increasing viscosity. Since the cause of the difficulty is dirty sand, to decrease the rate of wash may serve ultimately either to aggravate the condition or to cause other troubles in the filter operation. The ultimate effective remedy is to clean the sand.

28-58. Growth of Size of Sand Particles. Increase in the size of sand particles in a filter is due to the quality of the raw water resulting in the

[1] See also L. A. Marshall, *Water Works Eng.*, Sept. 24, 1930, p. 443.

[2] J. R. Baylis, *Pure Water*, June, 1951.

deposition of a scale or of a gelatinous layer on the surface of the sand.   A
hard scale of calcium carbonate may form in a lime-soda softening plant
as a result of incomplete recarbonation, dissolved calcium carbonate
being thrown out of solution through the absence of sufficient dissolved
carbon dioxide.   The increase of carbon dioxide may also serve to dissolve manganese that has deposited on the sand grains[1] The remedy
for the condition lies in the control of the quality of the water being
placed on the filter.

28-59. Displacement of Gravel.   Displacement of the gravel in a
filter may result from a break in the underdrainage system, from uneven
distribution of the wash water, or from the use of too high a rate of wash.
The condition aggravates the unevenness of the wash-water distribution,
mixes the gravel with the sand, and may permit the escape of sand into
the underdrains.

The condition may be remedied by diminishing the rate of filtration or
by repairing or renovating the underdrainage system.   The escape of
sand into the underdrains is dangerous, because its remedy is expensive,
usually involving the shutdown of the filter and the tearing up and replacing of the underdrain pipes.   Gravel that has become misplaced in a
filter may sometimes be replaced without shutting down the filter by
drawing a straightedge across the surface of the gravel while wash water
is running through the filter.   The fine gravel, which is almost suspended
in the rising wash water, is easily shifted about in this manner.

28-60. Permissible Loads on Treatment Plants.   Various authorities
have adopted standards of quality for raw water that is to enter a treatment plant.   A compilation of the general trend of these standards is
shown in Table 28-3.

Insofar as the load of zinc, manganese, iron, and similar substances in
the raw water is concerned, there seems to be no limit to the amount that
can be removed by purification, except the practical question of economy.
No practicable method has, as yet, been devised for the removal of sodium
chloride, the presence of which in the raw water supply is therefore
limited to the amount permissible in the effluent.   Other substances that
should be excluded from the plant influent are the phenols and cresols
and other tarry derivatives from gas and coke by-product manufacturing.
The presence of decayed vegetation and of excessive growths of microorganisms is undesirable in the influent and should therefore be excluded.

28-61. Results of Rapid Sand Filtration.   A rapid sand filter will
remove suspended matter, color, odor, and bacteria from water and will so
alter the characteristics of certain polluted or otherwise undesirable
waters as to make them suitable for domestic and most industrial uses.
The removal of bacteria is usually insufficiently effective to place dependence on the filter alone for the production of a hygienically safe water.

[1] See also L. V. Carpenter, *Am. J. Public Health,* October, 1931, p. 1153.

Where the bacterial load is at all heavy, the filtration process must be supplemented by sterilization. Raw water with turbidities as high as 35 to 40 ppm can be successfully treated by rapid sand filtration. Color can be reduced to 10 ppm or less.

TABLE 28-3. Standards of Quality of Raw Water Supplies Requiring Treatment*

Characteristic	Disinfection only	Filtration and disinfection	Filtration, special auxiliary treatment, and disinfection
BOD, ppm:			
Monthly avg..................	0.75	1.5–2.5	2.0–5.5
Max day or sample...........	1.0	3.0–3.5	4.0–7.5
Coliform, MPN per 100 ml:			
Monthly avg..................	50–100	240–5,000	10,000–20,000
Max day or sample...........	......	20% 5,000	(TVA)
		5% 20,000†	
Dissolved oxygen, ppm..........	4.0–7.5	2.5–7.0	2.5–6.5
% saturation...................	50–75	25–75	
pH avg.......................	6.0–8.5	5.0–9.0	3.8–10.5
Chlorides, max ppm.............	50	250	500
Fe plus Mn, max ppm...........	0.3	1.0	15
Fluorides, ppm.................	1.0	1.0	1.0
Phenolic compounds, max ppm....	None	0.005	0.025
Color, ppm....................	0–20	20–70	150
Turbidity, ppm................	0–10	40–250	

* From "Water Quality Criteria," State Water Pollution Control Board, Sacramento, Calif., 1952.

† See *J.A.W.W.A.*, Vol. 84, p. 61, 1946; *U.S. Public Health Service, Bull.* 296.

Streeter[1] has expressed the relation between the bacterial quality of raw water and the effluent resulting from coagulation and sedimentation as $E_a = cR^n/\log T$ in which R denotes the bacterial content of the raw water, E_a that of the effluent from the settling basin, and c and n are empirical constants. When T was expressed in hours, the values of c and n for the experimental plant were found to be 0.57 and 0.88, respectively. The U.S. Public Health Service[2] has expressed the relationship between the bacterial content of influent and effluent water in purification processes as

$$y = cx^n$$

in which x and y denote, respectively, the bacterial content of the influent and of the effluent water.

Some results of the operation of rapid sand filters are shown in Table 28-4. A comprehensive summary of such results is given in *Public Health Bulletin* 172, 1927.

[1] H. W. Streeter, *Public Works*, December, 1933, p. 17.

[2] The Efficiency of Water Purification Processes, *Public Health Bull.* 193, 1930.

TABLE 28-4. Removal of Bacteria by Various Water-purification Processes

	Cincinnati* B. coli per cc				Lousiville* B. coli per cc				Akron,† % removal		Cincinnati,† % removal		Ports- mouth,† % removal	
Raw water.............	685	3,150	9,190	26,400	845	3,350	7,620	30,900	Total	B. coli	Total	B. coli	Total	B. coli
Settled................	362	759	1,170	1,690	592	1,540	2,500	2,490	73	82	80 to 90 87.3‡	80 to 90 83.1§		
Coagulated............	84	183	256	524	116	228	369	633	38	69	70 to 90 83.8‡	70 to 80 77.5	70	
Filtered...............	10	26	43	140	9	13	16	30	81	61	80 or better	80 or better	50	
Chlorinated............	2.5	9	20	44	0.9	2.9	3.9	6	..	..	75.3‡	84.6†		
All combined§..........	99.63	99.68	99.78	99.84	99.89	99.91	99.95	99.98	..	..	99.93‡	99.95†		

* Studies of the Effect of Water Purification Processes, *Public Health Bull.* 172, 1927.

† Report, Ohio Conference on Water Purification, 1922.

‡ Average for 1917–1921, inclusive.

§ B. coli index, average for 1917–1921, inclusive.

28-62. Pressure Filters. A pressure filter is a rapid sand filter placed in a closed watertight tank, as shown in Fig. 28-26. The water passes through the sand and emerges from the filter under a pressure greater than atmospheric. The filter is operated similarly to a gravity-type

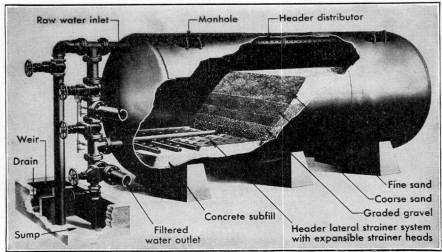

Raw water inlet — Manhole — Header distributor

Weir — Drain

Fine sand — Coarse sand — Graded gravel

Concrete subfill — Header lateral strainer system with expansible strainer heads

Sump — Filtered water outlet

Fig. 28-26. Horizontal pressure filter. (*Courtesy of the Permutit Co.*)

filter except that the coagulated water is usually applied directly to the filter without mixing, flocculation, or conditioning. Automatic filters are available in which the valves are manipulated automatically to backwash at a predetermined time or head loss. It is to be noted that the head loss through the filter is approximately the same as through a gravity filter. The term *pressure filter* does not imply that water is pumped through the filter under a high pressure loss.

Pressure filters are used primarily in small plants and in industries where the raw water is received, and the filtered water is discharged, under pressure, no pumps being required; and where automatic operation is suitable.

The coagulant, normally ammonium alum, is applied by means of an "alum pot." This is a pressure container placed in the influent line to the filter, the influent water dissolving the alum as it enters the filter. The arrangement is shown in Fig. 27-1. Ammonium alum is used because its solubility, lower than that of ordinary filter alum (aluminum sulphate), preserves it from too rapid solution. It also has some advantages where subsequent chloramine disinfection is applied.

The use of pressure filters for public water supplies is unusual because of cost, inefficiency of filtration, and the relatively poor quality of results obtained.

28-63. Double Filtration. Double filtration consists of the filtration of water through two or more slow sand filters in series, or through a rapid sand filter and then through a slow sand filter or through another rapid sand filter. Where double filtration is practiced, the use of preliminary, or "roughing" filters, of the rapid sand type is common. Whatever the type of the preliminary filter, its filtering material is coarser than that in the final filter, and the rate of filtration is higher. Roughing filters of the rapid sand type seldom require the use of coagulant, and they may be operated at rates as high as 130 gpm per sq ft.

Double filtration is found useful primarily in increasing the capacity of existing slow sand filters where the available area of land is restricted or in the construction of slow-sand-filter plants on restricted areas. As a result of the preliminary treatment at Walton, England,[1] the slow sand filters were more than doubled in capacity.

[1] See *Water Works*, September, 1926, p. 419.

CHAPTER 29

WATER SOFTENING

29-1. Purposes.[1] Among the principal purposes of water softening may be included (1) conservation of soap, (2) reduction of work in the laundry, (3) prevention of the formation of scale in steam boilers, and (4) preparation of water for domestic and industrial uses. Softening increases the efficiency of filtration; aids in the removal of color, iron, and manganese; makes possible, through proper operation, the production of a noncorrosive water; improves the cooking of foods and is desirable for other domestic purposes; and increases the efficiency of reduction of bacteria when filtration follows softening. Where soap is used in hard water, an undesirable precipitate of calcium and magnesium compounds, combined or mixed with other substances, is formed which deposits a scum or scale that is difficult to remove. Although "soaps and detergents are similar chemical compounds,"[2] and both will soften water, it is more economical to use chemicals for the purpose. In general, savings of soap resulting from water softening vary directly with the volume of water used, the hardness removed by softening, and the cost of soap. Where these values are, respectively, 100 gal per day, 200 ppm hardness removed, and 16 cents per pound, the annual per capita savings computed for soap would be about $2.80. Actually the savings would probably be much less than this due to (1) unnecessary use of soap in soft water, and (2) the income group of the family involved.[3] The cost of domestic water softening in the home, as compared with municipal water softening, may be reduced by by-passing hard water to be used in flushing, sprinkling, and similar purposes. In some buildings only the hot water is softened. The increasing use of synthetic detergents to replace soap in the home and in industry is destined to limit the economic advantages of softening water.

[1] See H. W. Hudson, *Illinois State Water Survey, Circ.* 13, 1934; W. H. Walker, *J.A.W.W.A.*, January, 1934, p. 77; H. R. Green, *ibid.*, Vol. 25, p. 982, 1933; H. M. Olson, *ibid.*, April, 1939, p. 607; R. S. Banks, *ibid.*, April, 1950, p. 395.

[2] See also T. E. Larson, *ibid.*, April, 1949, p. 315; Task Group Report, *ibid.*, August, 1954, p. 751.

[3] See also "Water Quality and Treatment," pp. 313*ff.*, American Water Works Association, 1950.

29-2. Results Desired. In the operation of a municipal water-softening plant it is now customary to reduce the carbonate hardness to 35 to 40 ppm, and the total hardness to 50 to 100 ppm. The solubility of calcium carbonate in softened water is an important criterion of its desired quality. Water that is supersaturated with calcium carbonate will deposit a coating on pipes and sand grains, whereas water that is undersaturated is apt to be corrosive. The solubility equilibrium of calcium carbonate is controlled by the lime-soda ash dose, the addition of alum, recarbonation, or the use of sodium hexametaphosphate (Calgon). The carbonate balance of the water is determined as explained in Sec. 31-23. In general, it is considered good practice to carry a calcium carbonate alkalinity of about 25 ppm, which calls for a pH of 8.2 to 8.5. If the pH is low, soda ash should be added and if too high, alum or carbon dioxide should be used.

29-3. Methods of Softening Water. Public water supplies are softened either by the lime-soda process or by base exchange. Catalytic precipitation has been introduced in England.[1] Water to be used for industrial purposes may be softened by the above methods or by the use of synthetic organic detergents, the so-called "sulphonated-oil soaps" and related substances, and proprietary preparations usually containing organic compounds.

29-4. The Lime-Soda Process. A flowing-through diagram of a municipal water-softening plant is shown in Fig. 29-1. The process involves the thorough mixing of the chemical with the water, followed by slow agitation for 30 to 60 min to allow completion of the chemical reaction. The proper time to be allowed is greatly affected by the temperature because the chemical reactions and sedimentation take place rapidly at higher temperatures. When the temperature of the water approaches 39°F, the settling area needs to be double that at 74°F. Precipitated chemicals are removed by sedimentation or filtration, or both. The water may be recarbonated after sedimentation to restore the carbonate balance. The process may be operated intermittently or continuously, either cold (50 to 70°F) or hot (212°F).

The continuous cold process is most commonly used in municipal practice. For industrial purposes intermittent operation may be used and, where the softened water must be heated, as for boiler-feed-water water conditioning, the hot process is most economical. Boiling reduces the carbonate hardness by driving off the dissolved carbon dioxide, resulting in the precipitation of insoluble carbonates. The complete softening of boiler feed water requires the use of excess chemicals and the unit cost may be higher than for municipal water softening.

[1] See "Manual of British Water Supply Practice," Institution of Water Engineers, 1950.

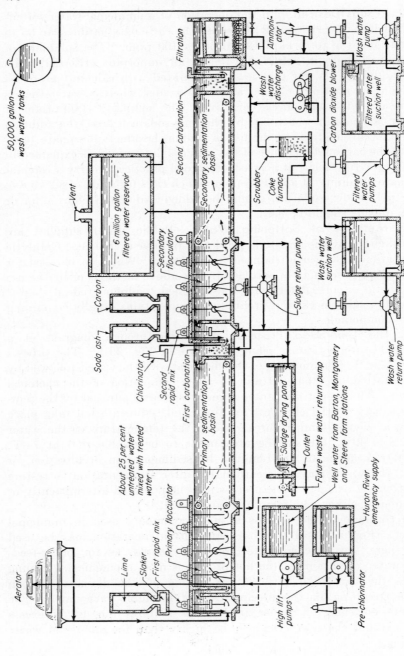

Fig. 29-1. Flowing-through diagram of the municipal water-softening plant at Ann Arbor, Mich. (*From H. E. McEntee, J.A.W.W.A., September, 1940, p. 1602.*)

29-5. Chemistry of the Lime-Soda Process. The following typical reactions occur when lime is added to hard water:

$$CaO + 2H_2CO_3 = Ca(HCO_3)_2 + H_2O \qquad (29\text{-}1)$$

Lime,   carbonic   calcium bicarbonate,   water
insoluble   acid   soluble, causes hardness

$$Ca(HCO_3)_2 + Ca(OH)_2 = 2CaCO_3 + 2H_2O \qquad (29\text{-}2)$$

Calcium bicarbonate,   lime   calcium carbonate,   water
soluble, causes hardness   insoluble

$$CaSO_4 + Na_2CO_3 = CaCO_3 + Na_2SO_4 \qquad (29\text{-}3)$$

Calcium sulphate,   sodium carbonate   calcium   sodium sulphate,
insoluble, causes   or   carbonate,   soluble, does not
hardness   soda ash   insoluble   cause hardness

Reactions (29-1) and (29-2) express the conditions that occur in nature to cause hardness. The calcium carbonate of the limestone is dissolved by water containing dissolved carbon dioxide. Reaction (29-3) occurs when sulphate hardness is removed by the addition of soda ash. Normally, reaction (29-3) would be followed by reaction (29-2) in the process of removing both sulphate and carbonate hardness.

The amount of lime and sodium carbonate necessary to complete these reactions is dependent on the amount of calcium and magnesium dissolved in the water and on such conditions as temperature, return of precipitated sludge, thoroughness of mixing, and time of contact. The necessary amount of chemical can be computed approximately by stoichiometrical computations.[1] It is not possible to determine the precise amount of chemical required because of other substances present in the water. Various rational and empirical formulas, all based on stoichiometrical principles, have been devised to express the quantities of lime and soda ash needed.[2] Caldwell and Lawrence[3] have described a graphical method for the determination of softening and conditioning chemicals based on the establishment of equilibrium of pH, alkalinity, magnesium, and calcium. Larson and Buswell[4] have shown that a residual hardness of about 20 to 27.4 ppm is the theoretical minimum to which hardness can be reduced by the cold process using only lime and soda ash.

The cold-water lime-soda process of softening cannot be expected to produce a water with much less than 80 to 100 ppm of hardness. The Spiroacter, a proprietary device, uses the cold lime-soda process com-

[1] See also C. P. Hoover, *Natl. Lime Assoc., Bull.* 211, 1934.

[2] See Alkalies and Chlorine in the Treatment of Municipal and Industrial Water, *Solvay Tech. Eng. Service, Tech. Bull.* 8, 1941.

[3] D. H. Caldwell and W. B. Lawrence, "Solution of Water Softening and Water Conditioning Problems by Chemical Equilibrium Methods," presented before American Chemical Society, Sept. 7, 1948.

[4] C. C. Larson and A. M. Buswell, *Ind. Eng. Chem.*, January, 1940, p. 130.

bined with upward flow through suspended catalytic granules of calcium and carbonate that, it is said,[1] will produce an effluent with a total hardness of 50 to 70 ppm.

29-6. Chemicals Used. Either hydrated lime or quicklime may be used in water softening, the choice depending on the available equipment for handling the chemicals and their relative cost. Commercial grades of hydrated lime and of quicklime are about 90 per cent pure, with calcium carbonate and silica as the principal impurities. Hydrated lime keeps better in storage and it does not require the slaking equipment needed for quicklime. The latter, however, is less bulky and costs less per unit weight of calcium oxide and is, therefore, more economical for larger plants.

In the preparation of the chemical to be added to the water it is better to prepare a well-agitated milk-of-lime suspension rather than a solution of lime water because of the relatively large volume of lime water required to give adequate dosage of lime. A difficulty involved in the use of milk of lime, however, is the continuous agitation required to prevent stratification and sedimentation in the storage tank and in pipes. A trough with an easily removable top or a soft rubber hose that is accessible for pressing or kneading in order to break down scale or to move deposits is preferable to inflexible pipe for conveying milk of lime. If high temperatures occur in slaking quicklime, the slaker should be provided with a ventilating hood in order to remove vapors.

The slaking of quicklime to produce a satisfactory milk-of-lime solution requires about 3 to 5 lb water per pound of lime. In practice the quicklime, after being crushed to a size convenient to be handled by the available equipment, is applied through a dry feeder to a covered container in which the lime is slaked at a temperature of about 200°F, requiring about 15 to 20 min for complete reaction during which the milk of lime is thoroughly stirred.

It apparently makes no difference whether the lime and soda ash are mixed together or fed as one solution. The measurement and feeding of the chemicals may be controlled either volumetrically or gravimetrically by dry-feed machines which control the dose with precision. In practice, charges of lime and of soda ash are made up in batches sufficient to last for one 8-hr period, or watch. Solutions should not contain more than about 5 per cent of the active ingredient, because stronger concentrations decrease the accuracy of feeding, although 10 per cent milk-of-lime solutions are used in practice.

Overdosing with lime and soda ash is undesirable because of possible residual caustic alkalinity and of physiological effects on consumers. It is desirable, therefore, that the increased alkalinity resulting from treatment should not exceed the hardness by more than 35 ppm; phenol-

---

[1] "Water Conditioning Handbook," p. 14/1, the Permutit Co., 1949.

phthalein alkalinity not more than 15 ppm plus 0.4 of the total alkalinity; and normal carbonate alkalinity not more than 120 ppm.

29-7. Hot-process Softening. The hot process of water softening is used principally in the preparation of boiler feed water and in industry where a soft hot water is desired. The softening reactions occur more rapidly in hot water and less chemical is required. Hot-process softeners are commonly proprietary devices. A flow diagram through such a device is shown in Fig. 29-2.

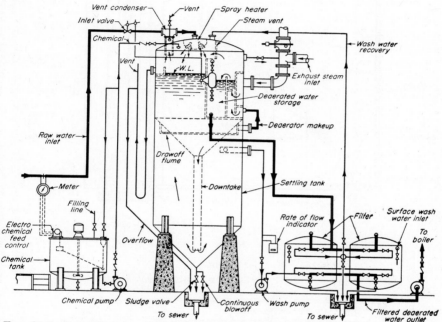

FIG. 29-2. Permutit type "BD" hot lime-soda water softener. (*Courtesy of the Permutit Co.*)

29-8. Sedimentation Basins. Because of the relatively large volume of sludge accumulated in the softening process, sedimentation basins with mechanical devices for continuous removal of sludge are often used. One form of such basins, commonly called *clarifiers*, is illustrated in Fig. 29-3. In general, the period of detention lies between 2 and 4 hr.

Proprietary devices, such as the Accelator,[1] illustrated in Fig. 27-7, combine the functions of mixing and sedimentation. Mixing is done in the inner cone, which is provided with a mechanical stirring device and which has a detention period of about 30 min. After mixing, the water passes through a V-shaped annular slot between the inner and the outer

[1] See also the Permutit (Spaulding) Precipitator, *J.A.W.W.A.*, November, 1937, p. 1697.

cone and rises with a velocity of 4 to 8 ft per hr[1] through a blanket of sludge that acts as an adsorbent medium and effects removal of precipitated solids. Sludge is drawn off continuously and slowly enough to maintain the essential blanket of sludge.

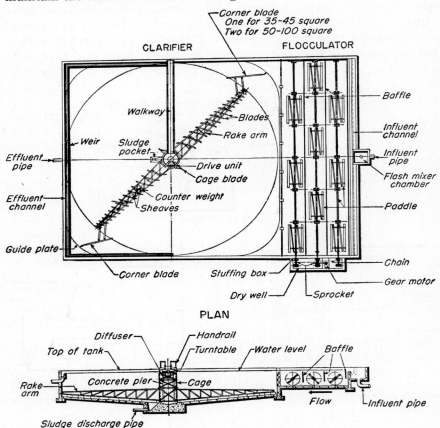

FIG. 29-3. Clarifier and flocculator. (*Courtesy of the Dorr Co.*)

29-9. Recarbonation. The addition of lime to water reduces the carbonate saturation index[2] and increases the tendency of the water to deposit calcium carbonate on filter sand, pipes, boiler tubes, etc. The carbonate balance may be partly or completely restored and other advantages may be gained by the recarbonation of the water.[3] This

---

[1] See Alkalies and Chlorine in the Treatment of Municipal and Industrial Water, *Solvay Tech. Eng. Service, Tech. Bull.* 8, 1941.

[2] See also Secs. 31-23 and 31-24.

[3] See also: C. H. Spaulding, *Eng. News-Record*, June 8, 1933, p. 747; C. P. Hoover, *Ind. Eng. Chem.*, Vol. 19, p. 784, 1927.

may be accomplished by diffusing carbon dioxide gas through the water, by underwater combustion,[1] by the use of dry ice,[2] or by the use of liquid carbon dioxide.[3]

Where diffused carbon dioxide is used it may be obtained from scrubbed flue gases or air may be blown through a coke or anthracite burner, functioning under pressure, all gases of combustion being discharged without scrubbing, into the recarbonation chamber. If it is necessary to cool the generator the heated water from the cooling jacket may be applied to some useful purpose as, e.g., heating the building. Adequate oxygen must be supplied for complete combustion, or deadly carbon monoxide may be produced.[4]

Diffused gas may be applied after the water has passed through the settling basins. The volume of carbon dioxide required can be computed from the equation

$$CaCO_3 + CO_2 + H_2O = Ca(HCO_3)_2 \qquad (29\text{-}4)$$

It can be shown from this equation that the pounds of CO_2 per million gallons of water is $3.7 \times CaCO_3$ in parts per million. The reaction time allowed in the recarbonation basin does not always return the water to chemical balance. Recarbonation should not be carried below a pH of 9.7 to 9.2 to avoid redissolving precipitated carbonates and to avoid the formation of a colloidal precipitate of calcium carbonate. Although water with a pH above 9.2 to 9.7 may be incrusting it is preferable to water that is corrosively aggressive.

The maximum amount of carbon dioxide that might be required should not exceed 500 lb per million gal water treated.

A period of settling should be provided before and after recarbonation to remove the sludges formed by softening and to remove any possible precipitate formed by the neutralization of excess caustic alkalinity $(Ca(OH)_2)$ by the carbon dioxide. The secondary period of sedimentation is, however, commonly omitted.

29-10. Disposal of Sludge. The large quantity of sludge accumulated in the lime-soda process presents a problem in its disposal.[5] Many expedients have been adopted such as (1) discharge into a stream providing sufficient dilution and carrying capacity to prevent the formation of sludge banks or the discoloration of the stream, (2) temporary storage to

---

[1] See also: L. H. Scott and F. C. Abbott, *Water Works & Sewerage*, October, 1939; L. H. Scott, *J.A.W.W.A.*, January, 1940, p. 93.

[2] See also A. F. Mellen, *ibid.*, February, 1950, p. 204.

[3] See also: Mellen, *loc. cit.*; Harry Stock, *Eng. News-Record*, Apr. 29, 1948, p. 107.

[4] See also R. D. Schafer, *Water & Sewage Works*, July, 1952, p. 266.

[5] See also: Committee Report, *J.A.W.W.A.*, December, 1947, p. 1211; H. V. Pederson, *Am. City*, May, 1948, p. 86; B. H. Swab, *J.A.W.W.A.*, April, 1948, p. 461; C. F. Wertz, *Eng. News-Record*, July 8, 1948, p. 113.

permit discharge into the stream during high-water period, (3) filling of depressions or excavations, (4) discharge into city sewers to the sewage-treatment plant, (5) drying the sludge and using it for liming soil, (6) reburning for the production of lime,[1] and (7) use as a filler for paint.

29-11. Operating Expedients. Greater economy and better results can be obtained by various expedients during operation that combine or modify the normal steps in the water-softening process. These expedients include (1) the use of excess lime, (2) the use of aluminum or ferrous compounds, (3) the recirculation of sludge, (4) the softening of only a part of the water, and (5) the combination of the lime-soda process and the zeolite process.

The addition of an excess of 2 to 3 grains of lime per gallon followed by the addition of sufficient soda ash to react with the noncarbonate hardness and the excess lime has been found to precipitate magnesium almost completely. The presence of an excess of lime can be determined by the test for alkalinity. If the phenolphthalein alkalinity is equal to one-half of the methyl orange alkalinity, only normal carbonate alkalinity is present. If the phenolphthalein alkalinity is greater than one-half of the methyl orange alkalinity, the water contains caustic alkalinity or excess lime.

Aluminum compounds are sometimes added to the water to coagulate finely divided precipitates, thus shortening the reaction and settling periods that might otherwise be required. Compounds used include alum and sodium aluminate; a dosage of 0.5 to 1.0 grain of alum per gallon or 0.5 grain of sodium aluminate per gallon may be used. Ferrous sulphate may be used in place of alum. The use of alum slightly increases the sulphate hardness, necessitating the use of additional soda ash. The reduction of hardness by sodium aluminate may be greater than would be calculated, possibly due to excess hydroxide ions released by the hydrolysis of sodium aluminate to aluminum hydroxide.

The recirculation of water-softening sludge alone, or combined with some finely divided insoluble compound, such as bleaching clay, applied to the water with the milk of lime, has been found beneficial in many plants.[2] The amount of returned sludge should be sufficient to maintain about 10,000 ppm of suspended solids in the mixing chamber, but the exact number for any particular plant must be determined by experience. The procedure has been found particularly beneficial when the bicarbonate has been changed to normal carbonate, the magnesium has been precipitated as magnesium hydroxide, and the excess caustic lime $(Ca(OH)_2)$ has been neutralized to carbonate. The recirculation of sludge may be combined with the excess-lime treatment.

[1] See also A. P. Black and others, *Water Works Eng.*, March, 1951, p. 227.
[2] See also C. P. Hoover, *Rept. 8th Ann. Water Works School Univ. Kansas*, 1930.

Recirculation of sludge may result in an effluent containing 50 to 70 ppm of hardness, approximately 30 ppm less than would be obtained without recirculation. The Spiroacter, a proprietary device,[1] produces an effluent of 50 to 70 ppm of hardness by the cold lime process with a period of retention between 6 and 12 min, compared with 4 hr in the conventional cold lime softening process without recirculation of sludge and 1 hr with recirculation.

In some cases it has been found desirable, and economical in the use of chemicals, to reduce the hardness of a portion of the water to a degree below that required and to mix the softened water with a portion of unsoftened raw water to produce the desired degree of hardness. This method is known as "split treatment."

A combination of the lime-soda process with the zeolite process may be found economical, particularly where the sulphate hardness is high. The carbonate hardness is first removed by lime treatment. The water is then recarbonated, to prevent incrustation of the ion-exchange material, and the water is passed through the ion exchanger to remove sulphate hardness. The hardness of the effluent is zero.

29-12. A Softening Plant. Municipal softening plants are usually designed to meet local conditions. Small plants and equipment for industrial purposes may be selected from standard designs offered by equipment manufacturers. Olson,[2] in 1945, reported costs of softening plants under 1 mgd capacity to be $75,000 per million gallons per day; and from $50,000 to $155,000 per million gallons per day for plants of 3 to 4 mgd capacity; and from $25,000 up for plants from 5 to 50 mgd capacity.

A typical small softening plant is illustrated in Fig. 29-1.[3] Such a plant, with a capacity of 250,000 gal per day, would consist of (1) a mixing basin 4 by 25 ft in plan and 12 ft deep, the mixing being done by paddles revolving on a horizontal shaft at right angles to the direction of flow of the water; (2) a settling basin 25 by 25 by 12 ft, equipped for the continuous removal of sludge; (3) a recarbonation basin 2 by 25 by 8 ft, equipped with perforated pipes for the diffusion of carbon dioxide; and (4) a secondary recarbonation tank about 5 ft square and 5 ft deep, which will act also as a clear well.

In small softening plants, precise chemical control is important because of the high percentage of error in the treatment resulting from small errors in the rate of application of chemicals. Precise control may be obtained by automatic equipment, which will apply the chemicals in proportion to the rate of water treatment.

[1] "Water Conditioning," the Permutit Co., 1943.
[2] H. M. Olson, *J.A.W.W.A.*, October, 1945, p. 1002.
[3] See also C. P. Hoover, *Water Works Eng.*, May 26, 1937, p. 734.

Softening with Ion-exchange Materials[1]

29-13. Cation and Anion Exchangers. Ion-exchange materials are substances so loosely bound chemically that, when they are placed in a solution of greater ionic concentration, cations will be exchanged by cation exchangers and anions will be exchanged by anion exchangers. New resins[2] available for water treatment include cation-exchange resins of the weakly and strongly acidic types, anion-exchange resins of the weakly and strongly basic types, and highly porous modifications of the strong-acid cation exchangers and strong-base exchangers. Ion-exchange substances have been widely known as zeolites but, in its 1949 Manual of Test Procedures the American Water Works Association recommended the adoption of the term cation exchanger or anion exchanger.

Cation-exchange materials may be classified as (1) inorganic gels or hydrated sodium aluminum silicates, (2) greensand, (3) sulfonated coals, and (4) synthetic resins, (*a*) phenol formaldehyde, (*b*) sulfonated poly-styrene resins, and (*c*) carboxylic-type cation-exchange resin.

The inorganic gel zeolites are commonly used in household water softeners and in some municipal plants. Both glauconite or greensand, and a synthetic proprietary zeolite known as Permutit, are widely used in practice. Permutit is a precipitated, synthetic compound protected by patent rights as are many other proprietary zeolites. Permutit ($NaAlSiO_4 \cdot 3H_2O$) is an artificial sodium zeolite that will exchange the sodium for calcium. It has the appearance of sand, with even-sized, hard, lustrous grains. It will absorb moisture from the air and must therefore be stored in a dry place. Although used in domestic and municipal water softening synthetic zeolites are being replaced in municipal practice by high-capacity organic materials.

Hydrogen exchange for metallic ions is known as demineralization. It is used principally for the production of water for industrial and laboratory processes, although it may be applied to municipal softening and to the reduction of solids in water. It is to be noted that softening with sodium-base exchangers results in an increase of dissolved solids in the softened water.

Anion-exchange materials on the market are synthetic resins the activity of which derives from basic nitrogen groups. The materials may be classified as (1) medium-capacity resins, (*a*) guanidine-melamine-formaldehyde type; (2) high-capacity weakly basic resins, (*a*) polyamine-

[1] See: also L. Streicher, *J.A.W.W.A.*, November, 1947, p. 1133, with bibliography; A. S. Behrman, Ion Exchange Materials, Conference on Water Resources, *Illinois State Water Survey*, Bull. 41, 1952, p. 175; Water Quality and Treatment, *A.W.W.A. Manual*, 1952, pp. 344*ff.*; Standard Manual of Cation Exchange Test Procedures, *J.A.W.W.A.*, May, 1949, p. 451; M. P. Robinson, *Water & Sewage Works*, April, 1952, p. 152; J. Thompson and F. X. McGarvey, *J.A.W.W.A.*, April, 1953, p. 145.

[2] See also Thompson and McGarvey, *loc. cit.*

aldehyde condensation products; and (3) strongly basic resins. Anion exchangers are used principally in industrial processes. The high-capacity weakly basic resins are effective for removing strong acids such as sulphuric or hydrochloric but are only slightly effective with weak acids such as carbonic or silicic. These resins are commonly used in deionization plants. The strongly basic resins are effective in the removal of weak acids.

29-14. Chemistry of Cation Exchangers. Reactions that occur in the exchange process of softening, demineralization, and regeneration with cationic exchangers can be symbolized as

Softening:

$$Na_2R^1 + \begin{cases} Ca(Cl_2) \\ Mg(HCO_3)_2 \end{cases} \rightarrow \begin{aligned} Ca \\ Mg \end{aligned} \bigg\} R + \begin{aligned} 2NaCl \\ 2NaHCO_3 \end{aligned} \qquad (29\text{-}5)$$

Sodium exchanger   calcium or magnesium bicarbonate hardness   calcium or magnesium exchanger   sodium bicarbonate, soluble, not hardness

Softening:

$$Na_2R + \begin{aligned} Ca \\ Mg \end{aligned}\bigg\} SO_4 \rightarrow \begin{aligned} Ca \\ Mg \end{aligned}\bigg\} R + Na_2SO_4 \qquad (29\text{-}6)$$

Sulphate hardness   sodium sulphate, soluble, not hardness

Regeneration:

$$\begin{aligned} Ca \\ Mg \end{aligned}\bigg\} R + 2NaCl \rightarrow Na_2R + CaCl_2 \qquad (29\text{-}7)$$

Sodium exchanger   calcium chlorid e, soluble

Hydrogen exchange for metallic ions:

$$(Ca, Mg, or Na_2)(HCO_3) + H_2R \rightarrow (Ca, Mg, or Na_2)R$$
$$+ 2H_2O + 2CO_2 \quad (29\text{-}8)$$
$$(Ca, Mg, or Na_2)(SO_4 or Cl_2) \rightarrow (Ca, Mg, or Na_2)R$$
$$+ (H_2SO or 2HCl) \quad (29\text{-}9)$$

Hydrogen exchange for metallic ions or regeneration:

$$(Ca, Mg, or Na_2)(SO_4 or Cl_2) + H_2R \rightarrow (Ca, Mg, or Na_2)R$$
$$+ (H_2SO_4 or HCl) \quad (29\text{-}10)$$
$$(Ca, Mg, or Na_2)R + (H_2SO_4 or 2HCl) \rightarrow (Ca, Mg, or Na_2)(SO_4 or Cl_2)$$
$$+ H_2R \quad (29\text{-}11)$$

Absorption of excess acid by De-Acidite ("D"), a proprietary substance regenerated with sodium carbonate:

$$D + (H_2SO_4 or 2HCl) \rightarrow D(H_2SO_4 or 2HCl) \qquad (29\text{-}12)$$
$$D(H_2SO_4 or 2HCl) + Na_2CO_3 \rightarrow D + Na_2(SO_4 or Cl) + H_2O + CO_2$$
$$(29\text{-}13)$$

---

[1] Organic component of exchanger.

29-15. Characteristics of Cation-exchange Materials. Characteristics desirable in an exchange material include (1) high operating exchange value which minimizes the size of the equipment required; (2) freedom from aggressive attack by the water being treated; (3) freedom from injury when overrun; (4) low salt requirements for regeneration; (5) availability and low first cost; (6) durability to resist the wear of rewashing; (7) freedom from the effects of turbidity, iron, manganese, or other substance not causing hardness in the water being treated; and (8) a grain of proper size, neither so fine as to cause too great a loss of head in operation or in backwashing, nor so coarse as noticeably to diminish the exchange value.

The glauconites or greensands usually have a lower exchange value but are more rugged than the precipitated synthetic exchange materials. In domestic installations, where the volume of material involved is small and the intensity of service is low compared with that in industrial and municipal use, the precipitated synthetic exchange materials are advantageous. Where the hard water has not been treated previous to softening, properly stabilized greensands may be desirable, as they are less affected by turbidity, iron, or other foreign substances. Unfortunately, however, because of their relatively low exchange value, undesirably large equipment may be required.

In precipitated synthetic exchange materials the exchange value and resistance to aggressive attack are indicated by the chemical composition. The composition of such materials may be expressed as the ratio of $Na_2O:Al_2O_3:SiO_2$. Thus a $1:1:6$ material contains 1 mole of Na_2O, 1 mole of Al_2O_3, and 6 moles of SiO_2. Most of the synthetic materials on the market fall within the range of $1:1:4$ and $1:1:15$. In general, other things being equal, an increase of SiO_2 content decreases the exchange value of the material but increases its resistance to aggressive attack. Procedures for the determination of the qualities of exchange materials are covered in a manual published by the American Water Works Association.[1]

29-16. Exchange Values and Characteristics of Exchange Materials. Exchange capacities of materials are measured in grains of calcium carbonate, or its equivalent, per cubic foot of the exchange material. Capacities of some materials are: greensand, 2,500 to 3,000; gel zeolites, 5,000 to 12,000; sulphonated coals, 7,000 to 10,000; cation-exchange resins, low capacity 7,000 to 10,000, medium 12,000 to 15,000, and high 25,000 to 35,000; and anion exchangers, medium 15,000 to 20,000, and high 25,000 to 35,000.

The greensands or glauconites are greenish-black rounded granules like fine sand, weighing about 80 lb per cu ft. They are resistant to wear and to aggressive waters. The gel, or wet-process, precipitated synthetic

[1] See *J.A.W.W.A.*, Vol. 35, p. 721, 1943.

zeolites are pale gray grains, about 0.3 to 0.5 mm in diameter. They weigh about 50 lb per cu ft, are porous, are relatively easily abraded, and are subject to attack by aggressive waters. The sulphonated coals are black grains, coarser than greensands, and are corrosion-resistant.

The exchange capacities of cation exchangers in terms of calcium carbonate removed depend, to some extent, on the weight of sodium chloride used per unit volume of exchange material. The capacity rises with increased salt concentration up to a maximum limit. The capacities of materials to remove magnesium hardness are somewhat less than to remove calcium hardness and the capacity diminishes in excessively hard waters high in sodium salts. The diminished capacity may be compensated for in operation by the use of more sodium chloride in regeneration.

29-17. Municipal Water Softening with Exchange Materials. Water containing either, or both, carbonate and sulphate hardness can be softened by passing it through a layer of sodium base-exchange material at a temperature not to exceed 100°F, so as not to injure the exchange material. The hardness of the water will be reduced almost to zero. In municipal practice it is the custom to soften only a portion of the water supply to zero hardness, mixing it with unsoftened water so that the resulting hardness is about 50 to 100 ppm. On the exhaustion of the exchange material it is regenerated with sodium chloride. The process may be carried on almost indefinitely, if properly operated, without renewing the exchange material. Under good operation it may be anticipated that no more than about 5 per cent of the exchange material will be lost annually.

29-18. Control of Base-exchange Softening. Water softened to zero hardness by base exchange requires adjustment of its pH and calcium carbonate content to be noncorrosive to iron. The adjustment is important, because undersaturation with calcium carbonate results in corrosion, and supersaturation builds up scale. A device is available, actuated by a soap test, that will indicate and sound an alarm when treated water has passed a predetermined maximum permissible hardness.

The corrosiveness of unadjusted hot softened water may be so great that pipes and equipment can be quickly ruined unless the aggressiveness is neutralized. This fact cannot be too greatly stressed. The ignorant use of base-exchange materials in the softening of hot water may be disastrous.

29-19. Treatment of Industrial Waters. The most important use of water in industry is for boiler feed. For this purpose a soft unaggressive water, relatively free from solids, is desired. Unfortunately treatment by means of most cationic exchangers produces aggressive water containing more dissolved solids than were in the raw water. This condition can be overcome by demineralization, and by the use of anionic exchangers.

The strongly basic resins are particularly effective in the removal of silica from water, a most undesirable scale-forming material.

29-20. Limitations of the Process. Raw waters with a hardness above 850 to 1,000 ppm cannot be softened economically in cation exchangers, partly because of the size of the softener required and the volume of salt and of wash water involved. Raw waters containing turbidity, suspended matter, dissolved iron or manganese, or high in certain salts, particularly chlorides, or other substances deleterious to the exchange material should be treated before softening. It must be emphasized that the

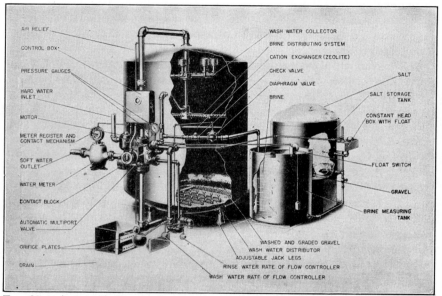

Fig. 29-4. Automatic base-exchange water softener. (*Courtesy of the Permutit Co.*)

softener is not a filter and should not be used as one. In general, waters with temperatures above 100° F will have an injurious effect on exchange materials.

The removal of calcium and magnesium compounds with the reduction of hardness to extremely low amounts sometimes creates an aggressive water that requires subsequent pH adjustment to avoid corrosion.

29-21. Description of Equipment. A base-exchange water softener, as used in municipal and industrial practice, resembles a rapid sand filter of either gravity or pressure type. A pressure-type softener is shown in Fig. 29-4 and a gravity type is shown in Fig. 29-5. The layer of zeolite shown in the figure may be from 30 to 75 in. thick. The smaller thickness is most common. Although the flow of water through the bed may be upward or downward, the latter is more common practice as there is less danger of loss of material and the filtering action of the bed is better.

The pressure-type softener is more commonly used in industrial and in small municipal plants. Such softeners are sometimes equipped with automatic regeneration controls to regenerate either at fixed periods of time or in accordance with the volume of water softened.

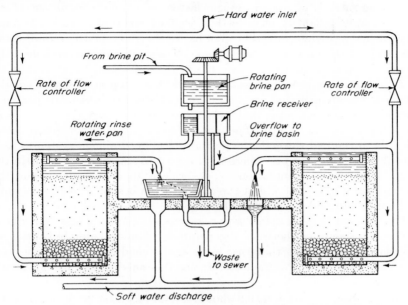

FIG. 29-5. Automatic gravity base-exchange water softener. (*J.A.W.W.A., September*, 1932, *p.* 1384.)

29-22. Size of Equipment. Factors affecting the volume of exchange material required may be formulated as

$$E = \frac{KQH}{G} \qquad (29\text{-}14)$$

where E = volume of exchange material to be used, cu ft
   Q = volume of water to be treated between restorations, cu ft
   H = hardness of water, grains per gal
   G = hardness to be removed between regenerations per unit volume of exchange material, grains per cu ft
   K = a factor dependent on the units, = 0.133 for units stated.

The volume of exchange material required varies directly as the volume of water softened between regenerations. The more frequent the regeneration the smaller the softener required, the lower its first cost, and the greater the attention required in operation. Automatic softeners[1] for municipal and industrial plants have been designed for regeneration every 2 hr or more. Manually operated softeners for such plants may be

[1] See also S. P. Oppenheim, *J.A.W.W.A.*, 1934, p. 607.

on a minimum of 8 hr between regeneration, and household softeners may run for a month or more between regenerations.

29-23. Regeneration with Sodium Chloride. The hardness of water issuing from a softener between regenerations increases slowly but at an increasing rate. Softeners are regenerated on a time schedule or after a predetermined quantity of water has been softened, or when the effluent has reached a predetermined level of hardness. The first two limitations are subject to automatic regulation. The last can be measured by laboratory test or by field soap test.

When the time comes to regenerate the first step is to backwash the softener in a manner similar to a rapid sand filter, to loosen the particles and remove any material that might have been deposited on the bed. The proper amount of 5 to 10 per cent brine solution is then either introduced into the bed through the perforated underdrainage system or run onto the surface of the bed where it is allowed to stand in contact with the entire bed during regeneration. The brine is then flushed out and the unit put back into service, but the effluent from it should be wasted until it shows a hardness of less than 1 ppm.

The softener is not satisfactorily regenerated unless the first 10 per cent of the water softened between regenerations shows a chloride content of less than 10 ppm higher than that in the unsoftened water and no increase in the chloride content of the water during the remainder of a run between regenerations.

The salt used in regeneration should contain at least 96 per cent NaCl and should be free from iron, mud, chips, and other foreign matter.[1] The amount of salt required depends on the volume of exchange material present, its exchange capacity, and the assumed allowance of salt per unit of hardness removed. As salt is the most important item in the cost of base-exchange softening, every effort should be bent toward the utilization of the minimum amount. The amount used, expressed in pounds of salt per cubic foot of exchange material is, in general, about: for glauconite, 1.4; for synthetic precipitated material, 4 to 8; for fused synthetic, 4; and for clays, 4. In no case should the amount exceed 6. About $\frac{1}{2}$ lb is used for 1,000 grains of hardness, regardless of the exchange material used, the minimum being in the range of 0.2 lb per 1,000 grains.[2] Salt may be stored in "wet storage," i.e., as a saturated brine solution containing about 25 per cent NaCl, in concrete tanks painted with a salt-resistant paint, such as Inertol or Acron.

The amount of salt required may be computed as follows:

Example. Let it be assumed that the unit contains 1,000 cu ft of zeolite and that it has a capacity, in terms of $CaCO_3$ removable, of 3,000 grains per cu ft. The unit will have, therefore, a softening capacity of 3,000,000 grains. If it is

[1] See Standard Specifications, *ibid.*, March, 1950, p. 317, December, 1951, p. 1067.
[2] See S. T. Powell, *ibid.*, November, 1937, p. 1733.

assumed that 0.5 lb of salt is required per 1,000 grains of hardness removed, there will be required $3,000 \times 0.5$, or 1,500, lb salt to regenerate the unit. Each gallon of saturated brine solution contains 2.479 lb salt. Approximately 605 gal saturated brine solution will be required, which should be diluted to 1,740 to 3,480 gal to form a 5 to 10 per cent solution.

29-24. Waste-brine Disposal.[1] The used wash water after it has regenerated and flushed the exchange material creates a problem in its disposal. It will contain approximately 35 SH lb chloride ions per million gallons, where S is salt, in pounds per 1,000 grains of hardness removed, and H is the reduction of hardness in parts per million as calcium carbonate.[2] The brine may inhibit fish life,[3] pollute underground water, and injure domestic water supplies.[4] Proposed methods of treatment include (1) evaporation ponds and (2) dilution, either controlled or uncontrolled. The wastes are not amenable to biological treatment.

29-25. Operation and Care of Softener. Base-exchange softeners require intelligent care in their operation to avoid injury to the exchange material, to the equipment, or to the quality of the water. For example, it may be desirable to flush the bed at intervals of a few months or a year to destroy bacterial growths. When not in operation a regenerated bed should not be left submerged for more than about 10 hr, and if the softener is to be out of service for more than a week it should be left unregenerated, and if a synthetic gel it should be kept damp but not submerged. The hardness of wash water should be less than about 175 ppm.

29-26. Loss of and Restoration of Softening Capacity. Loss of softening capacity may be due to such factors as (1) physical and chemical conditions of the grains of the softening material, (2) the temperature of the raw water, (3) the rate at which water is passed through the exchange material, (4) the amount of salt used, and (5) the uniformity of distribution of brine during regeneration. Under normal conditions the loss of exchange value should not exceed about 5 per cent per year for 3 years. Manufacturers' guarantees seldom extend beyond that period.

Exchange capacity may be improved or restored by such measures as (1) cleaning with dilute acid (acetic) or dilute caustic solutions, depending on the nature of the material coating or plugging the grains or the bed; (2) treatment successively with brine, sodium hydroxide, sodium silicate, and finally alum; (3) treatment with ammonium sulphate solution; (4) intermittent high-dosage chlorination to remove bacterial slimes;[5] and (5) grinding and screening of the exchange material, using the particles passing a No. 16 sieve and held on a No. 50 sieve.

[1] See *Public Works*, February, 1948, p. 66.
[2] See also P. D. Haney, *J.A.W.W.A.*, December, 1947, p. 1215.
[3] See also M. M. Ellis, *U.S. Bur. Fisheries, Bull.* 22, 1937.
[4] See also *J.A.W.W.A.*, September, 1949, p. 829.
[5] See also L. Streicher, *ibid.*, November, 1947, p. 1133.

29-27. Washing Equipment. In designing the washing equipment for an upward-flow wash, a rate of 6 to 8 gpm per sq ft of exchange surface will expand synthetic base-exchange materials about 50 per cent, and a 6-gal rate through greensand will expand it about 25 per cent. A rate higher than about 2 to 3 cu ft per sq ft per min may result in disturbing the gravel layer, causing an undesirable mixture with the exchange material unless provision is made for holding the gravel in place. The washwater gutters should be high enough above the surface of the bed to permit at least 50 per cent expansion without loss of exchange material. In designing the underdrainage system the provision of $\frac{3}{16}$-in. holes on 6-in. centers will provide sufficient area, giving a loss of head of about 8 ft when washing at an 8-gal rate.

29-28. Comparison of Lime-Soda and Base-exchange Processes. Advantages sometimes attributed to these competitive processes are

Advantages of the lime-soda process

1. Suitable for turbid, chalybeate, and acid waters where base exchange cannot be used
2. The effluent contains lower total solids than that from base-exchange softening
3. Control of corrosion prevention is comparatively simple
4. May be more economical
5. Has bactericidal effect
6. May be better for excessively hard waters, particularly those high in magnesium hardness, and for water high in sodium
7. Easily added to an existing filter plant
8. Freedom from patent complications
9. Freedom from danger of loss or disintegration of material

Advantages of the base-exchange process

1. Freedom from sludge
2. First cost and operating cost are comparatively low
3. Free from danger of excess chemicals in the effluent
4. Independent of change in quality of raw water
5. No deposits in the distribution system
6. The chemicals involved are easy to handle
7. Highly skilled labor is unnecessary
8. Any desired reduction of hardness is attainable
9. Repumping is unnecessary by the use of pressure softener
10. Small space is required
11. Almost completely automatic

29-29. Combination of Lime with Base-exchange Process. It is economical, under favorable conditions, to remove carbonate hardness with lime, residual carbonate and sulphate hardness being removed by base exchange. The steps in this process are usually (1) treatment with sufficient lime to reduce carbonate hardness followed by coagulation and sedimentation to remove the precipitated carbonates; (2) recarbonation to prevent deposition of carbonates, and pH control below 9.5 to prevent deterioration of the base-exchange material; (3) filtration, if desired; (4) passage through a cation exchanger to produce zero hardness; and (5) restoration of some hardness, if desired, by mixing with unsoftened or partly softened water.

Synthetic Organic Detergents[1]

29-30. Other Substances Used. Synthetic organic detergents, the so-called "sulphonated-oil soaps" and related compounds, and proprietary products usually containing organic compounds are used in corrosion control in the processing of industrial water supplies and for domestic purposes, but are not used in the softening of public water supplies. The sulphonated compounds lather in hard water without producing a precipitate. They include sodium metaphosphate ($NaPO_3$), trisodium phosphate ($Na_3PO_4 \cdot 12H_2O$),[2] sodium hexametaphosphate ($NaPO_3$)$_6$, called Calgon,[3] and sodium pyrophosphate ($Na_4P_2O_7$). In high-pressure steam boilers sodium phosphate or certain organic compounds may be used to inhibit scale formation. These compounds include lignin sulphonate, concentrated sulphite waste liquor, and a host of proprietary compounds for some of which great claims are made.

Sodium hexametaphosphate, or Calgon,[4] is a proprietary compound. It is a highly hygroscopic chemical, added in about 25 per cent solution in a concentration of about 1 ppm. Close control is not essential.[5] These substances are used also to control the corrosive aggressiveness of water, as explained in Sec. 31-22.

[1] Task Group Report, *ibid.*, August, 1954, p. 751.
[2] See *ibid.*, June, 1950, p. 601.
[3] See also K. K. Jones, *ibid.*, September, 1940, p. 1471.
[4] See also Owen Rice, *ibid.*, June, 1947, p. 552.
[5] See also Owen Rice, *Southwest Water Works J.*, Vol. 22, p. 21. April, 1940.

CHAPTER 30

DISINFECTION

30-1. Purposes and Methods. Water is disinfected to kill bacteria and thus prevent water-borne disease. Disinfection is not a substitute for filtration. Chlorination, the most common method of disinfection, frequently causes an increase in taste and odor. Disinfection usually requires complicated mechanisms that need the attention of skilled operators to avoid breakdown and incorrect dosage. The dangers from the interruption of service are so great that they must be avoided by every means possible.

Bacteria in water may be killed by chlorination, the addition of ozone, exposure to the ultraviolet ray, heating, the addition of lime, the addition of iodine, and in other ways. All microscopic organisms and larger forms of life in water may not be removed by all these methods; *e.g.*, *Entamoeba histolytica* are not removed by ordinary chlorination. Sterilization by heating is suitable only for domestic use. The expense involved in heating and cooling and the undesirable tastes likely to result therefrom preclude this method from use for public water supplies. Sterilization with lime alone has not been extensively practiced. It has been found that *E. coli* will die in water with a pH greater than about 9.5. Hence, when enough lime is added to bring the pH to this figure, sterilization of *E. coli* occurs.

30-2. Chlorination. The use of chlorine has become practically universal in the disinfection of water supplies in the United States. It is to be emphasized and repeated that chlorine, as normally applied, may not kill all pathogenic organisms. It will not kill cysts of *E. histolytica*, and it is ineffective against certain microscopic organisms. It is, however, an effective barrier against water-borne pathogenic organisms under normal conditions.

Knowledge of how chlorine kills is needed to explain its selective action in killing algae, protozoa, and other microorganisms. The disinfection efficiency of chlorine decreases noticeably with an increase in pH. This may be explained on the assumption that HOCl is the effective agent in disinfection with chlorine, and HOCl decreases rapidly in a solution with increasing pH. If, however, high organic matter is present, with which the chlorine must first react, the significance of pH will be reduced. It may be stated, however, that under normal circumstances the bactericidal effectiveness of chlorine may be expected to be greater at low than at high values of pH. Authoritative experimental data and conclusions on this matter will be found in *U.S. Public Health Reports* (Vol. 58, p. 1837; Vol. 59, p. 1661, in articles by C. T. Butterfield and others). For equal concentrations of chlorine added, other conditions being equal, 150 times as much chlorine must be added at a pH of 10 than at a pH of 5 to produce the same killing effect. The bactericidal action of chlorine increases appreciably with increase of temperature[1] within the range found in potable water.

Other conditions that may affect the bactericidal power of chlorine include organic matter and turbidity.[2] Organic matter and turbidity react with the chlorine to neutralize its effect and prevent the formation of hypochlorous acid. Within the normal range of temperature of potable water, temperature has little effect on chlorine activity.

Hypotheses that have been advanced to explain the bactericidal effect of chlorine include (1) the effect of *nascent oxygen*, which assumes that the decomposition of HOCl releases nascent oxygen that oxidizes the organic matter of which the bacteria are composed; (2) the effect of direct chlorination resulting from the reaction of free chlorine with the bacterial protoplasm; (3) the fact that toxic substances are formed by the reaction of the chlorine with substances in the bacterial cell wall; and (4) that it inhibits a key enzymatic process.[3] None of these hypotheses has been generally accepted. The nascent-oxygen hypothesis is obsolete, and the enzymatic hypothesis has, however, been applied to a quantitative determination of chlorine, as mentioned in Sec. 30-10.

Although chlorine is used principally for the killing of bacteria, it may be applied to water also to aid in the removal of iron and manganese, for the cleaning of sand filters, for the sterilization of water mains, and for other purposes.

Chlorine may be applied to water with equal effectiveness in the form of bleaching powder or as a gas, or it may be formed in the water by the electrolysis of chloride solutions. Its effectiveness as a bactericide does not depend on the method of its application. Conditions that may affect its results include the quality of the water and the period of contact permitted. The addition of chlorine to polluted water is inefficient and expensive and may be undesirable owing to the tastes and odors created.

30-3. Effect of Chlorine on E. Histolytica. In order to find a sterilizing agent capable of destroying cysts of *E. histolytica*, which are not satisfactorily destroyed by chlorine alone at less than 4 ppm after 30 min

[1] See also E. A. Whitlock, *Water and Water Eng.*, January, 1953, p. 12.

[2] See also S. M. Costigan, *J.A.W.W.A.*, March, 1942, p. 353.

[3] See also D. E. Green and P. K. Stumpf, *ibid.*, November, 1946, p. 1301.

under ideal conditions,[1] studies have been made[2] of the cyst-penetrating power of chlorine and chloramine compounds in water. These compounds are as follows, arranged in relative order of activity:

Chlorine (Cl_2)

Hypochlorous acid (HOCl)

Halazone[3]

Dichloramine ($NHCl_2$)

Succinchloramide

Monochloramine (NH_2Cl)

All these substances, except chlorine and hypochlorous acid, are chloramine compounds; halazone and succinchloramide include sulphur.[3] In the presence of water they break down to produce HOCl, as indicated by the following reactions:

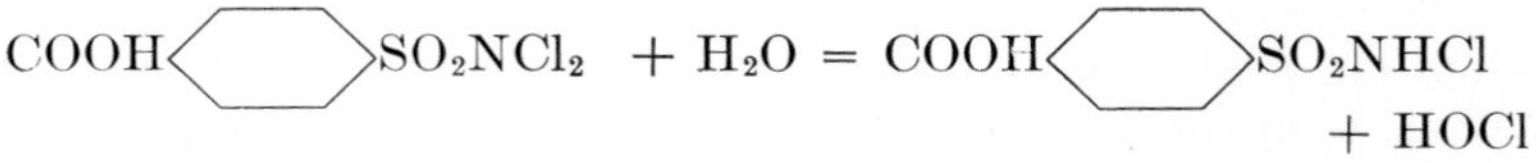

$$COOH\langle\bigcirc\rangle SO_2NCl_2 + H_2O = COOH\langle\bigcirc\rangle SO_2NHCl + HOCl \quad (30\text{-}1)$$

$$COOH\langle\bigcirc\rangle SO_2NHCl + H_2O = COOH\langle\bigcirc\rangle SO_2NH_2 + HOCl \quad (30\text{-}2)$$

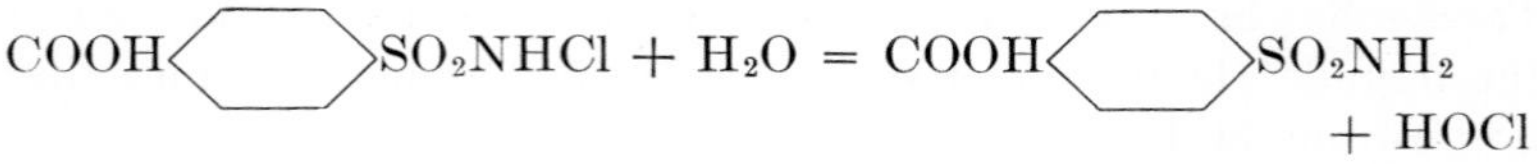

The very important effect of pH on the bactericidal and cyst-penetrating power of chlorine is to be noted because it may greatly affect the concentrations of chlorine required for satisfactory disinfection. It is generally assumed that the disinfecting effect of chlorine is proportional to the concentration of undissociated hypochlorous acid present and that this weak acid is but slightly ionized in acid solution but almost completely ionized in basic solution. These facts may help to explain why it takes 300 times as many units of titratable chlorine at pH 11 than at pH 5 to have an appreciable cysticidal effect on *E. histolytica*.[4]

30-4. Amount of Chlorine Required. The amount of chlorine required is dependent on the organic content of the water to be treated, its hydrogen-ion content, the amount of carbon dioxide present, the temperature, the time of contact, the desired results, and other factors. In practice, it is customary to apply the chlorine until the residual found in the treated water is between a trace and about 0.05 to 0.10 or 0.20 ppm.[5] The amount of chlorine commonly required to produce this residual is between a trace and about 1 ppm provided the contact period is more than 20 min before the water reaches the consumer after chlorination.[5]

[1] See also T. C. St. C. Morton, *Trop. Diseases Bull.*, May, 1948, p. 377.

[2] See also S. L. Chang, *J.A.W.W.A.*, November, 1944, p. 1192.

[3] See also H. D. Dakin and E. K. Dunham, *Brit. Med. J.*, May 26, 1917, p. 682; Halazone, *ibid.*, is ρ-sulphonidichloramidobenzoic acid.

[4] See also F. J. Brady and others, *War Med.*, April, 1943, p. 409.

[5] See Manual of Recommended Water Sanitation Practice, *Public Health Bull.*, 296, 1946, p. 21.

30-5. Bleaching Powder and Quicklime.[1] Bleaching powder, or calcium hypochlorite ($CaOCl_2$), is a chlorinated lime containing, when freshly made, about 33 per cent, by weight, of chlorine available for disinfection. The material was used when the chlorination of water supplies was introduced. It is now rarely used for public water supplies, having been superseded by liquid chlorine. It is less effective than liquid chlorine because it tends to raise the pH. Dry powders impregnated with chlorine, such as H.T.H. (high-test hypochlorite), Pittchlor, and Pittcide, are available. They contain, respectively, about 65 per cent, 70 per cent, and 50 per cent of available chlorine. Their use overcomes many of the disadvantages found in the use of bleaching powder, and the cost, per unit of available chlorine, may be no greater. They are used most often in the chlorination of water mains, filter sands, and storage reservoirs, and under emergency conditions where liquid chlorinators are unavailable or unsuitable.[2]

It has been found that the application of quicklime (CaO) to water in doses of about 12 grains per gal has a distinct bactericidal effect.

30-6. Handling Chlorine.[3] Some important characteristics of chlorine that affect its handling are (1) *color*, of gas, greenish-yellow; of liquid, amber; (2) *odor*, typical; (3) *weight*, of gas at room temperature, about 2.5 times that of air; of liquid, about 1.5 times that of water; (4) *solubility*, in water, low; at 50°F, 0.083 lb per gal; at 100°F, 0.051 lb per gal; (5) *crystalline hydrates*, formed at temperatures below 49.2°F; these are sometimes called "ice"; (6) *critical temperature*, at atmospheric pressure 291.2°F; (7) *vapor pressure*, at 68°F 81.9 psi; at 100°F 140 psi; at 150°F 270 psi; and at 212°F 536 psi; (8) *critical pressure*, 1,118.7 psi; (9) *viscosity*, of gas 94×10^{-7} and of liquid 23×10^{-5} in pounds per second per foot at 68°F; (10) *compressibility coefficient*, 0.0118 per cent per unit volume per unit of atmospheric pressures; this is the highest compressibility of any liquid element and results in rapid increase in pressure with rise in temperature; (11) ratio of volume of gas to volume of liquid at 32°F and a pressure of 776 mm mercury is 462, or 1 lb liquid forms about 5 cu ft gas.

Chlorine gas will neither burn nor explode. In the presence of water vapor it is extremely active chemically and will combine rapidly with most metals. The dry gas is highly corrosive to metals at temperatures above 300°F, and it may become corrosive at 195°F. It does not react appreciably with metals at lower temperatures. Commercial liquid chlorine is anhydrous and about 99.5 per cent pure.

The dry gas and liquid can be stored safely and indefinitely in steel

---

[1] See also *Public Works*, September, 1948, p. 36.

[2] See also J. A. Kienle, *Water Works & Sewerage*, October, 1932, p. 359.

[3] See Committee Report, *J.A.W.W.A.*, October, 1953, p. 1060; and "Chlorine," a technical brochure, Pittsburgh Plate Glass Co., 1948.

cylinders, under proper conditions.[1] Cylinders are constructed under specifications of the Interstate Commerce Commission to hold 100 lb to more than 150 tons of chlorine in containers that are transported on barges. One-ton containers and 55-ton tank cars are used by large water supplies. The cylinders are usually filled to 80 per cent of their capacity with liquid chlorine at 68°F, although they may be filled legally to 88 per cent at 70°F. They are built to withstand a bursting pressure of about 500 psi, corresponding to a temperature of about 190°F. Small cylinders should be kept below 150°F, should be stored upright, and should be handled carefully, rolling or dropping being dangerous. One-ton containers are used and stored with the axis horizontal.

Care must be taken to prevent the escape of liquid chlorine because of its highly toxic nature except in high dilution. It is desirable to have gas masks in good condition available nearby where chlorine is stored or used, but not in the same room. Minor leaks in chlorine equipment can be detected by the use of ammonia fumes which combine with the chlorine to form dense white clouds of ammonium chloride. Moisture should be kept away from a leak to avoid accelerating corrosion. An observer should stand with his head above the leak because chlorine, being heavier than air, will sink rapidly before diffusing appreciably.

Dangerous compounds may be formed when chlorine comes in contact with other gases. For example, the escape of chlorine into a poorly ventilated space containing carbon monoxide will result in the formation of phosgene, a highly toxic gas. In the use of ammonia with chlorine, in the chloramine process, care must be taken not to mix the gases before they are applied to the water, because of the danger of forming the highly explosive substance nitrogen trichloride.

Steel burns brightly in dry chlorine at temperatures above 194°F. It is essential, therefore, that chlorine be kept in a cool, well-ventilated room until ready for use. The temperature in the dosing room may be raised to 100 to 110°F to enhance the volatilization of the liquid. Liquefaction of chlorine in the chlorinator or in cooler portions of the pipe carrying chlorine will result if the containers are stored at higher temperatures than the area through which the pipe passes. The chlorine gas, if dry, may be conveyed to the point of application in pipes of any serviceable material, but if moist, rubber, glass, or silver may be used. However, neither hard nor soft rubber may be used with liquid chlorine. The pipe should be at least ¾ in. in diameter and arranged to drain back without traps into the container. Otherwise drip legs may be provided at low points to collect any condensate. If the room is insufficiently heated the upper portion of the drip traps may be insulated and the lower portion kept warm by a 100-watt electric light bulb. The sucking of water back

[1] See also A. S. Woodward and L. L. Hedgepeth, *J.A.W.W.A.*, May, 1953, p. 738.

into the chlorine container should be prevented by the use of a safety loop or vacuum-breaking device.

Provision should be made for forcing air into the top of the chlorinator or storage room so that the chlorine gas, which is heavier than air, can escape through ports at the floor level. Steam eductors may be satisfactory for this purpose as the steam will absorb the chlorine, assisting in the disposal problem.

Some recommendations made by a committee of the American Water Works Association for the handling of chlorine[1] include the following: (1) never connect a full container onto a header with other containers until temperatures (pressures) or both are approximately the same; (2) never apply flame or blowtorch to a container; (3) keep valves closed except when delivering chlorine. Other do's and don't's include: Don't put water on a chlorine leak. The resulting heat may increase the rate of chlorine vaporization; look for chlorine leaks with a rag soaked in ammonia on the end of a stick; try to stay above the leak; if possible absorb the escaping chlorine in an alkaline solution such as caustic soda, soda ash, or hydrated lime.

30-7. Application of Gaseous Chlorine. Chlorine gas may be fed directly to the point of application to the water supply or, preferably, the gas may first be dissolved in a small flow of water and the solution fed to the point of application. Direct application of chlorine to the water to be treated is less satisfactory because of unsatisfactory diffusion, possibility of the concentration of chlorine around the diffuser at low temperatures, and possibility of corrosion in pipes and valves resulting from accumulation of undissolved gas. On the other hand direct application is less expensive than solution-feed application.

30-8. Application of Liquid Chlorine. Liquid chlorine is most effective in disinfection when applied to filtered water at such a point that adequate mixing is assured. The application of chlorine to a reservoir or a suction line is usually to be preferred to application to a pipe under internal pressure. Where chlorine is applied under pressure, it is found to be as effective but not so easily handled. The use of direct-feed chlorinators is limited to pressures of 25 to 30 psi in the delivery pipe, whereas solution-feed equipment will carry to any pressure.

The rate of application of chlorine may be manually controlled, automatically controlled in proportion to the rate of flow of water, or mechanically controlled at various predetermined rates by means of a mechanically driven cam which raises and lowers the level of the make-up water to the chlorine injector.[2]

---

[1] See "Water Quality Treatment Manual," 1941, p. 141; and first-aid recommendations by C. R. Cox, Water Supply Control, *New York State Dept. Health, Bull.* 22, pp. 88*ff.*, 1943.

[2] See also E. W. Barbee, *J.A.W.W.A.*, September, 1946, p. 1064.

Provision is usually made to mix the chlorine and the water immediately after application and during the period of reaction. This provision need not be elaborate, the mixing and the time in the distributing mains frequently being adequate. Care should be taken in the design of distributing mains that water cannot be drawn from the mains in a shorter time than about 15 min after the application of the chlorine because of possible ineffectiveness of the chlorine in a shorter time, or of the receipt, by the consumer, of overdoses of chlorine.

30-9. Liquid Chlorinators.[1] Reliable and satisfactory apparatus for the application of chlorine to water is in extensive use. One form is illustrated in Fig. 30-1.[2]

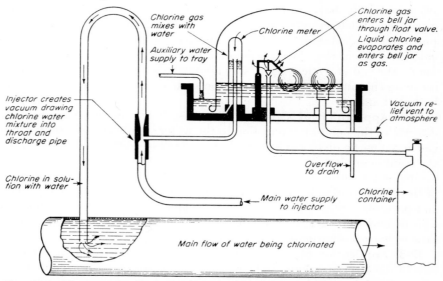

Fig. 30-1. Diagram showing operation of a chlorinator. (*Courtesy of Wallace and Tiernan Co., Inc.*)

Care is necessary to keep such machines and the lines leading to them free from dirt and deposits to avoid fluctuations in their operation and other difficulties. Gummy deposits of material collected from the lines by the chlorine occur in the orifices or on the bell jar. Such material may come from the pipe linings, oil used in valve packing, etc., and from unsatisfactory cleaning materials. Only the methane derivatives such as chloroform, wood alcohol, or carbon tetrachloride are satisfactory for cleaning chlorine equipment, as they are not converted into troublesome solids by the chlorine.[3]

[1] See also Panel Discussion, *ibid.*, September, 1954, p. 869.
[2] See also "Water Supply and Treatment," p. 119, National Lime Association, Washington, D.C., 1951.
[3] See also C. R. Cox, *J.A.W.W.A.*, 1934, p. 1587.

30-10. Determination of Residual Chlorine. It is desirable to know something of the method of determination of residual chlorine[1] before a conclusion can be safely based on the results reported. Five methods are recognized by the American Water Works Association.[2]

The orthotolidine method is probably most widely used.[3] However, the method is not foolproof as substances in the water may interfere with the results obtained, and impurities in the chemicals used in making up solutions may likewise affect the results. Interfering substances include nitrite, ferric compounds, manganic compounds, organic iron compounds, lignocellulose, and microorganisms. The effect of these substances is to increase the apparent content of chlorine. Suspended matter, turbidity, and color may affect the results. It is apparent that the standard orthotolidine test for chlorine must be conducted under well-controlled and understood conditions in order to avoid error in the interpretation of its results. The orthotolidine-arsenite test[4] has been developed to overcome difficulties in determinations of chlorine or chloramine residuals that might result from the presence of iron, manganese, nitrites, and ammonia.

The iodometric method can be made more precise than the orthotolidine method, particularly when residual chlorine is greater than 1 ppm. Colorimetric methods for the iodometric determination of chlorine are available.

The amperometric method[5] is the only procedure known that will differentiate between free chlorine and free chlorine combined with nitrogenous compounds. The "flash" test[6] is a colorimetric test in which the color must be standardized. It is rendered inapplicable in the presence of oxidized manganese.

An enzymatic method for estimating chlorine[7] involves the measurement of the clotting time of milk, containing an unknown amount of chlorine, incubated with the proteolytic enzyme, *papain*. The concentration of chlorine is a function of the clotting time of the milk.

The drop-dilution test is a rapid field method applicable especially where chlorine concentrations are greater than 10 ppm, as in water-main sterilization. The method is a modification of the orthotolidine test, using orthotolidine as a reagent. The chlorine-demand test for field use,

---

[1] See also: N. S. Chamberlin and J. R. Glass, *ibid.*, August, 1943, p. 1065; D. B. Williams, *Water & Sewage Works*, Vol. 98, pp. 429, 475, 1951.

[2] See Committee American Water Works Association, *J.A.W.W.A.*, October, 1943, p. 1315.

[3] See also C. H. Connell, *ibid.*, March, 1947, p. 209.

[4] See also: T. J. Hallinan, *ibid.*, Vol. 36, p. 296, 1944; and F. W. Gilcrease and F. J. Hallinan, *ibid.*, p. 1343.

[5] See also H. C. Marks, *J. New Engl. Water Works Assoc.*, March, 1952, p. 1.

[6] See *J.A.W.W.A.*, Vol. 32, p. 1027, 1940.

[7] See P. K. Stumpf and D. E. Green, *ibid.*, November, 1946, p. 1306.

depending on orthotolidine reagent, gives only rough approximations of the true chlorine demand.

The continuous recording of residual chlorine[1] has been found advantageous in practice. The operation of the recorder depends on the depolarization of a copper electrode immersed in an electrolytic cell through which the chlorinated water flows continuously. The electric current flowing through the cell is proportional to the concentration of residual chlorine in the water. The variations in electric current are translated and recorded on an indicating and recording instrument. Factors affecting the sensitivity of the cell include electrode deterioration, temperature, pH, and chloramines. Concentrations of dissolved solids in potable water are said to have no significant effect on the cell.

30-11. Tastes and Odors Due to Chlorine. The addition of chlorine to water may result in an unpleasant taste due to the presence of too much residual chlorine or to a combination between the chlorine and matter in the water. Tastes may be avoided by adding a larger amount of chlorine than is required for sterilization alone, called "superchlorination"; by superchlorination followed by aeration; by superchlorination, a long period of contact, followed by dechlorination; by chlorination before and after filtration, called "double chlorination"; by chlorination preceding filtration; by chlorination after filtration; by the use of ammonia in conjunction with prechlorination or double chlorination; by lowering the pH of the water to assure a more rapid dissipation of the residual chlorine; by passing the water after chlorination through a filter of activated carbon; or by various combinations of these methods.[2]

Chlorophenol tastes are the most difficult to combat because of the very faint traces of phenol that will produce tastes. Tests made by Howard[3] showed that iodoform tastes were observed in the filtered water with a phenol content of 0.006 ppm after chlorination with 0.2 ppm of chlorine. Authorities differ as to the concentration of phenol necessary to produce tastes when water is chlorinated. Thresh[4] reported that as little as 0.0002 ppm of phenol with 0.25 ppm of chlorine produced a taste.

The presence of 0.005 ppm of iodine in water may result in iodoform tastes after chlorination. Superchlorination and oxidation with potassium permanganate may overcome them, but dechlorination with sulphur dioxide has no effect. The use of activated carbons is reported to have beneficial effects in removing such tastes.

30-12. Prechlorination, Double Chlorination, and Superchlorination. Prechlorination is the application of chlorine preceding filtration in such

[1] See also: J. R. Baylis and others, *ibid.*, September, 1946, p. 105; S. C. Gray and D. V. Moses, *ibid.*, July, 1947, p. 693.

[2] See also: N. J. Howard, *ibid.*, Vol. 9, p. 766, 1922; J. H. Enslow, *ibid.*, Vol. 18, p. 621, 1927.

[3] See also W. Donaldson and R. W. Furman, *ibid.*, Vol. 18, p. 605, 1927.

[4] See 19*th Rept., Metropolitan (London) Water Board.*

an amount that no chlorine will pass through the filter. When it is necessary to use a dechlorinating agent the process is superchlorination. It has been found that double chlorination, *i.e.*, the application of chlorine at two points in the treatment process, is advantageous under some conditions. Prechlorination will reduce the bacterial load on the filters so as to minimize the possibility of the passage of bacteria into the filtered water, without diminishing the efficiency of filtration. The amount of coagulant required may also be reduced because of the oxidation of the organic matter by prechlorination. Chlorination may precede aeration without appreciable loss of chlorine, especially in alkaline waters. Advantages claimed[1] for prechlorination include (1) reduction of bacterial load on the filters, (2) increased factor of safety, (3) better color removal in certain instances, (4) increased filter runs, (5) control of growths in basins and filters, (6) deferred putrefaction of settling-basin sludge, and (7) destruction of hydrogen sulphide and other oxidizable tastes and odors. Despite the advantages of prechlorination, postchlorination should not be abandoned because of the safety barrier interposed by it.

Among the advantages of double chlorination are the load on the filters is lightened; the maintenance of two chlorinating plants serves as a factor of safety; the exposure of bacteria to high concentrations of chlorine for short periods of time is more effective than exposure to small concentrations for a long period of time; the long period of retention in the coagulating basin permits relatively large overdoses of chlorine before free chlorine appears in the filter effluents; tastes and odors are reduced; algae and slime are avoided in coagulating basins and filters; and coagulation is aided.

Superchlorination is occasionally used to destroy odors and tastes. Raw-water chlorination, preceded or followed by the application of activated carbon, is a widely followed practice to destroy tastes and odors. The excess chlorine may be applied to any point or points in the treatment process. It is most commonly applied after filtration. Excess chlorine must be removed to avoid tastes in the water.

In general, the minimum amount of chlorine necessary to disinfect water will be required by the postfiltration application of the chlorine. At this time there is the least amount of organic matter in the water to consume the chlorine, its effect being concentrated on the remaining bacteria. Although the amount of chlorine required is increased by its application at other points, the results of disinfection may be improved.[2]

30-13. Dechlorination. The purpose of dechlorination is to remove excess chlorine from the water before distribution to the consumer to avoid chlorinous taste. Dechlorination may be accomplished by the application of sodium thiosulphate ($Na_2S_2O_3$), sodium metabisulphate

[1] See G. D. Norcom, *Eng. News-Record*, June 8, 1933, p. 745.
[2] See *ibid.*, Vol. 100, p. 407, 1928.

($Na_2S_2O_5$), sodium sulphite (Na_2SO_3), sodium bisulphite ($NaHSO_3$), ammonia (NH_4OH), or sulphur dioxide (SO_2) to the water. The sulphites are granular solids that may be added to water by dry or by solution feed. Sodium sulphite is probably the lowest cost per unit weight, but the required dose of sodium thiosulphate is lower for the same results. Ammonia may be useful and economical as a dechlorinator because of its reaction to form chloramines. Sulphur dioxide, applied somewhat in the same manner as chlorine, is relatively inexpensive as a dechlorinator. Activated carbon removes chlorine by adsorption. It may be applied as a powder to the water before filtration.[1]

Sulphur dioxide gas is applied with a contact period of not less than 10 to 15 min. Experience has shown that 0.3 to 0.6 ppm of sulphur dioxide may be required for success with dechlorination. The relationship between sulphur dioxide and an excess of chlorine is about 1.0 part of chlorine to 1.12 parts of sulphur dioxide. This is about 25 per cent in excess of the theoretical requirements. Dechlorination may be accomplished also by treating water with magnesium metal,[2] by prolonged storage of the water particularly when exposed to sunlight, and by aeration.[3]

30-14. Break-point Chlorination. If chlorine is added to water that has no chlorine demand the concentration of residual chlorine should equal the concentration of applied chlorine, as indicated by line A in Fig. 30-2. If, however, the water does have some chlorine demand and chlorine is added in ever-increasing concentration, the relation between applied and residual chlorine may appear as indicated by line B. Point D on line B is called the "break point." The break point in the chlorination of water may be defined as the point on the applied-residual chlorine curve at which all, or nearly all, the residual is free chlorine.

The shape of line B results from the fact that when chlorine is first applied the immediate chlorine demand results in the formation of stable chlorides and some unstable chloramines. The latter give color in the conventional orthotolidine test and are reported as residual chlorine. At point C on the curve the increasing concentration of the applied chlorine breaks down the chloramines that have been recorded as residual chlorine, and the true residual free chlorine is revealed at point D where chlorine demand has been satisfied.

It has been found by experience that the application of chlorine at, or slightly higher than, break-point concentration will remove tastes and odors, will have adequate bactericidal effect, and will leave a desired chlorine residual. Unfortunately the universal adoption of the method is

---

[1] See also C. J. Lauter, *J.A.W.W.A.*, December, 1947, p. 1237.
[2] See also H. Bach, *Water Works & Sewerage*, July, 1934, p. 241.
[3] See also N. J. Howard, *J.A.W.W.A.*, December, 1947, p. 1241.

made difficult by the fact that all waters do not present a distinguishable break point, and in some the changes in the quality of the raw water may effect rapid changes in the break point. The break point is caused by the presence of nitrogen compounds in the water. In some cases a recognizable break point has been induced by the addition of ammonia, NH_3, NH_4OH, or $(NH_4)_2SO_4$.

Before attempting sterilization by break-point chlorination, laboratory tests should be made to show that the process is practical on that particular water.

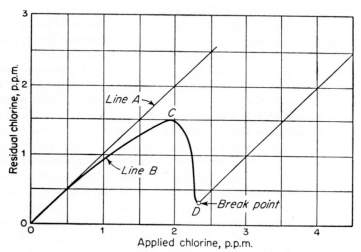

FIG. 30-2. Break-point chlorination.

30-15. Chlorine-Ammonia Treatment. The application of ammonia to water prior to the addition of chlorine has the advantages[1] of (1) the prevention of tastes, particularly those due to phenols; (2) the control of microorganisms in settling basins, filters, and the distribution system, due to the possibility of dosing heavily with chlorine and the carrying of high chlorine residuals without the production of tastes; (3) the bactericidal effects stronger than with chlorine alone where considerable quantities of organic matter are present; (4) longer period of persistence of the bactericidal effect, which inhibits aftergrowths; (5) reduction of chlorine requirements; (6) a reducing action which renders its effects independent of the presence of organic matter; (7) less irritation of the eyes and nose when used in swimming pools; (8) operators, no longer fearing to overdose with chlorine, will feed an adequate dose; and (9) freedom from danger, since chloramines are nontoxic and involve no danger either to employees

[1] See also: Committee Report, *ibid.*, December, 1941, p. 279; M. C. Smith, *ibid.*, September, 1951, p. 763; A. E. Griffin, *Am. J. Public Health*, 1937, p. 226.

or to consumers.   Ammonia should not be combined with chlorine when the chlorine is used as an oxidizing agent, as in the coagulation of colored water.   Under such circumstances ammonia may be applied with chlorine after filtration.   The chloramination of water is recommended primarily for water low in organic matter except where the detention period is brief, or the pH is above about 8.0.

Studies conducted by the U.S. Public Health Service indicate that chloramine is less effective than chlorine as a disinfecting[1] agent, and that in equal time the ratio of chloramine to produce 100 per cent kill is about 25:1, depending on the pH and the temperature.

It is important that the ammonia be applied at the right point and that adequate mixing and time of contact be provided before the application of the chlorine.   This time should be between 20 min and 1 to 2 hr.   The ammonia may be applied at any convenient point, an open reservoir or a closed conduit, where the efficacy of application has been proved by experience.   Because the ammonia dissolves quickly in the water but does not diffuse readily, it should be mixed by mechanical means.   It should be released near the bottom of a reservoir, because its specific gravity is less than that of water.   The period of contact may be from a few minutes to a few hours, but it must not be made too long, because the ammonia is a food for nitrifying bacteria which may remove the ammonia before it is available for the action of the chlorine, resulting in an increase in the bacteria and nitrite content of the filtered water.[2]   The resistance of these bacteria makes it appear impracticable to control nitrification by chlorination.[3]   If insufficient chlorine is added to carry a residual through the filters, the addition of more chlorine will probably cause tastes, as chloramines do not remove phenols from water, and the postaddition of chlorine, unprotected by ammonia, will cause phenol tastes.   Rapid disinfection will not occur, even with low ammonia ratio with waters high in pH, and chloramination should not be used for rapid disinfection with waters with a pH greater than about 7.2.

Ammonia gas is highly soluble in cool water, making its addition to water easy.   It can be applied through devices similar to those used for the application of liquid chlorine.   The ammonia water should be fed directly to the water supply through an orifice box.   The cost of this treatment has been found, about 1940, to be about 40 to 60 cents per million gallons of water treated.[4]

[1] Manual of Recommended Water Sanitation Practice, *Public Health Bull.* 296, 1946, p. 22.

[2] See also R. Hulbert, *Eng. News-Record*, Sept. 4, 1933, p. 315.

[3] See also D. Feben, *J.A.W.W.A.*, April, 1935, p. 439.

[4] See also: J. W. McAmis, *ibid.*, Vol. 17, p. 341, 1927; C. H. Spaulding, *ibid.*, Vol. 21, p. 1085, 1929; L. B. Harrison, *ibid*, Vol. 21, p. 542, 1929; L. L. Jenne and H. R. Welsford, *Ind. Eng. Chem.*, Vol. 23, p. 32, 1931; M. L. Koshkin, *J.A.W.W.A.*, Vol. 27, p. 1477, 1935.

30-16. Handling Ammonia. Care must be taken in the handling of liquid ammonia, as in the handling of liquid chlorine.[1] A mixture of ammonia and air in the ratio of 1:5 is inflammable. When moist, ammonia is corrosive to metals, is highly irritating to mucous membranes, and is especially corrosive to copper and copper-bearing alloys. Ammonia containers should be stored under conditions similar to those recommended for the storage of chlorine in containers.

30-17. Nitrogen Trichloride. The possibility of the formation of nitrogen trichloride (NCl_3) with resultant tastes and odors and ineffective disinfection is a hindrance to free residual chlorination. It will occur if the pH of the water is 4.4 or less and in alkaline waters high in nitrogenous matter. Nitrogen trichloride can be removed by dechlorination with sulphur dioxide followed by the application of the chlorine-ammonia treatment.[2]

30-18. Chlorine Dioxide.[3] Chlorine dioxide is an unstable compound that is commonly generated[4] at the point of its use by the introduction of sodium chlorite solution into the chlorinator discharge line. It is introduced in a proportion of equal weights of chlorine and of chlorine dioxide, with concentration of 0.2 to 0.3 ppm sodium chlorite. The theoretical ratio of chlorine to chloride is 1:4, but a ratio of 1:2 or less is recommended to obtain efficient evolution of chlorine dioxide. The dose required for effective taste and odor control has varied in practice between 0.5 and 1.5 ppm of chlorine dioxide. The chemical is most economically applied at any point after oxidation of the organic matter by chlorine. Chlorine dioxide has an oxidizing capacity $2\frac{1}{2}$ times that of chlorine, but its use as a disinfectant alone is not economical. It is most effective in the removal of tastes and odors, particularly against phenolic matter and algal growths, the effects being rapid. It is reported also[5] to be more effective than chlorine as a bactericide and as a sporicide. The action is relatively unaffected by pH values between 6 and 10. This fact is important in waters of high alkalinity.

Procedure in the use of chlorine dioxide involves chlorination for disinfection followed by the application of chlorine dioxide to destroy

[1] For first-aid measures see C. R. Cox, Water Supply Control, *New York State Dept. Health, Bull.* 22, pp. 110ff., 1943.

[2] See also D. B. Williams, *J.A.W.W.A.*, May, 1949, p. 441.

[3] See also: J. F. Synau and others, *J. New Engl. Water Works Assoc.*, September, 1944, p. 3; W. D. MacLean, *Water and Sewage*, May, 1946, p. 21; R. J. Mounsey and M. C. Hagar, *J.A.W.W.A.*, September, 1946, p. 1051; F. W. Gilcrease, *Water Works Eng.*, April, 1950, p. 297; Symposium, *Public Works*, May, 1948, pp. 35ff., 49.

[4] See also: A. E. Berry, *Water and Sewage*, February, 1945, p. 21; R. J. Mounsey and M. C. Hagan, *loc. cit.*

[5] See G. M. Ridenour and R. S. Nichols, *ibid.*, June, 1947, p. 561; G. M. Ridenour and E. H. Armbruster, *ibid.*, June, 1949, p. 537.

tastes and odors. Coagulation and filtration may precede or follow chlorination and precede the application of chlorine dioxide.[1]

30-19. Ozone.[2] Ozone is an unstable isotope of oxygen which, in the process of breaking down from O_3 to O_2, releases an atom of nascent oxygen. Advantages claimed for the use of ozone as a disinfectant include (1) no chemical remains in the water after disinfection; (2) odors, tastes, and color are removed; and (3) the cost of the process is not prohibitive.[3] Disadvantages include (1) high cost as compared with chlorination; (2) complicated apparatus is required; (3) application is inefficient since ozone disintegrates rapidly and solubility is low, with a solubility coefficient of only 0.29 in distilled water at 14 to 15°C;[4] and (4) the absence of residual chemical leaves no safeguard against postcontamination.

Hann[5] states that the power cost may vary between one and several dollars per million gallons, dependent on power rates and ozone requirements. To generate and apply 1 lb ozone will require 14 to 16 kwhr. It is economical to apply ozone only to clear filtered water so that the ozone demand may be less than 2 to 3 ppm. Adequate disinfection will be obtained with a brief residual of 0.1 ppm or more. Dosages up to 4 and 5 ppm are reported in taste and odor control.

Ozone is manufactured by the silent discharge of a high-tension electric current passing through a stream of air in an enclosed chamber. It must be mixed intimately with the water to be treated, since its solubility in water is slight and the process is inefficient without the best mixing. The mixing may be accomplished by allowing ozone to bubble up through the water or by allowing the gas to rise through a tower filled with pumice stone down which the water is trickling. A flow diagram of the ozonization plant at Philadelphia, Pa., is shown in Fig. 30-3. This plant,[6] with a capacity of 39 mgd, is probably the largest in the United States. It has been found at this plant that, for each pound of ozone produced, 8 to 9 kwhr are required by the ozone generator plus 2 to 3 kwhr for the operation of auxiliary equipment. A maximum capacity of 1.5 to 3.0 million cu ft of air is required daily. The air is dried, cleaned, and cooled before passing through the electrical corona where the voltage between electrodes is about 15,000. The ozonated air is introduced through porous plates at the bottom of the diffuser tank. The air rises through 18 ft depth of water which is passing downward through the

---

[1] See also N. H. Brown and L. B. Miller, *Public Works*, June, 1948, p. 38.

[2] See also: E. Howlett, *Water and Water Eng.*, January, 1947, p. 25; A. E. Rawson, *ibid.*, January, 1954, p. 9.

[3] See also M. T. B. Whitson, *J. Roy. Sanit. Inst.*, 1948, p. 448.

[4] See also A. E. Rawson, *Water and Water Eng.*, March, 1943, p. 102.

[5] V. Hann, *J.A.W.W.A.*, May, 1943, p. 585.

[6] See also: E. J. Taylor, *Water Works Eng.*, March, 1949, p. 217; *J.A.W.W.A.*, April, 1949, p. 322.

tank with a contact period of better than 10 min. At Whiting, Ind.,[1] ozone cost $1.95 per million gallons of water treated.

The process is used more extensively in Europe than in the United States.[2]

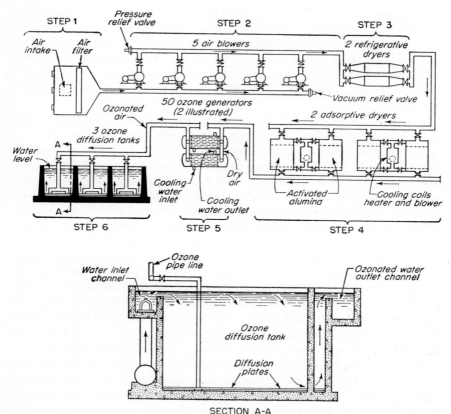

FIG. 30-3. Flowing-through diagram of an ozone plant. *(From E. J. Taylor and E. L. Bean, Eng. News-Record, July 28, 1949, p. 32.)*

30-20. Ultraviolet Ray.[3] The ultraviolet ray offers an effective method for the disinfection of clear water. The light kills both active bacteria and spores, which are difficult to exterminate by other means. The destructive power of light begins in the blue-green region of the spectrum with a wave length of 0.490μ and increases in effectiveness to

[1] See J. A. K. Van Hasselt, *Proc. 10th Ann. Short Course for Water and Sewage Plant Supts. and Operators*, Louisiana State University, 1947, 1, 43.

[2] See also: T. B. Whitson, *J. Inst. Civil Engrs.*, Vol. 21, p. 83, 1943; H. V. Over-field, *Water and Water Eng.*, October, 1943, p. 427.

[3] See also F. W. Gilcrease and L. DeLalla, *J. New Engl. Water Works Assoc.*, June, 1953, p. 130.

0.149μ. In this connection, it is interesting to note that the shortest visible violet rays have a length of 0.410μ and the longest visible red rays a length of 0.810μ.

The ultraviolet-ray machine consists of a mercury-vapor lamp enclosed in a quartz globe. The conditions necessary for the effective operation of the sterilizing machine are that all the water shall flow in a thin clear film close to the sterilizing ray. The water should be well agitated (but not mixed with air), and the exposure to the ray should be continuous. Ultraviolet lamps commonly use 220-volt direct current and about $3\frac{1}{2}$ amp. The effective penetration of the ray in clear and colorless water is about 12 in.

The amount of current consumed is dependent on the type of the machine and whether one or a number of machines are used in series. A single machine can be expected to consume about $\frac{3}{8}$ kw in passing 120 gal of water in 1 hr. Two large machines in series consumed 1.54 kwhr while delivering 3,000 gal water.[1] At Berea, Ohio, the cost of treatment was \$4.52 per million gallons with current at 1 cent per kilowatthour.[2]

30-21. Oligodynamic Action of Metals. Certain metals, particularly silver,[3] when immersed in water have been observed to exert an inhibiting action on bacterial life. The process is in the experimental stage, there being no installations of the type for the sterilization of a public water supply. In this process[4] silver, with or without "activators," such as palladium or gold, is deposited on the surface of sand, porcelain, or filter candles. Water is then passed through the filter or allowed to remain in contact with the silvered surface for a certain time. Although great claims have been made for the advantages of the process, there have been no applications where practical experience might support these claims.[5]

30-22. Excess Lime. The "excess-lime" process involves the application of sufficient lime for softening and clarification and, in addition, sufficient lime to exert a bactericidal effect. The necessary dose is between 10 and 20 ppm calcium oxide. After its bactericidal effect has been exerted the excess lime must be removed, preferably by any one of the various methods of recarbonation.[6]

30-23. Iodine. The disinfection of water with iodine is suitable for small water supplies and for troops in the field. The addition of 1 cc of a tincture comprising 7 parts iodine, 3 parts potassium iodide, and 90 parts alcohol to 7 liters water with a contact period of 5 min has been found

[1] See also *Plumbers' Trade J.*, Vol. 73, p. 897, 1923; Vol. 74, p. 36, 1924.

[2] See also J. F. Springer, *Public Works Mag.*, October, 1931, p. 39.

[3] See also A. Goetz, *J.A.W.W.A.*, May, 1943, p. 585.

[4] See also J. H. Gibbard, *Am. J. Public Health*, September, 1933, p. 910.

[5] See also: S. V. Moiseev, *J.A.W.W.A.*, February, 1934, p. 217; E. V. Suckling, *Water and Water Eng.*, Dec. 21, 1931, p. 625; Just and Szniolis, *J.A.W.W.A.*, April, 1936, p. 492.

[6] See also A. Houston, *Munic. Sanit.*, April, 1932, p. 148.

to give satisfactory disinfection.[1] Iodine is available also in pellet form for disinfection purposes. Chang[2] states that the dosage for disinfection should be about 8 ppm of iodine.

30-24. Control of Microscopic Organisms. The growth of microscopic organisms in a lake or open reservoir may be controlled in whole or in part by the construction or by the method of operation of the reservoir; by the application of toxic chemicals such as copper sulphate, chlorine, and chloramine, which are used in public water supplies; and compounds of mercury and other heavy metals, oxidizing agents, acids, caustic alkali, and other toxic substances used in industrial water supplies under exceptional circumstances; by the use of activated carbon; and by physical methods such as aeration, sedimentation, cutting weeds, cleaning the reservoir, or changing the quality of the water.[3] It is better, however, to prevent the growth of the organisms than to attempt to remove them after they have become a nuisance.

In the construction of a reservoir to inhibit the growth of certain types of microscopic organisms, shallow reaches and stagnant areas should be avoided. In general, it is undesirable to impound water high in organic matter drawn from a swampy area or to store ground water or treated waters in open reservoirs. In the operation of a reservoir, care should be taken to prevent the seeding of the reservoir by the admission into it of water impregnated with organisms. The admission of microscopic organisms into a water supply may be avoided by drawing the water from depths at which undesirable organisms are not found or by allowing a contaminated reservoir to rest until the crop of undesirable organisms has disappeared.

It is usually preferable to treat infected water continuously at the inlet to a reservoir, a distribution system, or other container than to attempt the destruction of large masses of zoogloeal matter that have accumulated in them. In other words, prevention is easier than removal. Some important considerations in the removal of microscopic organisms are[4] (1) certain algal spores can resist any form of algicidal treatment and will later develop on reaching a suitable environment; (2) where any portion of the raw water is exposed to light for a lengthy period in the purification works, several successive applications of algicide may be necessary to prevent growths and may be preferable to a single application; (3) applications of algicides should be made at points immediately before the water approaches any known focus of algal development; (4) certain organisms multiply at certain times of the day, and a concentration of the treatment around such time is frequently most effective;

[1] See also T. J. Burgers and W. Kalies, *Public Health Eng. Abs.*, July, 1948, p. 23.
[2] S. L. Chang and J. C. Morris, *Ind. Eng. Chem.*, Vol. 45, pp. 1009, 1013, 1953.
[3] See also H. K. Nason, *J.A.W.W.A.*, March, 1938, p. 436.
[4] See also J. W. Husband, *Water and Water Eng.*, Vol. 35, p. 765, 1933.

(5) improved circulation or increased velocity of flow in pipes and channels may markedly favor the development of some organisms throughout the system, although the growth of others may be inhibited in this manner; (6) all microscopic growths are subject to decay and thereby produce soluble organic matter which can pass through any form of filter; (7) in some cases it is desirable to alter the chemical quality of the water to discourage the growth of an organism.

The "carbon-blackout" method[1] of controlling algae involves the feeding of activated carbon to produce sufficient turbidity to inhibit growths by the diminution of light. The dosage of activated carbon, applied as a slurry, is in the order of 0.2 to 0.5 lb per 1,000 sq ft water surface, the greater the normal turbidity of the water the less the amount of carbon required.

When organic growths are giving trouble in closed conduits and in covered reservoirs, effective methods of treatment include chlorination, chloramine treatment, the use of copper sulphate, and the cleaning of the pipes or reservoirs. These remedies must be applied with caution, as the use of chlorine will probably produce tastes and odors, if not properly applied; the use of chloramine serves primarily to delay the action of the chlorine so that it may be more effective in remote portions of the distribution system; cleaning of pipes, if done mechanically, may accelerate the effects of corrosion. In spite of their objectionable features, each of the methods has been used in some instances with satisfaction.

30-25. Copper Sulphate.[2] Copper sulphate is the chemical most frequently used in the control of microscopic organisms in reservoirs, in pipe lines, and in distribution systems. Copper sulphate may be applied to open water surfaces by (1) towing a porous sack containing the requisite quantity of copper sulphate behind a boat that travels in parallel swaths 25 to 50 ft wide; (2) using a perforated wooden box, or other prepared container, to which copper sulphate crystals are added under controlled conditions; (3) spraying the solution over the water surface from a moving boat; (4) blowing dry copper sulphate from a boat or airplane or scattering it over surface ice or open water,[3] and by other ingenious methods.[4] Where water is entering a closed pipe line the copper sulphate may be added in the form of a solution at a concentration of about 0.5 to 0.65 ppm.[5]

[1] See also H. O. Hartung, "Taste and Odor Control in Water Purification," pp. 25, 55, Industrial and Chemical Sales, New York, 1947.

[2] See also F. E. Hale, "The Use of Copper Sulphate in Control of Microscopic Organisms," 1950 ed., Phelps Dodge Refining Corp., New York.

[3] For details of procedures see C. R. Cox, Water Supply Control, *New York State Dept. Health, Bull.* 22.

[4] See also "Water Quality and Treatment," p. 116, American Water Works Association, 1950.

[5] See also F. C. Amsbary, Jr., *J.A.W.W.A.*, March, 1945, p. 294.

Continuous feeding is said to be most effective, and it will leave a residue that remains toxic for as long as 4 months.[1] The presence of copper sulphate in water in the amount necessary to kill microorganisms has no detrimental effect on human beings or on the suitability of the water for a public water supply or for most industrial processes. It may, however, have a detrimental effect on fish, the most susceptible of which are certain species of trout which may be killed in concentrations higher than about 0.15 ppm. Some concentrations of copper sulphate that will kill fish are listed in Table 30-1.[2]

TABLE 30-1. The Amount of Copper Sulphate Necessary to Kill Fish*

Species of fish	Copper sulphate, lb per million gal	Species of fish	Copper sulphate, lb per million gal
Trout	1.2	Pickerel	3.5
Carp	2.8	Goldfish	4.2
Suckers	2.8	Sunfish	11.1
Catfish	3.5	Black bass	16.6
Perch	5.5		

* W. S. Mahlie, *J.A.W.W.A.*, Vol. 10, p. 1000, 1923; F. E. Hale, *Water & Sewage Works*, Vol. 93, p. R-73, 1946.

Crystals of copper sulphate ($CuSO_4 \cdot 7H_2O$) are available in sizes from a fine powder to those which will just pass a 1-in. mesh. The crystals are readily soluble in water and can be made up into solutions with a strength of about 25 per cent. Commercial copper sulphate contains about 25 per cent copper. Hence, the application of 0.8 ppm of copper sulphate, or 6.5 lb per million gal, will create a copper concentration of 0.2 ppm in otherwise non-copper-bearing water. This is the highest concentration permitted by the U.S. Public Health Service standards for potable waters. The amount of copper sulphate necessary for the control of different microorganisms is listed in Table 25-1.

30-26. Chlorine as an Algicide. The use of chlorine as an algicide is not extensive, because of the greater satisfaction found with copper sulphate and the difficulty of applying chlorine to a quiescent body of water.[3] Where there is a flow of water through a narrow channel or into or away from a body of surface water or from one body of water to another, chlorine gas can be applied at such a point by the method described in Sec. 30-7. The method may be used in the control of algae

[1] See also R. L. Derby and D. W. Graham, *Proc. Am. Soc. Civil Engrs.*, July, 1953, p. 203-1.

[2] For a test to determine the amount of copper sulphate required, see *Water Works Eng.*, September, 1950, p. 848.

[3] See also: C. Cohen, *J.A.W.W.A.*, Vol. 17, p. 444, 1926; F. J. Sette, *Eng. News-Record*, May 28, 1931, p. 885.

in a distribution reservoir.[1] The amounts of chlorine required to kill algae are listed in Table 25-1. It is to be noted that sufficient chlorine must be added to accomplish the purpose, followed by dechlorination, if necessary, or undesirable tastes are likely to develop. The successful use of "cuprichloramine," a compound of ammonia, chlorine, and copper sulphate, is reported.[2]

30-27. Control of Weeds and of Fish.[3] Weeds are undesirable in water-supply reservoirs and open channels because they are unsightly, obstruct the flow of water, cause tastes, odors, and color in the water, and supply food for other undesirable organisms. Time-honored methods for the removal of weeds from watersheds include oiling, burning, raking, cutting,[4] dragging, and chaining.[5] Spraying from airplanes has been done successfully.[6]

The use of chemicals can be the least costly and may be satisfactory. Chemical weed control around reservoirs[7] may serve to avoid tastes and odors and to prevent fires. Care must be taken that the chemicals used do not create tastes, odors, and toxic hazards in the water. For example, the popular weed killer 2,4-D is to be avoided because of its phenolic base. Acceptable chemicals include "Ammate" (ammonium sulphamate) and the sodium salt of trichlor acetic acid (90 per cent sodium trichlor acetate).

Emergent aquatic weeds, such as cattails and tules, formerly controlled by 2,4-D, may be treated with 2,4,5-T and hydrocarbons such as naphtha, trichlorbenzol, and orthodichlorobenzene. Loiselle[8] concludes that Ammate and CMU "look like the two best herbicides to use on watersheds." These are both proprietary compounds. Many proprietary weed killers of the dichlorphenoxyacetic acid type are used successfully.

Aquatic weeds, other than emergent weeds, that grow under water[9] can be controlled by the use of sodium arsenite, copper sulphate, chlorine, and Benchlor (trichlorinated benzines). Since arsenical compounds are toxic to man and animals they must not be applied in concentrations greater than 0.5 ppm. Dosages up to 10 ppm have been used[10] without

[1] See also L. B. Mangum, *J.A.W.W.A.*, 1929, p. 44.

[2] See "Water Quality and Treatment," American Water Works Association, 1950, p. 122.

[3] See also: R. F. Goudey, *Water & Sewage Works*, Vol. 94, p. R-121, 1947; M. Flentje, *J.A.W.W.A.*, August, 1952, p. 727.

[4] See also *Water Works Eng.*, February, 1954, p. 118.

[5] See *ibid.*, June 4, 1941, p. 630.

[6] See *Public Works*, May, 1949, p. 23.

[7] See W. I. Boyd, *Am. City*, December, 1952, p. 87.

[8] D. W. Loiselle, *J. New Engl. Water Works Assoc.*, June, 1953, p. 140; Anon., *Public Works*, June, 1948, p. 36.

[9] See also E. W. Surber, *J.A.W.W.A.*, August, 1950, p. 735.

[10] See also K. M. Mackenthum, *Sewage and Ind. Wastes*, August, 1950, p. 1062.

harm to fish life. Such dosages must be used with great caution and the water may not be used for bathing, irrigation, or as a beverage until its potability is assured. Chlorinated hydrocarbons, such as Benchlor No. 3, may be applied at a rate of about 50 gal per acre and allowed at least 4 days of contact, with precautions to avoid tastes and odors.

Fish are not always desirable in reservoirs and their removal is sometimes attempted. Methods used include (1) seining, which is not always successful because of snags; (2) draining of the reservoir; and (3) poisoning, particularly with rotenone, which is effective as a piscicide but is nontoxic to man in the quantities required to kill fish.[1]

30-28. Control of Small Animal Life. Infestations of public water supplies by the larvae of flying insects, by crustaceae, and by other small macroscopic animal life have been recorded.[2] The larvae giving trouble most frequently are the aquatic larval stages of the Chironomidae, called midges. The aquatic period involves the egg, pupal, and larval stages. Eggs may be laid in the water, in a protective gelatinous coating, either anchored or free-floating. The larvae resemble an animated letter S or figure 8, are from a few millimeters up to 25 mm in size, and are called white worms or bloodworms according to their size and color. In most cases the larvae will be found embedded in the debris and fine dirt at the bottom of the reservoir. They breathe and feed without leaving this environment. An entire cycle from egg to adult may occur in 1 to 5 weeks. Mechanical control involves covering the reservoir and screening all openings or the use of excelsior filters, which may be useful also in removing crustaceae. Biological methods include (1) keeping down vegetation near the reservoir, (2) keeping down algal growths, thus removing the food supply, (3) placing predatory fish in the reservoir, and (4) holding the reservoir empty for the needed period of time. Chemical methods involve (1) the use of mineral oil (Acme white oil, viscosity 80 to 85 at 100°F) to keep air from the eggs, to prevent the pupae from emerging, and to imprison flies alighting for oviposition; and (2) the use of DDT in a concentration of about 0.01 ppm. DDT should be used only under experienced supervision. The more common algicides, such as copper sulphate, chlorine, and chloramines, have not given universal satisfaction as larvicides.

[1] See also *Public Works*, September, 1948, p. 61.
[2] See also M. Flentje, *J.A.W.W.A.*, November, 1945, p. 1194.

CHAPTER 31

MISCELLANEOUS METHODS OF WATER PURIFICATION

31-1. The Removal of Compounds of Iron and of Manganese. Objectionable features of, and the similarity of the behavior of, compounds of iron and of manganese in water are discussed in Secs. 24-29 and 24-31. These compounds are soluble in water as ferrous or manganous hydroxides, and in other forms combined with organic matter. Methods for their removal include (1) aeration, (2) the application of lime, possibly supplemented with chlorine, (3) chlorination alone, and (4) the use of base-exchange substances. In all but the last-named method sedimentation either with or without filtration is used to remove precipitated compounds. Precipitation is enhanced by the catalytic action of previously deposited hydrates or oxides which may be added for the purpose. Iron alone may be removed by oxidation with potassium permanganate, or, if in the proper form, by coagulation and sedimentation.

Manganese alone may be removed by (1) biologic action through contact with *Crenothrix magnifera;* (2) hydrogen cation exchange; (3) on contact beds followed by aeration, particularly where pyrolusite, a native manganic oxide, is used as contact material; (4) by the use of potassium permanganate;[1] (5) by manganese base exchange; or (6) by break-point chlorination followed by filtration.[2] Craig[3] has removed manganese by the addition of copper and lime, maintaining the pH at 10 for coagulation. Nordell[4] calls attention to the catalytic effect of manganese hydroxides on oxides and their effect on the ripening of filters and in lowering of the required pH, and to the need for measures for overcoming the formation of thick coatings in the filter medium.

Methods for the removal of iron and of manganese are listed in Table 31-1. Other methods have been used.

---

[1] See also I. W. Mendelsohn, *Water Works & Sewerage,* January, 1935, p. 3.

[2] See also S. E. Edwards and G. B. McCall, *Eng. News-Record,* Aug. 8, 1946, p. 89.

[3] E. C. Craig and others, *J.A.W.W.A.,* Vol. 24, p. 1762, 1932.

[4] E. Nordell, "Water Treatment for Industrial Uses," p. 334, Reinhold Publishing Corporation, New York, 1951.

TABLE 31-1. Processes for the Removal of Iron and of Manganese[a]

Character of water	Treatment process[b]	Equipment[b]	pH	Chemicals	Oxidation	Remarks
Iron alone. No appreciable organic matter	A SD SF	A SB SF	Over 6.5	None	Yes	Easily operated
Iron and manganese loosely bound to organic matter. No excessive organic matter or organic acids	A CO Sd SF	Contact aerator of coke or crushed pyrolusite SB SF	Over 6.5	None	Yes	Double pumping, easily controlled
Iron and manganese bound to organic matter. No excessive organic matter	A CF	A and bed of manganese-coated sand, "Birm," crushed limestone ore, or manganese zeolite	Over 6.5 ±	None	Yes	c
Iron and manganese bound to organic matter. No excessive carbon dioxide or organic acid	CF	Filter bed of manganese-coated sand, "Birm," crushed limestone ore, or manganese zeolite	Over 6.5	None[d]	e	Single pumping, aeration not required
Iron and manganese loosely bound to organic matter	A L Sd SF	Effective A. Lime feeder and mixing basin SB SF	8.5–9.6	Lime	Yes	pH control required
Colored, turbid surface water plus iron and manganese with organic matter	A Co L Sd SF	Conventional rapid-sand-filter plant	8.5–9.6	f	Yes	Complete laboratory control required
Well water devoid of oxygen with less than about 1.5 to 2.0 ppm iron and manganese	Z	Conventional sodium zeolite unit, with manganese zeolite or equivalent to treat by-passed water	Over 6.5 ±	g	No	h
Soft well water devoid of oxygen with iron as ferrous bicarbonate	L Sd SF	Lime feeder, enclosed mixing and settling tanks, and pressure filter	8.0–8.5	Lime	No	i

[a] Condensed from C. R. Cox, Water Supply Control, *N.Y. State Dept. Health, Bull.* 22.

[b] A = aeration; Sd = sedimentation; SE = sand filtration; CO = contact oxidation; CG = contact filtration; C = chlorination; L = lime treatment; Co = coagulation; Z = zeolite or base exchange; SB = settling basin.

[c] Double pumping required unless air compressor or "sniffler valve" is used to force air into water. Limited air supply adequate. Easily controlled.

[d] Filter bed reactivated or oxidized at intervals with chlorine or sodium permanganate.

[e] Yes, but not by aeration.

[f] Lime and ferric chloride or ferric sulphate or chlorinated copperas, or lime and copperas.

[g] None added continuously but bed is regenerated at intervals with salt solution.

[h] Only soluble ferrous and manganous compounds can be removed by base exchange; so aeration or double pumping is not required.

[i] Precipitation of iron in absence of air occurs at lower pH than otherwise. Absence of oxygen minimizes or prevents corrosion. Double pumping is not required.

Aeration, followed by sedimentation, either with or without filtration, is probably the most common method for the removal of iron and of manganese. It is especially applicable when iron is present in the carbonate form alone. The amount of oxygen required for the oxidation of ferrous iron is only about 0.14 part per part of iron, so that only slight agitation with air is usually sufficient. The oxidation of ferrous iron may be accelerated, particularly in waters high in carbon dioxide, by raising the pH through aeration or the addition of such alkaline substances as lime, soda ash, or caustic soda. Acid waters must be made alkaline. Aeration can be overdone, because of excessive agitation, thus increasing the difficulty of sedimentation of precipitated iron. This may be removed also by adsorption by allowing the water, after aeration, to trickle over contact beds of coke or similar material. Settling basins, following aeration, may be designed for detention periods of 30 min to 2 hr and should be equipped for ease in cleaning. The presence of organic matter, carbon dioxide, and organic acids renders the removal of iron and of manganese difficult. Iron is more easily removed than manganese.

Iron and manganese can be precipitated from aerated water by the addition of lime. A pH of 9.4 to 9.6 is usually adequate for the precipitation of manganese. A pH of 8.2 is needed for the precipitation of iron. In softening water by the excess-lime process the iron and manganese are removed in an oxidized condition. Chlorine is used[1] to supplement lime. Chlorination beyond the break point,[2] preceding contact aeration, sedimentation, or filtration, alone or combined, can be effective in iron and manganese removal from waters at normal pH.

The oxidation of iron, particularly of organic origin, can be effected by the use of potassium permanganate. It is most effective, and is less likely to produce taste, if applied in the pH range from 8.8 to 9.8.

The precipitation of insoluble iron may be hastened by coagulation with alum, ferrous sulphate, or other coagulants, possibly with the adjustment of pH to secure optimum results.

It is to be noted that the removal of iron alone is more simple and more successful than the removal of manganese or iron combined with manganese.

31-2. Removal of Iron and Manganese Compounds by Base Exchange. Iron and manganese can be removed by base exchange. It is essential in the process that the raw water has not been aerated before entering the base exchanger as otherwise the precipitation of hydrated metallic oxides may clog the beds or coat the base-exchange material. Proprietary substances are in successful use. Synthetic zeolites are not recommended.

One process of removal involves both filtration and base exchange. The substance involved is a contact oxidizer made by treating the base-

---

[1] See also F. E. Hale, *J.A.W.W.A.*, October, 1936, p. 1577.

[2] See also E. R. Mathews, *ibid.*, July, 1947, p. 680.

exchange material used in water softening with manganous sulphate and potassium permanganate, thus causing the deposit of higher oxides of manganese. As raw water meets this material iron and manganese are oxidized to insoluble hydrated oxides that are removed by the mechanical filtering action of the base-exchange material which must be washed like a rapid sand filter, and then regenerated with potassium permanganate. The process is applicable to clear waters that do not contain large amounts of iron or manganese, or from which large quantities have been removed by other processes.

31-3. Removal of Silica.[1] Silica is removed from water to prevent scale formation in industrial processes, especially in steam boilers. Methods for the removal of colloidal silica include: (1) The application of ferric sulphate and lime to produce ferric hydroxide which absorbs the silica. The process may be undesirable because from 7 to 25 ppm of ferric sulphate are required for each part per million of silica removed, increasing the sodium sulphate content of the water by 1.1 ppm for each part per million of ferric sulphate added. The resultant increase in solids and sulphate hardness may be objectionable. (2) The use of magnesium hydroxide with either carbon dioxide, calcium bicarbonate, or magnesium bicarbonate which may be present in or added to the raw water, to produce magnesium carbonate which serves to absorb the silica. Dissolved silica is more difficult to remove, and study is being given to methods to remove it.

31-4. Removal of Fluorides. Methods for the removal of fluorides, proposed or studied, include (1) contact of the water with specially prepared ground bone; (2) the use of the carbonate radical of the apatite comprising bone $[Ca_9(PO_4)_6 \cdot CaCO_3]$;[2] (3) overtreatment with lime to a causticity of about 34 ppm in the presence of sufficient magnesium;[3] (4) passing the water through a bed of activated alum; (5) passing the water through a bed of tricalcium phosphate, with backwash of clear water followed by caustic solution to convert insoluble calcium fluoride to soluble sodium fluoride, then with clear water, then with carbonic acid to adjust the pH to about 7.0, and finally with clear water;[4] (6) absorption by hydroxy apatites in a pressure tank regenerating the medium with caustic soda, similar to the preceding method;[5] and (7) various forms of base exchangers.[6] Possibly the use of activated alum in conjunction with

[1] See also E. J. Roberts and W. W. Jukkola, *Public Health Eng. Abst.*, November–December, 1950, p. 27.

[2] See also: F. J. Maier, *Am. J. Public Health*, December, 1947, p. 1559; *J.A.W.W.A.*, August, 1953, p. 879.

[3] See R. D. Scott and others, *ibid.*, January, 1937, p. 9.

[4] See also R. Wamsley and W. E. Jones, *Water & Sewage Works*, August, 1947, p. 272.

[5] See also *Eng. News-Record*, Jan. 19, 1950.

[6] See also F. J. Maier, *J.A.W.W.A.*, August, 1953, p. 879.

ion exchangers is giving the greatest promise of satisfactory defluoridation of water.[1]

31-5. Removal of Dissolved Minerals. It is possible, by means of base exchange, to remove any amount of dissolved mineral matter from water, or to rearrange the dissolved minerals to produce an effluent of any desired qualities, within limits, for analytical or industrial purposes, even superior in quality to distilled water.[2] Kenzelite and Zepholite, proprietary base-exchange compounds, have been used successfully in the removal of lead, zinc, copper, and tin.[3] Streicher[4] states that waters with 1,000 to 3,000 ppm dissolved solids may be demineralized successfully by the application of a direct electric current in specially designed cells with canvas or similar diaphragms.

31-6. Fresh Water from Salt Water.[5] The recovery of fresh water from sea water has not yet been successfully accomplished as a source of public water supply. The great rewards which such recovery promises have encouraged extensive research.[6] Evaporation and ion-exchange demineralization are the only methods so far considered as feasible. Sources of heat for evaporation include various types of fuels and solar radiation.[7]

31-7. Removal of Oil. Oil must be removed from water principally in power plants and for industrial purposes. It may be removed by adsorption by passing the water through containers of excelsior, or similar material, which can be renewed frequently; by sand filters, similar to pressure filters, possibly combined with proprietary preformed floc, and equipped with mechanical agitation to supplement backwashing; and by other methods.

31-8. Removal of Radioactivity. Radioactive materials, discussed in Sec. 24-37, may be partly removed from water by the ordinary methods of coagulation and sedimentation followed by filtration.[8] Removals up to 80 to 90 per cent can be expected. No other feasible methods have been devised.

31-9. Removal of Color. Color may be removed, as other colloids are removed, by adsorption and by chemical precipitation, possibly followed

---

[1] See also J. A. Lee, *Chem. Eng.*, July, 1952, p. 400.

[2] See also H. B. Gustafson, *Ind. Eng. Chem.*, March, 1949, p. 464.

[3] See also B. A. Adams, *Water and Water Eng.*, Sept. 20, 1930, p. 415.

[4] L. Streicher and others, *Ind. Eng. Chem.*, Vol. 45, p. 2394, 1953.

[5] See also: E. D. Howe, *J.A.W.W.A.*, August, 1952, p. 690; *Eng. News-Record*, May 18, 1950, p. 32; "Fresh Water from the Ocean," The Ronald Press Company, New York, 1954.

[6] See also A. M. Buswell, *Public Health Eng. Abst.*, March, 1951, p. 27.

[7] See also W. A. Aultman, *J.A.W.W.A.*, August, 1950, p. 786.

[8] See also: W. A. Rodger, *ibid.*, June, 1950, p. 533; R. Eliassen and others, *ibid.*, August, 1951, p. 615; C. P. Straub and others, *ibid.*, October, 1951, p. 773; W. J. Lacy, *ibid.*, September, 1952, p. 824; A. L. Downing and others, *J. Inst. Water Engrs.*, Vol. 6, p. 511, 1952; Vol. 7, p. 555, 1953.

by sand filtration. No one method will remove all colors. Other methods include bleaching by sunlight in open reservoirs or by the use of chlorine. Coagulation with alum, followed by filtration, is probably the most widely used procedure. About 1 grain of alum per gallon of water should remove 10 ppm of color under favorable circumstances. In the removal of color by chemical coagulants the same principles apply as in the addition of coagulants for other purposes.

31-10. Removal of Taste and Odor.[1] Among the principal causes of tastes and odors in public water supplies may be included algae, industrial wastes, sewage, dissolved gases, dissolved mineral matter, and others. Since tastes and odors are closely associated the removal of one will generally result in the removal of the other.

Methods for the removal of tastes and odors include (1) aeration, (2) prechlorination, (3) superchlorination followed by dechlorination, (4) ammoniation or chloramination, (5) the use of chlorine dioxide, (6) the application of activated carbon, (7) the use of potassium permanganate,[2] (8) copper sulphate, (9) bleaching clay,[3] (10) lime alone or combined with ferrous hydroxide, (11) ozone, (12) the removal of iron and manganese, and (13) coagulation, sedimentation, and filtration. None of these methods is applicable to the removal of all tastes and odors, nor are all widely used for this purpose alone. For example, tastes and odors due to the presence of inorganic compounds may be controlled by aeration or by several methods of chemical treatment. Aeration or activated carbon is especially applicable to the removal of tastes and odors resulting from dissolved gases, whereas chloramination or lime[4] is applicable in the removal of phenol tastes. It has been found that the application of approximately 0.25 ppm ammonia (NH_3) is sufficient in most cases to prevent taste production when followed by chlorination. The theoretical ratio of chlorine to ammonia is 4:1 at pH of 8.5, and 8:1 at pH of 4.5. Ratios should vary with pH values. In practice it has been found that ratios of 3:1 to 2:1 will produce satisfactory results.

Where tastes have been exceptionally severe the combination of prechlorination and split treatment with activated carbon added also just ahead of the filters may be effective. Potassium permanganate has been found effective in controlling some tastes produced by microscopic organisms. Gibbons[5] found that it removed tastes and odors caused by

[1] See also: W. T. Bailey, *J.A.W.W.A.*, April, 1935, p. 458; J. R. Baylis, "Elimination of Taste and Odor in Water," McGraw-Hill Book Company, Inc., New York, 1935; Oscar Gullans, *J.A.W.W.A.*, July, 1933, p. 974; J. R. Baylis and O. Gullans, *ibid.*, April, 1936, p. 507.

[2] See also: A. Houston, *Munic. Sanit.*, April, 1932, p. 148; L. L. LaShell, *5th Ann. Rept. W. Va. Conf. on Water Purif.*, 1930, p. 37; L. Haines, *ibid.*, p. 35.

[3] See also R. I. Dodd, *J. Penna. Water Works Operators' Assoc.*, 1932, p. 65.

[4] See also J. S. Scott, *9th Ann. Rept. Ohio Conf. on Water Purif.*, 1929, p. 61.

[5] See also N. J. Howard, *Water Works & Sewerage*, January, 1938, p. 1.

solvent naphtha wastes, rosin, soap, and fermenting cereal wastes. It may be used also in combination with chlorine, being applied at such a rate that no pink color passes the filter. Doses between 0.2 and 0.4 ppm have been reported.

The most effective treatment seems to be superchlorination followed by a later application of activated carbon, or the use of activated carbon alone.[1]

31-11. Removal of Dissolved Gases. Dissolved gases can be removed by boiling, decompression, and the addition of chemicals. Dissolved gases, other than oxygen and nitrogen, in natural waters can normally be reduced by aeration because of the physical reduction of their partial pressure when exposed to air. Advantages of aeration in the degasification of water include (1) freedom from chemical control, (2) unskilled operation is possible, (3) simplicity of equipment which may function without moving parts, (4) there is no change in the mineral content of the water, and (5) low operating costs. It may be expected that a single-stage degasifier will deliver water with less than 0.2 ml oxygen per liter, and carbon dioxide not exceeding 2 ppm. The pH will increase because of the removal of carbon dioxide.

Carbon dioxide cannot be reduced below 2 to 5 ppm by aeration alone. Hence aeration will not prevent corrosion by carbon dioxide when the alkalinity is less than about 80 ppm. It is usually undesirable, in corrosion control, to aerate to remove carbon dioxide because the oxygen introduced will counteract the benefit of the reduction of carbon dioxide. Carbon dioxide may be further reduced by the use of calcium or barium hydroxide, but since the latter chemical is toxic it may not be used in potable water. Carbon dioxide can be reduced also by passing the water over beds of crushed limestone.[2] Such beds may be contained in closed tanks like pressure filters, called neutralizing filters.

Hydrogen sulphide cannot always be removed by aeration alone.[3] Scrubbed flue gases containing carbon dioxide are first diffused through the water containing the hydrogen sulphide. The dissolved carbon dioxide lowers the pH, thus releasing the hydrogen sulphide. Excess carbon dioxide is thereafter removed by aeration. Where precipitated sulphur compounds are formed they must be removed by filtration to avoid reversion to hydrogen sulphide.

31-12. Aeration.[4] Water can be aerated by (1) exposing it to the atmosphere, as in open aqueducts and reservoirs; (2) flowing over cascades, weirs, steps, troughs, etc.; (3) flowing through trickling devices such as coke beds and perforated trays; (4) spraying it through the air;

---

[1] See also Oscar Gullans, *J.A.W.W.A.*, January, 1937, p. 60.
[2] See also "Water Conditioning Handbook," the Permutit Co., 1949.
[3] See also S. W. Wells, *J.A.W.W.A.*, February, 1954, p. 160.
[4] See also: S. W. Wells, *loc. cit.;* P. D. Haney, *ibid.*, April, 1954, p. 353.

(5) diffusing air through it;[1] (6) aspirating air through the water;[2] (7) mixing air and water under pressure to increase the solubility of the air; and by other methods.[3] The first four methods involve the exposure of water to air and are most commonly used. Various types of aerators are illustrated in Fig. 31-1.

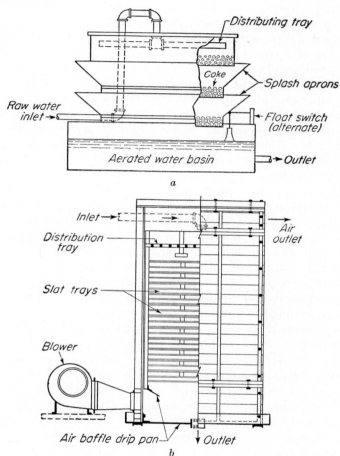

FIG. 31-1. Aerators. (a) Coke-tray aerator. (*Courtesy of the Permutit Co.*) (b) Infilco forced-draft aerator. (*Courtesy of Infilco.*)

Coke trays, such as are shown in the figure, are widely used. Short falls with many trays are preferred to long falls and few trays. Aeration is most effective when the flow of air is upward against the direction of

[1] See also F. C. Roe, *Eng. and Contract Record*, Apr. 14, 1937, p. 54.

[2] See also H. L. Kaufman, *J.A.W.W.A.*, Vol. 25, p. 1030, 1925.

[3] See also: F. E. Hale, *ibid.*, 1932, p. 1401; M. Flentje, *ibid.*, June, 1937, p. 872; R. McNamee, *Univ. Mich. Eng. Research Bull.* 16, June, 1930.

the falling water.   If it is desired to remove entrained air bubbles after aeration, the water may flow from the aerator into a basin with a detention period of about 15 min to 2 hr and with adequate surface area. Spray nozzles need a pressure of about 10 psi at the throat.   Air-diffuser basins may have a detention period of about 15 min, a depth of 9 to 15 ft, and use 0.05 to 0.10 cu ft free air per gallon of water treated, and requiring about 1 kw of power per million gallons per day of plant capacity.

Aeration under pressure is sometimes accomplished by pumping water into the top of a closed tank into which air is pumped to maintain a constant predetermined water level in the tank.   The device has the advantage of avoiding double pumping but aeration must be controlled to avoid supersaturation at normal atmospheric pressure with resulting visible escape of air from the water.

Efficiencies of aerators may be expressed in percentage removal of carbon dioxide.   This is not always a good measure since the higher the initial concentration the higher the percentage efficiency of the aerator.[1]

31-13. Deaeration.   Water may be deaerated to diminish its corrosiveness.[2]   Deaeration may prove more economical than corrosion control by the application of chemicals and it is aesthetically more desirable in that in some methods of deaeration nothing is added to the water. Methods for the removal of dissolved oxygen include (1) passing the water through vessels containing a large surface of scrap iron,[3] followed by filtration through sand, all under pressure in a closed vessel; (2) the formation of ferrous hydroxide in the water by the addition of ferrous sulphate and calcium or sodium hydroxide; (3) the addition of sodium sulphite; (4) boiling the water; and (5) exposing the water to a vacuum.[4] In any of these methods the surface of the water must be insulated from the atmosphere in order to prevent the rapid reabsorption of oxygen. In the last two methods listed the oxygen released must be removed promptly to prevent reabsorption.   Not more than about 95 per cent of the dissolved oxygen can be removed by the last two methods.   Chemical methods can deoxygenate water completely, but a combination of mechanical means to remove the first 95 per cent of the oxygen, followed by chemical treatment, may be economical.[5]   The addition of sodium sulphite to a public water supply is undesirable unless done under competent control, because of the toxicity of the chemical.

31-14. Activated Carbon.[6]   Activated carbon is a form of vegetable carbon, or charcoal, that has been heated in a closed retort in an atmos-

---

[1] See also "Water Conditioning Handbook," *loc. cit.*

[2] See also S. T. Powell and others, *J.A.W.W.A.*, July, 1946, p. 808.

[3] See also F. N. Speller, *Trans. Am. Soc. Heating Ventilating Engrs,*, Vol. 23, p. 125, 1917.

[4] See also S. T. Powell, *Water & Sewage Works*, March, 1946, p. 93.

[5] See also D. J. Pye, *J.A.W.W.A.*, November, 1947, p. 1121.

[6] See Specifications, *ibid.*, February, 1951, p. 161.

phere of such gases as carbon dioxide, air, steam, or chlorine. Occasionally chemical agents, such as phosphoric acid or zinc chloride, may be added. This "activation" and the greatly increased power of the carbon to adsorb gases distinguishes activated carbon from charcoal. Activated carbons differ between themselves depending on the raw material used and the process of activation. A carbon good for one purpose, such as gas adsorption, may be of little value in the treatment of a liquid.[1] Most of the activated carbons used in water purification are proprietary substances sold under such trade names as Darco, Minchar, and Nuchar.

Since it is not possible to measure the degree of odor and taste removal by chemical analysis, tests for the quality of activated carbon aim toward the physical measurement of its odor-removing ability. Three methods have been proposed for this purpose: (1) the phenol-absorption test, (2) the dilute-iodine test, and (3) the threshold-odor test.

The phenol-absorption test[2] gives a measure of the capacity of activated carbon to absorb phenol. Since carbons are highly selective in their action, the test may give no indication of the value of the carbon for absorbing other odors. Baylis suggests that the phenol-absorption requirement of a satisfactory carbon be limited to 35 ppm. The limits of adsorption of which activated carbon is capable have been formulated by Freundlich.[3]

In the iodine test a known weight of the carbon is shaken for a predetermined time with a solution containing a known weight of iodine. The iodine absorbed is a measure of the odor-absorbing power of the carbon. The test has the advantage of being simple, but it may indicate even less than the phenol test with respect to the quality of the carbon.

The threshold-odor[2] test is difficult to make but it has the advantage that it may measure directly the characteristic most desired in the activated carbon under observation.

It can be expected, in general, that good activated carbon will weigh 10 to 11 lb per cu ft, that it will contain not less than 90 per cent of pure carbon, and that not over 6 per cent will be retained on a 200-mesh sieve. Activated carbon is shipped in bags weighing about 75 lb. When supplied in carload lots of 15 tons, it can be bought for about 5 cents per pound. The cost of treatment, in 1950, ranged between 40 cents and $1 per million gallons.

31-15. The Use of Activated Carbon. Activated carbon is used in water purification principally for the control of tastes and odors resulting

[1] See also D. Colebaugh and others, *Water & Sewage Works*, April, 1952, p. R-101.

[2] See also: J. R. Baylis, *Water Works & Sewerage*, June, 1933, p. 220; F. R. Theroux and others, "Laboratory Manual for Chemical and Bacterial Analysis of Water and Sewage," 3d ed., McGraw-Hill Book Company, Inc., New York, 1943.

[3] See discussion in "Water Quality and Treatment," p. 160, Manual American Water Works Association, 1940.

from the presence of dissolved gases. It has been found effective in aiding in coagulation, in the removal of color, in the control of algae, in preventing or retarding the decomposition of sludge in settling basins, and in the reduction of the chlorine demand of treated water. It aids in water conditioning and lengthens filter runs by increasing the turbidity and producing better sedimentation of microorganisms. Among its advantages may be included the fact that no chemical reagent is added to the water, because the carbon is filtered out, there is no danger of an overdose of activated carbon, and excess chlorination is made easier.[1] If powdered activated carbon is added to the influent to a rapid-sand-filter plant in an amount less than 5 ppm, the filter runs will probably not be shortened,[2] but in some cases the reduction of length of run has been as much as 50 per cent.

In the removal of tastes and odors from water by activated carbon the material may be applied as a dry powder directly to the water at one or more points preceding filtration or sedimentation, or filtered water may be passed through the bed of activated carbon.[3] If a dry powder is used it may be applied to the water before filtration either alone or mixed with other chemicals such as alum.

Activated carbon may be stored and fed also as a slurry containing about 1.25 lb carbon per gallon of water. The amount of carbon in the slurry being fed can be determined most quickly by determining the specific gravity of the slurry and reading the carbon content on a prepared calibration curve.[4]

The material can be fed before, during, or after coagulation or at more than one point. This is known as "split treatment." The most common point of application is preceding coagulation. Wherever the carbon is applied, it should be so controlled that a small portion reaches the filter. It may be desirable occasionally to "bump" the filter shortly after washing or after commencing the application of carbon to work it into the interstices of the sand. Dosages vary widely between 1 and 100 ppm but averaging, in practice, about 20 to 25 lb per million gal.

The following points should be considered in the feeding of dry activated carbon: (1) the carbon should be handled in a separate room to minimize the dust nuisance; (2) the feeding machine should have considerable overcapacity because of the wide fluctuations of load that come to most plants; (3) a plentiful supply of water should be provided to carry the carbon to the point of application without danger of clogging

[1] See also: E. A. Sigworth, *J.A.W.W.A.*, Vol. 29, p. 688, 1937; *ibid.*, January, 1934, p. 6.

[2] See also M. M. Gibbons, *Eng. News-Record*, Mar. 17, 1932, p. 391.

[3] See also "Taste and Odor Control in Water Purification," Chap. 7, Industrial and Chemical Sales, New York, 1947.

[4] See also: J. T. Cross, *Pure Water*, November, 1949, p. 162; J. R. Baylis, *Taste Odor Control*, March, 1950; *J.A.W.W.A.*, December, 1952, p. 1161.

the slurry pipe; and (4) the strength of slurry, where slurry feed is used, should be about 4 per cent. Rubber or iron pipes may be used for conveying the slurry.

Care must be observed in the storage of activated carbon since it is furnished in so finely divided a state that an explosive mixture with the atmosphere can result. Because of the high absorptive properties of the material, enough heat might be generated in an improperly designed storage room to reach the ignition point. Storage space of 40 to 150 cu ft per ton should be allowed. Storage as a slurry avoids dust and fire hazards and does not injure the adsorptive properties of the carbon.

31-16. Microstraining.[1] Treatment of water by microstraining makes possible the removal of some microscopic organisms and fine suspended matter. The microstraining fabric most commonly used has about 80,000 apertures per square inch, having a nominal size of about 35μ. This fabric forms the inner layer of the surface of a cylinder, almost completely submerged in the water to be treated, revolving on a horizontal axis. Units with capacities up to 10 mgd are manufactured. There are many installations in England where the strainers have been found useful in conjunction with slow sand filters, and as complete-treatment devices.

31-17. Puech-Chabal Filters. In the Puech-Chabal system of filtration the water is passed at a progressively slower rate through a series of progressively finer gravity sand filters of the slow sand type. The use of these filters is confined almost exclusively to French installations. Although the quality of the water produced is excellent, the first cost is high and the head loss is appreciable.

31-18. Drifting-sand Filters and Magnetite Filters. These filters are of primary interest historically since neither is in general use. The drifting-sand filter at Toronto, Ont.,[2] the only one of its kind that was ever in use, has been abandoned. The magnetite sand filter[3] operated somewhat similarly to a slow sand filter. When the head loss through the filter reached a predetermined limit the filter sand was washed without shutting down the filter, by passing an electromagnet and a wash-water circulating pump over the bed. The magnetic sand was lifted by the electromagnet and washed as it was allowed to drop through the circulating wash water back into place on the surface of the bed. The dirty wash water from the pump was allowed to run to waste. The washing device moved across the filter, washing and replacing the sand without shutting down the filter.

[1] See also: P. L. Boucher, *Inst. Water Engrs., Scottish Section,* Apr. 6, 1951; A. W. Consoer, *Eng. News-Record,* Apr. 9, 1953, p. 36; R. Hazen, *J.A.W.W.A.,* July, 1953, p. 723.

[2] See G. G. Nasmith, *Can. Engr.,* Apr. 8, 1915.

[3] See S. I. Zack, *Water Works & Sewerage,* June, 1937, p. 201.

31-19. Diatomite Filters.   Diatomite filters for the treatment of water were first used during the Second World War.[1]   For civilian purposes they are now used mainly for special industrial processes, for swimming pools, and for other relatively small demands.   Their use for public water supplies is not extensive.[2]   Among the advantages of the diatomite filter for the production of potable water is its relatively low weight and low volume of filter compared with a conventional rapid sand filter of either the gravity or pressure type.   The diatomite filter operates under pressure with the advantages of a pressure-type rapid sand filter.   Its

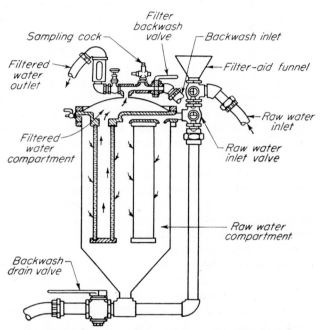

FIG. 31-2. Diatomite filter, showing normal operation.

bacteriological removal efficiency is good, and when properly designed and operated, it will remove cysts of *E. histolytica* and probably other organisms that are not affected by chlorination.

In operation[3] the water enters the bottom of the filter shown in Fig. 31-2, carrying filter aid with it in suspension.   The filter aid, consisting of diatomaceous earth, is deposited on the surface of the porous septa as

[1] See H. H. Black and C. H. Spaulding, *J.A.W.W.A.*, November, 1944, p. 1208; Military Water Supply and Purification, *War Dept. Tech. Manual* TM 295, August, 1945.

[2] See also: E. R. Baumann and H. E. Babbitt, *Water Works Eng.*, June, 1953, p. 526; J. K. Fraser, *J.A.W.W.A.*, February, 1954, p. 151.

[3] See also *Water Works Eng.*, January, 1954, p. 47.

the water passes through them to the filtered-water outlet.   When a head loss of approximately 5 to 50 ft of water has been attained the flow of water through the filter is reversed briefly to wash the cake of filter aid off the septum.   The dirty water and cake are washed to waste, and raw water carrying filter aid is sent through the filter, thus resuming normal operation.

The rate of filtration is greatly affected by the character of the water to be treated, its preconditioning, the character of the filter aid, and other conditions.   Rates of 1 to 15 gpm per sq ft filter surface may be used, with rates of 2 to 3 gpm per sq ft giving satisfactory results.   Between 800 and 1,000 lb filter aid may be used per million gallons of water treated.

31-20. Chemical Control of Metallic Corrosion.   The corrosion of metals is discussed in Chap. 19.   It follows from the explanation in that chapter that the corrosivity of water may be reduced by (1) controlling the carbonate balance of the water so that it will lay down a carbonate film to protect the metal from the electrolyte; (2) increasing the pH of the water,[1] i.e., by decreasing the hydrogen ions available to replace metallic ions discharged from the metal; (3) deaerating the water so that oxygen[1] is not available to react with the protective film of hydrogen formed by electrolytic action; and (4) by creating a protective coating of sodium silicate.

31-21. Sodium Silicate.[2]   The addition of sodium silicate ($Na_2O \cdot 3.3 \cdot SiO_2$) to corrosive waters has been found to inhibit corrosive attack on most metals used in water works.[3]   The material has been used in industrial and in hot-water supplies more than in public water supplies.   The application of 20 to 30 ppm sodium silicate should lay down an effective coating which may be maintained with routine dosage of about 4 ppm. Where the pH of the water to be treated is below 6.0 the more alkaline form of water glass ($Na_2O \cdot 2SiO_2$) may be used.

The use of sodium silicate is most effective in the presence of calcium and magnesium salts.   In order to form the first protective coating, enough silicate should be added to increase the hydroxide alkalinity 15 to 30 ppm.   Thereafter the maintenance of 5 to 10 ppm will probably be sufficient to provide protection in either hot-water or cold-water pipes. The use of sodium silicate in public water supplies must be controlled with intelligence, as an excessive amount, increasing the alkalinity to 100 ppm or more, produces a taste, discolors foods in cooking, and produces an unctuous feeling on the hands.

31-22. Threshold Treatment.   The application of sodium phosphate (Nalco) or of sodium hexametaphosphate (Calgon ($NaPO_3)_6$) in a concentration of 0.5 to 1.0 ppm, as described in Sec. 29-30, has been found

---

[1] See also T. E. Larson and R. M. King, *J.A.W.W.A.*, Jan. 1, 1954, p. 1.

[2] See also L. Lehman and H. L. Schuldener, *ibid.*, March, 1951, p. 175.

[3] See also W. Stricker, *Ind. Eng. Chem.*, August, 1945, p. 716.

to be effective in the prevention of corrosion.[1]   Close control of the dose
is unnecessary, but too large concentrations may be detrimental rather
than helpful.   The term "threshold treatment" has been applied to this
process because apparently the molecular dehydrated phosphate acts to
remove the crystal nuclei from contact with the solution on the threshold
of the crystallization process.   The name is equally appropriate with
respect to the inhibition of corrosion.[2]   Precipitation of calcium carbonate is prevented by threshold treatment because the sodium hexametaphosphate segregates nuclei of calcium carbonate as they develop.   The
isolation or adsorption of each nucleus prevents crystalline growth.

The effectiveness of threshold treatment to prevent corrosion is doubtful.   This doubt is expressed by a committee of the American Water
Works Association[3] when it states that threshold treatment "will nearly
always eliminate, or at least minimize, the outward manifestations of
corrosion" and adds "conflicting evidence forbids a definite statement as
to whether metaphosphate does or does not prevent actual corrosion of
ferrous metals."   Pallo[4] adds that "under conditions of low rates of flow
and up to and including some critical rate of flow, the rate of corrosion
was found to be higher on the threshold-treated lines than in those lines
receiving no treatment."

31-23. Carbonate Balance.   Waters containing carbonate hardness
may deposit a protective carbonate film on metals exposed to the water if
the carbonic acid content of the water is reduced.   If the acid content is
increased, the water may dissolve calcium carbonate.   The deposition of
calcium carbonate forms a film that protects metal from corrosion.   The
solution of the film exposes metal to corrosion.   Too active a tendency
to deposit carbonate is undesirable as it may clog pipes.   To prevent
clogging or corrosion the water should neither deposit nor dissolve carbonate, i.e., it should be in carbonate balance.   The point of carbonate
balance varies with the pH, the temperature, and other chemical characteristics of the water.   The point can be determined by laboratory tests.

31-24. Langelier and Other Indexes of Carbonate Balance.   Langelier[5] has devised an expression to indicate the pH at which a water should
be in equilibrium with calcium carbonate.[6]   It is in the form

$$\mathrm{pH}_s = (pK_2' - pK_s') + pCa + pAlk \qquad (31\text{-}1)$$

[1] See also Owen Rice, *J. Penna. Water Works Operators' Assoc.*, Vol. 12, p. 110, 1940.
[2] See also Owen Rice and G. B. Hatch, *J.A.W.W.A.*, Vol. 31, p. 1171, 1939.
[3] See Committee Report, *ibid.*, December, 1942, pp. 1807, 1826.
[4] P. E. Pallo, *ibid.*, April, 1946, p. 499.
[5] W. F. Langelier, *ibid.*, October, 1936, p. 1500.
[6] See also "Water Supply and Treatment," National Lime Association, Washington,
D.C., 1951, p. 197; and see *Water Works Eng.*, Nov. 13, 1946, p. 1345; and C. P.
Hoover, *J.A.W.W.A.*, November, 1938, p. 1802 for nomographs which greatly
simplify the solution of Langelier's formula.

where pH_s = pH that the water should have to be in equilibrium with $CaCO_3$

pK_s', pK_2' = negative logarithms of the second dissociation constant for carbonic acid and activity product of $CaCO_3$, respectively

pCa = negative logarithm of molal concentration of Ca

$pAlk$ = negative logarithm of equivalent concentration of titratable base

The *saturation index* is obtained by subtracting pH_s from the pH of the water. A negative index indicates that the water is undersaturated with calcium carbonate. A positive index indicates the reverse. The determination of the index involves an analysis in which total solids, temperature, calcium, and alkalinity are reported.

The Langelier index is useful to determine in which direction a water is out of carbonate balance and to estimate the dosage of lime necessary to produce equilibrium. Little difficulty from corrosiveness is to be expected from cold waters with an index more positive than -0.5, and from hot waters with an index more positive than zero. Although the Langelier index is used more widely than any other corrosion index, it is not always dependable because of (1) the formation of soft, bulky, porous, or otherwise undesirable sludge; (2) the formation of an insulating layer on heat-exchange surfaces and on household and industrial equipment; (3) uncertainties of scale precipitation with temperature changes in the water; and (4) probably the most important of all, failure to form scale despite indications by the index. Some of the difficulties, being due to

TABLE 31-2. Alkalinity : pH Limits Which Will Minimize the Effect of Temperature on the Amount of Scale Deposition*

Alkalinity, ppm $CaCO_3$........	50	100	150	200
Actual pH measured in cold water.....................	8.10–8.65	8.60–9.20	8.90–9.50	8.90–9.70

* From S. T. Powell and others, *J.A.W.W.A.*, July, 1946, p. 808. The limits of alkalinity and of pH are those within which scale deposition has been found to be sufficiently uniform on both cold and hot surfaces to provide satisfactory results when the calcium hardness was manipulated to maintain the proper saturation index.

organic matter in the water, can be controlled by chlorination or by pretreatment to remove organic matter. Larson and Buswell[1] have shown that for any specific methyl orange alkalinity there is a corresponding pH value at which the saturation index, and consequently the rate of scaling, is uniform, regardless of temperature. Such values of pH for a temperature range from 80 to 90°F are shown in Table 31-2.

[1] T. E. Larson and A. M. Buswell, *J.A.W.W.A.*, Vol. 34, p. 1667, 1942.

Other corrosion indexes are reported in the literature include Ryznar's stability index,[1] McLaughlin's,[2] Hoover's marble test,[3] and Enslow's continuous-stability indicator.[4]

31-25. Chemical Adjustment of pH. Lime is the chemical most commonly used in the adjustment of pH to control corrosion either to obtain carbonate balance or to reduce the concentration of hydrogen ions available to replace metallic ions. Other alkaline compounds, such as sodium or potassium hydroxides, will have no effect on the hardness of the water, but their cost is so high, compared with the cost of lime, that their use for public water supplies is uneconomical.

31-26. Chemical Formation of Carbonate Coatings. Protective coatings may be formed on metals by the adjustment of the pH to lay down a coating of calcium carbonate, by the addition of sodium silicate, and by the reaction between constituents of the water and of the metal. The addition of sodium silicate to water is discussed in Sec. 31-21.

The formation of protective coatings by reaction between constituents of the water and the metal is exemplified by the deposition of a protective layer of hydroxide of iron, formed by the reaction between the iron and dissolved oxygen. Similarly, lead reacts with certain hard waters to form basic lead carbonate, which deposits on the lead pipe to delay further corrosion. Such naturally formed coatings are important in the protection of many pipe lines and, in some cases, disastrous results have followed treatment of water that has dissolved these coatings.

31-27. Carbonate-scale Prevention with Sulphuric Acid. The addition of sulphuric acid to water is effective in diminishing some scale formation so long as the calcium sulphate content is kept below about 1,700 ppm. The acid converts the less soluble carbonates to the more highly soluble sulphates, thus preventing their deposition and the formation of scale. The amount of acid used should be sufficient to reduce the alkalinity to about 35 ppm. The process is used only in the treatment of water to prevent scale formation due to carbonate hardness. It is not suitable for use in potable water.

31-28. Chlorination to Control Corrosion. The corrosive action of bacteria is discussed in Sec. 19-7. The addition of chlorine may aggravate rather than diminish such bacterial activity. When chlorine is added to water containing organic matter it reacts with the organic matter to diminish the bactericidal effect and possibly to furnish food for aftergrowths of bacteria. The addition of ammonia with the chlorine will retard the exhaustion of the chlorine so that it may be carried into

[1] See *ibid.*, April, 1944, p. 472.

[2] See *Proc. 10th Ann. Conf. on Water Purif.*, *W. Va. State Univ.*, *Tech. Bull.* 8, p. 19, Apr. 15, 1936.

[3] See C. P. Hoover, *J.A.W.W.A.*, Vol. 30, p. 1802, 1938.

[4] L. H. Enslow, *Water Works & Sewerage*, Vol. 86, p. 107, 1939.

remote parts of the distribution system where its bactericidal effects will be felt further and endure longer.

In a few instances the use of ammonia has been found to aggravate the difficulties from corrosion in certain parts of the distribution system, probably because of the fact that when the chlorine is finally exhausted the remaining ammonia furnishes food for the undesirable aftergrowths. Under such circumstances the remedy is to stop the application of the ammonia, to change the conditions of its application, to study the effectiveness of copper sulphate, or to attempt other methods for the control of corrosion.

31-29. Corrosion by Hot Water. Responsibility of the management of the public water works extends to the corrosion of the consumer's plumbing as well as to the corrosion of the pipes belonging to the water department. Since it is common practice on the part of consumers to heat a part of the water used and to distribute it in the plumbing system, the corrosive characteristics of the public water supply when heated should be minimized. Hot water is more corrosive than cold; corrosive characteristics of water when heated are greatly changed; and methods for correction of the corrosiveness of hot water differ somewhat from the correction of cold water. Water with a pH of 7.5 to 8.0 may be only mildly corrosive to steel at temperatures of 50 to 60°F but will become actively corrosive at temperatures of 120 to 150°F, or higher, and the greatest corrosive action occurs at 160 to 180°F. The complete deaeration of waters to be heated to high temperatures will greatly reduce their corrosiveness. However, the disconcerting conclusion was reached by Hoover[1] that some waters high in pH and devoid of dissolved oxygen may be highly corrosive when heated. In general, it is desirable to maintain a more positive Langelier index, or lower stability index, in hot than in cold water because of the higher solubility of carbonate in hot water.

31-30. Cooling of Water. Water is cooled, principally in industrial processes, primarily to conserve water. Methods of cooling include[2] evaporative condensers such as spray ponds, natural-draft towers, forced-draft towers, induced-draft towers, and dry-surface coolers or air-cooled exchangers. An evaporative condenser is a device, such as a spray pond, in which air is moved across exposed water surfaces; the evaporation of about 1 per cent of the water will cool the remainder about 10 to 15°F. A spray pond consists of a number of spray nozzles over a collecting basin. Water passing down the various types of cooling towers comes in contact with moving air and is thus evaporated.

[1] C. P. Hoover, *J. Penna. Water Works Operators' Assoc.*, Vol. 9, p. 106; *Water Works & Sewerage*, Vol. 83, p. 384, 1936.

[2] See also H. E. Degler, Conference on Water Resources, *Illinois State Water Survey, Bull.* 41, p. 135, 1952.

31-31. The Treatment of Cooling Water. Waters used in cooling condensers and in other industrial processes are themselves cooled as indicated in Sec. 31-30. Scale may be formed at any point in the heat-exchange process with resultant damage or loss of efficiency. The principal purposes of treating cooling waters are to prevent scale formation and possibly to remove oil. The principal methods of treatment include softening and the application of sulphuric acid. Where scale or deposits are a result of other characteristics than hardness the causative substance is removed by an appropriate procedure such as iron and manganese removal, hydrogen sulphide removal, or disinfection.

31-32. Effect of pH Correction on Zinc and Copper. It is generally accepted that the higher the pH of water the less corrosive it will be to iron, but this is not altogether true with respect to zinc and copper. Moore[1] has shown that loss of zinc from brass diminishes as the pH is raised from 6.0 to 10.0 and that up to a pH of 11.0 it increases again; that the rate of corrosion of copper from brass is inversely proportional to that of zinc, and that protective films will retard the loss of zinc in a pH range of 7.5 to 9.5.

31-33. Chemically Poisoned Water. Water may be poisoned accidentally, by sabotage, by enemy action, and in other ways. Among the chemical poisons that may be used are[2] (1) alkaloids, such as nicotine, strychnine, and colchicine; (2) organic arsenic compounds, called arsenicals; (3) inorganic arsenic compounds, called arsenites and arsenates; (4) cyanides; and (5) heavy-metal salts such as acetates and nitrates of lead and of mercury. Among the most dangerous agents are the blister gases and substances containing cyanides.

Poisoned water may be detected most rapidly in the field by physical observations of unusual color and odor, or of dead fish or vegetation or animals in contact with the water. Chemical indications include low pH or high chlorine demand.

Some poisons may be removed from water by first aerating it and then adding about 200 ppm of activated carbon. This should be followed by coagulation with alum, sufficient being added to carry down the activated carbon. This may require as much as 7 grains per gal, the amount being in proportion to the activated carbon added. If the water is subsequently filtered a small dose of activated carbon and of coagulant may be used.

---

[1] E. W. Moore, *J. New Engl. Water Works Assoc.*, 1934, p. 47.

[2] Based mainly on Military Water Supplies and Purification, *War Dept. Tech. Man.* TM5-295, 1945.

OUTLINE OF A REPORT ON A WATER-WORKS DESIGN[1]

Address a letter of transmittal to the mayor and city council, or other authority, conveying the report, stating briefly your reasons for doing the work, and containing a general description of the plan recommended.

In the Body of the Report

1. State the causes leading to the installation of the water works, its history, its ownership, its legal status, and its rights to sources of water.

2. Describe those features and characteristics of the city which may affect the water works such as location, climate, industry, economic position, and transportation.

3. Population, present and future, with discussion of sources of information, and conditions affecting your prediction.

4. Area within corporate limits and within districts to be served, both present and future, with discussion of conditions affecting prediction.

5. Topographic features, with emphasis on conditions affecting pumping and distribution. Include contour map of the region.

6. Financial status of water works, past, present, and future. Management and administration. Rates charged for water, past and future. Proposed method of payment for plan recommended.

7. Demand for water, past and future, with reasons for prediction. Conditions affecting demand. Anticipated average, maximum, and minimum rates or normal demand, and fire demand.

8. Description of sources of supply investigated (if a surface source is included report must be extended to cover character of watershed and other features applicable to such source), underground conditions, and history and description of nearby wells.

9. Location of proposed wells, with plot of well field showing location of each well. Area of land now owned or available for purchase in well field. Nature of surroundings of well field, and their control to prevent contamination of the field. Possibilities of flooding, or other hazards.

10. Details of proposed wells: depth, diameter, distance to water, specific capacity, quantity of water available, type of casing and of screen, and size and area of screen openings. Features to avoid contamination.

[1] Applied especially to a ground-water source.

11. Total quantity of water available, average and peak loads. Quality of water and general features of proposed method of treatment.

12. Well pumps; type and characteristics. Power for operation. Description of hazards and plans for avoiding or preventing shutdowns. Point of discharge from wells. Lift to ground surface and lift above ground surface.

13. Location and description of collecting reservoir, or reservoirs, whether surface or elevated. Include sketch showing such things as plan, elevation, sections, with details of floors, walls, columns, roofs, ventilation, drainage, facilities for access and for cleaning. Possibilities of contamination.

14. Pumping station or stations: location, type of building, accessibility, hazards. Power available, its characteristics and possibilities of interruption. Emergency sources of power, and precautions against shutdown. Floor plan showing location of pumps, engines, or motors. Other equipment and accessories such as pipes, boilers, electrical equipment, wiring and controls. Heating, lighting, ventilation. Protection of operators, of building, and of equipment against hazards.

15. Description of each pump and its motor. Loads and pressures on each pump, and on the pumping station. Show hydrographs for average, maximum, and minimum days. Discussion of methods for meeting fire demands.

16. The distribution system: include contour map showing street plan, classification and location of fire hazards, and location and sizes of pipes, valves, and fire hydrants with circles showing area protected against fire by each hydrant. Tabulate feet, or miles, and percentage of total length of each size of pipe, and number of valves of each size. State number of persons living within 50 ft of, and within 400 ft of, a 4-in. or larger main. State the number of valves and of hydrants per 1,000 ft of pipe, and the average distance along pipe between valves, and between hydrants. Show a map of distribution system only, with piezometric contours for critical conditions.

17. Storage available on distribution system: amount, description of reservoirs, capacities, locations, effect on pressures and on supply. Hydrograph of flow in and out of each reservoir.

18. Fire protection: range of elevation within distribution system above and below pumping station; are mobile fire pumps to be used; ordinary and fire pressures at hydrants during fires at strategic locations. Number, size, and pressures of fire streams possible in various regions.

19. Cost: give an itemized account of the estimated cost of the water works, including *all* expenses. The following style is suggested for making this statement:

General Items

Land (2 acres on corner of . . . streets)................................ $ 1,000
Buildings:
    Low-lift pumping station at.. 4,700
    High-lift station at.. 89,500
Rights of way (private) from . . . to................................ 750
    Total... $95,950

Low-lift Pumping-station Equipment

3 8-in. wells, ready for service but not including pumps................ $ 0,000
3 pump heads and pumps, for above wells, ready for service............. 0,000
Details of other accessories... 0,000
    Total... $00,000

Finally state estimated cost per inhabitant, the probable estimate per lot or per front foot, and the general assessment for public benefits.

20. A brief summary including description of the plan, its total cost, and cost per inhabitant.

It is to be noted that this outline is not complete and is suggestive only. Details of any particular plan must be filled in, and inapplicable portions of this outline omitted.

$$n \quad \bigg| \quad \frac{r}{(1+r)^{n}-1} \quad \text{for } r=.04$$

n	
10	.0833
15	.0499
20	.0336
50	.0066
100	.00081
40	.01052

APPENDIX 2

PROBLEMS

Chapter 1

1-1. The first cost of a centrifugal pump and motor is $1,500; the annual cost of operation and maintenance is $1,200; the life of the unit is 15 years; the annual rate of interest is 4 per cent. Determine: (*a*) the capital invested; (*b*) the capitalized cost; (*c*) the annual expense; (*d*) the straight-line rate of depreciation; (*e*) the sinking-fund rate of depreciation; (*f*) the amount of the annual straight-line depreciation; (*g*) the amount of the annual sinking-fund rate of depreciation; and (*h*) the value of the unit after 10 years of service, assuming sinking-fund rate of depreciation.

1-2. Solve the preceding problem on the assumption that the salvage value is $300. $C = \$1200$

1-3. Two choices are available in the selection of a pumping unit: unit A with a first cost of $5,000, an annual operating cost of $600, and a life of 15 years; and unit B, with a first cost of $4,000, an annual operating cost of $800, and a life of 20 years. No other costs are to be considered. The annual interest rate is 4 per cent. What will be the annual savings if the more economical unit is purchased?

1-4. The cost of a water works for a city of 10,000 population is $500,000. The first cost and the life of the various parts of the works are as follows: land, $10,000, life indefinite; buildings, $30,000, life 40 years; mechanical equipment, $200,000, life 20 years; distribution system, $260,000, life 50 years. The annual cost of operation is $50,000, and the interest rate of the bond issue of $500,000 is 4 per cent. The average amount of water sold is 75 gal per capita per day. (*a*) If the only source of income is from water sold and the commerce commission allows 6 per cent return on capital invested, what should be the charge for water, in dollars per 1,000 gal? (*b*) For 1 ton water, in cents?

1-5. A pipe line costing $35,000 requires an annual charge of $1,600 for repairs. It is estimated that the annual cost of these repairs is $528 for materials and $1,072 for labor. If annual interest on capital invested is 6 per cent, taxes on capital costs are $1\frac{1}{2}$ per cent, the life of the pipe line is 25 years, and expenditures to prevent repairs are considered as capital investment, how many dollars could justifiably be spent to avoid the annual repair charge? It may be assumed that the prevention of repairs will not affect the life of the pipe.[1]

1-6. In developing an enterprise two choices are presented: (*a*) to install temporary equipment to function for 10 years, followed by the installation of more permanent equipment, or (*b*) to install the permanent equipment now.

[1] See W. R. Schneider, *J.A.W.W.A.*, February, 1947, p. 145.

The temporary equipment will cost $50,000, operating cost is $10,000 per year, and life is 15 years. At the end of 10 years its salvage value will be $2,500. The permanent equipment will cost $100,000, operation $12,500 per year, life 30 years, and salvage value $7,500. If interest is 4 per cent per annum, how many dollars are saved annually by adopting the more economical enterprise?

1-7. Eight thousand dollars is paid annually to retire principal and pay interest on a serial bond issue of $100,000 bearing interest at 4 per cent, annually. (a) How long would be required to retire the entire issue? (b) If all the bonds were to be retired serially in 10 years, what annual payment would be required?

Chapter 2

2-1. A circular leaf gate, 5 ft in diameter, is set at an angle of 30 deg with the horizontal. The depth of water over the center of the gate leaf is 20 ft. (a) What is the total pressure on the gate? (b) What is the direction of its line of action with respect to the plane of the gate leaf? (c) What is its point of application on the gate leaf?

2-2. The accompanying sketch shows a radial gate against which water is pressing. (a) Locate the distance of the center of pressure against the gate. (b) What are the magnitudes of the total pressure and of its horizontal and vertical components? Answer in pounds.

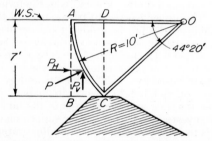

2-3. Assume that the center (point O in the accompanying sketch) of the gate is 3 ft below the water surface and that point A, the upper edge of the gate, is at the water surface. (a) Locate the distance from the surface to the center of pressure. (b) Determine the magnitude of the total pressure and its horizontal and vertical components.

2-4. A trapezoidal weir, shown in the accompanying sketch, is placed in the end of a sluiceway. Locate the distance from the water surface and from the line AA to the center of pressure of the area $abdc$.

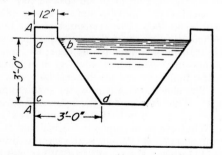

2-5. A right triangle with a 4-ft base and an 8-ft side is submerged with apex down and its base horizontal and 2 ft below the water surface. The plane of the triangle makes an angle of 45 deg with the vertical. Locate the center of pressure with respect to the surface and a vertical plane passing through the 8-ft side of the triangle.

2-6. A rectangular gate 20 ft wide and 10 ft high is set in a vertical plane. It is made to turn on horizontal hinges the centers of which are 4 ft up from the bottom of the gate. A stop block at the bottom prevents the bottom of the gate from turning in the direction of the water pressure, but it is free to rotate in the opposite direction. How deep would the water flow over the top of the gate before it would open? Neglect friction and limitations imposed by pressure and velocity conditions in the stream flowing over the top.

2-7. A cylindrical tank, 15 ft in diameter, holds a depth of 10 ft of water. It is to be emptied through a 6-in. standard circular orifice lying in a horizontal plane in the bottom of the tank. How long will it take to empty the tank? Answer in seconds.

2-8. A conical tank is 6 ft in diameter at the water surface, and 2 ft in diameter at the bottom. The vertical distance between the two diameters is 10 ft. How long will it take to empty the tank through a 6-in. standard circular orifice in the bottom of the tank? Answer in seconds.

2-9. A steel storage bin in a water-purification plant is 8 ft deep and is designed to hold a dry chemical weighing 90 lb per cu ft. The pressure produced by the chemical is assumed to act as a fluid. The bin is in the form of an inverted right truncated pyramid. The upper base is 10 ft square, and the lower base is 4 ft square. One entire side of the bin is divided by a vertical plane through the center of the bin into two doors, each being hinged along the sloping edges of the bin. When the bin is filled with chemical, (a) where is the center of pressure on each door with respect to its top and the line where the two doors come together? (b) If the doors were held closed by a bolt at the top, and by a bolt at the bottom, what would be the shear on each bolt? Answer in pounds. Assume that there is no connection between the door and the bottom of the bin.

2-10. A railroad is investigating a new water-supply plan involving a flow of 6 mgd. The supply is to consist of a dam impounding water at A, from which it must be pumped over a summit at B. From B it runs by gravity to the shops at D. Since the head available at the shops is much more than would be required in the shops for power development, a hydroelectric plant at C has been suggested to utilize all the available power. The electric power will be transmitted back to A for use in pumping water over the summit at B. The pipe line is to consist of 60,000 ft of 24-in. cast-iron pipe with C = 100. It will cost $8 per foot, in place. The works at A will cost as follows: dam, $80,000; land for reservoir, $5,500; buildings and machinery, $25,000. The annual operating expense will be about $2,500. The reservoir on the summit at B will cost $3,000. The works at C will cost: buildings and machinery, $35,000; and reservoir, $5,000. The annual operating cost at C will be $3,000. The transmission line between A and C will cost $30,000. The efficiencies are as follows: hydraulic turbine, 80 per cent; generator, 90 per cent; transmission line, 95 per cent; motors, 85 per cent; pump, 75 per cent. Life of masonry structures, such as dams, may be taken as 100 years; pipe line, 50 years; buildings and machinery, 30 years. Rate of interest is 4 per cent annually. The elevations of the water surfaces are as follows: at A, 1,200 ft; at B, 1,400 ft. The elevation of the hydraulic turbines at C is 400 ft. The length of the pipe from A to B is 15,000 ft, from B to C, 40,000 ft, and from C to D, 5,000 ft. (a) What excess horsepower is available at C for operating the shops and for other purposes? (b) What is the capital invested in the plant? (c) What is the annual expense of the plant? (d) What will be the cost of water per 1,000 gal? (e) If electricity could be sold at 1 cent per kilowatthour at C, what would be the net cost of water per 1,000 gal?

2-11. Determine the rate of discharge over a submerged weir 20 ft wide and operating under a head of 4 ft. The submergence is 30 per cent. Contractions are suppressed. Use the Francis weir formula.

2-12. A rectangular channel terminates in a standard weir whose length is equal to the width of the channel. When the velocity of flow through the channel is 1.65 fps, the rate of flow is 500 cfs. When the velocity of flow through the channel is 0.78 fps, the rate of flow is 200 cfs. Determine: (a) width of channel; (b) maximum head on weir; (c) minimum head on weir; (d) height of weir crest above bottom of channel. Use Francis weir formula.

2-13. An overflow spillway 20 ft wide is so shaped that when operating under a head of 6 ft the stream at the crest has the same longitudinal cross section and the same pressure and velocity characteristics as a section discharging over a sharp-crested weir. What is the rate of discharge? Assume contractions are suppressed, and use Francis weir formula.

2-14. A 27-in-diameter pipe with $C = 140$ is carrying 2,000 gpm. Compute the hydraulic gradient using the Darcy formula with the value of f found in Fig. 2-6.

2-15. The value of Darcy's f for a 27-in. pipe is 0.015. The pipe is carrying 2,800 gpm on a hydraulic slope of 0.25 per 1,000. What would be the rate of flow in this pipe if the Hazen and Williams coefficient were 120?

2-16. Two horizontal pipes are joined end to end, in series. AB is 8 in. in diameter and is 2,000 ft long. BC is 6 in. in diameter and 2,000 ft long. The pressure at A is 120 psi, and at C, which is on the same elevation as A, the pressure is 50 psi. (a) If the Hazen and Williams coefficient C is 100, what is the flow through the pipe, in gallons per minute? (b) If $C = 150$, what would be the rate of flow through the pipe, in gallons per minute? Neglect all losses other than those due to friction in straight pipe.

2-17. Three pipes ABC, ADC, and AEC are in parallel, being joined at A and at C. The rate of flow through all three pipes is 3,000 gpm. Pipe B is 10 in. in diameter and 3,000 ft long; D is 6 in. in diameter and 1,000 ft long; and E is 8 in. in diameter and 2,000 ft long. If point C is 10 ft lower than A, coefficient $C = 100$, the direction of flow is from A toward C, and the pressure at C is 20 psi, what is the pressure at A?

2-18. The pressure at point A in a pipe is 100 psi; from A to B is 2,000 ft of 8-in. pipe; between B and C there are two lines of pipe, one 6-in. in diameter and 1,000 ft long, and the other, parallel to it, 4 in. in diameter and 1,500 ft long. From C to D the pipe line consists of 1,000 ft of 6-in. pipe. If the pressure at D is 80 psi, D is 23 ft higher than A, and $C = 120$, what is the rate of flow through the pipe line? Answer in gallons per minute.

2-19. The following values were computed from a table in Merriman's "Hydraulics" and represent the head lost H' in 100 ft of clean cast-iron pipe for various rates of flow Q in cubic feet per second ($D =$ diameter of pipe):

D = 0.75 ft		D = 1.00 ft		D = 1.25 ft		D = 1.5 ft	
Q	ft/100*	Q	ft/100*	Q	ft/100*	Q	ft/100*
1.38	0.45	1.57	0.15	2.46	0.16	5.28	0.20
1.76	0.73	2.36	0.32	3.69	0.25	7.05	0.33
2.64	1.57	3.14	0.55	4.91	0.42	10.55	0.67
4.40	3.94	4.71	1.12	7.37	0.85	17.6	1.66
6.60	8.40	7.85	2.80	12.3	2.11	26.4	3.50
....	....	11.85	5.95	18.4	4.48		

* This represents head lost in feet per 100 ft of pipe.

a. Plot the values of Q and of H' for each value of D, using logarithmic cross-section paper with Q as abscissas and H' as ordinates. Draw a straight line through the points for each diameter of pipe.

b. Draw the lines lightly so that erasures can be made, if necessary.

c. Make the lines parallel and determine their slopes.

d. Assume value of D and plot H' against D.

e. Determine the slope of this line, H' relative to D.

f. Locate lines for 10-, 14-, 16-, and 24-in. pipes.

g. Determine the value of K from the expression $K = H'D^n/Q^m$, substituting one corresponding value of H' and Q for each diameter of pipe. Tabulate as follows:

D	Q	D^n	Q^m	H'	K

h. Use the average value of K' in the equation $H' = K'Q^m/D^n$.

i. Transpose the equation into the form $H' = K''V^{m'}/D^{n'}$.

j. Change the equation into the form $V = Cs^pD^q$, and compare with the Hazen and Williams formula.

2-20. Three reservoirs are joined by cast-iron pipe, as shown in the accompanying sketch. What are the rate and direction of flow in each pipe? Assume $C = 120$. Answer in gallons per minute.

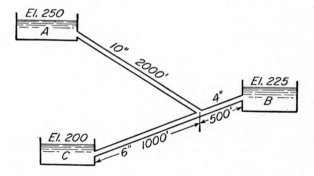

2-21. Two reservoirs are connected by 10,000 ft of riveted-steel pipe 48 in. in diameter. The difference between the elevations of the water surfaces in the two reservoirs is 16 ft. What is the rate of flow in the pipe? Answer in gallons per minute. What would be the rate of flow if a wood pipe of the same diameter had been used?

2-22. Construct the hydraulic grade line and the total-energy line for the pipe shown in the following sketch. Use a horizontal scale of 1 in. = 1,000 ft, and choose a vertical scale that will show clearly the changes of elevations of the two lines where the gradient changes. Use Hazen and Williams formula with

$C = 100$, and compute elevations to nearest 0.1 ft, making allowances for *all* head losses due to any cause whatsoever.

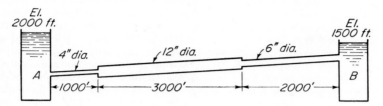

2-23. Two lines of $2\frac{1}{2}$-in. smooth rubber-lined fire hose are connected to a fire hydrant. One line is 400 ft long and terminates at A in a 1-in. smooth nozzle. The other is 300 ft long and terminates at B in a 1-in. smooth nozzle. During a fire it is found that with A open and B closed the pressure at A is 45 psi. What will be the pressure and the rate of discharge at each nozzle with both A and B open? Assume that the pressure at the hydrant is constant under all conditions.

Chapter 3

3-1. Population figures are shown in the accompanying table for three communities, all residential with similar characteristics. Predict the population of B in 1970 by each of the methods explained.

City	1950	1940	1930	1920	1910	1900	1890
A............	102,492	94,192	79,421	64,561	41,353	28,372	25,694
B............	67,647	64,748	57,486	42,492	37,001	17,210	9,874
C............	105,343	102,157	80,809	65,655	49,675	42,359	30,931

3-2. (*a*) If the average rate of demand is 40 mgd, what is the maximum hourly rate of demand on the maximum day for high-service pumping shown by the curve for Toledo, Ohio, in Fig. 3-2? Answer in gallons per minute. (*b*) What is the maximum daily high-service pumping demand during the period shown? Answer in millions of gallons.

3-3. Answer the questions in the preceding problem for Springfield, Mass., for the week of Mar. 17, 1940, as shown in Fig. 3-4. Assume that the radial scale represents rates in millions of gallons per day. (*c*) What is the average daily rate of demand for the high-service pumping for the week shown? Answer in millions of gallons. Assume that the higher curve represents the week of Mar. 17.

3-4. Construct a demand-duration curve, on the basis of hours per day, for the maximum day at Toledo, Ohio, similar to the curve shown in Fig. 3-5. Abscissas are to be in per cent of time for one day, and ordinates are in per cent of average rate for the maximum day.

3-5. (*a*) Estimate the water demand by the residential city B in 1950 shown in Prob. 3-1, exclusive of fire demand, for the following periods of time: (1) maximum day, (2) average day, (3) maximum hour. Answers are to be based on the data in Tables 3-3 and 3-9 and are to be in gallons and in gallons per minute for the time covered. (*b*) What would be the proper allowance for fire protection for this city, expressed in gallons per minute and in accordance with each of the formulas in Table 3-8?

Chapter 4

4-1. A 24-in. gravity well is being pumped at a rate of 300 gpm. Measurements in nearby test wells were made at the same time, as follows: At a distance of 20 ft from the well being pumped, the drawdown was 20 ft, and at 50 ft the drawdown was 5 ft. The bottom of the well is 300 ft below the ground-water table. (*a*) If all observed points were on the Dupuit curve, what was the drawdown in the well during pumping? (*b*) Assuming the water surfaces in the test well at a distance of 50 ft to have been on the "free surface," what was the drawdown of the ground-water table immediately adjacent to the well being pumped? (*c*) What is the specific capacity of the well? (*d*) What is the maximum rate at which water can be drawn from this well?

4-2. Assuming that the conditions in the preceding problem apply to a pressure well, answer all but (*b*) of the preceding questions. What is the ratio of the specific capacity of the pressure well to that of the gravity well?

4-3. A 24-in. gravity well is discharging 400 gpm when $h_e = 100$ ft, $h_w = 68.5$ ft, and the vertical distance from the ground-water table to the free surface, at a distance of 50 ft from the well, is 10 ft. What is the height of the surface of seepage in the well being pumped?

4-4. (*a*) Plot a curve whose abscissas are the percentage of maximum rate of discharge from the well in Prob. 4-1, and whose ordinates are the corresponding percentage of total possible drawdown. Let the length of the abscissa and of the ordinate, for maximum conditions, each be 5 in. (*b*) Plot a similar curve for the pressure well in Prob. 4-2. Use the same abscissas and ordinates as in part (*a*) of this problem.

4-5. What is the specific capacity of a gravity well 18 in. in diameter and 300 ft deep? The distance to the ground-water table under static conditions is 75 ft. When being pumped at a rate of 250 gpm, the drawdown in the well is 5 ft and at 485 gpm it is 12 ft.

4-6. A 24-in. pressure well is 500 ft deep. The static depth of water in the well is 400 ft. When being pumped at 500 gpm, the drawdown is 12 ft and at 700 gpm it is 20 ft. What would be the discharge from the well with a drawdown of 50 ft?

4-7. To determine the velocities of flow of water through a porous dam embankment, test holes A and B were driven into the embankment 6 ft apart. The following observations were made: (*a*) temperature of water, 62°F; (*b*) elevation of water at A, 589.3 ft; (*c*) elevation of water at B, 584.2 ft; (*d*) velocity of flow from A to B, 12 ft per day. If the water in the lower part of the dam is drained down so that the elevation in hole B drops to 575.0 ft, the elevation at A drops to 584.2 ft, and the temperature rises to 70°F, what will be the velocity of flow of water through the dam, in feet per day? Use Hazen's formula $V = ke^2s[(t + 10)/60]$, where V = velocity in feet per day, k = a constant, e = Hazen's effective size of sand, s = slope of hydraulic grade line, and t = temperature in degrees Fahrenheit.

4-8. If the distance between A and B in Fig. 4-7 is 8.5 ft and point A in Fig. 4-8 indicates the time at which the electrolyte was added to the well at A, what was the velocity of flow between the wells? Answer in feet per day.

4-9. The distance from the ground surface to the static surface of the water in an 18-in. gravity well is 50 ft, and the depth of water in the well is 100 ft. When the well is being pumped at 700 gpm and equilibrium has been established, the distance from the ground surface, which is level, to the water in the well is 69.6 ft, and to the water surface in a bore hole (not being pumped) 10 ft from the well is 55 ft. Let $r_e = 100$ ft. (*a*) What is the vertical height of the surface of seepage in the well? (b) What is the distance from the ground surface to the Dupuit surface in the bore hole? (c) Draw a diagram of the Dupuit and the free-surface curves, using 1 in. = 10 ft horizontal and 1 in. = 5 ft vertical.

4-10. If it is known that the well in Prob. 4-5 penetrates only 20 per cent of the aquifer, what will be the discharge from the well when the drawdown is 12 ft, if Eq. (4-11) is applied?

4-11. (a) Construct the drawdown curve (time as abscissas and depth of water in the well as ordinates) for the well in Prob. 4-5, if it is pumped at 200 gpm for 5 hr. Assume $f = 0.20$. (b) Construct the recovery curve for the same well if pumping at 200 gpm is stopped after 5 hr.

4-12. At what drawdown in the well in Prob. 4-11 would equilibrium (maximum drawdown) have been reached, and how long (hours and minutes) after pumping started, if pumping at 600 gpm had continued? Let $f = 0.2$.

4-13. A pressure well was constructed 30 ft in diameter for a depth of 40 ft. In the bottom of the 30-ft portion an 8-in. tubular well was drilled to an additional depth of 124 ft. A test was conducted by pumping the water down in the 30-ft-diameter portion of the well and observing the rate of recovery of water level in the well. The following observations were made of the distance from the ground surface to the surface of the water in the well: 9 A.M., 40 ft; 3 P.M., 36.2 ft; 9 P.M., 32.8 ft; 3 A.M., 29.7 ft; 9 A.M., 26.9 ft. (a) What quantity of water, in gallons per day, can be obtained from the well if the pump is operated to lower the water 40 ft below the ground surface in 1 hr daily? (b) What quantity of water, in gallons per day, can be obtained if the pump is operated twice daily for about 45 min so as to lower the water 40 ft below the ground surface at each period of operation? (c) What is the maximum quantity of water that could be pumped from the well under continuous operation of the pump with water held 40 ft below the ground surface? (d) If the 30-ft-diameter portion of the well were deepened 10 ft, what quantity of water could be obtained per day from the well if the pump were operated 1 hr daily so as to lower the water 50 ft below the ground surface at each period of operation?

4-14. A number of wells like the well described in Prob. 4-1 are driven across a buried river valley under identical conditions. The wells are in a straight line 10 ft apart. (a) What would be the combined discharge from two adjacent wells being pumped simultaneously, with no other wells being pumped, if the drawdown in each well were 15 ft? (b) What would be the discharge from three adjacent wells being pumped simultaneously, with no other wells being pumped, if the drawdown in each well were 15 ft?

4-15. A water works owns a rectangular plot of land 30 by 51.9 ft, on which three gravity wells A, B, and C are located. B is in the center of the plot, and A and C are in diagonally opposite corners. All have hydraulic characteristics similar to the well described in Prob. 4-1. (a) What flow could be pumped from wells A and C simultaneously, with a drawdown in each well of 60 ft? (b) What flow could be pumped from all three wells if they were pumped simultaneously with a drawdown of 60 ft? (c) If two additional wells were constructed in the remaining corners of the plot, estimate the amount of water that could be drawn by pumping all wells simultaneously with a drawdown of 60 ft. (d) If each well costs $2,500, if it costs 10 cents per 1,000 gal for power to pump water from each well, if the rate of interest plus depreciation and other annual overhead charges is 12 per cent, and if water can be sold for 15 cents per 1,000 gal, how many wells of the same type as these wells, all being pumped simultaneously and continuously, can be economically located on this plot, assuming the drawdown to be 60 ft? Note: some formulas needed in this problem are to be found in the reference given in Sec. 4-18.

Chapter 6

6-1. (*a*) Tabulate the maximum rate of rainfall, the month of its occurrence, and the percentage of deviation from the annual mean in each of the regions shown in Fig. 6-2. (*b*) What would be the mean annual rainfall in Denver, Colo., if the rainfall in each of the months from April to September, inclusive, were increased by 50 per cent, the rainfall for other months remaining as shown in the figure?

6-2. The drainage area of the Scioto River, above the storage dam at Columbus, Ohio, is 1,080 sq miles. The extreme length of the watershed above the dam is 80 miles. When the watershed was covered with snow, a heavy warm rainfall occurred. For the 24-hr period beginning at 8 P.M. on the first day, the average rainfall over the drainage area was 4.9 in.; for the 48-hr period following the start of the storm, ending at 8 P.M., it was 6.4 in.; and for the 72-hr period ending at 8 P.M., it was 7.9 in. The apex of the flood was reached at noon on the third day after the start of the storm. At this time the depth of water over the spillway of the dam was 13.6 ft. The crest of the dam is 500 ft long. Determine the percentage runoff, calculating the discharge over the dam from the expression $Q = 3.7Lh^{3/2}$.

6-3. (*a*) Determine the annual runoff from a watershed of 100 sq miles near Seattle, Wash., on which the seasonal rainfall distribution is similar to that shown in Fig. 6-2, using M in Vermuele's formula as 1.0. Answer in millions of gallons. (*b*) Solve the same problem by the Justin formula, using S as 0.03 and T as 55. Answer in millions of gallons.

6-4. Let the outlet of the drainage area in Fig. 6-3 be at the lower left point of the figure, the greatest distance of flow on the area be 15 miles, and the total area be 78 sq miles. Determine the maximum rate of runoff in cubic feet per second, assuming the time of concentration as 10 hr and the imperviousness as 75 per cent and computing the rate of rainfall from Brackenbury's formula in Table 6-3.

6-5. Tabulate the maximum hourly rate of rainfall that may be expected once in 10 years for 5-min storms in at least five of the regions shown in Table 6-4. In each case use the larger value of K, x, and n shown in the table for the chosen time period.

6-6. What might be the maximum intensities of a 10- and a 100-year rainfall of 60 min duration in New England, according to the figures given in Table 6-4?

6-7. A rectangular drainage area is 4 miles wide from east to west and 3 miles from north to south. Rainfall observations during a storm were, at the northwest corner, 5 in.; at the northeast corner, 6 in.; at the southeast corner, 4 in.; at the southwest corner, 3 in.; and in the center of the area, 4.5 in. What was the average rainfall on the area?

6-8. Plot a hydrograph, a unit hydrograph, a flow-duration curve, and a mass curve for the data given for the Wabash River above Logansport, Ind., using the data given on page 141 of *U.S. Geological Survey Water Supply Paper* 772, changing the watershed area to 3,000 sq miles.

Chapter 7

7-1. Draw, to scale, the cross section of a rolled-fill earth dam holding a depth of water of 50 ft. The dam is to be on a slightly porous clay foundation. Three classes of material are to be used: grade *A* is a highly impervious mixture of sand and clay, suitable for puddle core wall; grade *B* is only slightly pervious sandy clay; and grade *C* is quite pervious. The upstream side of the dam is to be paved, and one or more berms are to be included on each side of the dam. The extreme length of exposed water surface from the face of the dam is $2\frac{1}{2}$ miles. All other conditions affecting the design are to be assumed and explained.

7-2. The core material in the dam shown in Fig. 7-2 (i) consists of clay, sand, and gravel weighing 110 lb per cu ft when dry. It has a moisture content of 16.3 per cent when saturated; and the pervious material on the upstream face weighs 114 lb per cu ft when dry, and contains 13.3 per cent moisture when wet. The depth of water behind the dam is 40 ft. (a) What is the weight, per foot of length of the dam, of each of the materials? (b) What will be the effective weight, per foot of length of the dam, of the material on the upstream face, to resist overturning when the reservoir is full? (c) What must be the coefficient of friction of this material to prevent sliding at the upstream face?

7-3. What should be the thickness of the lower edge of the apron on the dam shown in Fig. 7-1 to withstand uplift, assuming a factor of safety of 2 against uplift? Assume that the weight of concrete is 150 lb per cu ft.

7-4. Sketch the cross section of a masonry dam with water pressing on one side of it, and demonstrate that the resultant of all forces acting must pass within the middle third of the base of the dam in order to prevent tension in the upstream face of the dam.

7-5. If the section of a masonry dam shown in Fig. 7-3a is 60 ft high with a depth of water behind it of 55 ft, and the dam weighs 150 lb per cu ft, draw an enlarged section of the dam, to scale, and show the approximate magnitude, direction, and point of application of each force, or the resultant of the forces, listed in Sec. 7-19.

7-6. (a) If the base of the dam shown in Fig. 7-1 is 80 ft thick from toe to heel, what is the uplift per foot length of the dam? (b) How far from the upstream edge of the dam will the resultant of the uplift act? Assume the distribution of the uplift to be linear across the base of the dam.

7-7. What would be the thrust of the ice, per foot length of the top of a masonry dam, where ice may form to a thickness of 30 in., with no lateral restraint? Give an answer for each of the conditions listed in Fig. 7-4.

7-8. If the masonry dam described in Prob. 7-5 and shown in Fig. 7-3a is 60 ft high with 55 ft of water behind it, what must be the value of α in Eq. (7-2) in order that the dam will be on the point of overturning? Neglect ice thrust.

Chapter 9

9-1. A trapezoidal canal with side slopes 1:1 is to be constructed to carry 500 cfs at a velocity of 5 fps. What should be the base width and the depth of flow in the channel to give the greatest hydraulic radius?

9-2. Determine the economical diameter of a cast-iron pipe, to the nearest inch, to carry water at a constant rate of 6 mgd. The pipe costs $75 per ton; hourly wages for common labor are $1.25; the cost of pumping is 10 cents per million-gallon-foot; and interest plus depreciation is 7 per cent. Assume that the value of B, in Sec. 9-5, is 7.5.

9-3. Solve the preceding problem on the basis that the total quantity of water pumped through the pipe in a day is 6 million gal and that the rate of pumping for 6 hr daily is three times the rate for the remaining 18 hr.

9-4. If all the data concerning a cast-iron pipe are as in Prob. 9-2 except that the rate of pumping is to be 3 mgd, what should be the economical velocity in the pipe line? Answer in cubic feet per second.

9-5. Ten million gallons of water are to be pumped daily through a pipe line 1,000 ft long, with a value of $C = 120$. The water is to be lifted 80 ft. Other information concerning this pipe line is given in Prob. 9-2. (a) What would be the economical diameter of pipe through which water is to be pumped continuously? (b) What would be the least cost of pumping under the conditions? (c) What would be the cost if a pipe 25 per cent smaller in diameter were used? (d) What would be the cost if a pipe 25 per cent larger were used? Answer in cents per million gallons raised 1 ft, including all costs.

9-6. Design the waterway of an economically shaped rectangular bench flume to carry 500 cfs on a slope of 0.006, using Manning's formula with $n = 0.013$. Give the inside width and depth of water, in feet.

9-7. An aqueduct consists only of sections typified by cost–head-loss curves I, II, and V, shown in Fig. 9-7. If the total permissible head loss is 90 ft, what should be the minimum cost of the aqueduct, in dollars?

Chapter 10

10-1. A 12-ft steel pipe line, ⅝ in. thick and 500 ft long, is connected with standard, bolted, cast-iron flanges. Each end of the pipe is rigidly embedded in a concrete anchor. If the joints are 20 ft apart and there is 200 lb tension in each bolt when the temperature is 120°F, what will be the tension in each bolt at 32°F?

10-2. A 48-in. cast-iron pipe is subjected to an internal pressure of 125 psi. Assuming a safe working stress of 8,000 psi in tension, calculate: (a) the thickness of the shell necessary to resist the pressure only. (b) If the pipe is buried in damp topsoil and wet sand, weighing 120 lb per cu ft, with a depth of cover of 12.5 ft, what is the load of backfill only, per foot length of pipe? The trench is 5 ft wide.

10-3. A check valve on a 48-in. steel pipe 2 miles long is closed in 30 sec when the rate of flow is 40 mgd. What is the excess pressure resulting from the closing of this valve? Assume E for steel is 30 million psi and that the thickness of the shell is ½ in.

10-4. If the pipe line in the preceding problem is conveying water at a velocity of 10 fps and a standard 90-deg bend with bolted, flanged ends is in the line, what minimum tension would be necessary in each bolt to keep the joint tight? See standards of the American Water Works Association for the number of bolts in a bolt circle. The static pressure is 100 psi.

10-5. (a) If the pipe line in Prob. 10-3 changed 40°F in temperature, what would be its change in length due to expansion or contraction? Answer in feet. (b) If the pipe line were held rigidly between two anchors and the temperature were increased 40°F, what force, in pounds, would be necessary to prevent movement of the pipe?

10-6. A circular concrete-lined intake tunnel from a lake intake is 6 ft in diameter and 3.48 miles long. Water flows through the tunnel at 65 mgd to a wet well or suction pit at the shore end of the tunnel. A vertical, cylindrical, concrete-lined surge tower, 4 ft in diameter, is connected to the intake tunnel just above the entrance to the suction pit. An automatic shutoff valve is located between the surge tower and the suction pit. The static water level in the surge tower is at elevation 100 ft, and the bottom of the tower is at elevation 70 ft. Assume $C = 130$ in the tunnel, and neglect all losses of head except those due to friction in straight conduits. The velocity of the pressure wave in the tunnel and in the surge tower is 3,000 fps, and the coefficient of discharge of the opening in the surge tower is 0.8. (a) What will be the elevation of the surface of water in the surge tower when the flow is 65 mgd, if the static elevation is 100? (b) What would be the height to which the water would rise in the surge tower if the check valve were closed in 30 sec?

Chapter 11

11-1. The runoff, evaporation, and rate of water use from a watershed of 100 sq miles are shown in the accompanying table. Lakes, ponds, and reservoirs now on the watershed constitute 5 per cent of the watershed area. It will be necessary to construct an impounding reservoir to supply the demand shown, and this reservoir will increase the water surface on the watershed to 10 per cent. (*a*) Determine, with the aid of a mass diagram, the capacity of a reservoir necessary to supply a steady demand of 50 mgd. (*b*) Determine, similarly, the capacities of reservoirs required to supply each of the following continuous rates of demand: 15, 30, and 60 mgd. Assume that the evaporation rates remain the same as for the reservoir supplying 50 mgd. (*c*) What would be the time, in months, that the water is flowing over each spillway? (*d*) What is the maximum rate of steady demand that could be supplied by this stream, with an impounding reservoir, assuming the evaporation to be due to a 10 per cent water surface on the watershed? (*e*) If the monthly rate of demand varied as shown in the accompanying table, what would be the capacity of the reservoir necessary to supply this demand? Suggestion: In constructing diagrams use as a scale of abscissas, 1 in. = 4 months, and for ordinates, 1 in. = 1 billion gal.

Monthly Runoff, Evaporation, and Demand in Inches on a Watershed, for Driest Years of Record

Year	January	February	March	April	May	June	July
1916	2.57	2.68	3.75	1.96	1.90	0.62	0.34
1917	0.80	3.96	3.29	3.75	1.88	0.98	0.36
1918	2.73	2.84	2.18	1.59	0.93	0.26	0.08
Mean evaporation rate, each year..........	0.96	1.05	1.70	2.97	4.46	5.54	5.98
Mean demand rate, each year..........	0.44	0.26	0.22	0.26	0.57	0.61	0.69

Year	August	September	October	November	December	Mean
1916	0.68	0.14	0.24	0.19	0.60	1.31
1917	0.30	0.32	0.14	0.56	0.83	1.42
1918	0.28	0.21	0.10	0.54	0.10	1.27
Mean evaporation rate, each year.....	5.50	4.12	3.16	2.25	2.51	
Mean demand rate, each year..........	0.66	0.21	0.31	0.24	0.30	

11-2. (*a*) Plot a flow-duration curve for the year 1918 in the preceding problem before the construction of the reservoir. (*b*) Plot a flow-duration curve for the year 1918 in the preceding problem for the stream below the reservoir when the rate of demand is constant at 60 mgd. (*c*) Plot a flow-duration curve for the year 1918 in the preceding problem for the stream below the reservoir when the rate of demand is as shown in the last line of the table.

11-3. An impounding reservoir has a surface area of 100 acres at the spillway crest. The banks of the reservoir slope evenly on all sides at a gradient of 1:1.

The spillway is 200 ft long with a rate of flow equal to $Q = 3.6Lh^{3/2}$. At the start of a storm $h = 0.5$ ft. For the first 8 hr of the storm the rate of flow into the reservoir averaged 4,000 cfs; during the next hour it was 5,000 cfs; and for the last 16 hr it averaged 3,000 cfs. (a) What was the maximum height of water on the spillway, in feet? (b) How long after the storm started did this occur, in hours? (c) What was the head on the spillway, in feet, at the end of 25 hr?

· **11-4.** If the impounding reservoir for which data are shown in Fig. 11-1 loses, annually, 2 per cent of its present capacity due to silting, how long, in years, before it will be able to supply no more than 50 per cent of the rate of demand that can now be supplied? The ordinates shown represent 10^9 gal.

11-5. It may be assumed that the spillway for the Geist reservoir (Fig. 11-2) is designed so that the maximum head on it will flood land to the 790 contour. (a) If the crest of the spillway is raised 5 ft, without increasing its discharge capacity, what will be the increased storage capacity and how many acres of land will be flooded? (b) If the cost of additional land flooded is $150 per acre, and the cost of raising the crest by an overflow spillway is $50,000, how much could be saved by the construction of a siphon spillway costing $60,000 that would provide the same additional storage without flooding additional land?

11-6. If the rate of flow into the Geist reservoir in Fig. 11-2 is constant at 6,000 cfs, in what length of time will the water level rise from 787 to 791, if at the same time the rate of discharge over the spillway is $400h^{3/2}$, where h is the head of water, in feet, on the spillway and the rate of discharge is in cubic feet per second?

11-7. Construct two routing curves, whose abscissas are time and whose ordinates are elevation of water above spillway crest, for the reservoir to which the following data are applicable:

Head above crest, ft........	0	0.5	1.0	1.5	2.0	2.5	3.0	3.5	4.0
Surface area, acres.........	239	243	248	252	265	270	275	281	286

The rates of flow into the reservoir, in cubic feet per second, during each 10-min increment of time after the flood reached the reservoir were 1,250; 2,500; 3,750; 5,000; 6,250; 7,500; 6,875; 6,250; 5,625; 5,000; 4,375; 3,750; 3,125; 2,500; 1,875; 1,250; and 625. The rate of discharge over the spillway is $3.8Lh^{3/2}$. Draw one routing curve for a spillway 90 ft long and another for a spillway 200 ft long. (a) How many acres of land were saved from inundation by the 200-ft spillway? (b) What was the ratio of the maximum rates of flow over the spillways to the maximum rate of flow into the reservoir?

Chapter 12

12-1. A small city purchased a centrifugal pump to be driven by an internal-combustion engine. When the bids were opened the following proposals were found:

Bidder	Cost of pump and engine	Efficiency of pump, %	Fuel consumption at full load, gal per hp-hr
A	$3,800	71	0.13
B	3,000	66	0.11
C	1,200	63	0.12

Assuming that the pump is to deliver 1,100 gpm against a total head of 125 ft for 10 hr per day and that fuel costs an average of 12.5 cents per gallon of fuel, which is the best pump to purchase? Assume that interest is 4 per cent per year and that depreciation is 10 per cent.

12-2. If the pumps in the preceding problem are to be driven by electric motors, with over-all costs of pump and motor the same as for engine and pump given in the table, and electric power costs 1 cent per kilowatthour, what would be the cost of lifting 1 million gal 1 ft high if the most economical unit and type of power were selected? Each pump is 100 hp.

12-3. Determine the maximum capacity of a 12-in. cast-iron suction pipe, with coefficient of 100. The pipe projects 5 ft into the reservoir; suction lift is 15 ft; maximum water temperature is 65°F; elevation above sea level is 8,000 ft. The pipe is straight and is 100 ft long. Assume entrance loss as one velocity head. Answer in gallons per minute. Note: Data on atmospheric pressure and on vapor tension must be found in other books.

12-4. If the average rate of pumping at Middleton, on Apr. 12, 1944, as shown in Fig. 3-3, was 6 mgd, what must have been the capacity of a wet well to permit the pumps to operate continuously at the average rate? Answer in gallons.

Chapter 13

13-1. An overhead traveling crane is to be installed in the pump room of a water-works pumping station. It is to have a rated capacity of 15 tons. Three electric motors will be required for its operation: one to move it along the room, one to move the load sideways across the room, and one to raise and lower the load. Only alternating current is available. What sizes and types of motors should be selected for these services, and why?

13-2. A water-works pumping station for a city of 30,000 population is to be electrically equipped for power and light. The power is to be taken from the high-tension lines near the pumping station. These lines carry current at 33,000 volts, three phase, 60 cycles, on three-wire feeders. If induction motors are to be used on the pumps: (*a*) What voltage should be used for operating them? (*b*) What voltage should be used for the lighting circuit in the building? (*c*) What electrical equipment should be installed from the feeder line to the pumps so that they can receive the proper current and be fully protected against any normal eventuality?

13-3. Make a complete descriptive list of all the electrical equipment required in the pumping station in the preceding problem. Assume that there are three pumps and motors and that there is no stand-by equipment. Each pump is to be driven by a 50-hp motor.

13-4. A d-c motor for low-service pumps is to be installed at the bottom of a pit where conditions are wet and the atmosphere is hot and humid. The motor must deliver between 50 and 200 hp continuously, through reducing gears, to a reciprocating pump whose speed may vary between 30 and 130 rpm. Any desired d-c voltage and current can be made available. The efficiency of the reducing gear is about 92 per cent. List the electrical equipment that should be installed for the operation of this pump and motor, including the equipment on the switchboard and the wiring to the motor in the pit. The linear distance along one wire from switchboard to motor is 65 ft.

13-5. If the pump in the preceding problem is to be operated only as a stand-by unit, starting under full load and operating only a relatively short time during the emergency, what electrical equipment should be provided for its operation, including wiring and equipment on the switchboard?

13-6. An electric motor is directly connected to a centrifugal pump to lift 4,000 gpm continuously against a pressure of 125 psi. The unit discharges into a pipe line 2 miles long, lifting water into an elevated tank. The pumping unit is one of several similar units in the station, all discharging into the same pipe. Alternating current is available at 220 volts, three phase, 60 cycles. What size and type of motor should be used (a) if the unit has to start with the discharge valve open; (b) if the unit can be started with the discharge valve closed; (c) if the unit can be started so that the water can be by-passed to a low-service reservoir and the pump and motor can be operated at any desired speed and load up to full load when the discharge valve is opened into the high-service line; and (d) if the elevated tank were shut off and the discharge pressure might lie between 50 and 125 psi? Note: Make necessary assumptions of data not supplied and appropriate to the conditions of the problem.

13-7. A water-works pumping station has an average load of 50 mgd and discharges at a constant pressure of 120 psi, with fluctuations in discharge as shown for the maximum day at Toledo in Fig. 3-3. There is an elevated storage tank on the distribution system with a capacity of 1,000,000 gal. The pumping station is equipped with four motor-driven centrifugal pumps of equal capacity, each having an efficiency of 80 per cent at all loads. Only three of the pumps are to be operated simultaneously, the fourth being held for emergency. Each pumping unit can be started under no load and slowly loaded up to full load, if desired. Additional equipment includes a diesel-engine-driven centrifugal pump to be used as a fire pump. Rates for electric current delivered to the transformer at the pumping station at 2,200 volts are first 1,000 kwhr at 6 cents per kilowatthour, next 2,000 kwhr at 4 cents per kilowatthour, next 3,000 kwhr at 2 cents per kilowatthour, all over 6,000 kwhr at 1.8 cents per kilowatthour. There will be the following demand charges in addition: 1,500 kw or over at 0.2 cent per kilowatthour; 2,500 kw or over at 0.3 cent per kilowatthour; and 4,000 kw or over at 0.5 cent per kilowatthour. (a) Name the power and type of motors that should be used for each pumping unit. (b) What would be the least cost for electric power to operate this station for 30 days with a hydrograph similar to the maximum day for Toledo shown in Fig. 3-3, without making use of the storage on the distribution system? (c) Answer question (b), utilizing the storage on the distribution system.

Chapter 14[1]

14-1. A 12 by 18 by 24 by 18 by 24, outside, center-packed, duplex, crank-and-flywheel pumping engine, when operating at 40 rpm, is found to have a slip of 20 per cent. What is the rate of discharge in gallons per minute?

14-2. A pump and engine with a duty of 150 million, based on steam, operates condensing with a water-works type of condenser. The water pressure is 90 psi at delivery. Steam is 200 psi absolute. Vacuum is 20 in. mercury. (a) How many degrees will the temperature of the water be raised? (b) If the duty were raised to 200 million, how much would the temperature be raised? (c) If the discharge pressure were doubled, how much would the temperature be raised?

14-3. A pump with a duty of 125 million, based on Btu, raises 100 million gal per day against a head of 231 ft. Neglecting steam-line and other losses, what should be the horsepower of the boiler?

14-4. Illinois coal, costing $8 per ton, will evaporate 7 lb water per pound coal from and at 212°F. Which will be the cheaper, and how much per horsepower

---

[1] Supplementary information from more basic texts will be necessary to solve some of these problems.

annually in dollars, a 100-million-duty plant on a coal basis or a 100-million-duty plant on a steam basis?

14-5. What is the lowest theoretical water rate for a simple direct-acting steam pump using dry steam if the boiler pressure is (a) 25 psi (absolute), (b) 250 psi (absolute), (c) 350 psi (absolute)?

14-6. What will be the power costs, in cents, of raising 1 million gal water 1 ft high by each of the following pumping units: (a) a steam pump with a duty of 100 million based on coal, (b) an electrically driven centrifugal pump with a maximum efficiency of 75 per cent, (c) a gasoline-engine-driven centrifugal pump with 75 per cent efficiency, (d) an oil-engine-driven centrifugal pump with an over-all efficiency of 75 per cent? The cost of coal is $8 per ton; electricity, 1.75 cents per kilowatthour; fuel oil, 14 cents per gallon; and gasoline, 20 cents per gallon. The consumption of gasoline is 0.10 gal per hp-hr, and of oil is 0.12 gal per hp-hr.

14-7. The over-all heat efficiency of a boiler in a water-works pumping station is 80 per cent. The coal used costs $7.50 per ton and contains 10,500 Btu per lb. A high-service steam pumping unit in the plant, discharging water at a gage pressure of 150 psi, delivers 550 hp under full load, with a mechanical efficiency of 89 per cent and a water rate of 50 lb. The boiler pressure is 150 psi. Steam is delivered with a moisture content of 2 per cent. What is the cost of fuel used by this pumping equipment, expressed in cents per 1,000 gal of water pumped?

Chapter 15

15-1. A single-stage centrifugal pump delivers 1,000 gpm against a head of 250 ft when running at 1,000 rpm. (a) What will be the rate of discharge and the discharge pressure at a rate of 1,200 rpm? (b) At what speed must it run to discharge 900 gpm, and what would be the discharge head at this speed?

15-2. A single-stage centrifugal pump, with an impeller 10 in. in diameter, delivers 1,800 gpm against a head of 100 ft when running at 1,200 rpm. What is its specific speed?

15-3. How many stages would be required for a centrifugal pump to deliver 2,400 gpm against a head of 450 ft at a speed of 1,750 rpm if the specific speed of the series is 2,000?

15-4. What is the safe upper limit of specific speed for a double-suction centrifugal pump with a total head of 100 ft and a total suction lift of 10 ft?

15-5. A three-stage centrifugal pump with 8-in.-diameter impellers is of the same type as the pump in Prob. 15-2. At what rate and against what head will it discharge at 1,000 rpm?

15-6. A 6-in. centrifugal pump has a straight 8-in. suction pipe lifting water 10 ft vertically from the sump. The pump is discharging into 1,000 ft of 6-in. cast-iron pipe with a value of $C = 100$. The outlet of the pipe is 120 ft above the pump. If the efficiency of the pump and motor is 78 per cent, at what rate is the pump discharging, in gallons per minute, when using 40 kw of current? Neglect all friction losses other than that due to flow in straight pipe.

15-7. If the centrifugal pump whose characteristics are shown in Fig. 15-3 is being driven by a steam turbine with a heat efficiency of 18 per cent, what is the duty of the combined turbine and pump when the pump is operating at its highest efficiency at a speed of 1,750 rpm?

15-8. Determine the number and capacities of electrically driven centrifugal pumps for a pumping station under the following conditions: (a) The hydrograph of load on the pumping station is shown for the maximum day at Toledo in Fig. 3-3. The load on this day is 3.92 million gal. (b) The discharge pressure is

240 ft. (c) Electric current at any demand rate less than 1.25 times the average for the day costs 0.8 cent per kilowatthour. Between 1.25 and 1.5 times the average rate, it costs 1 cent per kilowatthour; and between 1.5 and 2 times the average rate, it is 1.5 cents per kilowatthour. No load above twice the average is permitted. (d) Efficiency of the motors at all speeds may be assumed as 92 per cent. (e) The motors are to be variable-speed to drive the pumps at any desired speed, and the piping is such that any combination of pumps may be run in tandem or in series. (f) The characteristics of each pump are shown in Fig. 15-3. (g) The pumps are to be selected to give the least cost of power. What will be the daily cost under the conditions stated? Answer in dollars.[1]

15-9. Compute the diameter of the impeller of the centrifugal pump whose characteristic curves are shown in Fig. 15-3.

15-10. What will be the least cost of electric power to raise 1 million gal water 1 ft high if electric power costs 0.9 cent per kilowatthour and the pump whose characteristics are shown in Fig. 15-3 is driven by a motor with an efficiency of 93 per cent, when driving the pump at its maximum efficiency?

15-11. The accompanying tabulated data are the results of tests on a centrifugal pump.

rpm	Head, ft	Dis-charge, gpm	Effi-ciency, %	rpm	Head, ft	Dis-charge, gpm	Effi-ciency, %	rpm	Head, ft	Dis-charge, gpm	Effi-ciency, %
1,875	242	0	0	1,613	203	880	67	1,200	106	0	
	254	220	35		190	1,155	76		116	220	40
	256	440	45		182	1,298	75		118	440	56
	258	495	48		164	1,540	68		114	743	72
	254	803	62		140	1,685	62		102	990	75
	232	1,265	74		20	1,848	34		81	1,550	40
	200	1,650	69	1,425	158	0		900	70	0	
	140	1,881	56		166	242	40		74	275	46
	100	1,903	45		172	581	55		76	434	61
	0	1,936			168	750	63		74	605	69
1,613	192	200	39		160	1,077	75		66	825	72
	200	209	40		156	1,150	77		48	1,133	62
	204	369	54		130	1,573	67		30	1,364	41
	206	522	58		84	1,839	50				
	208	605	56		20	1,924	33				

Plot the characteristics of this pump, including horsepower, using discharge in gallons per minute as abscissas (1 in. = 200 gpm) and as ordinates, head (1 in. = 40 ft.), horsepower (1 in. = 10 hp), and efficiency. Superimpose on these curves isoefficiency curves for 40, 50, 60, 65, and 70 per cent and then every 1 per cent to the maximum efficiency. Plot also horsepower curves for every 10 hp up to the maximum horsepower. Then answer the following questions: (a) At what speed, head, and discharge is the pump most efficient? (b) What is the maximum efficiency, and what is the horsepower at that efficiency?

15-12. What is the specific speed of the pump in the preceding problem?

Chapter 16

16-1. A single-stroke pump with a stroke of 12 in. and a net piston surface of 5 sq in. is to discharge at an average rate of 7.5 gpm. The motion of the plunger is harmonic. (a) What is the maximum speed of travel of the piston in feet per

[1] See E. Condict, *Water Works Eng.*, August, 1951, p. 755, for a similar problem.

minute?   (*b*) What is the maximum momentary rate of discharge, in gallons per minute?

16-2. A two-stroke pump, with a 28-in. stroke and with each piston having a net lifting surface of 8 sq in., operates at 50 rpm, the pistons moving with harmonic motion.   What is the capacity of the pump, in gallons per minute?

16-3. The rod, or shaft, in a differential-plunger pump similar to that shown in Fig. 16-2 is 1.4 in. in diameter.   The weight of the moving parts is 154 lb, and they displace 1,500 cu in. of water.   The diameter of the piston is 6 in.   (*a*) If the total lift on each stroke is 200 ft, what must be the diameter of the differential plunger in order that equal work may be done by the pump on the upstroke and on the downstroke?   Neglect friction.   (*b*) How many gallons will be discharged on each stroke if the length of the stroke is 18 in.?

16-4. A deep-well turbine pump is to lift 800 gpm a height of 200 ft.   If the diameter of the well is to fit the pump, determine a satisfactory combination of pump casing and speed within the limits fixed in Sec. 16-9.

16-5. A deep-well turbine pump is to lift 400 gpm a height of 400 ft.   If the diameter of the pump casing cannot exceed 10 in., how many stages must be used and at what speed must the impellers run to remain between the limits fixed in Sec. 16-9?

16-6. It is desired to raise 500,000 gpd from a gravity well by means of an air lift.   The distance to ground water when not pumping is 80 ft.   The specific capacities of wells in the neighborhood have averaged about 15 gpm per ft drawdown.   The water-bearing stratum consists of fine running sand.   It is underlaid by impervious clay and overlaid by shale and sand not containing water.   The distance from the ground surface to the bottom of the aquifer is 200 ft.   Design the well and the air-lift equipment for conditions at Hattiesburg, Miss., using the highest efficiency shown in Table 16-1.   Determine each of the following: (*a*) depth of well, in feet, (*b*) capacity of air compressor, in cubic feet of free air per minute, (*c*) size of air pipe, nearest commercial size, in inches, (*d*) size of eductor pipe, nearest commercial size, in inches (use same diameter from top to bottom), (*e*) starting and operating air pressures, pounds per square inch, (*f*) velocity of water at bottom of eductor pipe, feet per second.

16-7. (*a*) Design an air lift to raise 1,000 gpm from a well, if the submergence is 40 per cent, the efficiency is 25 per cent, and the lift is 100 ft.   (*b*) If the specific capacity of the well is 20 gpm, what should be the starting and the operating pressures of the air compressor, in pounds per square inch?

Chapter 17

17-1. Determine the thickness of a cast-iron pipe for the following conditions (for nomenclature and procedure see Sec. 17-4): $d = 42$ in.; $S = 11,000$ psi; $R = 31,000$ psi; water-hammer allowance = 50 psi; static pressure = 100 psi; external load = 3,000 lb per ft; factor of safety = 2.0; field conditions E (Table 17-1) prevail.   In approximately what thickness class will this pipe lie (Table 17-2)?

17-2. First Street and Avenue A are each 35 ft wide between curb lines. They intersect at an angle of 30 deg, First Street running east and west, and Avenue A running at an angle of 30 deg to it in a northwest-southeast direction. A 24-in. cast-iron bell-and-spigot pipe line lies in Avenue A, 3 ft northeast of the southwest curb line, running parallel to it.   The center of the spigot end of a 12-ft length of pit-cast iron pipe lies in the south curb line (extended) of First Street.   It is desired to place a fire hydrant 2 ft north of the north curb line on First Street and 22 ft east of the intersection of the nearest curb lines on Avenue A and First Street.   This hydrant is connected by a 6-in. pit-cast iron pipe with bell-and-spigot ends to an 8-in. pipe of the same classification.   This 8-in. pipe runs east and west parallel to the north curb line on First Street and connects with the 24-in. line on the southwest side of Avenue A.   A gate valve is to be placed in the 6-in. line to the hydrant.   The 8-in. line is 3 ft south of the north curb line on First Street.   Prepare a sketch of the layout, to scale, showing the location of pipes and specials, and prepare a bill of material for everything needed to complete the installation of pipes and specials, valves, and hydrants at the intersection.

17-3. A pipe line 10 miles long is to be constructed to convey 15 cfs of water with a hydraulic gradient not to exceed 0.1 ft per 1,000 ft with a coefficient of 125. If unlined centrifugally cast iron pipe is to be used, what would be the cost of the pipe alone, assuming bell-and-spigot pipe with the longest lengths available. Base the cost of the pipe on the cost per pound at Birmingham, Ala., as shown in the latest issue of *Engineering News-Record* containing such unit costs.

17-4. In laying out the pipes in a pumping station, two flanged ends in a 12-in. line are found to be 7 ft $3\frac{1}{8}$ in. apart in a direction parallel to the axes of the two lines which are, themselves, parallel.   The axes of the two lines of pipe are 4 ft 9 in. apart in the same horizontal plane.   It is desired to connect these two pipes, inserting a 12-in. flanged gate valve in the line.   Make a sketch and prepare a bill of material for this connection.

17-5. A 48-in. circular aqueduct is to be constructed on the surface of the ground in a mountainous region in the Southwest where transportation is costly. The maximum internal pressure to be resisted is about 10 psi.   Transportation charges from railhead to job site are to be $7.50 per ton for any load of 1 ton or less.   For loads above 1 ton the cost in dollars will be $6W^2$, where W is the weight of the load in tons.   What would be the cost for 1,000 ft of aqueduct for transportation of each of the following kinds of pipe: wood-stave, spiral-riveted steel, asbestos-cement, and reinforced-concrete with 4-in. shell and 30 lb reinforcement per foot length of pipe?   Concrete pipe and wood pipe may be fabricated on the job.   Concrete contains 1 part of cement to 5 of aggregate.   Aggregate and water for concrete pipe need not be transported.   Steel pipe and asbestos-cement pipe must be transported prefabricated to the job.

17-6. A steel conduit 48 miles long was designed to resist only the pressure due to depth below the hydraulic grade line.   At station 1,052 + 96 it is 417 ft below the gradient and 653 ft below the highest reservoir surface elevation.   At this point it is 54 in. in diameter; the steel is $\frac{3}{8}$ in. thick with double-riveted lap joints in the longitudinal seams.   The joints have $\frac{5}{8}$-in. rivets, staggered, on a pitch of 2.28 in. in each row.   The rows are $1\frac{1}{8}$ in. apart.   The pitch line to the edge of the plate is $1\frac{5}{16}$ in., and the lap of the sheets is 3 in.   Compute the stress per square inch on the rivets, both in shear and in bearing, and on the net plate due to the depth below the hydraulic grade line.   Assume the diameter of the rivethole to be $\frac{1}{16}$ in. larger than the diameter of the rivets.   What is the efficiency of the joint?

17-7. Design a wood-stave pipe for the following conditions: diameter, 84 in.; maximum pressure head, 60 ft of water; allowable tension in bands, 20,000 psi; thickness of staves, 2 in.; swelling force of wood, 100 psi; safe crushing strength of wood, 650 psi.

17-8. How much wire, and of what size, would be needed for 1,000 ft of spirally wound wood-stave pipe 3 ft in diameter, subjected to 70 psi of internal water pressure?   The tensile strength of the wire is 20,000 psi, and the swelling strength and crushing strength of wood are as in the preceding problem.

17-9. A 10-ft diameter reinforced concrete conduit is under a hydrostatic head of 30 ft, with other conditions as shown in Fig. 17-25. Determine (a) the volume of concrete, in cubic yards per foot length of conduit, (b) the diameter of the circumferential reinforcing bars, (c) the weight, in pounds, of circumferential reinforcing steel per foot length of conduit.

Chapter 18

18-1. (a) How many turns of the wheel are necessary to open the valve in Fig. 18-2? (b) Is this valve right-handed? (c) Determine from the scale of the figure about how many turns of the handwheel are necessary to open the valve in Fig. 18-6, assuming the pitch of the threads on the valve stem and the size of valve to be the same as in Fig. 18-2.

18-2. Determine from the scale of the figure the approximate length of the key necessary to open the valve in Fig. 18-5.

18-3. How many pounds pull would be required to start opening the valve in Fig. 18-7, under the following conditions: 80 psi acting on the disk of a 10-in. gate valve; coefficient of friction of gate against seat, 0.2; area of contact between disk and seat is an annular ring 10 in. inside diameter and ¾ in. wide; length of valve-handle lever, 24 in.; effective distance from valve stem to fulcrum, 7 in.? Neglect all other friction and weights.

18-4. What will be the effect on the operation of the check valve in Fig. 18-11 if valve M is closed?

18-5. What will be the effect on the operation of the valve in Fig. 18-15 if valve L is closed?

18-6. If the valve disk shown in Fig. 18-22 is 18 in. in diameter and there is a depth of water of 20 ft over it, what weight must be lifted in order to open the valve?

18-7. A 78-in. steel pipe line runs in straight lines between lettered points. At A the elevation is 3,140 ft; the distance from A to B is 680 ft; at B the elevation is 3,110 ft; the distance from B to C is 1,140 ft; at C the elevation is 2,890 ft. There is a reservoir at A, and it is to be assumed that there is a complete rupture of the pipe at point C so that water flows freely from the pipe. What diameter of air-inlet valve would be required at B under the following conditions: thickness of pipe shell, 0.25 in.; stiffener rings placed 20 ft apart; factor of safety against collapse, 2; coefficient of discharge of air-inlet valve, 0.5? For the solution see *Proc. ASCE*, Vol. 75, p. 789, 1949.

Chapter 19

19-1. If electric current costs 1 cent per kilowatthour, what may be the range of annual costs, for current alone, of the cathodic protection of an elevated tank with 5,000 sq ft of submerged steel surface, assuming conversion from alternating to direct current at 10 volts to be 50 per cent efficient?

Chapter 20

20-1. If the average daily flow for a typical winter day in Kansas City is as shown in Fig. 3-3 and amounts to 30 mgd, what should be the capacity of an equalizing reservoir to equalize the rate of pumping if (a) the rate of pumping is to be continuous and (b) the pumps operate at 120 per cent of average rate from 8 A.M. to 6 P.M., and at a reduced rate for the remainder of the day, sufficient to supply the remainder of the full day's demand? The reduced rate of pumping is to be continuous from 6 P.M. to midnight, and from midnight to 8 A.M.

20-2. If the line for the average day at Toledo in Fig. 3-3 indicates the rate of pumping before the installation of an equalizing reservoir; if the minimum pressure pumped against is 70 psi when pumping at the average rate of 10 mgd, and for rates of pumping above this the pressure varies as the square root of the rate of pumping; and if the cost of pumping is 7.5 cents per million gallons raised 1 ft, what will be the approximate daily saving in pumping cost as a result of installing an equalizing reservoir to permit pumping continuously at the average rate of demand?

20-3. If, at Toledo, the average hourly rate of pumping on the average day shown in Fig. 3-3 is 50,000 gal, how much equalizing storage capacity would be required on the maximum day when the pumps were operated at a constant rate from 6 A.M. to 6 P.M.?

20-4. Solve the preceding problem using the curve for Middleton on Apr. 2, 1944, and assume that the pumps run at a constant rate from 7 A.M. to 7 P.M.

20-5. (a) What is the capacity of the tank necessary to equalize the pumping at a constant rate in Fig. 20-1? (b) If the distance from the ground to the bottom of the tank is 125 ft and the tank is 30 ft deep, plot a curve with time as abscissas and pressures in pounds per square inch as ordinates, in the distribution system at the base of the tank.

20-6. A pipe line is 8 in. in diameter and 1 mile long, with $C = 100$. An elevated tank, with a height from the ground to the base of the tank of 100 ft and a depth of water of 25 ft in the tank when full, is connected to the pipe line 4,000 ft from the pumping station. The ground level at the pumps and at the tank is the same. (a) When the rate of flow at the end of the pipe line, 1 mile from the pumping station, is 500 gpm, and the tank is not connected to the pipe, and the pressure at the end of the pipe, at the same elevation as the pumps, is 30 psi, what will be the pressure at the pumps? (b) If the pressure at the end of the pipe line remains at 30 psi and at the pumps is the same as found in the preceding step, and if the tank, containing 15 ft of water, is opened into the pipe line, what will be the rate of flow into or from the tank? Neglect all friction losses other than those due to losses in straight pipe.

20-7. A covered concrete reservoir to hold 15 million gal of water will cost $h^{3/2}$ dollars per foot of length of wall, where h is the depth of water in feet, and $1 per sq ft of reservoir area. What will be the least cost for which this reservoir can be constructed if appurtenances cost $1,000?

20-8. Determine the economical height of a steel standpipe in terms of the useful capacity Q and the following unit costs and conditions: cost of steel, a cents per pound; thickness of steel varies as $(BH)(CD)$, where H is useful height of water, B and C are constants, and D is the diameter of the standpipe. The cost of the foundation varies as ED^2, where E is a constant. All other costs are KQ, where K is a constant. Dimensions are in feet.

Chapter 21

21-1. A city has rectangular blocks 300 by 500 ft. There may be 3,500 gpm concentrated on one fire. Design the water-pipe system for the immediate district so that the loss of head in the pipes shall not exceed 10 ft per 1,000 ft of pipe. Use the smallest sizes of pipe possible, and design an economical layout. It is not necessary that all pipes shall be of the same size.

21-2. How many two-way fire hydrants throwing 250 gpm fire streams can be located on an 8-in. pipe connected to a larger main at each end where the pressure remains constant, if the hydrant spacing is 500 ft and the loss of head in the pipe does not exceed 10 psi?

21-3. Compute the flow distribution in each pipe of the crossover shown in the sketch if each pipe is 8 in. in diameter and 1,000 ft long. One hundred per cent put-in occurs at A and 100 per cent take-off at F. Use the Hardy Cross method, following the procedure given in Sec. 21-5.

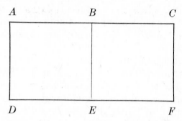

21-4. Water is entering a pipe junction at 2,600 gpm. It is leaving the junction through three pipes of the same length, A, B, and C, whose relative resistances are, respectively, 4, 9, and 16. The pipes are joined again at a common junction at the opposite end from which the flow enters. What is the rate of flow in each pipe in gallons per minute?

21-5. Compute the rate of flow in each pipe in the accompanying crossover, using the Hardy Cross method and computing rates of flow to the nearest 0.5 per cent. Construct the 5-ft piezometric contours with the pressure at F equal to 70 ft and at A to 90 if of water.

Chapter 22

22-1. Water is entering a 48-in. uninsulated pipe line 16,800 ft long, with E equal to zero and C equal to 110, at a rate of 25 mgd, and at a temperature of 35°F. The pipe is exposed to a surrounding-air temperature of −5°F and to a 35 mph wind. What are the heat input and the heat loss, expressed in Btu per hour? Compute for each of the following materials: riveted steel ¼ in. thick and concrete with 5 in. thickness of shell. Follow the procedure and use the heat coefficients given in *Engineering News-Record*, Nov. 9, 1950, p. 39.

22-2. A saturated clay having a dry density of 120 lb per cu ft has a surface temperature of 32°F on Dec. 10. It is exposed to an average temperature of 14°F until Jan. 29. There is no appreciable snow during the period, and the average annual ground temperature at a depth of 3 ft is 50°F. Would a service connection 3 ft deep in this soil be in danger of freezing?[1]

Chapter 24

24-1. How many grains of hardness are equivalent to the various concentrations of hardness expressed in parts per million in Table 24-4?

24-2. A sample of water is found to have a turbidity of 100. (*a*) How can its turbidity be changed in the laboratory to 75; (*b*) to 200?

24-3. (*a*) How much dilution water must be added to 1 gal of a 12 per cent strength sodium hypochlorite solution to produce a solution with a strength of 3 per cent? (*b*) How much of a solution of 3 per cent strength of sodium hypochlorite must be added to a solution of 12 per cent strength to produce a solution of 9 per cent strength sodium hypochlorite?

24-4. Study an analysis of your home-town water supply, or some other public water supply, and write a report on its sanitary quality as compared with U.S. Public Health Service Standards for potable water. See Sec. 23-12 and Table 24-2.

[1] See J. Petrica, *J.A.W.W.A.*, November, 1951, p. 911.

24-5. Fifty milliliters of water saturated with oxygen at 75°F are mixed with 100 ml of water saturated with oxygen at 55°F. What will be the temperature and the percentage saturation with oxygen of the mixture?

24-6. Compute the amount of oxygen that is soluble in water at 60°F and 760 mm mercury pressure, when the surface is exposed to the air containing 80 per cent nitrogen and 20 per cent oxygen. The results should be accurate to the nearest 0.1 ppm. Is it possible to formulate algebraically the relationship between temperature and dissolved oxygen?

24-7. Prepare a hypothetical analytical report on the sanitary analysis of a water supply that you think should be condemned. The report should be prepared in a manner similar to that recommended or used by your state health authority. Your reasons for condemning the water should be clearly stated.

24-8. On the evaporation of 1 liter of aqueous solution of sodium chloride it is found to contain 38 grams of NaCl. What was the concentration of NaCl in the solution? Answer in percentage by weight and in parts per million.

24-9. Water enters a purification plant with a pH of 6.6. The next day the pH is 8.6. What was the average pH for the 24-hr period, assuming straight-line variation of hydrogen-ion concentration?

24-10. Of two bases that are very slightly dissociated one has a dissociation constant of 0.0000010, and the other of 0.0000090. What are their relative ionic strengths?

24-11. If a molal solution of a nonelectrolyte will freeze at 1.86°C lower than pure water and a molal solution of HCl will freeze at 3.68° below 0°C, what is the percentage dissociation of the HCl?

24-12. (a) Compute the dissociation constant of a 0.1 molal solution of an acid that is 45 per cent dissociated. (b) What is the pH of a 0.01 molal solution of an acid if its dissociation constant is 0.0000171? (c) What is the pH of a molal solution of (R)OH that is 0.42 per cent dissociated, where the dissociation constant is 0.001?

24-13. Prepare hypothetical combinations for the water reported in Table 24-6, assuming the concentrations of Na, Ca, and Cl to be halved.

24-14. If it were possible to remove the chlorides from the water reported in Table 24-6, would it be potable? Why?

Chapter 25

25-1. What is the most probable number of *E. coli* per 100 ml, as determined by the following series of observations: of 5 10-ml portions, 4 were positive; of 3 1-ml portions, 2 were positive; and 1 0.1-ml portion was negative?

25-2. What was the *E. coli* index at a filter plant where the following observations were made for 2 months?

Quantities tested, ml	1.0	0.1	0.01	0.001
Number of tests	60	40	60	30
Number positive	40	6	6	1

25-3. A microscopic analysis of a public water supply is shown on page 130 of "The Microscopy of Drinking Water," by Fair and Whipple, John Wiley & Sons, Inc., New York, 1927. What are the probabilities of this water causing complaint by the consumers? What would be the probable nature of the complaint? How should you proceed to overcome the complaint?

25-4. A large impounding reservoir was heavily contaminated with anabaena. At the time of the condition the reservoir was about 30 miles long and 3 miles wide, with an average depth of about 5 ft and a maximum depth at the dam of 30 ft.   Estimate the cost of applying copper sulphate at the rate of 0.36 ppm, if the cost of the chemical is $1\frac{1}{2}$ cents per pound, and the cost of labor and equipment for applying the chemical from a boat running at 6 mph is $5 per hour.   The boat covers a swath of 50 ft.

25-5. If *B. butschlii* and *Dialister pneumosintes* were shaped as cylinders, and were packed together as closely as possible, how many of each could be packed into a cubic centimeter?

25-6. A boat to apply copper sulphate to a reservoir that is 15 ft deep is rowed at 2 mph in 25-ft parallel swaths.   How long will it take the boat to cover 1 acre? How many pounds of copper sulphate will be used per acre if only the upper 5 ft of the water is to be dosed at the rate of 1 ppm?

Chapter 26

26-1. Name the processes of water purification listed in Table 26-1 which rendered potable, according to the Standards of Quality of the U.S. Public Health Service, the water supplies at Toledo, Youngstown, Niagara Falls, Cincinnati, and Louisville.

26-2. What was the turbidity of the water leaving the plain sedimentation basin at Youngstown, Ohio, from October, 1923, to September, 1924, according to Table 26-1?

26-3. Compute the period, or periods, of detention possible in the sedimentation basin shown in Fig. 26-1*a*, making reasonable assumptions of dimensions not shown or that cannot be scaled.

26-4. Derive an expression for the economical depth of an open circular settling basin in terms of the depth of the water h, the diameter d, the capacity Q, and the cost of the appurtenances S.   Let the cost of floor per unit area $= k_1$, and of wall per unit length $= k_2 h^{3/2}$.

26-5. What would be the economical depth, in feet, of a rectangular reservoir with length four times the width, with a capacity of 760,000 gal, if the cost of floor and roof, including columns, is $10 per square foot; the cost of the walls, in dollars per foot of length, is 0.8 times the square of the water depth, in feet; and the cost of all appurtenances is $2,350?   There will be no excavation or other items to consider.

26-6. Three open rectangular sedimentation basins are to be constructed of concrete with the following possible periods of detention: 2, 4, 6, 8, 10, and 12 hr, depending on the manipulation of valves.   The rate of flow through the plant is 18 mgd.   The basins are to be placed in a row, side by side, using a common dividing wall between basins.   The floor will cost $5 per square foot; exterior walls, as in the preceding problem; interior dividing walls, 25 per cent more than exterior walls; all appurtenances and other charges not depending on dimensions, $10,000.   No other items of cost are to be considered.   What would be the least amount of money for which these basins could be constructed, and what would be the three dimensions of each basin if all are to have the same depth?

26-7. Sketch the basins designed in the preceding problem and show in diagrammatic form the piping and valve arrangement that would permit the periods of detention required.   Number, or letter, each valve and show in a table those which would be open and those which would be closed for each period of detention.

Chapter 27

27-1. (*a*) How many square feet of floor space would be required to store 6 months' supply of each chemical listed in Table 27-1 to permit the addition of

2 grains per gal to a flow of 15 mgd? (b) If the chemical fed as a solution is to be held in a solution storage tank, what would be the volume of each tank to hold sufficient solution of each soluble chemical listed in Table 27-1 for 8 hr supply to dose 2 grains per gal to 6 mgd, assuming that the greatest recommended solution strength shown in the table is prepared?

27-2. In the operation of a coagulation basin it is found that optimum coagulation is obtained at a pH of 6.7 at which point 0.9 grain alum is required per gallon of water treated. Unfortunately the natural pH of the water is 7.3, and when alum alone is added, 1.7 grains of alum is required per gallon of water treated. It is found by test that the addition of 0.6 grain of 66°Bé sulphuric acid will reduce the pH so that satisfactory coagulation can be obtained with 1.0 grain of alum per gallon. If the sulphuric acid costs 1½ cents per pound, and alum costs $2 per 100 lb, what will be the saving, if any, when sulphuric acid is added? Answer in dollars per million gallons of water.

27-3. How much natural alkalinity, expressed as parts per million of CaCO₃. will be required in water to be coagulated by the use of 2 grains of commercial alum per gallon water?

27-4. By how much is the total hardness of water increased by the addition of 2 grains per gal of commercial alum, containing 17 per cent aluminum sulphate?

27-5. In the coagulation of water with "lime and iron," 175 lb of crystallized ferrous sulphate is added per million gallons of water. (a) How many pounds of commercial quicklime, containing 85 per cent CaO, must be added to complete the reaction, assuming no natural alkalinity in the water? (b) Is it more or less economical to add the iron first? Why? (c) If the water contains 12 ppm of dissolved oxygen at the start of the reaction, how much will remain when coagulation is complete, assuming no reaeration or change in temperature during the process?

27-6. If 0.75 grain of pure aluminum sulphate is required per gallon of water treated, what would be the cost of commercial alum costing $2.50 per 100 lb, and containing 17 per cent of aluminum sulphate? Answer in dollars per million gallons.

27-7. The stirring paddles in a chemical mixing tank are so arranged that the shaft that drives them should revolve at 300 rpm. A three-phase 60-cycle 110-volt current is available but only a single-phase 60-cycle 110-volt motor can be obtained. The motor has a rated capacity of 4 hp. (a) If the cost of current is so low as to be negligible, what would be the proper thing to do in the situation? (b) If the current costs 4 cents per kilowatthour what should be done?

27-8. The nominal capacity of a rapid-sand-filter plant is 10 mgd. Alum is used as a coagulant at the rate of 1½ grains per gal of water treated. Three solution-storage tanks are to be used, each holding solution for 8 hr of operation. (a) What should be the capacity of each tank, in gallons, if the strongest permissible solution is used? (b) Of what materials should the tanks be made?

27-9. If stirring paddles were used in the tanks in the preceding problem, how fast should the paddles revolve, what should be the diameter of the paddle wheel, and what wattage would be required to drive the paddle in one tank? Each tank is cylindrical.

27-10. (a) Determine the dimensions of an around-the-end, baffled flocculation basin for a flow of 6 mgd and a detention period of 30 min. (b) What would be the probable loss of head through the basin? (c) What would be the difference between the power of an electric motor to drive a pump to lift the water this height, and the power that would be necessary to drive flocculating paddles in a straight-flow tank that would give equally satisfactory mix? Suggestion: See

Engineering News-Record, Vol. 99, p. 857, or *Journal of the American Water Works Association*, Vol. 21, p. 235.

27-11. Sketch, to scale, and show dimensions, the pipes and fittings for a solution pot similar to Fig. 27-1, to hold sufficient commercial alum to dose 2 mgd of water at a rate of 2 grains per gal, assuming a recharge every 8 hr. Dimensions of pipes and fittings are to accord with commonly used standards, insofar as is economical.

27-12. Draw to scale a rectangular flocculating basin, with mechanically driven paddles, through which the water flows horizontally from one paddle to the next, in series. The basin is to care for a flow of 2 mgd with a flocculation period of 45 min. It is to be 8 ft deep. Show over-all dimensions of the basins and details of the inlet and outlet devices or arrangements, state nominal horizontal flowing-through velocity, and estimate the daily cost of electric power required if the unit cost is 1 cent per kilowatthour. Use the maximum power requirements that are given in Sec. 27-35. Assume all necessary data not given in the statement of the problem.

27-13. If the Accelator shown in Fig. 27-7 is 30 ft in diameter at the top of the effluent collection trough, and it is treating a flow of 4.5 mgd, what would be the diameter, in millimeters, of the smallest particle of flocculent material removed within the "sludge-filter zone" according to Stokes' law? The water temperature is 20°C, at which the viscosity may be taken as 1 centipoise. The density of water is unity at this temperature. Stokes' law is

$$V = \frac{gd^2(D_2 - D_1)}{18\gamma}$$

in which V is the settling velocity of a particle of water, in centimeters per second; g is the acceleration of gravity; d is the diameter of the particle; D_1 is the density of water; D_2 is the density of the settling particle; and γ is the coefficient of viscosity, in poises. All units are in the cgs system. Solve the problem for a particle density of 1.05 and also of 2.65.

Chapter 28

28-1. If the dimensions of a slow-sand-filter unit are 220 by 140 ft in plan, and the underdrainage system consists of a manifold longitudinally down the center of the shorter dimension of the filter bed with underdrain branches on 16-ft centers, (*a*) what would be the approximate nominal capacity of the filter in gallons per day? (*b*) What would be the maximum rate of flow in any of the branch underdrains? Answer in cubic feet per second.

28-2. If the depth of water on the filter shown in Fig. 28-1 is 60 in., how many inches of negative head can be produced on the filter when it is dirty? Suggestion: Scale the necessary dimensions from the figure.

28-3. A slow sand filter costs $185,000 per acre, exclusive of walls. The appurtenances to each filter cost $4,000 in addition. The cost of outside walls is $22 per linear foot, and the cost of walls between filter units is $32.50 per foot. The cost of the administration building and of other items common to the entire plant is $80,000. If the plant is to occupy 12 acres for filter units alone, using rectangular units of equal area, laid out in the most economical manner, what would be the least cost for which the plant could be built?

28-4. If in an emergency the operator is called from the laboratory to the hydraulic jump in the chemical-feed house shown in Fig. 28-5, how long will it take him if he runs at 5 mph?

28-5. A concrete rapid-sand-filter box of the gravity type is one of a number of units in a double row on each side of a pipe gallery. Each unit has a capacity of 1 mgd and all units are rectangular, the filters in each row having a common wall between them. What should be the length and width of the sand surface in each filter? Show computations and give reasons for selection of each dimension.

28-6. What are the approximate length and width of the filter gallery shown in Fig. 28-7?

28-7. What is the maximum head loss possible between washings of the rapid sand filters in Fig. 28-8 when the clear well is full?

28-8. (a) At what rate must wash water be applied to the filter in Prob. 28-5 if the rate of rise of wash water is 24 in. per min? (b) If there are two wash-water gutters shaped and located as shown in Fig. 28-3, what should be the dimensions of the gutters?

28-9. A rapid-sand-filter plant with a capacity of 24 mgd is to include 12 filters of equal capacity, placed in two rows of 6 each. Each unit is to be a monolith with 12-in. rectangular walls, and a floor 6 in. thick. Each filter is rectangular in plan. A submerged rate controller is used on each filter, allowing a maximum negative head of 4 ft. Determine the length, width, and depth of each filter box, and explain each step in your solution.

28-10. What are the effective size and the uniformity coefficient of the sand within the "specified limits" shown in Fig. 28-13?

28-11. Compute the following for a perforated-pipe underdrainage system branching from a manifold down the center of a 2-mgd rapid-sand-filter unit, using wash water at a 24-in. rise per minute. The filter is 1.25 times as long as it is wide; there is a single manifold down its center, with branches on 6-in. centers along the manifold. Determine (a) the largest cross-sectional area of the manifold, in square inches; (b) the largest cross-sectional area of one branch, in square inches; (c) the diameter of each perforation in one lateral, in inches; (d) the number of such perforations; (e) the total area of perforations, in square inches.

28-12. Compute the cross-sectional area, in square inches, of the largest portion of the manifold and for each branch in a separate wash-air distribution system in a rapid-sand-filter unit of the size necessary in Prob. 28-11. Air is to be used at the highest rate allowed in Sec. 28-45. There is a single manifold down the center of the filter with branches on 6-in. centers.

28-13. If the distance H in Fig. 28-20 is 13.5 ft, what percentage of the total head loss may be represented by negative head?

28-14. If the diameter of the throat of the submerged rate controller shown in Fig. 28-22 is 8 in., the diameter of the entrance of the balanced valve is 16 in., the velocity through the throat is 18 fps, and the diameter of the flexible diaphragm exposed to the differential pressure is 12 in., what is the magnitude of the force available to open the rate controller?

28-15. If each filter in the plant illustrated in Fig. 28-3 has a nominal capacity of 2 mgd and is washed at a rate of 24-in. rise per minute, what should be the diameter and the velocity of flow in each pipe in the gallery, using the nearest commercial size of pipe and the highest velocities permitted in Table 28-1?

28-16. A 24 mgd rapid-sand-filter plant has 18 filter units. If water alone is used in washing and the wash water is supplied from a storage tank, what should be the capacity of the tank, in gallons? Rate of rise of wash water is 24 in. per min.

28-17. A 24 mgd rapid-sand-filter plant has 12 filter units. If air and water are both used in washing, but not simultaneously, and the air is supplied from a wash-air storage tank, what should be the capacity of the tank, in cubic feet?

28-18. What should be the cost of cleaning one of the 1 mgd filter units shown in Fig. 28-3, with caustic soda and soda ash, according to Table 28-2, if caustic soda costs $5.50 per 100 lb, and soda ash costs $2 per 100 lb?

28-19. If the raw water entering a treatment plant has an *E. coli* index of 5,000 per cubic centimeter, what should be the value of E_a in Streeter's formula in Sec. 28-61, and in what units is it expressed? T is 4 hr, and the constants are as expressed in Sec. 28-61.

Chapter 29

29-1. Examine *U.S. Geological Survey Water Supply Paper* 496, and name one city that has a very soft water, one that has a moderately soft water, and one that has a water so hard as to be on the verge of rejection as a public water supply. In each case state the hardness in parts per million and in grains per gallon.

29-2. How many pounds of lime ($Ca(OH)_2$) and of soda ash (Na_2CO_3) should be added per million gallons to reduce hardness of the water in Table 24-6 to 80 ppm on the basis of stoichiometrical computations?

29-3. What would be the annual per capita savings in a city with a population of 100,000, if the hardness of the water were reduced from 500 to 100 ppm?[1]

29-4. (a) How many pounds of lime ($Ca(OH)_2$) must be added to 1 mg water to reduce the carbonate hardness from 300 to 100 ppm, according to the reactions in Sec. 29-5? (b) How many pounds of CO_2 are required in the water to complete the reaction?

29-5. Water containing 300 ppm of total hardness is to be softened by base exchange through a medium with an exchange capacity of 12,000 grains per cubic foot, costing $60 per cubic foot. (a) What should be the cost of the softening medium for a plant to treat 4 mgd of water, regenerated hourly? Allow no standby equipment. (b) How many pounds of salt would be used at each regeneration on the basis of 0.5 lb per 1,000 grains hardness removed?

Chapter 30

30-1. (a) How many pounds of chlorine gas will be required to apply a dose of 0.2 ppm to a million gallons of water? (b) How many pounds of commercial calcium hypochlorite would be required for the same purpose? (c) How many pounds of H.T.H. would be required for the same purpose?

30-2. (a) How many parts per million of chlorine must be added to the water in Fig. 30-2 to obtain a residual of 1.5 ppm. (b) If 2.5 ppm of chlorine is added, what will be the residual?

30-3. What would be the cost of power for the sterilization of 1 million gal water by ultraviolet light if the unit cost of power is 1 cent per kilowatthour?[2]

30-4. What would be the cost of power for the ozonization of 1 million gal water at a dosage rate of 4 ppm if 10 kwhr is required to produce 1 lb ozone, and current costs 0.5 cent per kilowatthour?

[1] Base conclusions on the following references: *J.A.W.W.A.*, June, 1932, p. 859, and Vol. 12, p. 398; Vol. 14, p. 406; *Am. City*, Vol. 39, p. 131; and *Eng. News-Record*, Vol. 97, p. 780.

[2] The following references may be of assistance: *J.A.W.W.A.*, Vol. 1, p. 564; Vol. 4, p. 172; Vol. 7, p. 325; Vol. 18, p. 775; Vol. 22, pp. 959, 1290; *Eng. News-Record*, Vol. 79, p. 1021; *J. New Engl. Water Works Assoc.*, Vol. 29, p. 208; *Am. J. Public Health*, Vol. 12, p. 320; *Eng. and Contr.*, Vol. 57, p. 46.

Chapter 31

31-1. Water issuing from a well contains no dissolved gases and 4 ppm of ferrous carbonate. How many pounds of oxygen must be dissolved to oxidize 90 per cent of the ferrous carbonate to ferric carbonate?[1]

31-2. Plot curves with efficiencies as ordinates and concentration of CO_2 as abscissas for various types of aerators. Efficiencies are to be measured in percentage removal of CO_2.[2]

31-3. The tabulated figures show the changes in alkalinity and in pH resulting from the addition of calcium carbonate to 1 liter of water. What are the alkalinity and pH of the water at McLaughlin's saturation point? How many pounds of lime $(Ca(OH)_2)$ must be added to 1 million gal of this water to attain carbonate balance, if pH is 6.8?

Alkalinity, ppm	115	130	142	152	158	160	158	154	148
pH	4.3	5.3	6.4	6.8	7.2	7.7	8.0	8.4	9.0

31-4. Determine the Langelier index for a water with a temperature of 25°C; pH of 7.8; total solids, 300 ppm; Ca, 40 ppm; and alkalinity, 60 ppm.[3]

[1] Suggestion: See *Journal of the American Water Works Association*, Vol. 24, p. 65.

[2] Suggestion: Consult *Eng. News-Record*, Vol. 90, p. 874; *J.A.W.W.A.*, Vol. 11, p. 118; *Public Works*, Vol. 55, p. 251; *Eng. and Contr.*, Vol. 40, p. 302; *Water Works & Sewerage*, August, 1932, p. 275.

[3] Suggestion: Use the nomograph in *J.A.W.W.A.*, November, 1938, p, 1820, or in *Water Works Eng.*, Nov. 13, 1946, p. 1345.

INDEX

Diameter (Inches)	Area (sq. ft.)
1	0.005454
1½	0.01227
2	0.02182
2½	0.0341
4	0.0873
6	0.1963
8	0.349
10	0.5454
12	0.7854
14	1.069
16	1.396
18	1.767
20	2.182
24	3.1416

PIPE MAT'LS.

CAST IRON
STEEL
Wood
Conc.
Cement-asbestos

House Connections

Copper
Lead

$$H = A - (V_p + V_h + H_f) - L.B.$$

$$L.B. = 1.35 \, ft. \, H_2O$$

Atmos. Press
V_p = Vapor P.

$$Atm.P - V.P - h_f = \quad H.H_2O$$

lift that
can be made